FOODS

FACTS AND PRINCIPLES

SIXTH EDITION

N SHAKUNTALA MANAY
Former Head
Department of Food & Nutrition
Smt. V.H.D. Central Institute of Home Science
Bangalore, Karnataka

M SHADAKSHARASWAMY
Former
Professor of Biochemistry
Head, Department of Chemistry
and
Dean, Faculty of Science
Bangalore University
Bangalore, Karnataka

Committed to Educate the Nation

NEW AGE

Publishing Globally

IN INDIA
NEW AGE INTERNATIONAL (P) LIMITED, PUBLISHERS
LONDON • NEW DELHI
Bangalore • Chennai • Cochin • Guwahati • Hyderabad • Kolkata • Mumbai
Visit us at **www.newagepublishers.com**

Published by New Age International (P) Ltd., Publishers
Second Edition: 2001
Sixth Edition: 2026
Reprint: 2027

GLOBAL OFFICES

- **New Delhi** **NEW AGE INTERNATIONAL (P) LIMITED, PUBLISHERS**
7/30 A, Daryaganj, New Delhi-110002, (INDIA), **Tel.:** (011) 23253472, 23253771, **Mob.:** 9315905300
E-mail: contactus@newagepublishers.com • Visit us at www.newagepublishers.com

- **London** **NEW AGE INTERNATIONAL (UK) LTD.**
27 Old Gloucester Street, London, WC1N 3AX, UK
E-mail: info@newacademicscience.co.uk • Visit us at www.newacademicscience.co.uk

BRANCHES

- **Bangalore** 37/10, 8th Cross (Near Hanuman Temple), Azad Nagar, Chamarajpet, Bangalore- 560 018
Tel.: (080) 26756823, **Mob.:** 9315905288, **E-mail: bangalore@newagepublishers.com**

- **Chennai** 26, Damodaran Street, T. Nagar, Chennai-600 017, **Tel.:** (044) 24353401, **Mob.:** 9315905309
E-mail: chennai@newagepublishers.com

- **Cochin** CC-39/1016, Carrier Station Road, Ernakulam South, Cochin-682 016
Tel.: (0484) 4051304, **Mob.:** 9315905289, **E-mail: cochin@newagepublishers.com**

- **Guwahati** Hemsen Complex, Mohd. Shah Road, Paltan Bazar, Near Starline Hotel
Guwahati-781 008, **Tel.:** (0361) 2513881, **Mob.:** 9315905296, **E-mail: guwahati@newagepublishers.com**

- **Hyderabad** 105, 1st Floor, Madhiray Kaveri Tower, 3-2-19, Azam Jahi Road, Near Kumar Theater
Nimboliadda Kachiguda, Hyderabad-500 027, **Tel.:** (040) 24652456, **Mob.:** 9315905326
E-mail: hyderabad@newagepublishers.com

- **Kolkata** RDB Chambers (Formerly Lotus Cinema) 106A, 1st Floor, S N Banerjee Road
Kolkata-700 014, **Tel.:** (033) 22273773, **Mob.:** 9315905319, **E-mail: kolkata@newagepublishers.com**

- **Mumbai** 142C, Victor House, Ground Floor, N.M. Joshi Marg, Lower Parel, Mumbai-400 013
Tel.: (022) 24927869, 24915415, **Mob.:** 9315905282, **E-mail: mumbai@newagepublishers.com**

- **New Delhi** 22, Golden House, Daryaganj, New Delhi-110 002, **Tel.:** (011) 23262368, 23262370
Mob.: 9315905300, **E-mail: sales@newagepublishers.com**

C-26-07-15581

Printed in India at R. K Printers, Delhi.
Typeset at In-house, Delhi.

NEW AGE INTERNATIONAL (P) LIMITED, PUBLISHERS
7/30 A, Daryaganj, New Delhi-110002
Visit us at **www.newagepublishers.com**
(CIN: U74899DL1966PTC004618)

This Dedication is beyond debt and debit

To

Late Professor M. Shadaksharaswamy,

An aesthete, a harmonist, a luminous being, his wisdom balanced science of matter with Spirit.

The punctilio, momentous, memories, took the birth as a Sixth Edition of the book

Foreword

Foods: Facts and Principles, has evolved in three decades and the fourth edition has now explicitly and progressively shows two sides of the Food, one that Food is a matter of science and the other Food is the spirit. The knowledge is evergrowing aspect of life. Food is one of the fundamental needs of human beings. Archaeological records indicate that the naturally grown food, once were of wild varieties which were cereals, vegetables and fruits.

The emphasis currently is on Millets and a major issue to popularize Millet is not only for its nutritive value but yield per hectare. Also, to compensate for the deficit of commonly used cereal and cereal products. Population increase brings new demands, hence the food export and import makes countries interdependent. Global yield of cereals, fruits and vegetables are now easily available as fresh exotic produce.

Each country's culture has its own food preferences and priorities, thus food habits differ and influence Basis of Food Groups. The relation between nutrients and the classification of food has changed considerably. It is interesting to note that after World War II a wide range of changes has taken place to arrive at balanced food groups according to major needs of energies, that of carbohydrate, protein and fats and vice versa.

A balanced diet has undergone changes and transcends at times. The said standards of Recommended Dietary allowances have become arbitrary standard. Malnourishment is creating problems of obesity, cardiovascular diseases and metabolic disease like diabetes. The feature of food as a source of spirit and its qualitative psycho-physiological profiles is a more significant aspect of Indian Culture. The nature of food and man broadly being Satvic, Rajasic and Tamasic. India's Vedic and Upanishadic culture of five thousand years is coming to the forefront, is now recognized and has revived the concept that health of mind ensures physical health. The spirit behind food and man being the same, this is now established in experimental studies tried out on human subjects. This is an interesting aspect that the book covers exposing all aspects of food. Food plays a key role in this connection. The inner world of man and qualitative nature of food is simultaneously related and the gulf is now bridged.

Macro, Micro and Meso nutrients is an area that makes the diet more personalized and individuals can work out their diets based on their own wellbeing-(Swastya). This overall transformation of facts and principles has recently caught the attention from the physical, mental and shifting it to the centre of the spirit. This union is Yoga, lifestyle of this kind is Yogic Life and Food sadhana in this perspective is yogakshema for the global wellbeing.

The overall comprehensive revision has been a steady growth meaningfully brought forward to meet the ultimate wholesome health of body, mind and life through food.

M.S. Swaminathan

Preface to the Sixth Edition

The Sixth edition of **Foods: Facts and Principles** is a revision of the Fifth. All the production figures and some tables have been updated and necessary proof correction has also been undertaken. It is fulfilling to know that, the very first edition of this book, Foods: Facts and Principles, had received a grant, under the scheme of writing textbooks, from the University Grants Commission. My gratitude to the University Grants Commission is hereby acknowledged.

This sixth edition has empathized the understanding of the concepts of the fitness of "health and wellbeing". It is a qualitative Physical-Psychosocial and Spiritual change.

Earlier it was health, primarily that of physical wellbeing, taking into consideration the Nutrients and Nutrition and their contents in the food. Basic food groups underwent change from complex to simple groups.

This book has raised the standard from physical to mental, social and spiritual health. It recognizes energy, metabolism and utilization depending of the quality of food. This is Thermic Effect of Food (TEF), also known as Diet Induced Thermo genesis (DIT) or Specific effect of food (SEF). This has been not only discussed scientifically, but also compared to the ancient cultural concept of *Sattvic, Rajasic* and *Tamasic* food. There is no text, which compares these principles that have been experimentally proved on human subjects, based on research papers. The quality of food as per our culture influences the psychosocial status of the mind. This is experimented on human subjects and the resulting data has been utilized. Thus physical and psychosocial aspect has been integrated.

To practice food *Sadhana*, a disciplined yogic diet is required. The subjective changes occurring in such diets change the subjects' mood profile and the subjects are capable creating an environment of wellbeing not only for themselves but for the global wellbeing.

Here comes the challenge of food *Sadhana* of yogic diet to become aware of subtler energies embedded on the subtle bodies known as Chakras. These are ascending in order of colours similar to Rainbow, to experience oneself as per food; in nature food and colours of food is another interesting inner experimentation.

Thus, food *Sadhana* is a comprehensive state of wellbeing known as *Swastya*. Ascending plane of food consciousness means intrinsic change in health, heightened health and vastness of spirits, the sense of wellbeing in one's own life.

And social change is a natural result of this inner change as one's outlook of qualitative life brings vastness to be experienced which integrates socio-spiritual sense of wellbeing.

N. Shakuntala Manay

Preface to the First Edition

This book is written to meet the needs of students of Indian universities pursuing courses in foods, nutrition and allied courses, at the honours and postgraduate levels. The books currently used as a text and reference books, mostly written by western authors, do not satisfy the needs of Indian students. Such books deal at great length of foods like beef, cheese, etc. which are important in their diet, but hardly deal with foods like pulses, spices, etc., which are important in ours. Our book eliminates this imbalance.

The production, processing and utilization of each food are discussed from the Indian context. Indigenous food products from cereals like idli, dosa and chapatti, milk products like dahi and khoa, and Indian confectionery (sweetmeats) have received special attention. Nutritional foods mixes from oilseed cakes and pulses, which are important to overcome malnutrition of infants and young children of developing countries like India, are considered. Indian food laws and the role of Indian Standards Institute in the regulation of food standards are discussed.

The book gives a comprehensive account of foods. It consists of three parts. Part 1, constituting Chapters 1–11, deals with the constituents of foods and the basic science required for understanding foods. Chapters 12–26, constituting Part 2, deal with different kinds of foods, some individual members of each kind of food, their composition, and nutritive value and uses. The final four chapters (Part 3) deal with the method of food preparation, food quality, and processing and preservation of foods.

We trust that the book would be of interest to all students and scientists working in the field of food, and nutrition. Suggestions for improvement of the book are welcome.

The authors wish to convey their gratitude thanks to Dr. M.S. Swaminathan, Director General, International Rice Research Institute, Manila, Philippines, and President of the International Union of Conservation of Nature and Natural Resources, for writing the Foreword. Our thanks are also due to Prof. P.S. Veerabhadrappa and Sri L. Goverdhan of the Biochemistry Department, Bangalore University, for help at various stages of the preparation of the manuscript. One of us (N.S.M) thank the U.G.C for financial assistance for writing the book.

N. Shakuntala Manay

M. Shadaksharaswamy

Contents

PART II: FOOD AND FOOD PRODUCTS

PART III: FOOD PREPARATION, PRESERVATION AND PROCESSING

CHAPTER

1 Introduction

Man's basic drive is for food to satisfy his hunger. Food is intimately woven into the physical, economic, psychological, intellectual and social life of man. It is a part of his culture and is filled with many different meanings and symbolisms for all individuals at various ages and stages of their maturity.

Agricultural produce, such as cereals, pulses, fruits and vegetables, and reared animals for meat, milk, eggs, etc., are foods or food raw materials. When consumed, foods undergo digestive and other changes to supply the body with its requirements. After production and before consumption, foods are subjected to numerous adverse physical, chemical, microbial or parasitic factors that may cause their spoilage or cause disease when consumed. To prevent these and prepare food for immediate or future use requires processing, preservation and storage. Food for consumption should have the proper appearance, colour, juiciness, texture, odour and taste. During the past few decades, great advances have been made in the study of the whole field of the properties, preservation and processing of raw food and of the behaviour of finished food products.

There is a tremendous growth of world population. In spite of increased food production, there is a danger of shortfall in supply. Consequently, there must be greater and more efficient utilization of the existing food sources and development of entirely new ones. Also, artificial foods, which have been controlled with respect to the attributes of eating quality, nutritional content and ease of assimilation, have to be developed to meet the requirements of man.

1.1 Food as a Source of Nutrients

Food is a more basic need of man than shelter and clothing. It provides adequately for the body's growth, maintenance, repair and reproduction. Food furnishes the body with the energy required for all human activities—it provides materials required for the building and renewal of body tissues and the substances that act to regulate body processes. An individual food, such as milk, may fulfil all these functions or, as in the case of sugar, any one function. However, all the above functions of food must be served by the diet in order to maintain the body in good health. Most foods fulfil more than one function, as they are complex mixtures of a number of chemical substances.

1.1.1 Nutrients

Foods are composed of dozens or even hundreds of different kinds of substances—the "nutrients" which, when consumed in adequate amounts, fulfil all the functions of the body. Six general classes or kinds of nutrients found in all foods are carbohydrates, fats, proteins, vitamins, minerals and water.

Carbohydrates make up the bulk of our diet. They are our chief source of energy. About 70 per cent of the energy requirements for all body functions is obtained from carbohydrates. Energy is produced by the oxidation or "internal burning" (cellular respiration) of carbohydrates in the animal cells using oxygen. Carbohydrates also help in the utilization of proteins and fats. Carbohydrates, when consumed in excess, are converted into fats (some glycogen also) to be used when needed.

The main sources of carbohydrates in the diet are starch and sugar. The sources of the former are mainly cereal grains (wheat, rice, etc.) or tubers (potato, sweet potato, cassava) and those of the latter are sugarcane and fruits.

Fats or lipids are the most concentrated form of energy in the food. They furnish more than twice the number of calories per gram furnished by carbohydrates or proteins. When compared to carbohydrates, fats contain a lower percentage of oxygen and more (No of) hydrogen, and consequently, on oxidation, yield more energy. Generally about 30 per cent of human energy requirements are met by fats. When excess energy is supplied to the body, it is stored as fat.

Fats are abundant in both plant and animal materials. In plants, they may be confined to the cytoplasmic membrane or may also be present as reserve material. The fat content of fruits (except avocado and olive) is poor. Fat up to about 15 per cent is present in the germ of cereals. Nuts, such as groundnuts, are rich sources of fats. Butter from milk is an important source of fat. The adipose tissue of animals consists mainly of fats.

Proteins are the major source of building material for the body. They play an important role as structural constituents of cellular membranes and function in the maintenance and repair of body tissues. Proteins also function as biocatalysts. The food value of the protein depends upon the nature and content of its amino acids, which are its structural units. The excess of protein not required for building may be used as a source of energy.

Proteins are found in both animal and plant tissues. Meat, fish, poultry, eggs, milk and cheese are good sources of protein foods from animal sources. Pulses and cereals contain considerable amounts of storage proteins. Soybean contains over 40 per cent protein on a dry weight basis. Nuts and seeds are also good sources of proteins. Starchy vegetables contain up to 2 per cent protein. Other vegetables and fruits are poor sources of proteins.

Vitamins are "accessory nutrients." They are required for the proper utilization of the bulk food of the diet—carbohydrates, fats and proteins, and for the maintenance of good health. Vitamins, together with minerals are involved in small quantities in the regulation of body processes. They are constituents of enzymes, which function as catalysts for many biological reactions within the body.

Vitamins are found in plant and animal tissues. Their content in plant tissues varies widely depending upon the growing condition, stage of maturity, handling, processing and storage of these food materials. They are not uniformly distributed in plant tissues. Vegetables and fruits are good sources of vitamins. Wheat is an excellent source of B vitamins, but the bran and germ, containing the bulk of these nutrients, are usually removed during processing. Since vitamins are simple organic substances, they are easily synthesized and synthetic vitamins are therefore added to enrich or supplement those found in food products.

Minerals also act as catalysts for many biological reactions within the body. Their other functions include the building of bones and other structural parts of the body, muscular contraction, transmission of messages through the nervous system, and the digestion and utilization of nutrients in food. Some minerals like calcium, phosphorus, iron, magnesium and sulphur are required in large quantities, while others like zinc, copper, iodine, manganese, cobalt, etc., are required in small quantities.

Minerals are found in foods from animal and plant sources. The mineral content of plant foods varies depending upon the mineral elements present in the medium of cultivation. The distribution of a particular mineral element varies in different tissues. Minerals, like vitamins, are added to food to enrich it.

Water is second only to oxygen in importance for the body. It is an ideal medium for transporting dissolved nutrients and wastes throughout the body.

Apart from the consumption of water as such, the body's needs for water are supplied by the foods we consume. Some foods contain a high percentage of water. Besides from this, oxidation of carbohydrates, fats and proteins in the body yields water.

In addition to the above nutrients, foods contain enzymes that function as catalysts in chemical reaction, colouring, material and flavour compounds.

1.2 Food is More than Nutrients

All through history, food has played important roles besides that of nutrition. Ancient Indians, realizing the nature of this importance compared food with God (*Annam Brahma*). According to them, food, in addition to its physiological effects has psychological, organoleptic and healing properties. Indian thought goes even further; according to it energy stored in food is "Cosmic" energy for it also helps man experience enlightenment.

Wars have been fought for food. People have been known to steal, rob and kill for it. Explorers have searched the world for new foods. Sciences have been built on food and food–related discoveries have been rewarded. Fortunes have been made and lost in foodstuffs. Food has helped in creating history!

Food is also a source of power. People have been made to starve for submission. Wars have been won by blockading food supplies to the enemy. The power of food may be exerted in society, and in the family too through its use as a reward or punishment. A child may be sent to bed without food because of bad behaviour or may be given something special as a reward for some achievement. Denial of food is often being used against those who revolt against "the establishment."

Food is a source of security. An infant learns security from the way his mother feeds him. His behavioural patterns will be influenced by the extent to which he feels secure as regards his food supply. Similarly, a growing child gains confidence and a feeling of belonging when he knows there is food in the house and he will be fed. People feel reasonably secure when they have enough food stored up to take care of them during periods of scarcity. Familiar foods give a sense of security when one has to eat away from home.

Food is a status symbol. The well-to-do eat foods the common man cannot afford, even though they may not be so nutritious. It is prestigious to use polished white rice instead of brown rice, which protects one against beriberi. The same is true of white flour and white bread, which have replaced "black bread." The status factor associated with certain foods used by the so-called upper class makes others prefer them, to easily available, less expensive and often more nutritious foods. We serve certain foods for family meals and different foods when we have guests.

Food is a symbol of hospitality and friendship throughout the world. We express our hospitality to a guest through an offer of food or a drink. In times of disaster or sorrow we take food to the affected persons. In our country, offering a cup of coffee or tea is a symbol of friendship.

Food is an outlet for emotion. As a relief from tension, one may eat or overeat. For some people, loneliness and boredom are relieved by continuous nibbling of food. Anger and frustration may turn one against food. Specific foods are associated with unhappy experiences. Foods consumed by some people are unacceptable and even revolting for others. Such concepts have no rhyme or reason, nor are they related to nutritive value; they are just emotional reactions.

Thus, for an average man, food is much more than a substance supplying nutrients for health. It is the sum of his culture and traditions, emotional outlet, gratification of pleasure, relief from stress, means of communication, security, status— all of these interwoven in the fabric of life and unconsciously expressed in food likes and dislikes. The psychological and emotional reactions to food do not yield easily to reasoning or scientific facts about nutrition.

1.3 Food Intake and Its Regulations

All living beings must eat to live and all have mechanisms that direct them to take food. In almost every case, some control is exerted over the amount and kind of food that is taken. When hungry, living beings respond by locating and ingesting food and eating stops when hunger is satisfied. Thus eating behaviour is a complex interplay between hunger, appetite and satiety.

1.3.1 Hunger, Appetite and Satiety

Hunger is usually an unpleasant sensation that compels a person to seek food and eat it. It is a physiological condition that is associated with the contraction of the stomach. The contractions are forceful and occur for a period and then die away as the stomach passes into a resting stage. Hunger conditions that subside without eating will reappear later with greater intensity. In addition to stomach contractions resulting in tenseness, rumbling and a feeling of emptiness, a hungry person may experience certain general sensations, e.g., weakness, irritability, occasional headache or even nausea.

Hunger cannot truly be explained only by the biological component—as human beings, the psychological part and cognitive components of hunger cannot be ignored. Unlike any other beings, humans use an external clock in their daily routine, including when to sleep and when to eat; this external time device triggers our hunger. For instance, when the clock says 1p.m., lunch time, many people feel hungry just because it is lunch time. This hunger is triggered by learned behaviour. In addition, the smell, taste, or texture of food also triggers hunger.

Appetite in most people is a pleasant sensation that causes a person to desire and anticipate food. Appetite exists in all higher life forms, and serves to regulate adequate energy intake to maintain metabolic needs. It is regulated by a close interplay between the digestive tract, adipose tissue and the brain. Appetite has physiological components but is basically a psychological state. It is less easily localized than hunger, and is usually felt in the mouth or palate. It appears to depend more on the odour and memory of pleasant food. Appetite is clearly distinct from hunger, as a person may express a desire for some food at the end of dinner when he is comfortably replete. Absence of the desire for food, when it is needed, is an abnormal condition and is known as Anorexia.

Satiety: It is a sensation accompanying the satisfaction of the desire for food that comes after eating. It is not just the opposite of hunger and has far fewer sensations; while hunger builds up slowly, satiety occurs rapidly. The other side of hunger and appetite is satiety, which is the physiological and psychological experience of "fullness" that comes after eating and/or drinking.

1.3.2 Regulation of Hunger

The hypothalamus is a small portion of the brain located at its base near the brain stem. This has been identified as the area that evokes the sensation of hunger and satiety. In the central portion of the hypothalamus (the ventromedial hypothalamus), the destruction of a small area causes animals to eat voraciously and become obese, because of destruction of the satiety centre. Again, the destruction of a small centre in the side region of the hypothalamus (the lateral hypothalamus) results in the opposite effect, that is, the animals refuse to eat because of the destruction of the feeding centre and become anorexic. A stimulation of the satiety centre causes organisms to stop eating and that of the feeding centre causes them to eat.

The satiety and the feeding centres of the hypothalamus are connected by nerve fibres. When stimulated, the satiety centre sends signals to the feeding centre to inhibit feeding activity. That is, the feeding centre controls the feeding behaviour and the satiety centre regulates it.

A number of factors stimulate the satiety centre so that it can regulate the feeding centre. There are sensory, metabolic and hormonal influences controlling the food intake.

1. *Sensory influences:* Stomach contraction results in hunger. But hunger contraction is not the only feature of food intake regulation, as hunger contraction continues even when the main nerve to the stomach is severed. However, there are stretch and chemo receptors in the gastro-intestinal system that record the distensions of the stomach and the presence of food after a meal, which relay information to the brain resulting in short-term regulation.

   Several other stimuli involved in the gastrointestinal system contribute to the sensation of eating. Sensory stimuli coming from the taste, smell and texture of food are relayed to the cortex of the brain, which are then transmitted to the satiety centre in the hypothalamus, which results in signals to stop or to continue eating. Further, some psychological factors also have an influence on this centre.

2. *Metabolic factors:* There are glucose receptors in the satiety centre which are receptive to glucose utilization. When food is taken, the blood sugar level increases and the rate of utilization of glucose in the tissues rises. Then the receptors are stimulated, and the satiety centre signals responses to stop eating. Some hours after eating, the blood glucose level falls resulting in a low utilization rate. The satiety centre then stops sending signals to the feeding centre. This mechanism of food intake regulation is known as glucostatic regulation.

   The regulation of food intake over a long-term is regulated by the amount of fat stored in the adipose tissues (lipostatic regulation). According to this theory, precise information on the fat stores is relayed from the adipose tissues to the nervous control centre. If the stores are filled, signals are given to stop eating and when the fat level is reduced, eating continues till the satiety centre is activated. The manner in which the information on the fat content of adipose tissue is transmitted is still not clear.

   The plasma concentration of amino acid patterns produced by the diet have an effect on the amount of food intake. Since many brain neurotransmitters are affected by the supply of amino acids, it is definitely possible that the feeding behaviour could also be so influenced (aminostatic regulation).

3. *Hormonal centre*: A number of hormones, such as insulin, glucagons, etc., which are involved directly or indirectly in the regulation of the utilization of glucose which can be sensed by the hypothalamus glucose receptors, regulate the intake of food.

In addition to these physiological factors, emotional factors which have a psychological component come into play in the control of hunger and appetite. Further, according to the World Health Organization Spiritual factors also come in with respect to human beings. This aspect is considered in the last chapter of this book.

1.4 Food Patterns

Man eats what his forefathers ate, if possible, and what his environment offers. A young child does not form fixed food habits but is patterned by adults, who eat certain foods and not others. The foods that his father does not like, and which his mother therefore does not serve, do not become familiar to the child and would not be eaten by him. The environment—the physical, psychological and social settings, which relates to the culture of a group and also determines the food patterns.

Historical: Some of our knowledge of what early man ate comes from archaeological studies of cave drawings of food getting and preparation activities. Other evidence of what primitive people ate includes the study of remnants of discarded food found by archaeologists in mounds, pits, bogs, lake beds and tombs. The remnants of human faeces (coproliter) also tell the story of early human food. From such remains of prehistoric man a picture of the food eaten by him has been reconstituted with some degree of certainty from the study of anthropologists and other scientists.

Primitive men lived as hunters and gatherers. They collected their food from wild animals and plants. They depended upon fruits, nuts, roots and other plant foods, meat from animals and the fish catch from seas, lakes and rivers. They were forced to spend their days and nights in search of food. They roamed from place to place to correspond to the changing season, the appearance and disappearance of various fruits and leaves, or the migration and movement of game animals. They lived this way till about 10,000 years ago in a few places and 5,000 years ago in most of the world.

Gradually, food gatherers learned to domesticate plants and animals. They were no longer roaming about eating what was available. They settled down, built shelters and raised plants and animals to provide food. Plant domestication began in China about 10,000 B.C. followed by India, the eastern Mediterranean area and Africa. The first crops to be grown were wheat and barley from wild grasses. Simultaneously, livestock were domesticated. Cows were domesticated first and then sheep and goats. Milk was probably the first food to be extracted from animals. In the early stages, food production did not develop beyond an inefficient subsistence level and small farming communities developed around the areas of farming. The development of agricultural skills over the last two centuries and consequent supply of a sufficient amount of food, its preservation and storage, resulted in the emergence of cities and urban civilization.

One of the first great changes that occurred in man's food pattern must have been when he learnt to use fire to cook. It is not known when he first used fire for this purpose. Man eats most of his food cooked and this is one of the many characteristics that separate him from other animals. The type and amount of fuel available determine the pattern of food of a society. In areas where fuel is scarce, quick-cooking foods are prepared. The use of chapatis, thin unleavened bread, and stew-like mixtures has developed in our country and in other parts of Asia and Africa because their preparation requires meagre equipment and little fire.

Many changes took place in food patterns prior to the Middle Ages. As man moved from one place to another, he found new foods growing in his new settlement. Since he usually carried the seeds of foods grown where he lived to his new place of residence, there was a migration of foods. Thus, sugar went from India to other parts of the world. Sweet oranges from China and sour ones from India went to Europe with the early overland traders. The dispersion of foods indigenous to one country into another has always increased the variety of man's diet from ancient times. Today, with the rapid development of the means of communication and transportation, the differences in the diets of different countries are becoming less marked.

1.5 Population and Food Production

1.5.1 Population Growth

The population of the entire world when agriculture or settled cultivation was started over 10,000 years ago was about 15 million. The estimate of the world population about 2,000 years ago was 250 million. This was doubled in 1650 A.D. Since then there has been a threatening increase in the population growth reaching a billion in 1830, 2 billion in 1940 and 4.42 billion in 1980, with more than half of the world population living in Asia. The regions of fastest population growth are Africa and South and Central America, although the world's largest growth and largest absolute increase are in South Asia. It is estimated that by 2020, the world population would be 7.6 billion and 90% of this would be in developing countries. At present the world population is increasing by about 55 million per year.

The population of India at the time of partition of the country (1947), which was about 350 million, jumped to 683 million in 1981 and is expected to exceed 1.3 billion in 2020. Now, the annual addition to the population of India is over 14 million.

The world is already facing hunger. According to recent (2006) Food and Agricultural Organization (FAO) report, abnormal food shortages have been reported in 39 countries of Africa, Asia and Latin America. The present growth rate of the world population tends to further aggravate the food situation. Also, about one-third of humanity consumes two-thirds of the world's food supply. About one–quarter of the people in developing countries are undernourished. India is one of the countries which suffers from undernourishment on a vast scale.

The people of developing countries consume food corresponding to 2,800-2,900 kilocalories (Kcal) per day (Indian consumption is 2,440 kilocalories). The consumption in developed countries is in the range of 3,300-3,400 Kcal. A utilization of under 2,000 Kcal per person per day can be definitely said to be on the low side. Within any country, the distribution of food is very much in favour of the better-off.

In developing countries, the inadequacies of food are not only in the quantity of food, but also in its quality, leading to malnutrition as well as undernutrition. The diet of people in these countries is unbalanced, because the bulk of their diet consist mainly of cereals—rice, maize, millets and starchy roots. Over 80 per cent of their calories are derived from these food sources. The lack of variety in their food and particularly the shortage of protective foods leads to deficiency diseases. Protein-calorie malnutrition, particularly among children, is extremely common in these countries. In 1975, in Africa, Asia and Latin America, 20.9 million out of 34.6 million children of the age group 1-4 suffered from protein-calorie malnutrition.

1.5.2 Food Production

From 1950 to 1971 there was an unprecedented growth in world food production. Yields on existing crop land were raised dramatically by energy intensive agriculture. The introduction of high yielding wheat and rice strains in parts of Asia and Africa resulted in a large increase in yield and this is referred to as the "Green Revolution." During this period the world grain production increased from 631 million tonnes to 1,237 million tonnes; resulting in an increase in grain availability per head, per year from 251 to 330 kg.

Even after 1971, there has been a gradual increase in the world grain production. It stood at 1,432 million tonnes in 1980 as against 1,237 million tonnes in 1971. But the output per head barely kept pace with population growth. During this period, the availability of grain per head per year came down from 330 to 324 kg. The world production of grain in 2005-06 was 2,009 million tonnes.

The position in developing countries was even worse. There was a decline in their total grain production. These countries face a widening food gap between their production and consumption. Their food import needs to be increased dramatically. The total food import of developing countries in 1984 was of the order of 100 million tonnes.

In India, the progress in agricultural production during the last 35 years has been very impressive. There has been a consistent upward trend in food grain production except during the years marked by acute weather aberrations. The food grain production has risen from 51 million tonnes in 1950-51 to a record production of 151.5 million tonnes in 1983-84 and further increases are anticipated in the coming years. Our requirement in 2007 A.D. is of the order of about 220 million tonnes.

The increase in agricultural production during the last three decades is a result of the increase in the application of science and technology in agriculture. Great strides have been made in agricultural research, education and extension. However, we cannot be complacent and ignore major problems concerned with food production. Farm management efficiency has to be improved. Input factors like water, seeds and fertilizers are to be increased. The diminishing size of an average land holding and its adverse effect on the net income of the farmer has to be avoided. The consistent damage to the ecosystem whose maintenance is essential for sustained agricultural advance should be prevented. Our dry farming has to be improved.

1.6 Food and the Future

The shooting population growth, rising energy costs, doubts about the adequacy of the agricultural resource base, disproportionate share of available food by the well-to-do, lagging behind of new agricultural knowledge and unfavourable weather conditions have given rise to pessimism about the ability of the Earth to feed its people. This assessment is also explicit or implicit in the reports of a number of international institutions concerned with world food production and demand.

It appears as though one need not be frightened about the world food situation. Actually, hunger is not new; it is as old as history. The world lives from hand to mouth, never more than one crop away from hunger. Actually, the world food problem is diminishing. The average lifespan is lengthening even in the poorest countries. The life expectancy at birth is now said to be 67 years, which was 42 years in 1960. The child death rate is dropping. In the low–income countries the death rate among the children in the age group 1-5 declined from 200 per thousand in 1978 to 114 per thousand in 2005. These recently born children were getting the food and health care that increased their survival rate by 14 per cent in eighteen years.

There is a decline in the birth rate. In low-income countries, the birth rate in 1978 was 39 per thousand; by 2005 it had fallen to 31 per thousand. The decline in the birth rate has decreased the world population growth rate from 1.8 per cent to 1 per cent.

The average food production in developing countries has crept upwards, though it is not ahead of population growth. More land could be brought under cultivation, though such development would require enormous investment and much time. There is great scope for increasing food production in the developing countries; the yield per hectare in some of them is less than half of what it is in the developed countries. The poorer countries are arranging for proper distribution of available food through fair-price shops and food-for-work programmes.

Discoveries in agriculture are not lagging behind. International research has resulted in the production of high-yielding varieties of wheat and rice which has helped increase the world food supply. The number of agricultural research institutions with good financial resources is increasing. It may be hoped that the work in such institutions will result in technological breakthroughs in fields such as gene splicing, textured vegetable proteins, nitrogen fixation from non-leguminous crops, salt-tolerant crops, wild crosses of plants and of animals, improved photosynthesis, long-range weather forecasting or computer-aided agriculture management.

Food products are being used for nonfood purposes, e.g., because of fuel scarcity, some countries are using petrol mixed with alcohol. If this is practiced on a world scale, produce from 5 per cent of farmland would be required for this purpose. We can ill afford this when hunger is threatening the world.

Large amounts of vegetable material like grasses are available. They are not eaten because they consist largely of cellulose, which man is unable to digest. Proteins are extracted from grasses and other vegetable matter. Such protein concentrates are not used as foods now as they lack both taste and smell. But they could be used as foods after improved processing.

After the oils are extracted from nuts, a residue rich in proteins is left. This residue at present is mostly used as animal food or fertilizer. It is estimated that the amount of protein contained in such oilseed residues is sufficient to provide twice the world's deficit of protein. Oilseed cake can be processed and used as food. It is already being used to a certain extent in some poor countries. This could be expanded.

New foods can be obtained in the future. We are now mostly depending on foods derived from plants grown on land. Unicellular organisms, such as yeasts, algae and fungi may be cultivated on liquids. These are rich sources of high-quality proteins and could be developed as foods. New foods may also be developed by chemical synthesis.

1.6.1 Genetically Modified Foods

After World War II, the "Green Revolution" averted world wide famine. Half a century on, the world needs yet greater ingenuity to feed itself. Science is again at its wit's end. Agriculture in the future must be environmentally sensitive and, above all, sustainable. Much current debate on these issues concerns genetically modified crops, but this is only part of the story Sustainability has lessons for the whole agricultural enterprise, from high-tech agriculture to the depths of the ocean

Although "biotechnology" and "genetic modification" commonly are used interchangeably, GM is a special set of technologies that alter the genetic makeup of such living organisms as animals, plants, or bacteria. Biotechnology, a more general term, refers to using living organisms or their components, such as enzymes, to make products. Combining genes from different organisms is known as recombinant DNA technology, and the resulting organism is said to be "genetically modified," "genetically engineered," or "transgenic". GM products (current or in the pipeline) include medicines and vaccines, foods and food ingredients, feeds, and fibres.

Ten years after GM crops were first cultivated commercially, the debate over whether they should be grown at all still rages. It was in 1996 that GM crops became an industry, when cotton and maize engineered to be resistant to insecticides and soyabeans resistant to weed killer were grown for profit in significant quantities for the first time. Today some 8.5 million farmers in 21 countries grow GM varieties in developing countries. Between 1996 and 2005, the total surface area of land cultivated with genetically modified organisms had increased from 4.2 million acres to 222 million acres, of which 55% were in the United States. There has also been rapid and continuing expansion of GM cotton varieties in India since 2002.

According to the United States Department of Agriculture (USDA), there are over 40 plant varieties that have completed all of the federal requirements for commercialization. Some examples of these plants include tomatoes and cantaloupes that have modified ripening characteristics, soybeans and sugar beets that are resistant to herbicides, and corn and cotton plants with increased resistance to insect pests. While there are very few genetically modified whole fruits and vegetables available on the produce stands, highly processed foods, such as vegetable oils or breakfast cereals, most likely contain some tiny percentage of genetically-modified ingredients because the raw ingredients have been pooled into one processing stream from many different sources. In India, besides cotton, genetic engineering experiments are being conducted on maize, mustard, sugarcane, sorghum, pigeonpea, chickpea, rice, tomato, brinjal, potato, banana, papaya, cauliflower, oilseeds, castor, soybean and medicinal plants. Experiments are also underway on several species of fish.

There are some advantages of genetically modified foods, like pest resistance, herbicide tolerance, cold/drought tolerance, etc. Malnutrition is common in Third World countries where impoverished people rely on a single crop, such as rice, as the main staple of their diet. However, rice does not contain adequate amounts of all necessary nutrients to prevent malnutrition. If rice could be genetically engineered to contain additional vitamins and minerals, nutrient deficiencies could be alleviated.

There are also some risks associated with genetically modified foods which include some environmental hazards and human health risks. Also, the patenting of GM foods leads to economic concerns in developing countries.

Genetically modified foods have the potential to solve many of the world's hunger and malnutrition problems and to help protect and preserve the environment by increasing yield and reducing reliance upon chemical pesticides and herbicides. Yet there are many challenges ahead for governments, especially in the areas of safety testing, regulation, international policy and food labeling. Many people feel that genetic engineering is the inevitable wave of the future and that we cannot afford to ignore a technology that has such enormous potential benefits. However, we must proceed with caution to avoid causing unintended harm to human health and the environment as a result of our enthusiasm for this powerful technology.

1.6.2 Organic Foods

The excessive use of chemicals like insecticides, herbicides, pesticides, etc., used in food production during the Green Revolution, resulted in foods containing small quantities of these hazardous chemicals. This resulted in consumer awareness for foods grown by conventional methods. The risk factors of GM foods further increased the interest in organic foods, produced without using synthetic chemicals, including artificial fertilizers.

The interest in Organic Foods, which began in 1950, has been growing steadily and it accounts for 1-2% of the total food sales worldwide. The organic food market, which has been growing since early 1990 is expected to reach 10-50% annually depending on the country.

Thus, it should be possible to have sufficient food for future generations if we make the needed investment to develop and distribute new agricultural knowledge, the developed countries share their knowledge and experience with the less developed ones, and the developing countries are diligent enough to improve their agriculture and reduce the rate of growth of their population number. Action should also be taken to prevent the conversion of a high share of our food into non-food products and to develop food from non-traditional sources. Scientific and technological improvements will help meet the food needs of the future.

CHAPTER

2 Carbohydrates

Foods are complex substances composed of chemical constituents. The three major constituents of foods are carbohydrates, proteins and lipids. In addition, foods contain small amounts of vitamins, minerals, pigments, flavouring substances and enzymes. Another important constituent of all foods is water which is present in small or large quantities. These constituents give foods their structure, texture, colour, flavour and nutritive value. Thus, a knowledge of the constituents of foods and their properties is of central importance to the study of foods. This chapter will deal with the chemistry of carbohydrates.

2.1 Introduction

Carbohydrates are widely distributed in nature in the form of sugars, starches, celluloses and other complex substances. They contain carbon, hydrogen and oxygen, and can be represented by the formula $C_x (H_2O)_y$, where x and y may have values ranging from three to thousands. This suggested the nomenclature of this class of substances as hydrates of carbon or carbohydrates. There are many carbohydrates which do not fit into the general formula. The modern definition of carbohydrates is that they are polyhydroxy aldehydes or ketones and their derivatives.

Carbohydrates are the primary products of photosynthesis. They are organic compounds formed from carbon dioxide and water through the sun's radiations in photosynthetic plant cells. Light energy is thus converted into chemical energy in substances suitable for food and feed. Carbohydrates are easily digested and provide the necessary calories in the diets of most people of the world. They provide 4 $kcalg^{-1}$ and promote the utilization of fats and reduce wastage of proteins. They are ideal components of food from the point of view of energy. Carbohydrates are readily available as a source of food in roots, tubers, cereal grains, sugarcane and sugarbeet. Cereal grains provide the most economic source of food carbohydrates. Because of their high-carbohydrate and low-water content, cereals are easy to grow, harvest, store, transport and process. Ideally carbohydrates should supply 60 to 70 per cent of total calories required.

Carbohydrates are usually classified as monosaccharides, oligosaccharides and polysaccharides. The term "saccharide," meaning sugar or sweetness, is related to the characteristic taste of many of the simple carbohydrates. Monosaccharides are simple sugars, each consisting of a single polyhydroxy aldehyde or ketone unit, and they serve as the building blocks of complex sugars and polysaccharides. Oligosaccharides (*oligo* meaning "few") contain two to ten monosaccharide units joined in glycoside linkage. Polysaccharides contain many monosaccharide units, from hundreds to a few thousands, joined in linear or branched chains. Most polysaccharides contain recurring monosaccharide units of only one kind or two alternating kinds.

Carbohydrates were first named according to the sources from which they were obtained, e.g., grape sugar, cane sugar, malt sugar, milk sugar, corn starch, and liver glycogen. Then they were named from a prefix related to the sources followed by the suffix—"ose", e.g., fructose (fruit sugar), maltose (malt sugar), lactose (milk sugar), xylose (wood sugar), and cellulose (carbohydrates from cell membranes). These trivial names are still commonly used.

2.2 Monosaccharides

Monosaccharides are simple sugars containing short chains of carbon atoms with one aldehydic or ketonic group (carbonyl group), each of the remaining carbon atoms bearing a hydroxyl group. Those containing an aldehyde group are called "aldoses" (names ending in—"ose") and those with a ketone group are known as "ketoses" (names ending with—"ulose"). Depending upon the total number of carbon atoms present in the monosaccharide molecule, they are designated as trioses (3 C-atoms), tetroses (4 C-atoms), pentoses (5 C-atoms), hexoses (6 C-atoms) and so on.

The simplest sugars are glyceraldehyde and dihydroxyacetone. The most abundant monosaccharide is the six-carbon sugar, glucose (dextrose). It is the parent monosaccharide from which others are obtained. It is also the basic building block of the most abundant polysaccharides—starch and cellulose. Glucose occurs in ripe fruits, flowers, honey, beetroot, etc. Glucose in blood is the source of energy for animals. Other hexoses of importance in food are fructose and galactose. Fructose (levulose) is found in fruits and honey, is the building unit of the polysaccharide, inulin, and is one of the structural units of cane sugar (sucrose). Galactose, which is not found free in natural foods, is a component of milk sugar and agar agar. Mannose, another hexose, is present in alginic acids. The pentoses, arabinose and xylose, are components of plant gums.

2.2.1 Structure

Carbohydrates are represented by three types of formulae: The Fischer projection formula, the Haworth cyclic structure and the conformational formula. The Fischer projection formula is constructed on the convention that the tetrahedral apexes connecting the asymmetric carbon atoms be in a line in the plane of projection. The substituents at the "top" and "bottom" of the tetrahedral carbons and in a plane below it are also written along that straight line. The hydrogen atoms and hydroxyl groups that project forward above the carbon atoms in the plane are written on opposite sides of the straight line as shown:

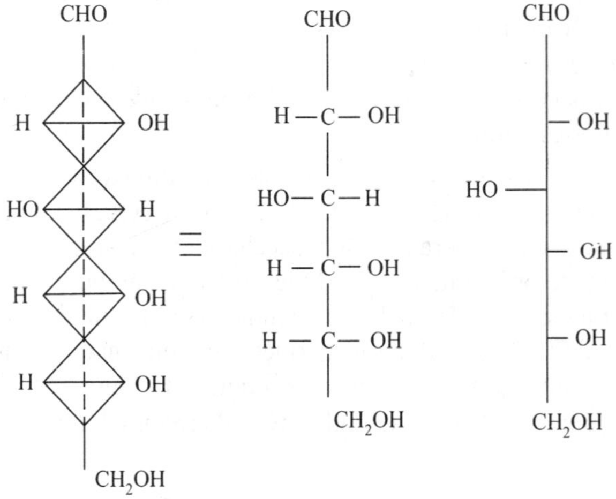

The above formula for a hexose shows four chiral centres (asymmetric carbon atoms), and thus 2^4 or 16 isomeric structures are possible and sixteen aldohexoses are known. Similarly all sugars, except dihydroxyacetone which has no chiral centre, occur in 2^n isomeric forms where *n* represents the number of asymmetric carbon atoms.

Chiral compounds exist in right-handed and left-handed forms, which are mirror images of each other. They are designated by the symbols D- and L- to indicate their absolute conformation. The sugars, whose configuration around the penultimate carbon atom (when the carbonyl group is at the top in the Fischer projection formula) is similar to D-glyceraldehyde, are designated as D-compounds and their mirror images as L-compounds.

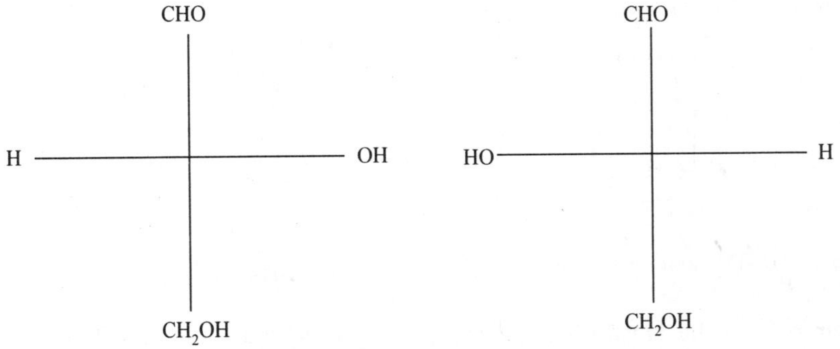

D-Glyceraldehyde L-Glyceraldehyde

When the flexible Fischer model is built for an aldohexose, the oxygen atom on the fourth and fifth carbon atoms can be turned to approach within the bonding distance of C-atom one. In such an event the hydroxyl group on C-4 or C-5 of the sugar molecule can form cyclic hemiacetals. If the ring closes by the parting of the hydroxyl on C-4, a five-membered heterocyclic ring called "furanose" is

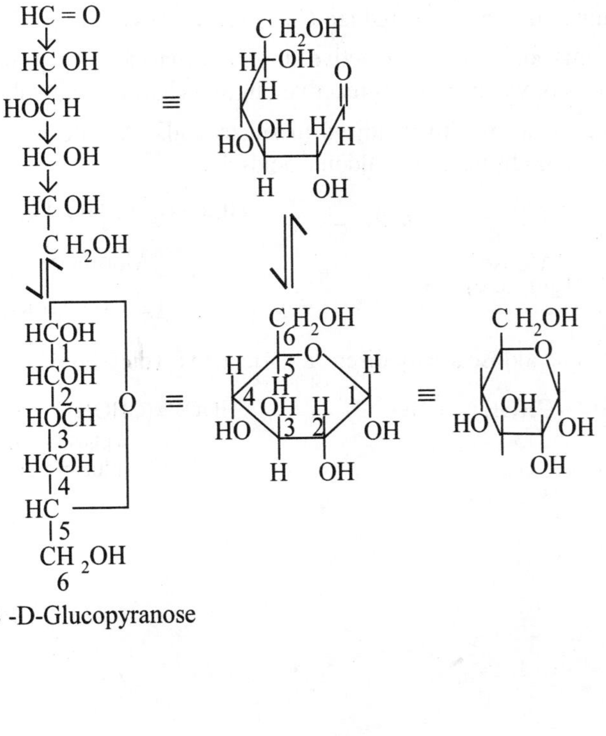

α -D-Glucopyranose

formed. If the ring closes by the participation of the C-5 hydroxyl, a six-membered "pyranose" ring is formed. Such rings are also formed with ketoses. Haworth, therefore, represented the carbohydrates as cyclic compounds.

When rings are formed, the new hydroxyl group on C-l, called the "anomeric hydroxyl group," can project forward on either side of the ring. Hence, two different furanoses or pyranoses can be formed. When the asymmetric anomeric hydroxyl group formed is on the same side of the ring as the hydroxyl group on the penultimate C-atom, the furanose and pyranose rings formed are called alpha (α-). When it is formed on the opposite side, the asymmetric ring is called beta (β -). The *α* and β sugars are known as anomers. The Haworth structures of some sugars are as follows:

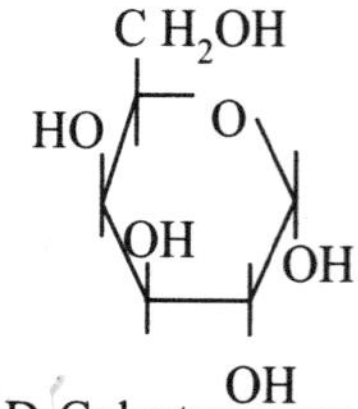

α -D-Galactopyranose

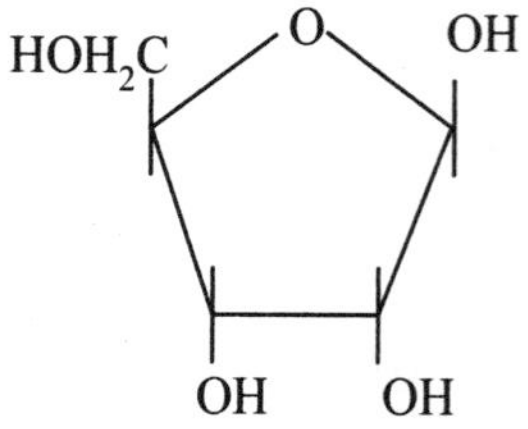

β -D-Ribofurnose

The sugar ring in the Haworth structure is not planar and therefore does not represent the correct conformation of monosaccharides. Modern spectroscopic investigations have displaced the conventional formula. The most stable conformational formulae of some sugars of interest in foods are given in Fig 2.1 The chair conformations of the pyranose rings predominate because of stearic relationships.

2.2.2 Properties of Monosaccharides

Because of the reactive groups present in them, monosaccharides undergo many reactions. They readily enolise in alkaline solutions and reduce $Cu^{2+}$and Fe $(CN)_6^{3+}$ ions. They are therefore called "reducing sugars." Plants protect the reactive monosaccharides for transport and storage by condensing them with loss of water into less reactive oligosaccharides and polysaccharides.

The reducing sugars are readily oxidised to sugar acids. A mild oxidation of aldoses, when only the aldehyde group is oxidised, gives "aldonic acids."

$$HOCH_2 \cdot (CHOH)_4 \cdot CHO \rightarrow HOCH_2 \cdot (CHOH)_4 \cdot COOH$$

Aldose (glucose) — Aldonic acid (gluconic acid)

When both ends of an aldose are oxidised "aldaric acids" (dicarboxylic acids) are formed.

$$HOCH_2 \cdot (CHOH)_4 \cdot CHO \rightarrow HOOC \cdot (CHOH)_4 \cdot COOH$$

Aldaric acid (glucaric acid)

Oxidation of the terminal alcoholic (–CH_2OH) group of aldose, without the oxidation of the aldehydic group, gives "alduronic acid."

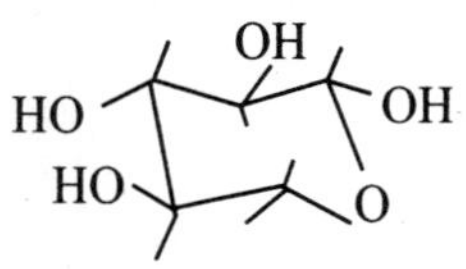

β -D-Xylopyranose

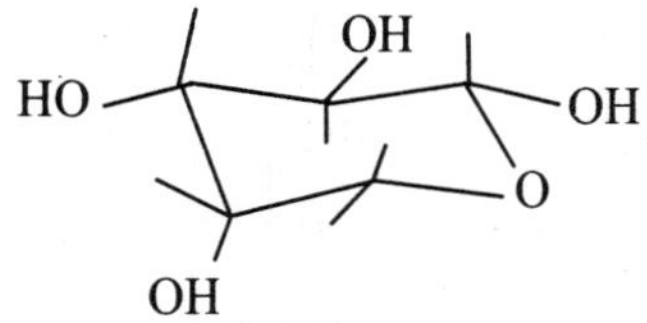

α -L-Arabinopyranose

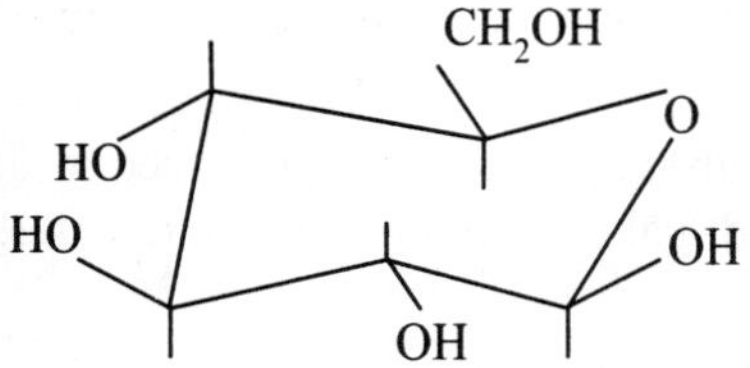

β -D-Glucopyranose

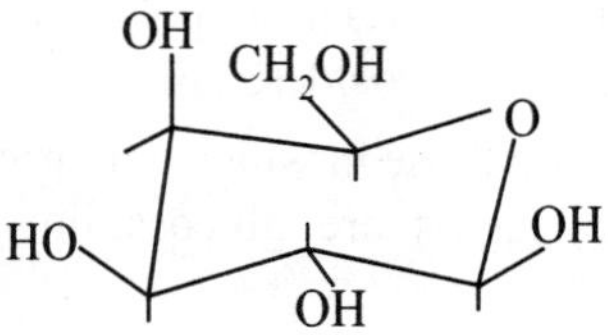

β -Galactopyranose

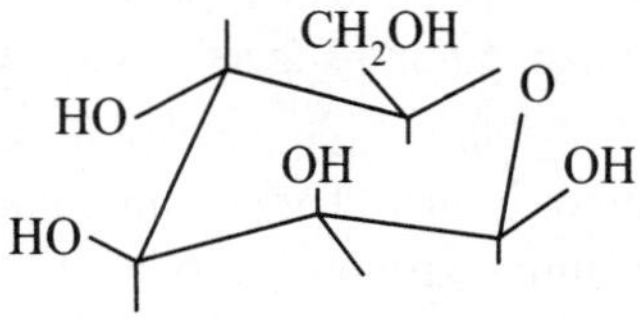

β-D-Mannopyranose

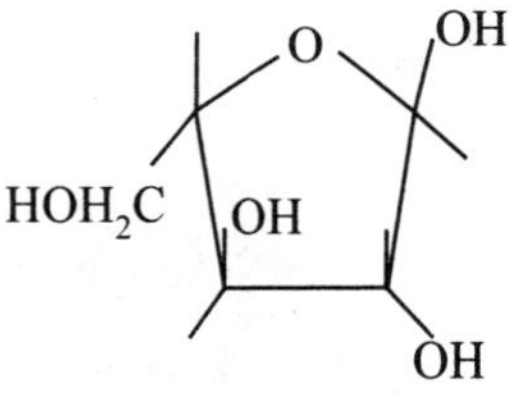

α-L-Arabinofuranose

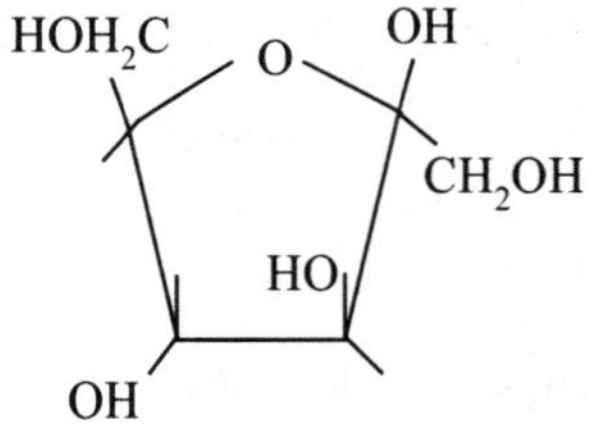

β -D-Fructofuranose

Fig. 2.1 Most stable ring conformation of some monosaccharides

$$HOCH_2 \cdot (CHOH)_4 \cdot CHO \quad \rightarrow \quad HOOC \cdot (CHOH)_4 \cdot CHO$$

Uronic acid
(glucronic acid)

Uronic acids are common monosaccharide constituents of polysaccharides, such as hemicelluloses, pectic substances, gums and others.

Reduction of the carboxyl group of monosaccharides yields sugar alcohols, "alditols."

$$HOCH_2 \cdot (CHOH)_4 \cdot CHO \quad \rightarrow \quad HOCH_2 \cdot (CHOH)_4 \cdot CH_2OH$$

Alditol
(glucitol or sorbitol)

Alditols are present in small amounts in many fruits and vegetables. Glyceritol (glycerol) and sorbitol are used in food processing because they keep food moist by virtue of their strong affinity for water. A cyclic alditol, inositol, is found as its hexaphosphate (phytic acid) or is mixed with its calcium-magnesium salt (phytin) in plants.

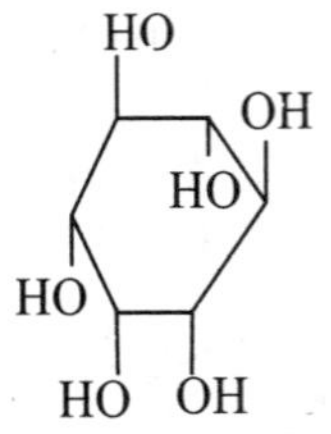

Inositol

2.2.3 Monosaccharide Derivatives

Some derivatives of monosaccharides are present as polysaccharide components of foods. Some of them are amino sugars, deoxy sugars and glycosides.

Amino sugars: Amino sugars are those in which a hydroxyl group in the sugar is replaced by an amino group. The common amino sugars are glucosamine and galactosamine. In some cases, the amino group is acetylated.

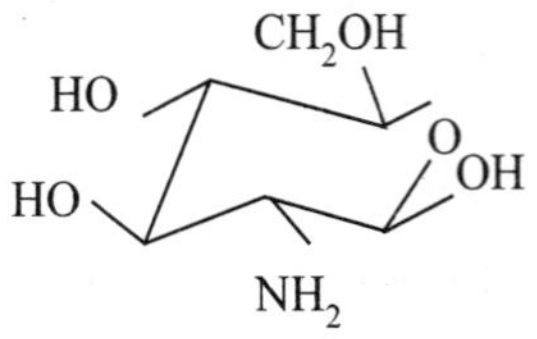

Glucosamine
(2-Amino-2-deoxy-D-glucose)

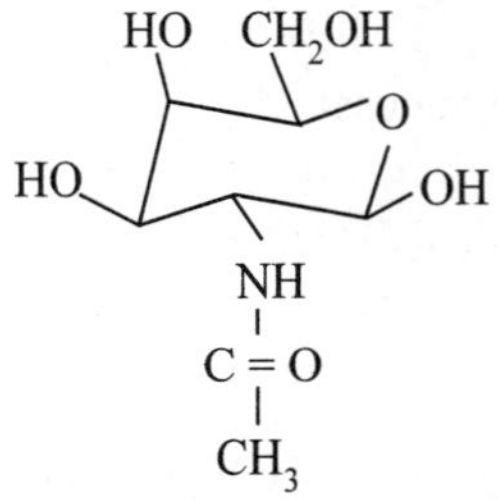

N-Acetylgalactosamine

Another important derivative of amino sugar is sialic acid, a component of glycoproteins.

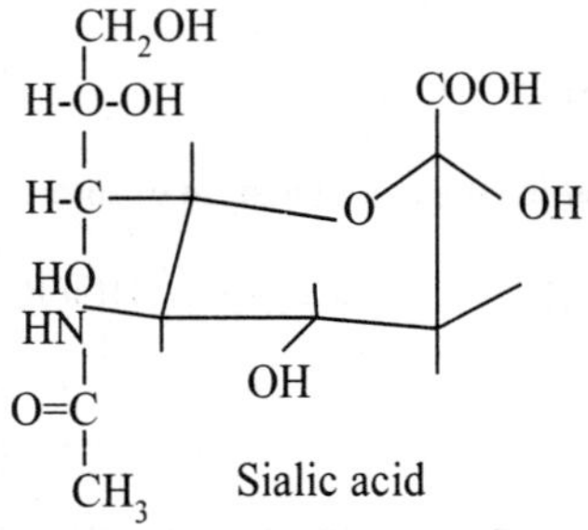

Sialic acid

Deoxy sugars: Deoxy sugars are those in which one oxygen atom is removed at a designated carbon atom. L-rhamnose and L-fucose are the deoxy sugars found in food polysaccharides. L-rhamnose is 6-deoxy-L-mannopyranose, while L-fucose is 6-deoxy-L-galactopyranose. 2-Deoxy-ribose is a constituent of DNA.

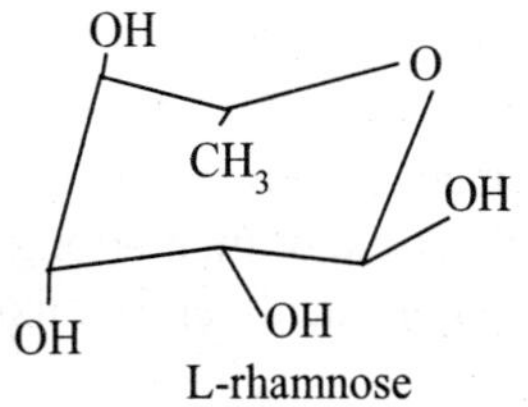

L-rhamnose

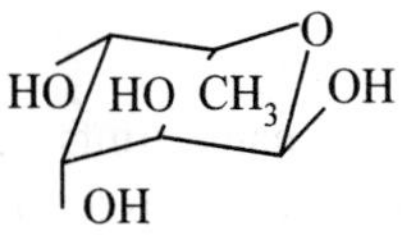

L-fucose

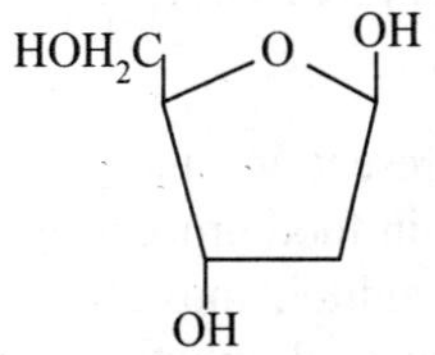

2-Deoxy-D-ribose

Glycosides; Glycosides are the condensation products of sugar (glycose) with nonsugars (aglycoses). When a molecule of water is removed by the condensation of the anomeric hydroxyl of glucose with the hydroxyl of an alcohol or phenol, an O-glycoside is formed. When amino and thiol compounds are aglycoses, N- and S-glycosides are formed. All the three types of glycosides are minor components of foods. Some glycosides are cyanogenic, i.e., they release hydrogen cyanide by enzymic hydrolysis in foods. Such types of glycosides could be a source of toxicity in foods.

2.3 Oligosaccharides

Oligosaccharides are formed by the polymerisation of *n* molecules of monosaccharides by the elimination of *n*-1 molecules of water. Depending on the value of *n,* the oligosaccharides are classified as di-, tri-, tetra-saccharides, etc. The water lost is between the anomeric hydroxyl group of one monosaccharide unit and one of the several possible hydroxyl groups of an adjacent unit. The linkages between monosaccharide units in oligosaccharides (and polysaccharides) are therefore glycosidic linkages. Reducing oligosaccharides are formed when the anomeric hydroxyl of one monosaccharide unit is linked with an alcoholic hydroxyl of the next. When water is eliminated between anomeric hydroxyls of different units, non-reducing oligosaccharides, such as sucrose, raffinose, etc., are formed.

The commonly found oligosaccharides in foods are sucrose, maltose, lactose, raffinose and stachyose. Some of these occur as such in food products while the others are partial hydrolytic products of naturally occurring polysaccharides. Sucrose found throughout the plant world is most abundant in sugarcane, sugarbeet and maple syrup. It is the familiar table sugar. It is manufactured from sugarcane or sugarbeet. It is composed of a molecule of glucose and a molecule of fructose linked through the elimination of a molecule of water through their anomeric hydroxyl groups. In the presence of mild acids or the enzyme invertase, sucrose undergoes hydrolysis (inversion). The hydrolysis product is known as invert sugar. Maltose consists of two molecules of glucose with a glycoside linkage formed between the anomeric hydroxyl of one glucose unit and the hydroxyl on the fourth carbon atom of the next. Maltose does not occur in natural foods. It is found as an intermediate product by the action of enzymes, amylases,on starch. Lactose is a constituent of mammalian milk and is composed of glucose and galactose. Raffinose and stachyose are formed by the additions of one and two galactose residues respectively to a sucrose molecule. The structures of food oligosaccharides are given in Fig.2.2.

2.4 Function of Sugars in Foods

Apart from their nutritional value, sugars have other functions in foods. They function as humecants (compounds which absorb moisture from air), plasticizers, texturizing agents, flavour producing agents, and sweeteners. The first three of these functions depend upon the sugar-water relationship. The flavour-producing function depends upon the reactions sugars undergo when subjected to heat in sterilization, cooking and dehydration processes. The sweetness of sugars depends upon their ability to form hydrogen bonds (see Sec. 11.3) with water, with other polar compounds and among themselves.

Carbohydrates are hydrophilic to different degrees depending upon their structures. The rates and extent of water absorption by sugars depend upon their absolute purity, their anomeric purity, whether or not they form stable crystalline hydrates and the homogeneity of their crystalline structure. Water uptake causes dissolution, equilibration of anomeric forms and acyclic forms, and hydrolysis of glycosidic bonds. The hygroscopicity of sugars, dextrins and their mixtures is an important factors affecting the acceptance of confections, bakery toppings, and instantly reconstitutable powders or granules that must not become sticky. Sugars like maltose and lactose, with their limited uptake of water, are particularly useful in such products. More hygroscopic liquid sugars, such as invert sugar or glucose syrup, are used to help retain moisture in baked foods, plastic confectionery, and fillings that should not become brittle. To retain plasticity and inhibit crystallization, starch hydrolysates (which contain non-crystallizing malto-oligosaccharides) or sorbitol, are used. Concentrated syrups are used to give a firm texture to fruits. These withdraw water from fruits by osmosis, and sugar molecules enter the cells to form complexes with cell-wall polysaccharides, resulting in a firmer structure.

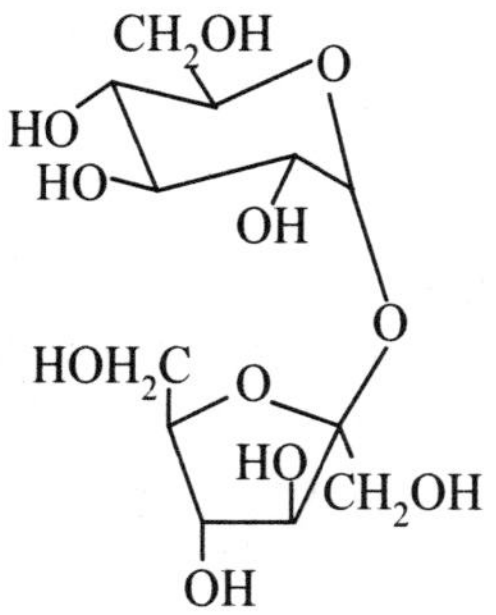

Sucrose
(β-D-Fructofuranosyl-
α-D-glucopyranose)

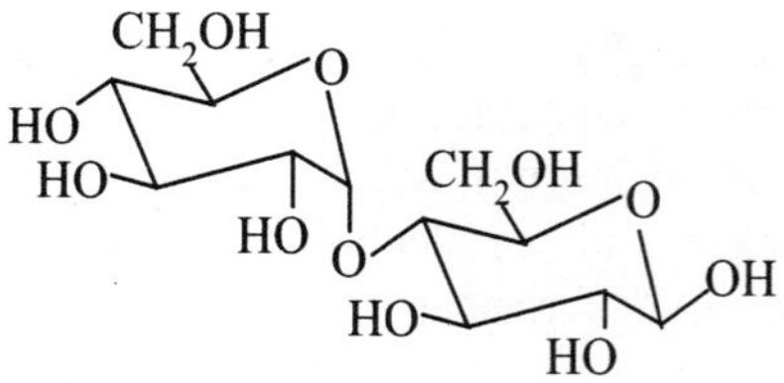

β-Maltose
(4-0- α-D. Glucopyranosyl-
β-D-glucopyranose)

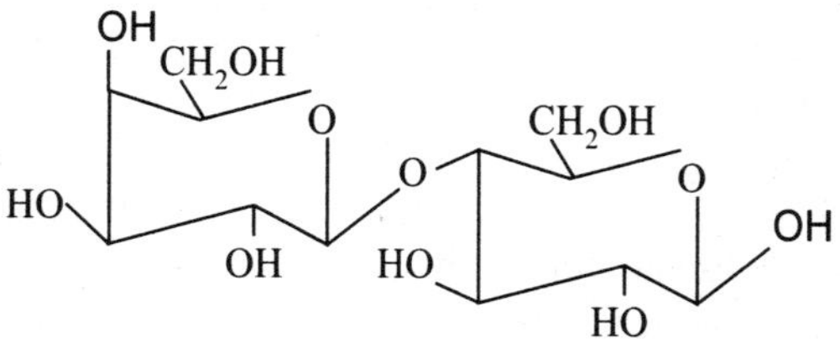

β -Lactose
(4-0-β-Galactopyranosyl-
β-D-glucopyranose)

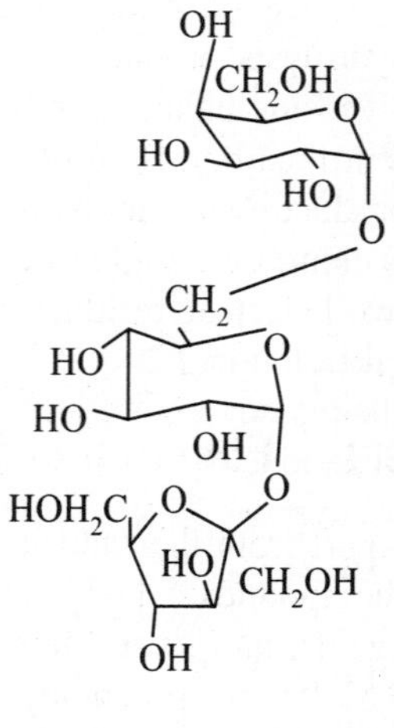

Raffinose
(α-D-Galactopyranosyl-(1→6)
O-α-D-glucopyranosyl-(1→2)
-D-fructofuranoside)

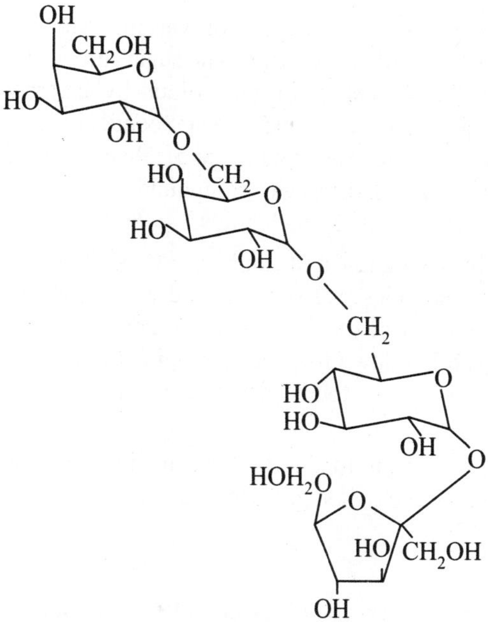

Stachyose
α-D-Galactopyranosyl-(1 → 6) – O –
α-D-galactopyranosyl-(1 → 6) – O –
α-D-glucopyranosyl-(1 → 2) – β – D –
fructofuranoside

Fig. 2.2 Conformational formula of common oligosaccharides

2.4.1 Browning Reactions (Non-enzymic)

The non-enzymic browning reactions are responsible for the colour and flavour of foods, such as dates, honey and chocolate. The distinctive flavours that coffee beans, groundnuts, cashewnuts and breakfast cereals develop after roasting is due to browning reactions. The presence of reactive reducing sugars is responsible for browning in foods. On heating they undergo ring opening, enolization, dehydration and fragmentation. The unsaturated carbonyl compounds that are formed react to produce brown polymers and flavour compounds. The heat-induced browning reactions occur in two ways; caramelization and the Maillard reaction.

Caramelization: Sugars in dry condition or their syrups, when heated, undergo a number of reactions, depending upon the temperature and presence of catalysts. Generally, there will be reactions leading to equilibration of anomeric and ring forms, inversion of sucrose, condensation reactions leading to the formation of oligosaccharides and polysaccharides, isomerization, dehydration and fragmentation, leading to the formation of unsaturated polymers with brown colour. With the use of proper catalysts it would be possible to conduct caramelization to provide either flavouring or colouring caramel for food use. For flavouring purposes, sucrose in concentrated syrups is caramelized. For the manufacture of caramel colours for use in beverages, glucose syrups treated with dilute sulphuric acid partially neutralized with ammonia are used.

Maillard reaction: The Maillard reaction is actually a complex group of many reactions. The carbonyl group of acyclic sugars readily combines with the basic amino groups of proteins, peptides, and amino acids, resulting in sugar amines. The set of various reactions sugar amines undergo, resulting in browning, is known as the Maillard reaction. The sugar-amines form a brown colour at a lower temperature than that for the formation of the colour by caramelization. Hence, Maillard reaction products predominate in browned foods. The condensation product of sugar and amines undergoes enolization and rearrangement and then undergoes condensation and polymerization, forming red-brown and dark-brown compounds. The brown to black, amorphous unsaturated, heterogeneous polymers are called "melanoids."

Inhibition of the Maillard-browning reaction can be accomplished by keeping the pH below the isoelectric pH of the amino acids, peptides and proteins and by keeping the temperature as low as possible during processing and storage. Use of non-reducing sugars, such as sucrose, under conditions not favouring inversion, also helps bring down Maillard browning. Sulphur dioxide and sulphites used in extending the storage life of dehydrated foods, fruit juices and wines also inhibit the browning reaction.

Sweetness of sugars: The most important function of sugars in food concerns their role as sweeteners. For an account of the sweetness of sugar, see Chap. 9

2.5 Polysaccharides

Most of the carbohydrates in nature occur as polysaccharides. They are formed by a few types of hexoses, hexose derivatives (uronic acids and sulphate esters) and pentoses. They are high-molecular-weight substances composed of a large number of monosaccharide units combined to form one large molecule or polymer. They consist of a primary chain and, in some, side chains or branches may exist. The primary chain usually consists of one, but sometimes two, types of monosaccharide units. The side chains may consist of sugars different from those of the main chain, with different types of glycosidic linkages. Polysaccharides commonly found in foods are starch, dextrins, glycogen, cellulose, hemicellulose, pentosans and pectic substances.

The generic name of polysaccharides is "glycans." If they are composed of a single type of monosaccharide unit, they are homoglycans, and if of two or more monosaccharide units, they are heteroglycans. Glycans that release only glucose on hydrolysis are glucans (hexosan) and xylose, xylans (pentosan). Similarly, other homoglycans are called mannan, galactan, fructan and araban depending upon the sugar released on the hydrolysis of the polysaccharide. Heteroglycans composed of two sugars are called galactomannan, glucomannan, arabinogalactan, etc., depending on the sugars present. The names of some well-known polysaccharides end in "in," for example, chitin, dextrin, inulin (fructan) and pectin.

Polysaccharides serve plants and animals in three ways: Cellulose, hemicellulose, pentosans and pectic substances provide structural material (cell walls, fibres, seed coats, peels and husks). Chitin and mucopolysaccharides (polysaccharides containing amino sugars) serve this purpose in animals. Structural polysaccharides are indigestible substances; nevertheless, they are important for human health. They provide the bulk in the diet and aid excretion. Starch, dextrin and fructan in plants, and glycogen in animals, provide food reserves. These polysaccharides are digested and utilized by the human body. They are nutritionally important. Polysaccharides attract and retain water so that life's enzymic processes are not impeded under dehydrating conditions.

2.5.1 Properties of Polysaccharides

There are great differences in the solution properties of various polysaccharides. Some disperse rapidly in water, some are quite insoluble, and others disperse as swollen particles or globules. A few form clear solutions at moderate concentrations. Some form gels at low concentrations, some gel only at high concentrations and others do not gel at all. Some form gels that are translucent and others opaque. The differences in the solution properties of polysaccharides are related to their monosaccharide composition, type of chemical linkages among sugar units, hydrogen bonding and ionic interaction between and among polymers and the gross conformation of the hydrated polymer in solution.

The structure of polysaccharides influences their interaction with water. Hydrogen bonds are formed between the hydroxyl groups of the polysaccharide and water. Layers of water molecules adjacent to the hydroxyl groups of polysaccharides are, therefore, partially ordered and immobilized, and assist the dissolution or dispersion of the large molecules. As the hydrated macromolecules move in circles the water aggregates can be rearranged or displaced. By folding or coiling, the polysaccharide molecule can associate with itself to form loops. Hydrogen bonding between sections of different molecules can result in the formation of crystalloid regions (micelles). Linear polysaccharides can associate through intramolecular hydrogen bonding to form gels and, if the solution is dilute, it may result in precipitation (retrogradation). Branching side-chains or negative charges like those of carboxyl groups of uronic acids distributed along the linear polysaccharide molecules inhibit intramolecular association.

At the same concentration, solutions of linear polysaccharides have greater viscosities than those of the branched polysaccharides of the same molecular weight. If the polysaccharide contains carboxyl groups the viscosity is more pH-dependent. At low pH values carboxyl groups are un-ionized. Therefore, solutions of polysaccharides containing acidic groups can form gels upon the addition of polyvalent cations since the ions readily form intermolecular salt bridges.

2.5.2 Starch

This is the principal food-reserve polysaccharide of the plant kingdom, where it occurs in cereal grains, pulses, tubers, bulbs and fruits in varying amounts from a few per cent to over 75 per cent in the case of several grains. Starch provides the major source of energy in the diet of man. Much of the starch is consumed without being isolated from the plant material in which it occurs. Refined starch, either natural or modified, also plays an important role in food preparations.

Starches contain only glucose residues. They are mixtures of the structurally distinct polysaccharides, amylose and amylopectin. Cereal starches usually contain 25 per cent amylose and 75 per cent amylopectin. Waxy or glutinous starches like waxy corn starch contain little or no amylose. Waxy varieties of corn and sorghum starches have found use in food-pie fillings and puddings. Amylose has great industrial possibilities and hence, by breeding, corn with starch of high amylose content (about 85 per cent), has been obtained. In addition to these components, starch granules commonly contain small amounts of proteins, fatty substances and inorganic material. The non-carbohydrate constituents are of relatively little importance in relation to food use, but they affect the physical properties of starch.

Amylose consists of glucose units linked by α -(1→4) bonds, i.e., the anomeric hydroxyl of one glucose unit is in glycosidic linkage with carbon-atom 4 of the next glucose unit (Fig. 2.3). The chain length of amylose varies and it is considered to have a molecular weight of 1.1 to 1.9 million. Amylose is not truely soluble in water but forms hydrated micelles. In such micelles the long chain is twisted into a helical coil. It is this structure of amylose that is responsible for the blue colour produced by iodine with starch. The structure of amylose contributes to the gelling characteristics of cooked and cooled starches.

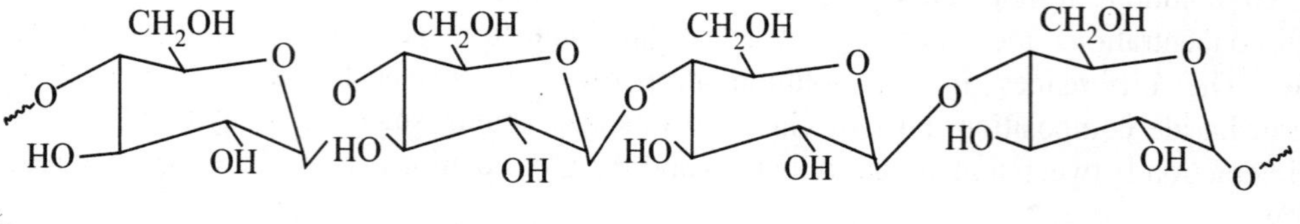

Fig. 2.3 Partial structure of amylose

Amylopectin also has a backbone of α -(1→4) linkages but, in addition, the molecule is branched through α -(1→6) linkages to the extent of 4-5 per cent. The length of the linear unit in amylopectin is about 20-25 glucose units. Amylopectin has a brushlike structure and its molecular weight is over 10 million. Amylopectin is responsible for the thickened properties of starch preparations, but it does not contribute to gel formation. The partial structure of amylopectin is given in Fig. 2.4.

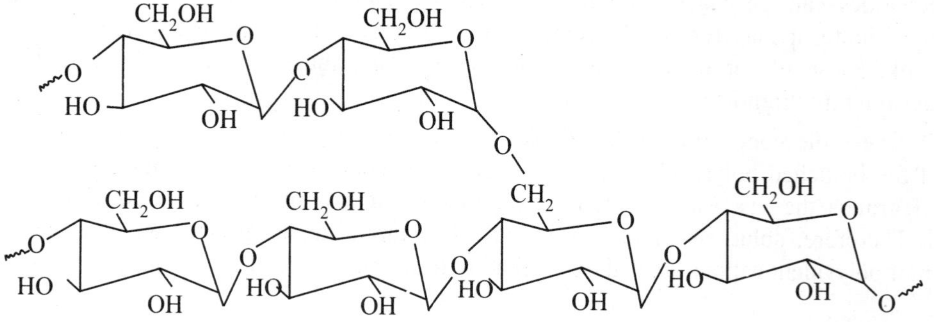

Fig. 2.4 Partial structure of amylopectin

Granular structure: Starch occurs as granules in the cytoplasm of the cells. The granules remain essentially intact during most types of processing, such as milling, separation and purification of starch, and even during most types of chemical modification. The microscopic appearance of starch granules from different sources is different, and thus they can be identified by this method alone. The unique characteristics of granules are their sizes, shapes, uniformity, location, and the appearance of granules under polarized light (birefringence).

Within the starch granules, a mixture of linear and branched molecules is arranged in concentric shells. When parallel association exists between adjacent linear molecules or between the outer branches of the branched molecules, they are held together by hydrogen bonds resulting in crystalloid regions or micelles, and this causes the granules to be birefringent. More loosely packed regions are amorphous and they exist between the micelles in each concentric shell. Water can easily enter the amorphous regions of the grain.

Gelatinization: Cereal starches under normal conditions usually have a moisture content of 12-14 per cent. Cold water can penetrate amorphous regions of starch without disturbing the micelles and a maximum water content of about 30 per cent can be obtained. If the mixture is heated, the intramolecular hydrogen bonding is broken, the grains absorb more water and swell. The swelling causes loss of birefringence. The temperature at which the granules begin to swell rapidly and lose birefringence is called the "gelatinization temperature." This change is completed with a given starch sample with a rise of a few degrees in temperature after gelatinization sets in because the individual granules within any starch sample differ not only in size and shape but also in the energy required for bringing about swelling. Thus, it is more appropriate to call the temperature of gelation the gelatinization temperature range. The gelatinization temperature range is somewhat specific for starches from different sources and this property is useful for the purposes of identification of starch.

As the temperature of the starch suspension is increased above the gelatinization range, the granules continue to swell, if sufficient water is present. Additional swelling increases the viscosity as the swollen granules begin to collide frequently. In some cases the fragile granules may be torn into fragments, causing a reduction in viscosity. The viscosity changes depend on the temperature, initial concentration of starch suspension, size of the granules, the internal forces holding the molecules together within the granule and the effect of the other ingredients in the system.

When a starch-thickened mixture is allowed to cool without stirring, there is a tendency for intramolecular bonds to form resulting in the formation of a more or less rigid gel. This is because the hydrogen bonding between molecules becomes more extensive, thereby increasing the micellar regions. The growth of micelles results in the gel becoming firm. When only amylopectin molecules are present, as in waxy starches, the branches prevent the degree of association for gel formation, except when an extremely high starch concentration of about 30 per cent or more is present. Waxy starches form a soft thick mass rather than stiff gels. This characteristic, together with translucence and slow retrogradation, make waxy corn and sorghum starches useful in pie fillings and similar products.

In a very dilute solution of starch, the individual amylose molecules are not sufficiently entangled to produce a gel so that the growing micelles eventually cause precipitation. This is known as "retrogradation." The rate and extent of retrogradation is also, influenced by temperature, size, shape of starch granules and other ingredients present. Retrogradation is more rapid at temperatures near 0° C. Even waxy starches, which do not form gels except at very high concentration, retrograde under frozen conditions.

Amylose can form strong and flexible films which are water soluble and edible. Presence of amylopectin decreases the intermolecular binding and prevents the formation of films. This difficulty can be overcome by using high-amylose starch. Foods can be coated with a thin film of amylose to improve water retention and decrease surface thickness in dehydrated fruits.

Modified starches: As has already been discussed, unmodified starches from different sources differ in size, shape, appearance and gelation temperature and gel-forming ability. Increased knowledge of the molecular and granular structure of starches has helped modify starches to meet the specific needs of food and other industries. Modified starches are not toxic and their digestibility appears to be little affected.

Pregelatinized starches are those that are cooked and dried to give products that readily disperse in cold water to give moderately stable suspensions. Dispersions of pregelatinized starch have a less desirable texture than cooked dispersions prepared from untreated starch. Nevertheless, pregelatinized starch dispersions have some characteristics of the original starches. This has led to their wide use in the preparation of instant puddings, pie fillings, soup mixes, salad dressings, etc.

Starches are modified by suspending granular starch in a very dilute acid at a temperature below its gelatinization temperature. This results in "thin boiling" starch. This method hydrolyzes sufficient molecules in the granules so that, on heating with water, a product with low viscosity but which can form a firm gel upon cooling and ageing is produced. Acid-modified starches are used in the manufacture of starch gum confections (gum drops).

The extent of swelling and ultimate breakdown of starch granules during cooking can be controlled by introducing cross bonding between starch molecules, using suitable reagents. Chemical crosslinking can induce gel formation in the hydrated starch. By appropriate treatments, starch granules whiter in colour, improved gel strength and clarity, greater paste stability and paste viscosity, can be obtained.

2.5.3 Dextrin

These are products of the partial breakdown of starches. Dextrins are intermediate in size between starches and sugars and exhibit properties that are intermediate between these classes of materials. These are formed, amongst other methods, when starch is subjected to dry heat. The toasting of bread converts a part of starch to dextrin. The sweet taste of toast is due to this change.

2.5.4 Glycogen

This is the storage polysaccharide in animals, and hence is sometimes called animal starch. This is mainly present in the liver and skeletal muscle. Liver glycogen rapidly hydrolyzes to D-glucose after slaughter of animals. Glycogen is a branched-chain polysaccharide resembling amylopectin rather than amylose, but is more branched than amylopectin.

2.5.5 Cellulose

Cellulose makes up more than 25 per cent of cell walls in higher plants and this one polysaccharide is said to account for nearly half the world's supply of carbon. In woody tissues, cellulose molecules are associated into partially crystalline microfibrils. However, in vegetable pulp cells it has little fibrous character. Cellulose is found embedded in an amorphous gel composed of hemicellulose and pectic substances. In the case of fruits and vegetables, texture is more important than flavour. Changes in cell wall constituents surrounding the cellulose, and in the interstitial matrix, are largely responsible for the changes in the texture of fruits and vegetables during ripening, storage and processing.

Cellulose, like amylose, is composed of long chains of glucose residues with (1→4) linkages, but the linkages in cellulose are β-rather than α-configuration of amylose. As with amylose, the cellulose has a very high molecular weight. The fibrous polysaccharide does not dissolve in water to any extent. Cellulose is not digested in the human system and acts as roughage or dietary fibre. It can be broken down to glucose by certain microbial enzymes. This is the way cellulose is hydrolyzed in the rumen of animals to provide them with sugar.

Some modified celluloses find use in food industries. Avicel is partially hydrolyzed cellulose and is sometimes added to foods to contribute bulk without calories. Carboxymethyl cellulose (CMC) is used in the manufacture of ice cream. It contributes a good body and smooth texture, retards the enlargement of ice crystals during storage and improves the melting characteristics of ice cream. CMC also finds numerous other uses in foods. Other derivatives of cellulose-hydroxypropylmethyl cellulose, methyl-methyl cellulose, etc., also find use in food industries.

2.5.6 Hemicelluloses

Hemicelluloses are a poorly defined group of substances. They cover the polysaccharides, other than cellulose, starch and pectic substances, that occur in land plants. They are insoluble in water but, unlike cellulose, are soluble in alkali. Some hemicelluloses are composed predominantly of pentoses (xylose); others contain hexuronic acids and occasionally L-rhamnose. Hemicellulose helps cement together closely packed cellulose microfilaments. Together with cellulose, hemicellulose forms a portion of undigested carbohydrate and is therefore a dietary fibre.

2.5.7 Pectic Substances

Pectic substances occur as constituents of plant cell walls and in the middle lamella. In the latter, they serve as cementing material to hold cells together. They are mixtures of polysaccharides formed from galactose, arabinose and galacturonic acid, the last being predominant. The carboxyl groups of galacturonic acids are partly esterified with methyl groups and partly or completely neutralized by one or more bases (Fig. 2.5).

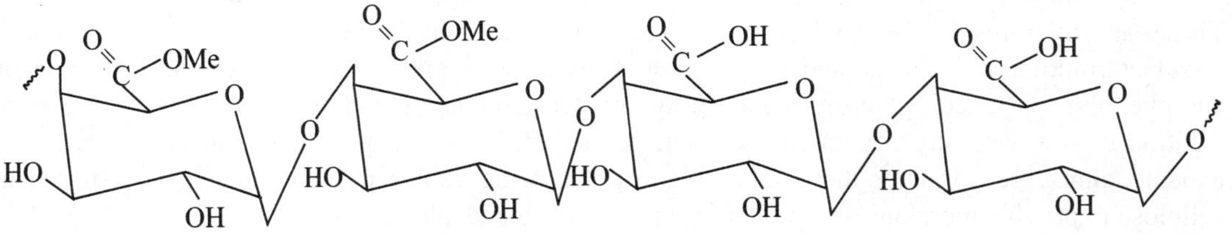

Fig. 2.5 Partial structure of pectic substances

The water-insoluble parent pectic substance that occurs in plants is protopectin. This, in fruits, decreases during ripening and soluble pectin increases. Protopectin on restricted hydrolysis, gives pectinic acid and pectin. Pectinic acid forms a colloidal solution and contains more than a negligible proportion of methylester groups. It is capable of forming gels with sugar and acid. Pectin is water-soluble pectinic acid with a varying methyl ester content and degree of neutralization. Pectin forms gel with sugar and acid under suitable conditions. Pectic acid is mostly galacturonic acid and is essentially free from methyl ester groups.

Commercial pectin is obtained by extraction of citrus peels (or from apple pomace) with dilute acid. The product in which at least 50 per cent of the carboxyl groups of galacturonic acids are methylated is used in the manufacture of jams and jellies. For rapid-set of jellies the degree of methylation should be high (about 60). For gel formation, sugar (65-70 per cent), acid (pH 2.3-3.2), water and pectin must be present. The acid increases the unionized carboxyl groups which decrease the attraction between pectin and water molecules, thus decreasing the ability of pectin to remain in a dispersed state. Sugar further decreases the hydration of pectin by competing for water. The unstable dispersion of the less hydrated pectin forms a gel when cooled. Pectin with a low methoxyl content forms a gel by the cross-linkages established between free carboxyl groups and divalent cations like calcium. Gel-formation does not require the presence of sugar in such cases.

2.5.8 Gums

Gums are hydrophilic substances that give a viscous solution or dispersion when treated with hot or cold water. Most gums are polysaccharides and included in this definition are starches, pectic substances and some derivatives of starches and cellulose, which have been already considered. Other natural polysaccharide gums are seed gums, plant exudates and seaweed gums.

Gums are incorporated to improve the texture, water retention and rehydration of many dehydrated, frozen and "instant" convenient foods. Ice cream, gelled desserts, salad dressings, baked goods, processed cheese and encased ground meats are some of the examples of the foods whose qualities have been improved by the addition of gums. Gums function as thickeners for gravies and sauces, moisture retention agents in baked goods, emulsion stabilizers in salad dressings, protective colloids in chocolate milk and syrup, foam stabilizers in whipped popping and beer, clarifying agents for wines and beer, flavour fixing agents and lubricants.

The seed gums commonly used are guar (guaran) obtained from the common Indian pulse guar *(Cyamopsis tetragonoloba)* and locust bean gum (from *Ceratonica siliqua*). These are long-chain polysaccharides of β -D mannose and α -D-galactose (galactomannans) with branched units. These give colloidal dispersions of high viscosity that are stable over the pH range of foods and are not affected by heat processing, freezing, acids, salts or proteins in the food product. They form complexes with other gums which help modify the texture of their gels.

The best-known plant exudates are gum arabic (Acacia), karaya (Sterculia) and tragacanth. These are mixtures of heteroglycans containing the monosaccharides D-galactose, L-arabinose, D-galacturonic acid, L-fucose and L-rhamnose. They are generally contaminated with proteinaceous and phenolic substances, glycosides and foreign matter. Gum arabic is more soluble in water giving a solution of low viscosity compared with other gums. Because the quality, quantity and markets of exudate gums are variable, these natural gums are being replaced by derivatives of starch and cellulose to provide more uniform properties and more dependable supplies,

Agar is an extract from red and brown algae. It is mainly β -D- and α -L-galactan where galactose residues are sulphated at various hydroxyl positions. Neutral fractions called "agarose" or "agaran" can be separated from agar. Agar forms the strongest and most stable gels at the lowest concentration. Agar gels are transparent and reversible upon heating and cooling. Therefore, agar finds several uses in stabilizing food products.

Carrageenans are also sulphated galactans from seaweed extracts. They are both gel-forming and non-gel-forming carrageenan fractions. Both form stable complexes with proteins and other gums. Carrageenans are especially useful in dairy products because they form the stabilizing complexes with milk proteins and suspended cocoa powder in milk, and give a more acceptable texture to processed cheese and cream.

Algin is a product of brown algae. It is composed of D-mannuronic and D-galacturonic acids. The carboxylic groups are neutralized by various natural cations. If they are replaced by a single cation (sodium, potassium, ammonium, etc.) the product is called an "alginate." When the cations are removed insoluble alginic acids are produced. Alginates give widely variable sols and viscosity properties in acid and salt solutions. They form gels and films and find a number of food uses.

Some microbial gums also find use in foods. Two important ones are dextran and xanthan gums. Dextran is formed by the action of *Leuconostoc mesenteroids* on sucrose. It is a polysaccharide consisting of α -D-glucose units, 95 per cent of the units being linked by α -(1→6) linkages and 5 per cent α -(1→3) linkages. Dextran of molecular weight below 100,000 is readily soluble in water and is used in many food products.

Xanthans are formed by the action of the bacterium *Xanthomonas comestris* on D-glucose. The gum contains D-glucose, D-mannose and D-galacturonic acid and has a high molecular weight. It dissolves in cold water and finds use in food as a stabilizer, emulsifier, thickener, suspending agent, bodying and foam enhancer.

CHAPTER

3 Lipids

The term "lipid" is used to denote diverse types of compounds which are insoluble in water but soluble in nonpolar solvents, such as chloroform, carbon disulphide, benzene and ether. The characteristic insolubility of lipids in water is, in several cases, due to the presence in them of one or more fatty acids which contain long aliphatic hydrocarbon chains. Lipids are widely distributed in nature. They rarely occur in an organism in the free state, but are more usually combined with proteins (lipoproteins) or carbohydrates (lipopolysaccharides or glycolipids).

3.1 Classification

Lipids are broadly classified into two groups, simple lipids and compound lipids. Simple lipids include fatty acids, fats which are esters of fatty acids with glycerol (triglycerides), and waxes which are esters of fatty acids with long chain monohydroxy alcohols. All other lipids are included under compound lipids. These include phosphoglycerides (phospholipids or phosphatides), steroids, carotenoids, and lipids functioning as vitamins or hormones.

Foods may contain any or all these substances but those of greatest interest are fats (acylglycerols or triglycerides) and phospholipids. The term "fat" is generally applied to all triglycerides regardless of whether they are normally non-liquid or liquid at room temperature. Triglycerides from animal sources contain a higher percentage of saturated fatty acids and are normally solids at room temperature and known as fats. The plant triglycerides are rich in unsaturated fatty acids, are generally liquids at room temperature and called "oils".

3.2 Role of Lipids

One of the major roles of lipids in foods is to serve as fuel molecules. Triglycerides constitute a pool of stored energy. They are a more highly concentrated form of metabolic energy than carbohydrates. When oxidized, a gram of fat gives more than twice (9 Kcal) as much energy as proteins or carbohydrates. This is because fats are more highly reduced than carbohydrates and proteins. It is desirable that lipids supply 20 to 30 per cent of the total calorie requirement. When energy supply from foods is in excess of energy demand, the excess is preferentially stored as fats in the adipose tissue. As a storage fuel, fats have an advantage as they can be stored in an anhydrous form while glycogen, the stored polysaccharide, is heavily hydrated. Taking into account these two properties of fats, a gram of fat stores more than six times as much energy as a gram of glycogen and this energy is mobilized for use by the body when needed. Carbohydrates and proteins can be converted into fat when energy and growth requirements have been satisfied. Fatty acids are not converted into proteins or carbohydrates. These complex processes are co-ordinated by hormones.

Lipids in the form of triglycerides, phospholipids, cholesterol and cholesterol esters, are important to the structure, composition and permeability of membranes and cell walls. They perform the function of energy storage in seeds and fruits. Lipids are a major component of adipose tissue. Skin waxes act as insulation barriers to avoid thermal and physical shock. Some fats play a solvent-like role—the dietary fats help carry fat-soluble vitamins so that they are efficiently absorbed. Fats serve as vitamins, emulsifiers, and flavour and aroma components.

3.3 Fatty Acids

A fatty acid is a long-chain carboxylic acid, $CH_3 (CH_2)_n COOH$. A considerable variety of fatty acids occur in nature. Most natural fatty acids contain an even number of carbon atoms due to their mode of biosynthesis, but odd-numbered fatty acids do occur naturally. Most fatty acids are linear, though some branched-chain and cyclic fatty acids are also found in nature.

3.3.1 Saturated Fatty Acids

Although straight-chain saturated fatty acids containing from 2 to 80 carbon atoms per molecule are known, generally those containing C_2 to C_{20} and particularly those containing C_{16} and C_{18} are found in most animal and vegetable fats. Table 3.1 gives the trivial name, systematic name and structure of some saturated fatty acids found in food lipids.

Table 3.1 Some saturated fatty acids found in food lipids

Trivial name	Systematic name	Structure
Butyric	Tetranoic acid	$CH_3 (CH_2)_2 COOH$
Valeric	Pentanoic	$CH_3 (CH_2)_3 COOH$
Caproic	Hexanoic	$CH_3 (CH_2)_4 COOH$
Enanthic	Heptanoic	$CH_3 (CH_2)_5 COOH$
Caprylic	Octanoic	$CH_3 (CH_2)_6 COOH$
Capric	Decanoic	$CH_3 (CH_2)_8 COOH$
Lauric	Dodecanoic	$CH_3 (CH_2)_{10} COOH$
Myristic	Tetradecanoic	$CH_3 (CH_2)_{12} COOH$
Palmitic	Hexadecanoic	$CH_3 (CH_2)_{14} COOH$
Stearic	Octadecanoic	$CH_3 (CH_2)_{16} COOH$
Arachidic	Eicosanoic	$CH_3 (CH_2)_{18} COOH$
Behenic	Docosanoic	$CH_3 (CH_2)_{20} COOH$
Lignoceric	Tetracosanoic	$CH_3 (CH_2)_{22} COOH$

Saturated fatty acids with more than 24 carbon atoms seldom occur in food triglycerides, but do so in waxes. The lower members C_4—C_{10} occur mainly in milk fat. Those of chain-length C_{12}—C_{24} are found in most animal and vegetable fats. Fatty acids with odd-numbered carbon atoms are found in animal and vegetable fats, but they seldom exceed 1-2 per cent of the total fat. The most commonly encountered saturated acids are lauric, myristic, palmitic and stearic.

3.3.2 Unsaturated Fatty Acids

Unsaturated fatty acids differing with respect to number of carbon atoms and double-bond characteristics are found in lipids. Unsaturated acids may have one to six double bonds. Polyunsaturated acids usually have a methylene (CH_2) group between double bonds. Double bonds occur in many locations but a regularity of position is seen in most of the acids commonly found in food fats. The unsaturation in different acids is at a definite location with respect to the carboxyl carbon number one or CH_3 ("ω" carbon atom) and they have *cis* configuration. The unsaturated fatty acids found in lipids are given in Table 3.2.

Table 3.2 Some unsaturated fatty acids found in food lipids

Trivial name	Systematic name	Structure
Myristoleic	9-Tetradecenoic	$CH_3(CH_2)_3CH{=}CH(CH_2)_7COOH$
Palmitoleic	9-Hexadecenoic	$CH_3(CH_2)_5CH{=}CH(CH_2)_7COOH$
Oleic	9-Octadecenoic	$CH_3(CH_2)_7CH{=}CH(CH_2)_7COOH$
Linoleic	9,12-Octadecadienoic	$CH_3(CH_2)_4CH{=}CH\ CH_2CH{=}CH\ (CH_2)_7COOH$
Linolenic	9,12.15-Octadecatrienoic	$CH_3(CH_2CH{=}CH)_3(CH_2)_7COOH$
Arachidonic	5,8,11,14-Eicosatetraenoic	$CH_3(CH_2)_3(CH_2CH{=}CH)_4(CH_2)_3COOH$

Oleic acid is found in almost all fats. It is a dominant compound of olive oil in which it is present up to a concentration of 75 per cent. Linoleic acid is present in high concentration in many fats and oils. It is present to the extent of 60-80 per cent in safflowerseed oil. This acid enters into a number of reactions involving oxidation, polymerization and lipoprotein interaction. Linolenic acid comprises 50-60 per cent of the fatty acid in linseed oil. Arachidonic acid which is C_{20} tetraenoic acid is found primarily in animal sources. It is a component of many phospholipids and a precursor of prostaglandins.

3.3.3 Essential Fatty Acids

Fatty acids containing more than one double bond (polyunsaturated) are derived from those containing one double bond. The way in which the new double bond is introduced between the existing double bond and the carboxyl group differs in plants and animals. Linoleic acid, which contains two double bonds, and certain acids derived from it, are necessary to maintain animals in a healthy condition. Animals are unable to desaturate oleic acid to linoleic acid. Therefore, the latter must be supplied in the diet from plant sources. Linoleic acid and other unsaturated acids formed from it are, therefore, known as essential fatty acids.

3.4 Triglycerides

Triglycerides are the acyl derivatives of glycerol. The position of an acyl group in glycerides is indicated by the term "Sn" (stereospecifically numbered) in which the carbon atoms of glycerol are projected in a vertical line, and the secondary hydroxyl is shown to the left and the top carbon atom is C-l. Thus, a triglyceride containing palmitic, oleic and stearic acid residues in positions 1, 2 and 3 respectively of glycerol is named Sn-glycerol-1 palmi–to-2-oleo-3-stearate or simply palmito-oleo-stearate.

In triglycerides, all the glycerol hydroxyl groups are esterified. Partial glycerides with only one or two hydroxyl groups esterified are called mono- and diglycerides respectively. The structures of these are given in Fig. 3.1. R_1, R_2 and R_3, represent fatty acid residues. If R_1 R_2, and R_3, are the same, i.e., only one fatty acid species is present, the triglyceride is a simple glyceride. If they are different, the glyceride is referred to as "mixed triglyceride." Natural triglycerides are mixtures of mixed triglycerides.

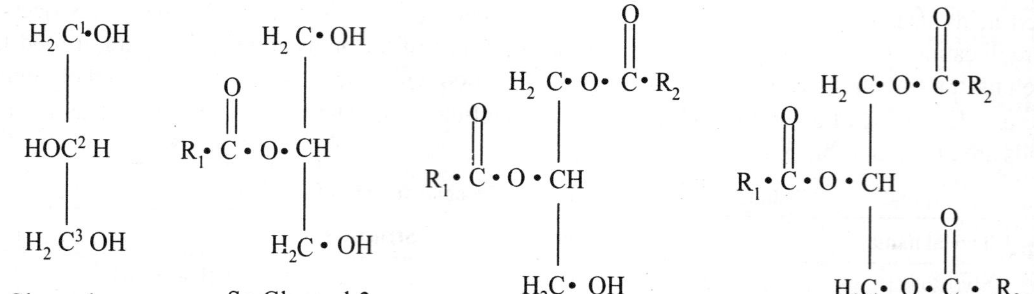

Glycerol Sn-Glycerol-2-monoglyceride Sn-Glycerol 1,2-diglyceride Sn-Glycerol-1,2,3-triglyceride

Fig. 3.1 Structure of glycerides

3.5 Physical Characteristics

Knowledge of the physical properties of fats is useful for evaluating the utility of a fat for a specific purpose and for determining the stage of processing. As fats are mixtures of triglycerides, they do not have a sharp melting point; they have a melting range. Fats with a narrow range or sharp melting point are required for confectionery purposes, while for shortenings, fats with a broad range or gradual melting range are required. The specific heat of fats is useful in processing operations. It increases with the increasing unsaturation of fatty acids. Viscosity increases with an increase in the average chain-length of fatty acids in triglycerides and decreases with increasing unsaturation. Viscosity is a factor that must be considered when designing systems for handling fats. Knowledge of the density of fats helps determine the solid-liquid ratio in commercial fats. This could be determined more rapidly by nuclear magnetic resonance (NMR) spectroscopy. The cold test, which is a measure of the time required for an oil to develop a cloudy appearance when held in an ice bath, is useful to determine the use of the oil for salad dressing. The refractive index of fat increases with the increasing chain-length of fatty acids in the triglycerides or with increasing unsaturation. The refractive index can, therefore, be used to control the process during hydrogenation.

3.5.1 Polymorphism

Polymorphism is the phenomenon in which a substance occurs in different crystalline forms, e.g., the existence of carbon in common black form or as diamond. Certain triglycerides are found to exist in polymorphic forms. The forms have different melting points. Tristearin can exist in three forms with melting points 53°, 64.2° and 71.7°C. Polymorphs also differ in X-ray diffraction patterns and infrared spectra. This is because of different modes of molecular packing in the crystal.

The X-ray analysis of polymorphic crystals provides information about the packing density of the molecules and, therefore, a measure of the degree of randomness of molecular orientation in a given polymorphic form. Infrared spectroscopy gives the characteristics of the subcell packing in the crystals. Based on this information, a monoacid trisaturated glyceride shows three forms— α , β' and β. Triglycerides containing different fatty acids with varying chain lengths and degrees of unsaturation exhibit even greater complex polymorphic behaviour.

Tempering: Newly processed fats may not be in the polymorphic form and physical state in which they are most useful. A process that permits the formation of the proper polymorphic form is known as tempering. This is done by the controlled removal of the heat of transformation during crystallization. Tempering at different temperatures allows the formation of different sets of mixed crystals, melting over a wide range of temperatures.

Shortening: The quality of shortening of fat depends on the incorporation of air, plasticity and consistency, and solid-liquid ratio. Polymorphs differ in their abilities to incorporate air during plasticizing (the whipping of air into fat during the crystallization stage, to give whiter, creamier, smoother and more uniform creaming). β' crystals assist in the incorporation of an abundant quantity of very small air bubbles, while β crystals result in the incorporation of a small amount of large bubbles.

Air incorporation in batters is important, since the volume, texture and tenderness of baked products depend upon the size and number of air bubbles in the batter. β' crystals are best for use in cakes, while β crystals are very unsatisfactory. Vegetable fats, partially hydrogenated in a manner that favours β' crystal formation, have good air incorporation properties.

3.6 Reactions of Fats

The stability of a fat or fatty food is important to maintain a fresh taste or odour during storage and use. The stability is related to the composition of the lipid moiety and the changes it is subjected to. Fats with substantial unsaturation in the fatty acids are usually unstable. The presence of agents causing oxidation (pro-oxidants) or preventing oxidation (anti-oxidants) and the methods of storage determine their stability. Vegetable fats are usually more stable than some of the animal fats, such as lard even though the total unsaturation of the vegetable oils may be greater, because of the natural anti-oxidants usually present in them.

3.6.1 Rancidity

The change that a lipid undergoes leading to an undesirable flavour and odour is known as rancidity. This is brought about in two ways: hydrolysis and oxidation.

The ester linkages of lipids are hydrolyzed to yield fatty acids. Hydrolysis is catalyzed by acids, bases, enzymes or thermal effects. When a base is the hydrolyzing agent, the liberated fatty acids are converted into their salts, or soaps, and the hydrolysis is termed "saponification." The other agents release free fatty acids and the reactions brought about by them are collectively known as lipolysis, "lipolytic rancidity"or "hydrolytic rancidity."

Hydrolytic rancidity occurs in raw milk and is important for the flavours of various milk products. The flavour of rancid milk is due to even numbered fatty acids from C_4 to C_{12}, and is not just due to butyric acid, as is commonly believed. Lipolysis seriously degrades the quality of cooking and frying of oils. The smoke point (temperature at which smoke is seen over the surface of heated fat) of a fat is seriously depressed due to lipolysis. For example, the smoke point of cottonseed oil decreases from 232.2°C to 160°C in the presence of 1 per cent free fatty acids. Foods fried in such oils exhibit cracked surfaces, have increased tendency for browning, and increased fat absorption.

Fats, when in contact with air, react with oxygen producing products with undesirable characteristics. This is known as "oxidative rancidity." This type of rancidity is more of a problem with foods than hydrolytic rancidity. In the case of the latter, the undesirable flavour is only owing to short-chain fatty acids. In oxidative rancidity, a large number of intermediates are formed and their condensation products lead to rancidity. This type of rancidity is promoted by heat, light, ionizing radiations, catalysts and enzymes (lipoxygenases). Usually, fats with substantial unsaturation in the fatty acids are more prone to oxidative rancidity.

Mechanism of oxidative rancidity: The mechanism of oxidative rancidity has been extensively studied. Rancidity takes place through auto-oxidation because the rate of oxidation increases as the reaction proceeds. Oxidation takes place through a free-radical chain mechanism involving three stages: (1) initiation, formation of free radicals, (2) propagation, free-radical chain reaction, and (3) termination, formation of nonradical products.

In the initiation stage, an unsaturated hydrocarbon loses a hydrogen atom to form a radical and oxygen adds on at the double bond to form a diradical:

$$RH \rightarrow R\cdot + H\cdot$$

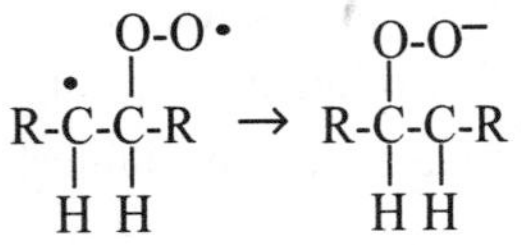

In some cases, initiation takes place by the direct incorporation of oxygen between a labile hydrogen atom to form a hydroperoxide:

$$RH + O_2 \rightarrow ROOH$$

The free radicals formed during the initiation reaction react with oxygen and the hydrocarbon, forming peroxy radicals, hydroperoxides and new hydrocarbon radicals

$$R\cdot + O_2 \rightarrow ROO\cdot$$

$$ROO\cdot + RH \rightarrow ROOH + R\cdot$$

Termination occurs when two radicals interact:

$$R\cdot + R\cdot \rightarrow RR$$

$$ROO\cdot + ROO\cdot \rightarrow ROOR + O_2$$

$$RO\cdot + R\cdot \rightarrow ROR$$

$$ROO\cdot + R\cdot \rightarrow ROOR$$

$$2RO\cdot + 2ROO\cdot \rightarrow 2ROOR + O_2$$

Hydroperoxides formed by the above method are readily decomposed by heat, metal catalysts or enzyme activity.

$$ROOH \rightarrow RO\cdot + \cdot OH\cdot$$

$$2ROOH \rightarrow RO\cdot ROO\cdot + H_2O$$

The radicals formed from hydroperoxides undergo a series of reactions leading to several products, such as hydroxy acids, keto acids and aldehydes. The short-chain aldehydes and the short-chain acids derived by their oxidation are largely responsible for the undesirable flavours and odours characteristic of rancid foods.

Anti-oxidants: An anti-oxidant is a substance that is added to fats or fat-containing foods to retard the oxidative breakdown of fat and thus prevent spoilage of foods. Naturally, an anti-oxidant should be fat soluble and should not contribute any objectionable flavour, odour or colour to the fat or foods in which it is used. Anti-oxidants function by combining with free radicals and thus interrupting the free-radical chain mechanism. Free-radical and anti-oxidant complexes have been isolated. Anti-oxidants, such as ascorbic acid, function by being preferentially oxidized and they afford poor protection. Tocopherols are naturally occurring anti-oxidants. For antioxidants used in foods, see Chap. 29.

3.6.2 Polymerization

Unsaturated fatty acids in lipids undergo polymerization owing to heat, oxidation, and the presence of free radicals or polar catalysts. Heating of fats and oils, as in frying operations, can produce changes in molecular weight, colour, viscosity or refractive index due to polymerization. Polymers decrease the heat transfer efficiency of an oil and also affect the quality of products fried in oil. Under extreme conditions it can also adversely affect the nutritional quality of oils and their wholesomeness.

3.7 Phospholipids

Phospholipids or phosphoglycerides differ from triglycerides in that one of the terminal hydroxyls of glycerol is esterified with phosphoric acid and the other two hydroxyls by fatty acids. The fatty acids occupying Sn_1, and Sn_2 positions vary in chain length and in unsaturation. Acids in position 2 are usually highly unsaturated and those in position 1 can be saturated or monoenoic.The phosphoric acid in position Sn_3 is,in turn, esterified to another moiety *x*,

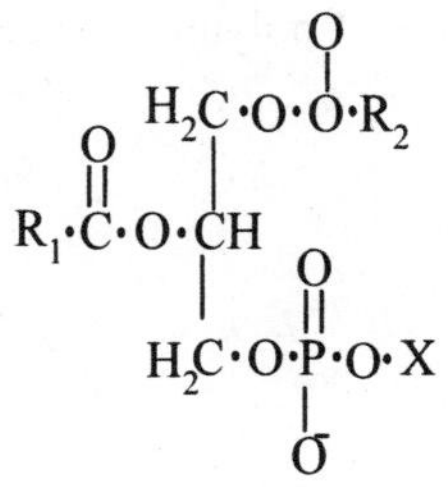

Phospholipids

In the above structure, *x* may be choline HO-CH_2-CH_2-$N^+(CH_3)_3$,ethanolamine (HO-CH_2-CH_2-NH_2), serine or inositol. Phosphoglycerides containing these components are all found in foods. The phospholipid containing choline (phosphatidylcholine) is known as "lecithin." Lecithin is a very good emulsifier. Egg yolk is rich in lecithin and is thus used in the preparation of emulsions.

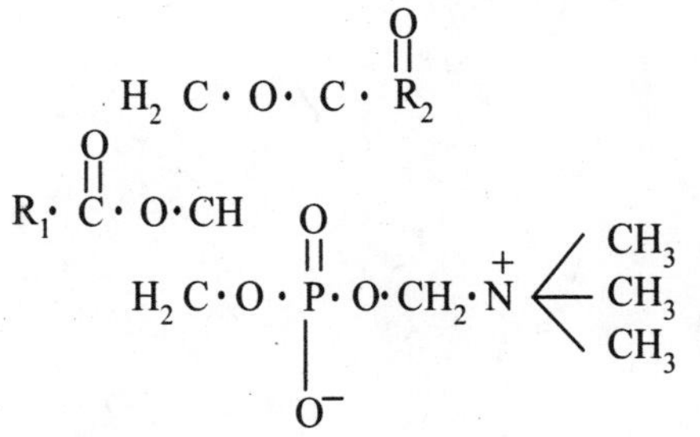

3-Sn-Phosphatidylcholine (Lecithin)

Phospholipids are important components of the cell membrane and considerably influence its structure and function. They are also involved in the transport of other lipids in the blood stream. Phospholipids are usually complexed as lipoproteins in their natural state.

3.8 Lipids in Foods

Ingested fats include the "visible" fats like those of butter, cooking oils, vanaspathi, margarine, etc. They also include "hidden" fats from sources, such as cereals, pulses, milk, cheese, egg, meats, nuts, fruits and vegetables. The latter group accounts for nearly 60 per cent of dietary fat.

Fats have important roles in foods. As already indicated, vitamin E plays the role of a natural anti-oxidant. Fats also influence food structure. Fats separate out from an aqueous medium on standing. To create a system that will exist as one phase the fat has to be emulsified. The body employs a mixture of bile salts, fatty acids, monoglycerides and phospholipids, to emulsify fats in the gut. In food processing also, monoglycerides, phospholipids and a wide range of synthetic compounds are used as emulsifiers. Therefore, the texture of foods can be influenced by a mixture of fat blends and appropriate emulsifiers. Often lipids themselves or their breakdown products contribute to the flavour and aroma of food. For example, the flavour of butter, milk and cheese is due to the short-chain fatty acids. Many flavours associated with vegetables, such as beans and cucumber, are formed by the oxidative enzyme breakdown of unsaturated tissue lipids.

Some dietary fats have some harmful effects also. Some cyclic fatty acids inhibit the desaturation of stearic acid to oleic acid. This alters membrane permeability and leads to some diseases. Abnormal lipid metabolism is the causative agent in the development of coronary artery disease. Some of the peroxidized products of polyunsaturated acids could be toxic.

CHAPTER

4

Proteins

The word protein is derived from the Greek word "proteios" which means "principal" or "prime". Proteins are the principal components of all living cells and are important in practically all aspects of cell structure and functions. They are molecules of great size, complexity and diversity. These macromolecules are characterized by their nitrogen content. In addition, some proteins contain small quantities of sulphur, phosphorus and minerals. Plants have the ability to synthesize proteins from inorganic nitrogen sources, such as ammonia, nitrate and nitrite. Animals, unlike plants, cannot synthesize proteins in this manner. Thus all animal life, either directly or indirectly, depends on plants to satisfy its protein needs.

In addition to being components of food, proteins are involved in a greater variety of functions than any other type of molecules of life. Some proteins function as biocatalysts (enzymes) and hormones to regulate chemical reactions in the body. Life processes, such as growth, digestion and metabolism, excretion and conversion of chemical energy to mechanical work, are all controlled by enzymes and hormones. Proteins are transport agents. Blood plasma proteins and haemoglobin regulate the osmotic pressure and pH of body fluids. Antibodies, the natural defence agents against invasion of foreign substances or micro-organisms that can cause various diseases, are proteins. Food allergies result when certain ingested proteins cause an apparent modification in the defence mechanisms.

4.1 Amino Acids

As briefly described above, proteins have different biological functions and properties. Yet, all proteins are built up of the same building blocks, the amino acids. There are twenty amino acids which are protein constituents. They contain both a basic amino group and an acidic carboxyl group attached to the same carbon atom, the α -carbon atom. In addition, they also possess a third group referred to as the side chain denoted by the letter R. The general structural formula of an α-amino acid in the unionized and ionized condition is:

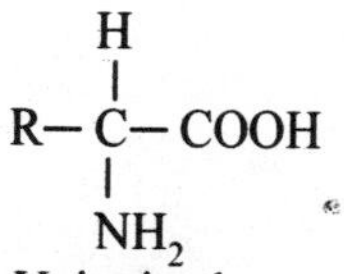

Unionized

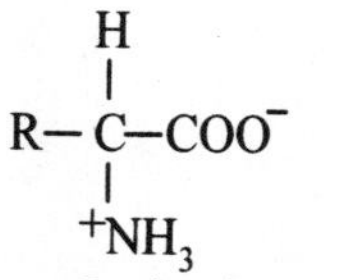

Ionized

4.1.1 Classification of Amino Acids

Since the amino and carboxyl groups are common to all amino acids, the R group differentiates one amino acid from the other. Based on side chains, amino acids are classified into four groups as shown in Table 4.1

Table 4.1 Classification of amino acids

Nonpolar R groups (name)	**Structure (pH-7)**
Alanine (Ala)	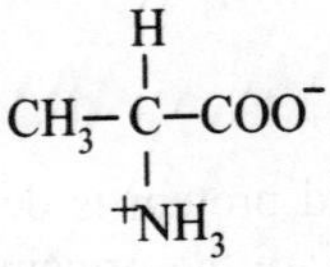
Valine (Val)	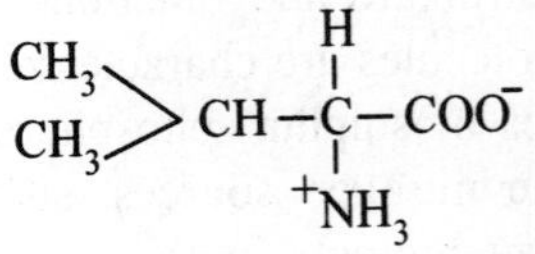
Leucine (Leu)	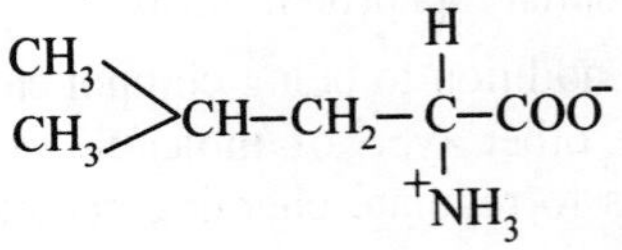
Isoleucine (Ile)	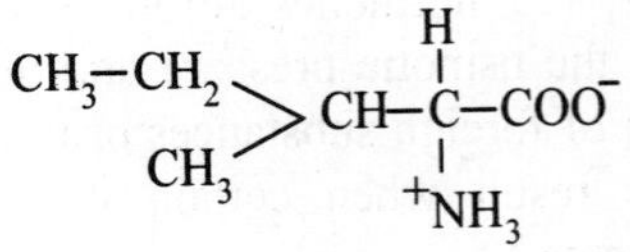
Proline (Pro)	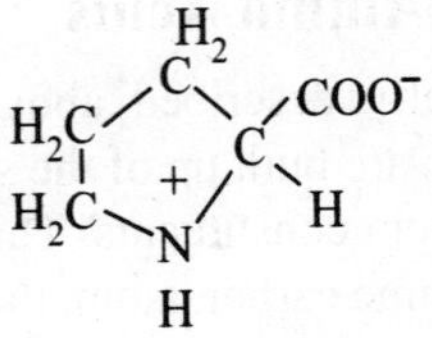
Phenylalanine (Phe)	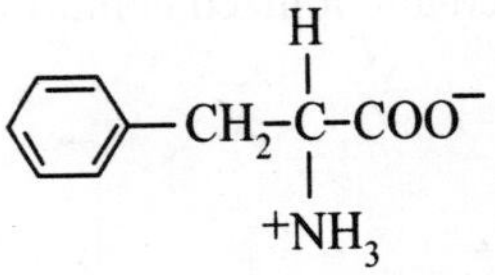
Tryptophan (Trp)	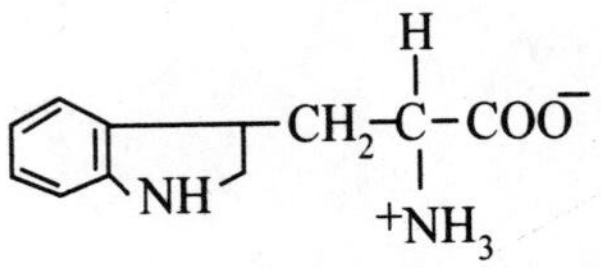

(Contd...)

Methionine (Met)	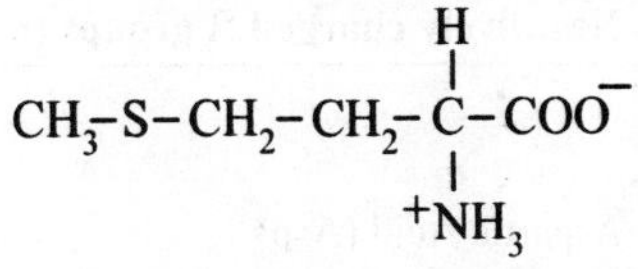
Polar uncharged R Group (name)	**Structure (pH-7)**
Glycine (Gly)	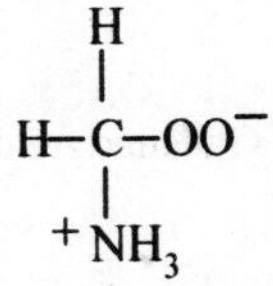
Serine (Ser)	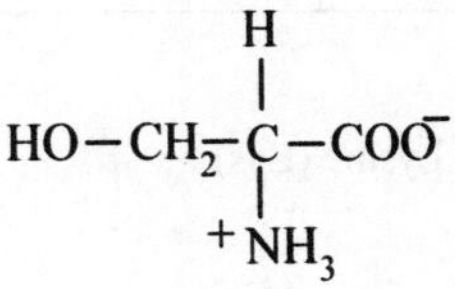
Threonine (Thr)	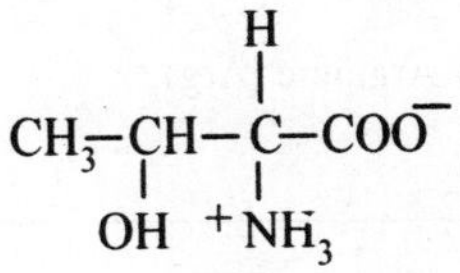
Cysteine (Cys)	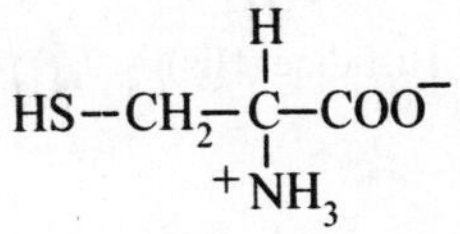
Tyrosine (Thr)	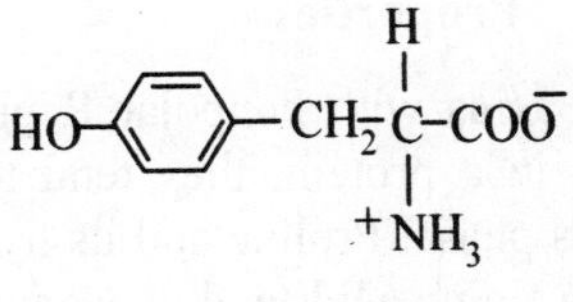
Asparagine (Asn)	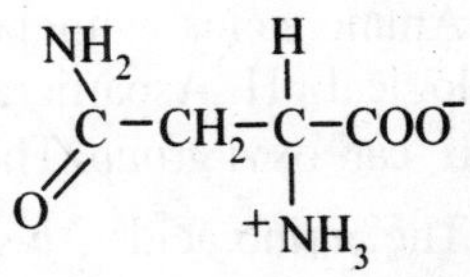
Glutamine (Gln)	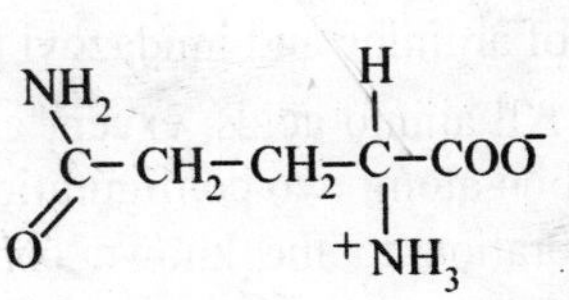

(Contd...)

Negatively charged R groups (name)	**Structure (pH-7)**
Aspartic Acid (Asp)	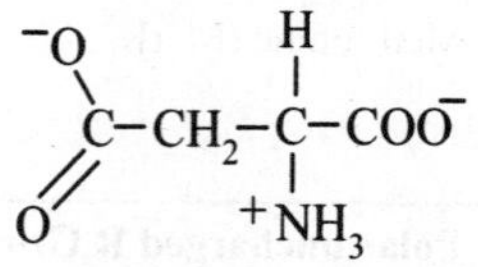
Glutamic Acid (Glu)	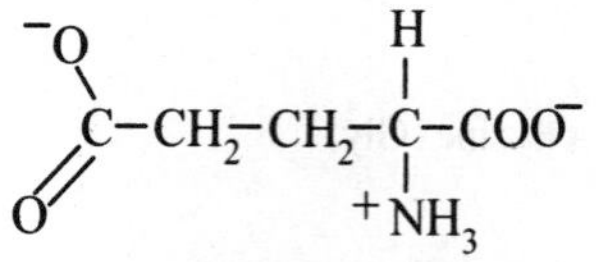
Positively charged R groups (name)	**Structure (pH-7)**
Lysine (Lys)	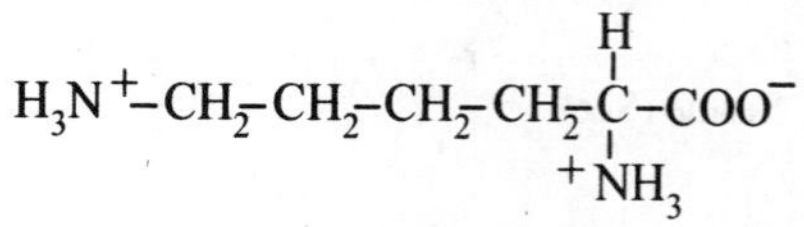
Arginine (Arg)	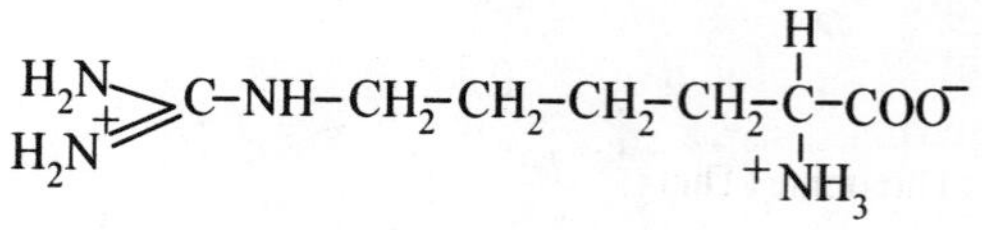
Histidine (His)	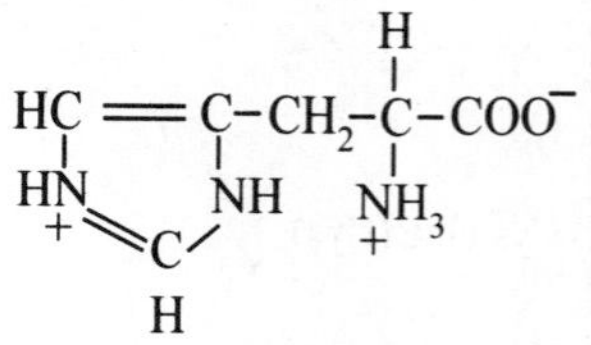

4.1.2 Properties

Amino acids with nonpolar R groups are hydrophobic. Consequently, when these amino acids are present in a protein, they tend to fold into the interior of the protein away from the surrounding aqueous phase. Proline and its hydroxy derivative, hydroxyproline, have a unique structure. They are actually amino acids and play a unique part in protein structure.

Amino acids with polar uncharged R groups are hydrophilic. Their side chains ionize at physiological pH. Aspartic and glutamic acids possess a terminal carboxyl group (acidic) in addition to the α -carboxyl group. These terminal carboxyl groups possess a net negative charge at neutral pH.

The amino acids—lysine, arginine and histidine—have a positively charged (basic) R group at pH 6-7. The groups responsible for the positive charge are the ε -amino group of lysine, guanidino group of arginine and imidazoyl group of histidine.

All amino acids, except glycine, have a chiral centre. Depending upon the chiral centre at the α -carbon atom, two configurations L- and D- are possible. Based on the relationship of the α -carbon configuration to the known configuration of the two isomers of glyceraldehyde, all amino acids isolated from protein hydrolysates have L-configuration. A second chiral centre is present in four amino acids: isoleucine, hydroxylysine, threonine and hydroxyproline.

All the amino acids in the crystalline state or in aqueous solution at neutral pH values are ionized. The carboxyl group loses a proton and acquires a negative charge, while the amino group gains a proton and hence acquires a positive charge. As a consequence, amino acids possess dipolar or zwitterion characteristics. Only at low pH, well below that normally encountered within healthy living cells, a proton will add on to the ionized carboxyl group producing a cation in which the α-amino group is ionized.

On raising the pH above neutrality, the amino group will give up a proton and the molecule will become an anion in which only the α -carboxyl group is ionized.

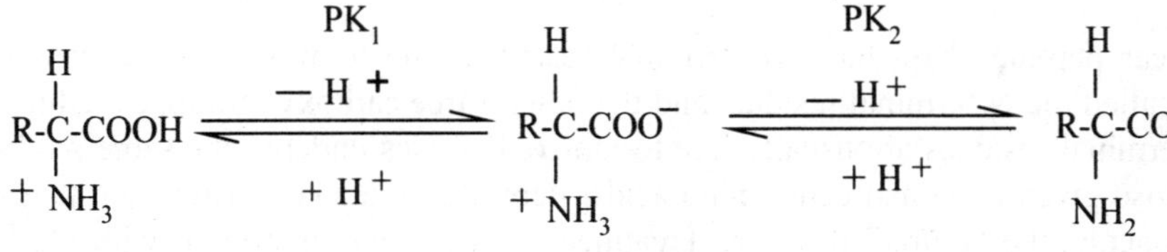

Cation Zwitterion Anion

At the pH equal to pK_1 of the carboxyl group, cation and zwitterion will exist in equal concentration. Similarly, at the pH equal to pK_2, of the amino group, zwitterion and anion will be present in equal concentration. The pH at which the amino acid exists as the zwitterion is called the isoelectric pH (pI) and is the mean of $pK_1$and pK_2 i.e.,

$$pI = \frac{pK_1 + pK_2}{2}$$

The aromatic amino acids—tryptophan, tyrosine and phenylalanine—absorb light significantly in the ultraviolet range. Since most proteins contain tyrosine, the spectroscopic measurement of light absorption at 280nm is a convenient and rapid method for estimating the protein concentration of a solution.

Amino acids undergo the usual reactions of carboxyl and amino groups. Thus, the α -carboxyl group participates in reactions leading to the formation of amides, esters and acylhalides. Similarly, the amino group reacts with ninhydrin, dinitrofluorobenzene, phenylisothiocyanate, dansyl chloride. nitrous acid, etc. In addition, amino acids show reactions characteristic of the side-chain hydroxyl, sulphydryl, amino, carboxyl, indoyl, imidazoyl and guanidino groups.

4.2 Peptides

When the α -amino group of one amino acid reacts with the α -carboxyl group of another, a peptide bond is formed with the elimination of a molecule of water.

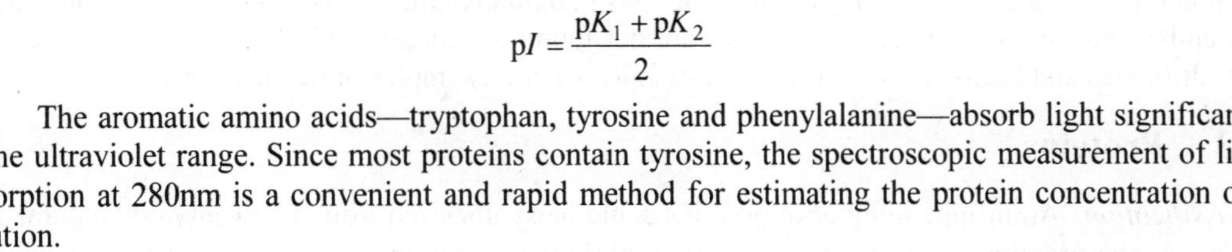

When a few (2-10) amino acids are joined together by peptide bonds the compound is called an oligopeptide. With more than ten amino acid residues the compound is termed a polypeptide. When the polypeptide contains about 100 amino acid units, it is called a protein. The general structure of a polypeptide can be represented thus:

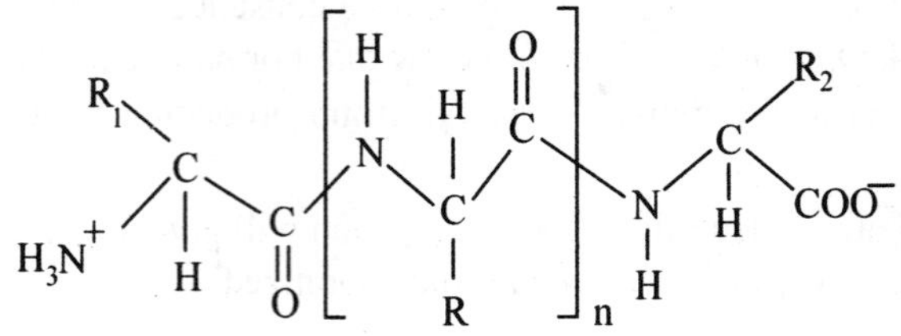

The linear peptide chain has two terminal residues, one terminal residue possessing a free amino group, called the N-terminal residue, and the other a free carboxyl group, called the C-terminal residue. The terminal residues are usually free to ionize. Peptides undergo the same kind of chemical reactions as those given by constituent amino acids. Peptides give a colour reaction that is not given by free amino acids, the "biuret" reaction. Treatment of a peptide or protein with Cu^{2+} in alkaline solution yields a purple colour, which has an absorption at 540nm. This property is used in the estimation of peptides and proteins.

Most peptides are the partial hydrolytic products of proteins. However, a few peptides are of metabolic importance and are found free in nature. Carnosine (β-alanyl-L-histidine) and anserine (β-alanyl-L-methylhistidine), are peptides found in muscle. Glutathione (γ-glutamyl-cysteinyl-glycine) is found in mammalian erythrocytes and functions in oxidative metabolism. The peptide bonds due to β- and γ-carboxyls in the above peptides are not found in proteins. Other natural peptides function as antibiotics and hormones. Oxytocin and vasopressin are examples of peptide hormones.

4.3 Proteins

Classification: An infinite number of proteins could be synthesized from the twenty odd natural amino acids. As the proteins perform a wide variety of biological functions, they are classified in a number of ways. They are classified on the basis of their function as catalytic proteins, contractile proteins, structural proteins, etc. On a compositional basis, proteins can be classified into two general classes—simple proteins and conjugated proteins. Simple proteins yield only amino acids on hydrolytic degradation, while conjugated proteins yield, in addition to amino acids, an organic or inorganic moiety called the prosthetic group. The simple proteins are further subclassified on the basis of their solubility as shown in Table 4.2. Most enzyme and hormone proteins belong to either the albumin or globulin class. The plantseed proteins are mostly glutelins.

The prosthetic groups of conjugated proteins are carbohydrates, lipids, nucleic acids, metal ions or phosphates. They are bound to the protein by linkages other than salt linkages. The protein component of a conjugated protein is stabilized by combination with the prosthetic group.

Lipoproteins are proteins complexed with lipids and are found in cells and the blood stream. The lipids are very firmly held to the proteins and cannot be easily removed. The lipids in lipoproteins are triglycerides, phospholipids, cholesterol or derivatives of cholesterol. Lipoproteins serve as transporters of lipids in blood. Based on density, the lipoproteins are grouped into three groups—high-density, low-density and very low-density lipoproteins.

Glycoproteins are proteins whose prosthetic groups are heterosaccharides containing hexosamine, galactose, mannose, fucose and sialic acid. A covalent bond joins the protein to the

Table 4.2 Classification of simple proteins

Name	Solubility in				Food Source
	Water	Salt Solution	Acid/Alkali	Alcohol 80%	
Albumins	Soluble	Soluble	—	—	Milk, egg, plant and animal cells
Globulins	—	Soluble	—	—	Milk, eggs, meat, plant cells, particularly in seed proteins
Glutelins	—	—	Soluble	—	Cereal grains and related plant materials
Prolamines	—	—	—	Soluble	Cereal grains and related plant materials.
Histones	Soluble	—	Soluble	—	Glandular tissues, pancreas, thymus, fish
Protamines	Soluble	—	Soluble	—	Fish sperm
Sclero-proteins (albuminoids)	—	—	—	—	Meat

heteropolysaccharide by either O-glycosidic (with serine or threonine) or N-glyosidic bonds (with asparagine). Glycoproteins are found in mucous secretions of mammals and they function as lubricating agents. Egg-white contains ovomucoid which cannot be coagulated by heat and is a glycoprotein. Certain fractions of pulse proteins are glycoproteins.

Metalloproteins are complexes of proteins and heavy metals. In most metalloproteins the metal is loosely bound and can be easily removed. However, in some proteins such as haemoglobin and myoglobin, the metal iron is firmly bound to the prosthetic group. Liver and spleen contain the metalloproteins ferritin and haemosiderin with about 20 per cent iron content. These are storage forms of iron in animals which release iron from the proteins when required. Conalbumin from egg can form a complex with iron and it also combines with copper and zinc.

Nucleoproteins are complexes of proteins and nucleic acids. Nucleic acids readily combine with proteins to form the complexes. Phosphoproteins are proteins conjugated with inorganic phosphate. The most widely known phosphoproteins are the milk protein casein and the enzyme pepsin.

4.3.1 Protein Structure

The diverse biological functions of proteins are a result of their structure. The structure of a protein is normally considered under four levels—primary structure, secondary structure, tertiary structure and quaternary structure.

Primary structure: The nature of amino acids and their linear sequence in the polypeptide chain is referred to as the primary structure. The determination of the primary structure, which was once a formidable job, has now become easy due to the modern analytical tools available for amino-acid analysis. The unique sequence of amino acids is résponsible for many of the fundamental properties of the proteins, e.g., the replacement of one amino acid residue in the β-chains of haemoglobin, which contains 574 amino acid residues, can bring about profound changes in its biological properties. The sequence of amino acids also determines, to a large extent, the secondary and tertiary structures of proteins.

Secondary structure: An extended peptide chain is not stable and it folds into itself. The three-dimensional manner in which relatively close members of the protein chain are arranged is referred to as the secondary structure. The native structure of a protein is that structure which possesses the lowest feasible free energy. Therefore, the structure of a protein is not random but somewhat ordered.

The secondary structure of the protein depends upon the structural characteristics of the peptide bond which repeats itself along the chain. X-ray studies indicate that the peptide bond is slightly shorter than other single C-N bonds. This indicates that the peptide bond has some characteristics of a double bond. Thus, groups adjacent to the peptide bond cannot rotate freely. The rigidity of the peptide bond holds the six atoms shown in the diagram in a single plane. The amino (-NH-) group does not ionize between pH 0 and 14 due to the double bond properties of the peptide bond. In addition, the R-groups of amino acid residues, because of stearic hindrance, force oxygen and hydrogen of the peptide bond to exist in a *trans* configuration. Therefore, the backbone of peptides and proteins has free rotation in two of the three bonds between amino acids as indicated below.

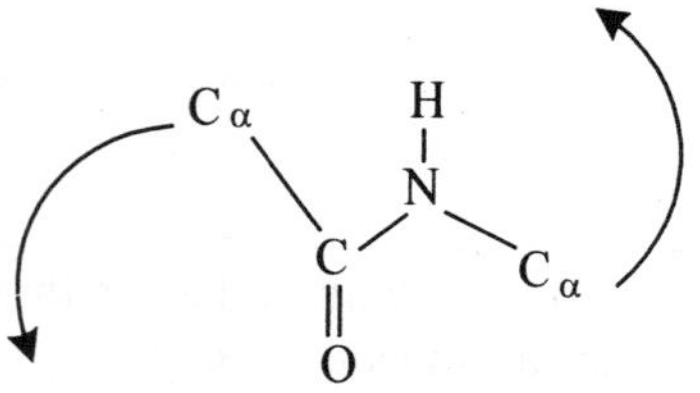

When the restrictions of the peptide bond are superimposed on a poly-amino acid chain of a globular protein, a right-handed coil, the α -helix, appears to be one of the most ordered and stable structures feasible (Fig. 4.1). The α -helix contains 3.6 amino acid residues per turn of the protein backbone, with the R-groups of the aminoacids extending outward from the axis of the helical structure. Hydrogen bonding occurs between the nitrogen of one peptide bond and the oxygen of another peptide bond in the four residues along the protein backbone structure. This arrangement enhances the stability of the structure.

Another secondary structure found in many fibrous proteins is the β-pleated sheet configuration. In this configuration, the peptide backbone forms a zigzag pattern, with the R-groups of the amino acids extending above and below the peptide chain. Since all the peptide bonds are available for hydrogen bonding,this configuration allows maximum cross - linking between adjacent polypeptide chains and thus ensures good stability. When the polypeptide chains run in the same direction, parallel-pleated sheets, and when they run in the opposite direction, antiparallel pleated sheets, are possible (Fig. 4.2). Silk and insect fibres are the best examples of the β-sheet structure.

Most proteins do not have the regular secondary structure due to some factors which prevent the formation of long uninterrupted regions of α-helix or β-pleated sheets. For example, if a proline residue is present in the polypeptide chain, the α-helix is interrupted because the amide nitrogen of proline, when involved in the peptide bond formation, does not possess an attached hydrogen bond. In addition, hydrogen bonding in both the pleated sheet and α-helical structures may be disturbed by

Fig. 4.1 Right-handed α -helix

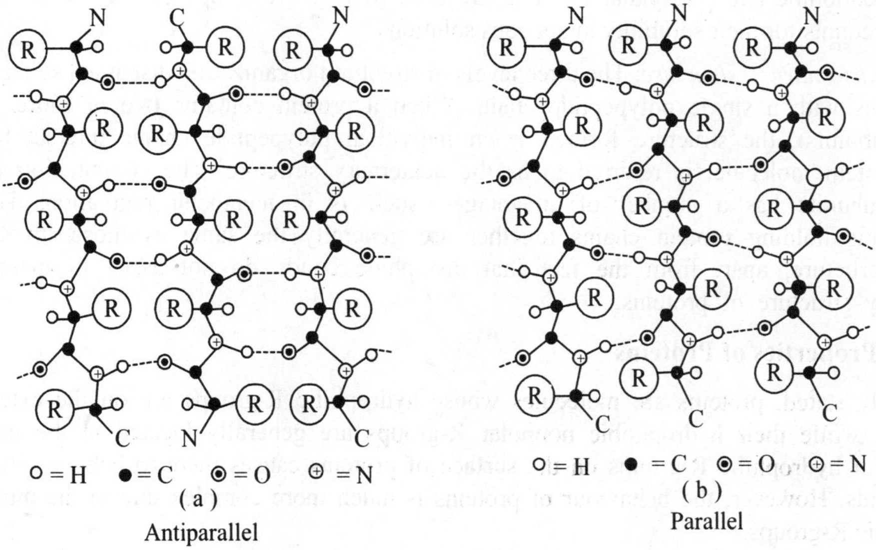

Fig. 4.2 Antiparallel and parallel β -pleated sheets

unfavourable side-chain interactions, such as the presence of two bulky side-chains next to each other or the electrostatic repulsion produced by the two similar groups.

Another type of secondary structure of fibrous proteins is the collagen helix. Collagen, found in skin, tendons and numerous other parts of the body, accounts for one-third of the total body protein. Collagen contains one-third glycine and one-fourth proline or hydroxyproline residues. The rigid R-groups, and the lack of hydrogen bonds by peptide linkages involving proline and hydroxyproline, force the collagen polypeptide chain into an odd kink-type helix. Peptide bonds composed of glycine form interchain hydrogen bonds with two other collagen polypeptide chains and this results in a stable triple helix. This triple helical structure is called "Tropocollagen"(Fig.4.3)

Fig. 4.3 Triple helix of Collagen

Tertiary structure: The tertiary structure of proteins defines a specific three-dimensional configuration. This involves the folding of regular units of the secondary structure as well as structuring of areas of the peptide chain devoid of secondary structure. The folded portions are held together by the hydrogen bonds formed between R-groups, by electrostatic interaction between chains possessing oppositely charged groups such as those of lysine, arginine, glutamic and aspartic acids hydrophobic interaction between nonpolar regions and covalent disulphide linkages.

In the formation of the tertiary structure, all the polar groups are on the surface of the molecule and the interior consists almost entirely of nonpolar hydrophobic residues, such as those of leucine, valine, methionine and phenylalanine. The presence of polar R-groups on the surface of proteins usually accounts for their solubility in aqueous solutions

Quarternary structure: The three levels of structural organization discussed so far apply to all the proteins with a single polypeptide chain. When a protein contains two or more polypeptide chains (subunits), the structure formed when individual polypeptide chains interact to form the native protein molecule, is referred to as the quaternary structure. The combination of different protein subunits has a number of advantages, such as in metabolic regulation. The bonding mechanisms holding protein chains together are generally the same as those involved in the tertiary structure, apart from the fact that disulphide bonds do not assist in maintaining the quaternary structure of proteins.

4.3.2 Properties of Proteins

As already stated, proteins are molecules whose hydrophilic R-groups are on the exterior of the molecule, while their hydrophobic nonpolar R-groups are generally located in the interior. The presence of hydrophilic R-groups on the surface of proteins causes them to behave somewhat like amino acids. However, the behaviour of proteins is much more complex due to the multiplicity of hydrophilic R-groups.

Proteins behave as electrolytes and they conform to the same physical and chemical principles of electrolytes. The amino acid compositions of individual proteins greatly vary and thus their net charge varies. If the protein contains a high content of acidic groups (aspartic and glutamic) its isoelectric pH is low; if basic amino acids (arginine and lysine) are more, the protein has a high isoelectric point.

The variation in the ionic properties of proteins leads to several methods for the fractionation of proteins from a biological system. Two methods have been successfully employed in the isolation and purification of proteins based on their ionic properties. They are electrophoresis, particularly zone electrophoresis on polyacrylamide gel, and ion-exchange chromatography.

Electrical charges also influence protein solubility. Proteins in solution show changes in solubility as a function of pH, ionic strength, temperature and dielectric properties of the solvent. Using these variables protein mixtures can be resolved.

Proteins can be hydrolyzed with acid, alkali or enzymes. Complete hydrolysis of proteins can be brought about by heating the proteins with 6 M HC1 for 8-10 hours at 120°C. Acid hydrolysis avoids recemization of amino acids. However, it results in the destruction of tryptophan. During acid hydrolysis, asparagine and glutamine are hydrolyzed to aspartic and glutamine acids, and sulphur-containing hydroxy amino acids undergo varying degrees of oxidation. Alkaline hydrolysis with 2 M sodium or barium hydroxide results in substantial recemisation of amino acids. The amino acids arginine and cysteine, and a portion of lysine, are destroyed, although tryptophan is retained. A complete hydrolysis of proteins can be brought about by enzymes without any destruction of amino acids. This type of hydrolysis takes place in the body during digestion of proteins.

Micro-organisms cause deterioration of protein foods. Growth of spoilage organisms occurs under unsatisfactory conditions when the food is not properly processed. Microbial proteases bring about decarboxylation and deamination resulting in undesirable changes in flavour and texture, and production of offensive odours and toxins. These changes are referred to as putrefaction.

4.3.3 Denaturation

The ordered three-dimensional structure of proteins is very delicate. It is subject to alterations by mild agents without any breaking of peptide bonds. The loss of native conformation brings about changes in specific properties characterizing the identity of proteins and this is known as "denaturation."

Denaturation brings about many changes in a protein. It makes the peptide bonds of the protein more readily available for hydrolysis by proteolytic enzyme, solubility is decreased and biological properties such as catalytic, hormonal, etc., are lost. The crystallization of protein is no longer possible, and viscosity and optical rotation increase. The increase in viscosity suggests the unfolding of the molecule resulting in more asymmetry. This would expose more hydrophobic residues resulting in the decreased solubility of proteins.

Denaturation is the result of the modification of the secondary, tertiary or quaternary structure of the protein molecule, excluding the breakage of covalent bonds. Denaturation is therefore a process by which hydrogen bonds, hydrophobic interactions and salt linkages are broken and the protein completely unfolds and assumes a random coil structure, in which state the protein molecules readily form aggregates (coagulation).

Denaturation is usually reversible if drastic methods of denaturation are not used and if the molecular weight of the native protein is very large. However, reversible denaturation (renaturation) is also observed in some smaller proteins when milder methods of denaturation are used.

Both physical and chemical agents bring about denaturation. Heat is the most important physical agent. For every 10°C rise in temperature the increase in denaturation rate is 600-fold. The effect of denaturation can be reduced by working at a reduced temperature. The rate of heat denaturation is affected by the water content of a protein, ionic strength, pH, and types of ions present in the solution. Layering of proteins at an interface can result in denaturation. Therefore, the creation of interfaces, such as those of foams, are to be avoided to preserve the native properties of proteins. Stirring, shaking, high pressure, and ultraviolet radiations bring about protein denaturation.

Amongst the chemical agents, the pH of the medium has a profound effect on denaturation of proteins. Most proteins are stable within a fairly narrow pH range and exposure to pH values outside this range causes denaturation. A 6-8 M concentration of urea, and guanidine hydrochloride, that tends to break hydrogen bonds, also cause denaturation of proteins. Synthetic detergents, such as sodium dodecyl sulphate (SDS), are the most effective among the denaturing agents known.

The phenomenon of denaturation is of a great importance in food processing. When most foods are prepared for eating, they have been heat coagulated or denatured. In some cases, however, precautions have to be taken to prevent coagulation as in the processing of milk by pasteurization, evaporation and spray drying where it is desirable to retain the natural properties of proteins.

4.3.4 Protein Gels

Dry proteins have the ability to absorb water. A few proteins can form gels capable of immobilizing (making nonflowable) water equal to nearly ten times the weight of the hydrated proteins. Proteins which form gels have structures with high degree of asymmetry. These long proteinaceous fibres that form a three-dimensional matrix, primarily by the establishment of inter-protein hydrogen bonds and this cross-linked structure is sufficiently well developed to hold water in an immobilized state. Ionized functional groups on the proteins also aid in immobilizing water. If the attractive forces on the proteins are increased, e.g., by changing the pH to a value closer to the isoelectric point of the proteins, the gel tends to shrink. The shrinkage would expel some of the immobilized water (syneresis). Gelatin and casein coagulated by the action of enzyme rennin are good example of gel forming proteins. They are discussed in the chapters on meat and milk, respectively.

4.4 Food Proteins

Both plants and animals require proteins for growth, survival and propagation of the species. Proteins are present in many of our foods in varying amounts. Most proteins have to be processed or modified prior to use by human beings. Some major food proteins are considered briefly in this section. For more details about proteins from different sources, the reader has to refer to the chapter dealing with the particular food.

Animal proteins: Meat is an important source of protein from animal sources. Meat is the edible muscle of cattle, sheep and swine. These are designated as "red meat" because the colour of the beef, lamb and mutton pork is light or dark red due to the presence of the respiratory pigment myoglobin in them. Muscle from adult mammalian sources, stripped of all external fat, contains about 18-20 per cent protein on a wet basis. They are categorized on the basis of their origin and solubility as myofibrillar, sarcoplasmic and stroma (connective tissue) proteins which range from 49-55, 30-34 and 10-17 per cent, respectively, of the total amount of protein.

Milk is an excellent source of protein in our diet. Cow milk contains about 3.5 per cent protein. Milk proteins are generally divided into two classes—casein and whey proteins. Casein which is insoluble in water is a heterogenous group of phosphoproteins and accounts for 80 per cent of total milk protein. Whey proteins, making up the other 20 per cent, are the soluble proteins of milk.

Egg contains 13-14 per cent protein, about 2/3 of which is present in egg-white and the rest in egg-yolk. Egg-white consists of a number of proteins which are readily denatured and coagulated. Yolk is a mixture of lipoproteins and phosphoproteins.

Fish contains between 40 to 60 per cent edible flesh. The protein content of fish varies from 10 to 21 per cent. Fish muscle is similar to mammalian skeletal muscle with respect to structure and function but, unlike the latter, is easily damaged. The pigmented reddish brown muscle of fish contains enzymes which, following harvest, cause changes responsible for much of the instability of fish proteins.

Vegetable proteins: Fresh vegetables are not good sources of proteins. Many contain less than 1 per cent protein. Potatoes and green beans contain about 2 per cent and fresh peas about 6.5 per cent protein. Proteins from potatoes are considered to be of good quality because they are relatively high in the levels of lysine and tryptophan.

Cereal grains contain proteins ranging from 6 to 20 per cent. The protein content of rice is 7-9 per cent while that of wheat is 12-15 per cent. Proteins are found in various morphological tissues of the grains like embryo, germ, bran or seed coat and the endosperm. The germ proteins are mainly globulins or albumins and several enzymes are present in them. Bran is poorly digested by man and bran proteins are difficult to separate. Bran is mostly used as animal feed. The endosperm proteins act as structural components and also as a food reserve for the growing seedling. The endosperm proteins of wheat are mostly prolamines, gliadins and glutelins. Rice contains high levels of glutelins and low prolamine. Cereal proteins are generally of relatively poor nutritional quality.

Seeds contain protein in excess of 15 per cent. Pulses (legumes) contain, on an average, more than 20 per cent proteins. Proteins of seeds are mostly concentrated in aleurone grains which are subcellular granules of the cotyledon cells. Seed proteins function as structural elements of cell walls and various membranes and also as food reserves. The proteins of most seeds are globular. Owing to a decrease in the availability of meat proteins, seed proteins are gaining importance. Newer techniques have been developed to produce textured or "shaped" proteins from seeds. Nutritionally, seed proteins contain less of lysine and are also deficient in methionine and threonine. Seed proteins contain some anti-nutritional factors. They should be subjected to proper heat treatment to destroy or inactivate anti-nutritional factors and maximize nutritional quality.(see sec 17.3)

4.5 Non-traditional Proteins

People in many parts of the world are experiencing varying degrees of protein malnutrition, largely because of rapid increase in population. Therefore, there is a need to increase the production of proteins from traditional sources and to develop proteins from non-traditional sources. Some success has been achieved in the production of proteins from some unconventional sources.

Micro-organisms grow rapidly, their yields are high, and their growing conditions can be controlled. Therefore, microbes have been used to obtain food proteins (single cell proteins).

Two species of yeasts, *Candida utilis* (torula yeast) and *Saccharomyces carlsbergensis* (brewer's yeast), have been used for human food. Torula yeast grows well on sulphite waste liquor (waste product from paper industry) and wood hydrolysates, by utilizing pentoses as carbon source. Brewer's yeast can be collected after beer fermentation. These yeasts contain approximately 50 per cent of proteins on a dry-weight basis. They are, however, deficient in methionine but by adding 0.3

per cent methionine their biological value can be increased to over 90. One disadvantage of food yeasts is their nucleic acid content. Nucleic acid metabolic products are relatively insoluble and may lead to the formation of kidney stones, or aggravate arthritic or gouty conditions.

Strains of the yeast *Candida lipolytica* can grow on petroleum. The carbon and energy for the growth of the organism is provided by alkanes (straight– chain hydrocarbon molecules of petroleum). A commercial product named toprina has been prepared by this method. Toprina is toxicologically safe. However, the product has not been a success due to the rising cost of petroleum.

The bacterium *Methylophilus methylotrophus* can oxidize and use methane (or methanol) as a source of carbon and energy. A product named pruteen, is being produced using this method.

Two genera of algae—*Chlorella* (green algae) and *Spirulina* (blue-gree algae, now classified as blue-green bacteria) – when grown under controlled conditions, contain 50-60 per cent protein on a dry-weight basis. Algal proteins contain all essential ammo acids (methionine content is low). But high algal protein in the diet results in nausea, vomiting and abdominal pain. Poor digestibility and other undersirable characteristics can be eliminated by proper processing.

Fungi are being used as a source of food. Mushroom, a filamentous fungus, containing 27 per cent protein (dry-weight basis), is commercially grown and used as food. Attempts are being made to produce large amounts of food protein by culturing fungi in liquid media containing carbohydrates and inorganic nitrogen salts. However, there is a danger of the formation of microbial toxins (mycotoxins) in proteins produced by this method.

Leaf proteins extracted from green plant leaves can be used as food protein. The dried product contains 50-70 per cent protein. The nutritional value of leaf proteins is greater than that of proteins of other plants. Their lysine content is high (5-7 per cent). The cost, yield and the palatability of leaf proteins come in the way of their use to alleviate the world's shortage of food proteins. However, attempts are being made to resolve these difficulties in using leaf proteins as food.

4.6 Nutritional Importance

Proteins play some functional roles in foods because they can form gels, sols and emulsions and can contribute colour and flavour. Their most important role, however, is their nutritional value.

The primary function of the dietary proteins is to supply nitrogen and amino acids for the synthesis of body proteins and other nitrogen-containing substances. Body tissues contain 20 amino acids. Of this number, nine cannot be synthesized by man and have to be supplied in the human diet. These amino acids are histidine, isoleucine, leucine, lysine, methionine, phenylalanine, threonine, tryptophan and valine. These amino acids are designated as "essential." The other amino acids called "non-essential" can be synthesized in the body from a utilizable source of nitrogen, usually protein. The diet should provide all the essential amino acids in amounts needed by the body, together with a sufficient amount of utilizable nitrogen for the synthesis of body proteins. If any single amino acid is deficient, protein synthesis ceases or is greatly slowed.

The "quality" or "balance" of a protein depends upon the kinds and amounts of amino acids it contains. A "balanced" or "high-quality" protein contains all the essential amino acids needed for the human body. Proteins of animal origin are generally of higher quality than those of plant origin. Cereal proteins are low in lysine and deficient in methionine, tryptophan and, occasionally, threonine. Pulse proteins are deficient in methionine, and oil-seed and nut proteins in lysine, methionine and sometimes in threonine. The amino acids not contained in a protein are designated as "limiting" amino acids.

When proteins deficient in some essential amino acids are fed in amounts sufficient to provide adequate amounts of limiting amino acids, then some amino acids which are in excess for body growth and maintenance will be utilized as sources of energy. When the dietary pattern of amino acids differs from the ideal pattern it results in "amino acid imbalance," leading to depressed growth and impairment of mental capabilities in children. Except mental impairment, other defects can be overcome by supplementing the diet with the limiting amino acids.

The level of protein intake required for adequate maintenance has been worked out by an expert group from FAO and the World Health Organization (WHO). According to them, the recommended daily intake is 0.59 g of protein per kilogram of body weight for an average individual. The daily requirement for protein remains constant during the lifetime of most adults. FAO-WHO suggest a daily intake of 0.88 g of protein per kg body weight for children in the age range of 1 to 10 years. Women during pregnancy and lactation require some 20-30 grams per day additional protein. During diseases and injury which cause breakdown of tissue proteins and increased excretion of nitrogen more protein is to be taken to compensate for losses.

Proteins yield 4.1 Kcal of energy per gram. At optimum nutritional level, proteins provide 10-14 per cent of the total energy of the diet. This range tends to remain constant irrespective of age, sex, pregnancy, work or illness. The working capacity of an individual may be affected when the calorific contribution of protein falls below 8 per cent in a mixed diet. It has been suggested that a daily diet containing 30 g of high quality protein makes for nutritional well-being irrespective of the quantity of the remaining protein. Supplements of proteins from different sources will increase the biological value in synergistic manner.

Protein quality: The value of protein as food depends upon its amino acid composition, especially that of essential amino acids. The nutritional value of a protein also depends upon the presence of amino acids in proper proportions, the digestibility of the protein and its absorption. A good protein should help growth, repair of damaged tissues, reproduction and the general well-being of the body. Therefore, protein quality is determined by biological methods, using a number of animal feeding experiments. The biological value of proteins of some foods is as follows:

Total Protein	**100**
Egg	95
Cow milk	84
Fish	76
Meat	74
Rice	68
Wheat	66
Maize	60
Groundnut	55
Pulses	49-63

A Joint FAO/WHO Expert Committee in 1989 recommended that the protein digestibility – corrected amino acid score is considered the most suitable regulatory method for evaluating protein quality of foods and infant formulas. Since this method is based on human amino acid requirements, it is inherently more appropriate than animal assays and is the preferred method of measuring protein values in reference to human nutrition.

Data on the digestibility of protein and/or bioavailability (true digestibility) of amino acids in diets of developing countries was poor due to use of less refined cereals and pulses as major sources of protein. Representative digestibility values for some common foods and food mixtures are shown in Table 4.3.

Table 4.3 Some values (%) for digestibility of proteins in man

Protein Source	True Digestibility	
	Mean	Reference
Egg	97	4
Milk, Cheese	95	4
Meat, Fish	94	4
Maize	85	4
Rice, polished	88	4
Cottonseed	90	115
Sunflower Seed, flour	90	115
Wheat, whole	86	4
Wheat, refined	96	4
Wheat flour, white	96	115
Wheat gluten	99	115
Oatmeal	86	4
Millet	79	4
Peas, mature	88	4
Peanuts	94	115
Peanut butter	95	4
Soya flour	86	4
Soya protein isolate	95	115
Beans	78	4
Corn, whole	87	115
Farina	99	115
Triticale	90	115
Corn, cereal	70	115
Wheat, cereal	77	115
Rice, cereal	75	115
Oats, cereal	72	115
Maize + beans	78	4
Maize + beans + milk	84	4

(Contd...)

Indian rice diet	77	4
Indian diet + milk	87	4
Chinese mixed diet	96	4
Brazilian mixed diet	78	4
Filipino mixed diet	88	4
American mixed diet	96	4
Indian rice + beans diet	78	4

Source : Report of the Joint FAO/WHO Expert Committee, Bethesda, Md., USA, 4-8 December 1989

CHAPTER

5 Vitamins

Towards the end of the 19th Century it was realized that in addition to carbohydrates, proteins, fats, minerals and water, small quantities of unknown substances were essential to life. Researches in the first two decades of this century resulted in the discovery of the unknown accessory dietary factors. These food factors were originally believed to be organic bases and thus the name "vitamine," meaning "vital amine" (amine is an organic base), was given to them. The final "e" was later dropped, since the chemical nature of the various factors has been proved and most of them are not amines

Vitamins are low-molecular-weight organic substances necessary in small amounts in the diet of higher animals for normal growth, maintenance of health, and reproduction. All animals need vitamins but every vitamin is not required by all of them. For example, human beings and guinea pigs get scurvy when fed diets that do not provide vitamin C, but dogs, cats, rats and many other species make this vitamin in their bodies and do not need it in their food. Plants and micro-organisms synthesize vitamins.

Classification: Vitamins are a group of heterogenous substances that differ widely in their chemical nature and function. They are classified based on their solubility in water or fats as water-soluble and fat-soluble vitamins. The fat-soluble vitamins A, D, E and K are found in foods in association with lipids. The water-soluble vitamins are the B complex vitamins and vitamin C. The B complex consists of several unrelated compounds, containing nitrogen as a part of their chemical structure. The different B vitamins are called vitamin B-l, B-2 and so on, or by their chemical names. As the chemical identity of different vitamins was established, chemical names have replaced original names. Many vitamins exist in several related forms.

Functions: Vitamins have different functions in various animal species. They regulate metabolism, help convert fats and carbohydrates into energy and assist in forming bones and teeth. The modes of action of the fat-soluble vitamins are not nearly as clear as those of water-soluble vitamins. The latter form the coenzyme part of many enzymes as discussed in Chap. 10. Vitamins taken in excess of the finite amounts utilized in the metabolic processes are valueless. Excess water-soluble vitamins are excreted mainly in urine but excess of fat-soluble vitamins will result in storage and this could be toxic.

Requirements: Vitamin requirements for various age-groups and in circumstances of additional needs such as pregnancy and lactation have been worked out. However, the actual daily requirements for man vary depending upon inheritance, microbiological flora of the intestines, and food and eating habits. Thus, the recommended dietary allowance (RDA) of vitamins differs for different countries. The standard set by FAO/WHO and India are given in Tables 5.1 and 5.2 respectively. The RDA of developed countries is given under individual vitamins.

Table 5.1 FAO/WHO recommended daily intake of some vitamins

		Vit.D (µg)	Vit.C (mg)	Thiamine (mg)	Riboflavin (mg)	Niacin (mg)	Folacin (µg)	Vit.B-12 (µg)
Infants	0–6 months	10	20	—	—	--	40	0.3
	7–12 months	10	20	0.4	0.6	6.6	60	0.3
Children	1–3 years	10	20	0.5–0.6	0.6–0.8	7.6 – 9.6		0.9
	4–6 years	10	20	0.7	0.9	11.2		1.5
	7–9 years	2.5	20	0.8	1.2	13.9	100	1.5
	10–12 years	2.5	20	1.0	1.4			2.0
						16.5		
Adolescents	13–19 years	2.5	30	1.0–1.4	1.3–1.7	15.8–20.4	200	2.0
Adults	Men	2.5	30	1.3	1.8	21.1	200	2.0
	Women			0.9	1.3	15.2		

Source: WHO Technical Report Series,Nos. 362 and 452, Geneva, WHO,1967 and 1970.

Table 5.2 Indian recommended daily intake of some vitamins

		Retinol (μg)	Vit.D (mg)	Thiamine (mg)	Riboflavin (mg)	Niacin (mg)	Folacin (μg)	Vit.B-12 (μg)	Ascorbic acid (mg)
Infants	0-6 months	400	5.0	-	-	–			
	7-12 months	300	5.0	-	-	–	25	0.2	30
Children	1-3 years	250		0.6	0.7	8.0			
	4-6 years	300		0.8	0.8	10.0			
	7-9 years	400	5.0	0.9	1.0	12.0	50-	0.5-	30-
	10-12 years	600		1.0	1.2	14.0	100	1.0	50
Boys	13-19 years	750		1.3-1.5	1.4-1.7	17 – 21	50	0.5-	
Girls	13-19 years	750	5.0	1.1	1.2	14	100	1.0	30-50
Adults	Men	750		1.2-2.0	1.3-2.2	16 – 26			
	Women	750	5.0	1.0-1.5	1.0-1.7	13 – 20	100	1.0	30-50

Source: Nutritive Value of Indian Foods, Natural Institute of Natural (NIN), Indian Council of Medical Research (ICMR), Hyderabad, India, 1984

The early method of determining the potency of vitamins was by bioassay. The potency of vitamins A, D and E, till recently, was expressed in "units"; of late they are expressed in terms of actual weight as in the case of other vitamins.

Distribution in foods: Vitamins are present in a variety of natural foods. Some foods are richer in some vitamins and poorer in others. Persons who eat a good amount of a wide variety of natural foods do not suffer from the effects of vitamin deficiency.

Green leafy vegetables are good sources of most vitamins. Pulses, nuts and cereal grains (whole seed) also have a good content of certain vitamins. Root vegetables and fruits usually have a lower content of most vitamins, although there are some exceptions. The vitamin content of fruits and vegetables depends upon variety, growing conditions and several other factors. Animal foods like milk, eggs, or meat are good sources of water-soluble vitamins, except vitamin C. Organ meat such as liver and kidney are much richer in their vitamin content.

Loss of vitamins: All foods which undergo processing are subject to some degree of loss of vitamins. The exceptions to this phenomenon are when the availability of vitamins increases or some anti-nutritional factors are inactivated. The loss due to processing may be due to trimming. The removal of skins and peels of fruits and vegetables results in loss of vitamin C. For example, vitamin C is lost in the case of apple and pineapple, and niacin in the case of carrot, in this way. Vitamins present in seed coats and germs of cereals are lost during milling. Water-soluble vitamins are lost owing to heating and blanching. Blanching is a mild heat treatment involving the exposure of plant tissues to water or steam for as few minutes at about 100°C and one atmosphere pressure. High temperatures used for short-time processing and added chemicals have detrimental effects on the content of certain vitamins. Vitamin losses also occur during storage.

To restore vitamins lost during processing or for fortification and enrichment purposes, vitamins are added to foods. The vitamins added may be synthetic or natural. There is no difference between the synthetic vitamins and those obtained from natural sources.

5.1 Fat-Soluble Vitamins

Fat-soluble vitamins are generally associated with fatty foods, such as butter, cream, vegetable oils and fats of meat and fish. These substances generally contain only traces of B vitamins. None of the fat-soluble vitamins contain nitrogen in their structure. They are more stable to heat than the B vitamins and are less likely to be lost during the cooking and processing of foods. They are absorbed from the intestines along with fats and lipids in foods. As already stated they are not excreted in the urine and get stored in the body to a considerable extent, and this can result in toxicity.

5.1.1 Vitamin A

Vitamin A is found in animal materials like meat, milk, fish, etc. In animals, the vitamin is found in highest concentration in the liver, where it is stored and exists generally as a free alcohol or its esterified form. Plants do not contain vitamin A, but contain its precursors (provitamin A), the carotenoids, which are converted to vitamin A after absorption by the ingesting animal. Carotenoids are the orange and yellow pigments of fruits and vegetables. Green leafy vegetables also contain carotenoids; in these, the green colour of chlorophyll masks the yellow carotenoids.

Vitamin A is an alcohol ($C_{20}H_{29}OH$). It has been named "retinol" because of its specific function in the retina of the eye. Metabolically active forms of the vitamin include the corresponding aldehyde (retinal) and the acid (retinoic acid).

Carotenoids (see Sec. 8.8) are C —40-unsaturated hydrocarbons. A number of structurally related carotenes (α -, β -, γ -carotenes) and cryptoxanthin occur widely distributed in nature. β -carotene has a symmetrical structure and the molecule splits into half to give two molecules of vitamin A.

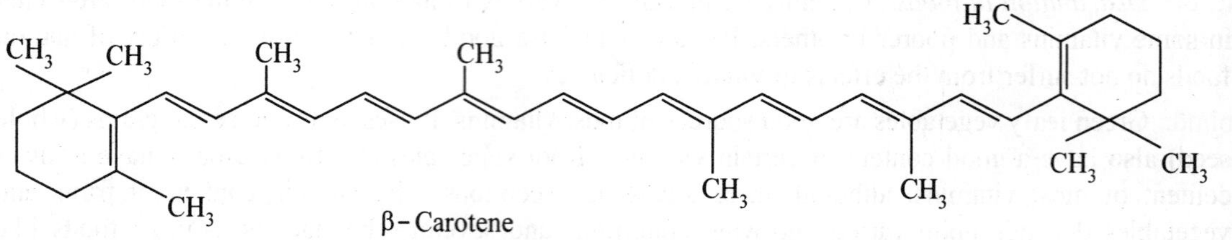

β - Carotene

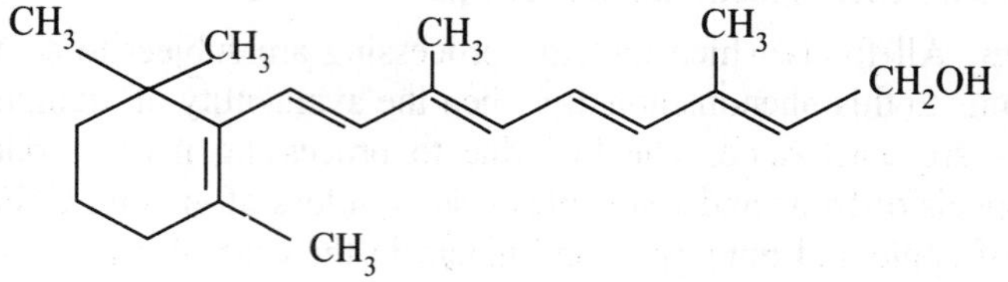

Vitamin A alcohol (Retinol)

Vitamin A is fairly stable to heat, but prolonged heating in contact with the air destroys it. It is easily destroyed by oxidation and ultraviolet light. Fats and oils lose their vitamin content by oxidation as they become rancid. Anti-oxidants prevent the loss of vitamin A, by oxidation.

Until recently the vitamin A activity in foods was expressed in international units (IU); 1 IU being equivalent to 0.3 μg of retinol or 0.6 μg of β-carotene. Because of the considerably poorer utilization of dietary provitamins when compared with retinol, the FAO/WHO Expert Committee has decided to abandon the expression of vitamin A value of foods as IU and proposed that vitamin A activity be stated as the equivalent weight of retinol (retinol equivalent, RE). By definition, one retinol equivalent is equal to one μ g of retinol or 6 μg of β-carotene, or 12μg of other provitamin A carotenoids. In terms of IU, one retinol equivalent is equal to 3.33 IU of retinol or 10 IU of β-carotene. The recommended daily allowances for adult males is 1,000 retinol, equivalents and that for adult females 800 retinol equivalents.

Functions: Vitamin A is essential for night vision. The retina is the layer of light sensitive cells lining the back inside of the eye, consisting of rods and cones. Cones respond to light by day and rods by night. Rods contain the photosensitive pigment rhodopsin (visual purple). The pigment is composed of a protein called opsin, bonded to a molecule of retinal. The pigment is photosensitive. When light falls on the retina, oxidation–reduction of retinol–retinal and stereochemical changes of vitamin A molecules (11-*cis* retinal to all *trans* retinal) take place. When there is a deficiency of vitamin A the rods cannot adjust to light changes, resulting in night blindness.

One of the chief functions of vitamin A is to maintain the health of epithelial cells, namely, the skin and membranes that line all passages that open to the exterior of the body, as well as the glands and their ducts. These cells secrete mucous which coats and protects them against invasive micro-organisms and other harmful particles. Vitamin A plays a role in the maintenance of normal epithelial structure. When vitamin A is not present, the cells cannot produce mucous and undergo, changes leading to keratinization of the mucous membrane. This renders less effective the protective barrier role played by these membranes in protecting the body against infection. It is from this function that vitamin A has become known as the anti-infective vitamin.

Vitamin A is also necessary for the growth and development of skeletal and soft tissues through its effects upon protein synthesis and differentiation of the bone cells. It is also required for the proper formation and maintenance of tooth enamel and healthy gums.

Deficiency disorders: Prolonged deficiency of vitamin A may produce skin changes, night blindness and corneal ulceration. In extreme deficiency states, the mucous membranes of the respiratory, gastrointestinal and genitourinary tracks do not function normally and are less of a defence against infecting organisms. Night blindness is attributed to the functional failure of the retina in the proper regeneration of visual purple. Vitamin A deficiency can lead to keratinization of the cornea, resulting in xerophthalmia. This is an important cause of blindness in poorly fed children in developing countries like India. Vitamin A deficiency results in the skin becoming dry, scaly and rough (xeroderma).

5.1.2 Vitamin D (Calciferol)

Rickets or osteomalacia is a bone disorder and it also occurs as a result of calcium and phosphorus deficiency. Cod liver oil has been used to cure this disease since the Middle Ages. It was noticed in the 1920s that when certain foods are exposed to ultraviolet light, they develop the ability to protect animals against rickets. Vitamin D isolated in crystalline form was named calciferol.

Most foods are low in vitamin D, although it is found in small quantities in butter, cream, egg-yolk and liver. Milk is a poor source of vitamin D; therefore, in some countries milk is fortified with this vitamin. The best food sources of vitamin D are fish liver oils.

There are at least 10 sterols which are provitamins D. Two major sterols that are converted into vitamin D by the action of ultraviolet light are the plant sterol, ergosterol, which gives ergocalciferol (vitamin D_2) and 7-dehydrocholesterol from animal tissues, which gives cholecalciferol (vitamin D_3). Vitamin D is remarkably stable and preparations of foods containing it can be warmed or kept for long periods without its deterioration. Storage, processing and cooking do not affect its activity.

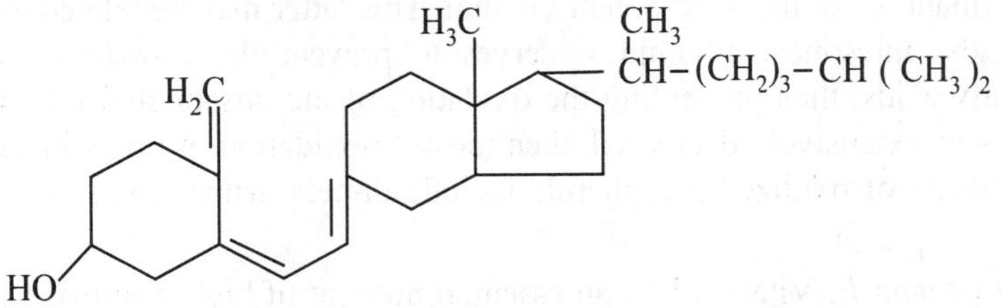

Vitamin D_3 (Cholecalciferol)

Function: Like other fat-soluble vitamins, vitamin D can be stored in the body to a large extent. The overall function of vitamin D is to produce a vital hormone called 1, 25-dihydroxycholecalciferol (1, 25-dihydroxy D_3 or vitamin D_3 hormone). This is formed by the liver and kidney, and the hormone is essential for the overall effects of dietary vitamin D, which include promotion of growth and proper mineralization of the bones and teeth. Vitamin D increases the intestinal absorption of calcium, phosphate transport in the intestines, maintains proper calcium and phosphorus levels in the serum and increases the reabsorption of calcium by the kidney.

Deficiency: The deficiency of vitamin D in children during the period of active skeletal growth causes rickets, which results from the defective mineralization of the ends of the growing bones. As a result, the ends remain abnormally pliable and eventually assume a bent form resulting in bowlegs, enlargement of bones about the joints and a narrow distorted chest with beading of the ribs. In adults, the deficiency of vitamin D causes osteomalacia, owing to defective mineralization. In this case, there is decalcification of bone shafts and the tendency is for fractures rather than bending to occur.

One international unit of vitamin D is defined as the activity contained in 0.025 mg of cholecalciferol. For infants, children and adolescents a daily allowance of 10 mg is required for better calcium absorption and some increase in growth. With cessation of skeletal growth, the requirement for vitamin D decreases; an allowance of 5 mg could do after 22 years. During pregnancy and lactation, an additional allowance of 5 mg over the non-pregnant allowance is required.

5.1.3 Vitamin E (Tocopherol)

Vitamin E is the most widely available of the vitamins in common foods. Wheat germ oil is the richest source of the vitamin. It is also present in other cereals, green plants, egg-yolk, milk-fat, butter, meat, nuts and vegetable oils (soyabean, corn, cottonseed).

Vitamin E activity in food derives from four tocopherols (α-,β-,γ- and δ-) and four tocotrienols. The α-tocopherol is biologically the most active form of vitamin E. The other compounds (β-γ-, and δ;-tocopherols and α-, β-,γ-and δ -tocotrienols) have lower biological activities, estimated to be 1–50 per cent of α-tocopherol.

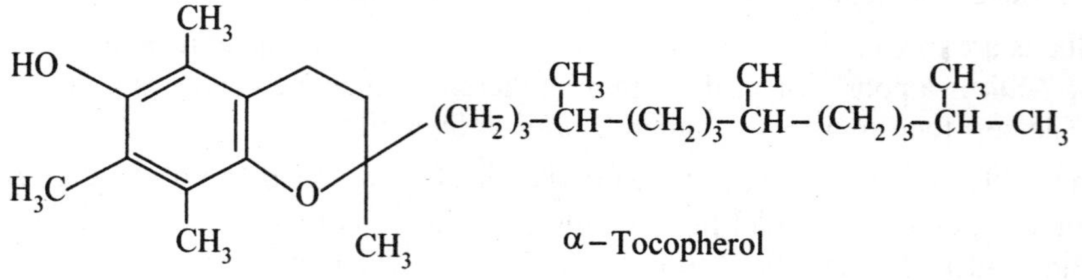

α – Tocopherol

The most important chemical property of vitamin E is its anti-oxidant property. However, the most potent anti-oxidant is not the most potent vitamin. This latter may be related to the absorption of the vitamin from the intestines. Vitamin E serves to prevent the formation of peroxides from polyunsaturated fatty acids, thus preventing the oxidation of the unsaturated fats. In the process, the vitamin E content gets extensively decreased, then the auto-oxidation of lipids in foods is severe. The decomposition products of oxidized tocopherols include dimers, trimers, dihydroxy compounds and quinones.

Function of vitamin E: Vitamin E is an essential nutrient of higher animals, including man. Its function at the molecular level in the biological processes of the body is not fully known. Its role in the body appears to be related entirely to its anti-oxidation role to prevent the formation of peroxides. Vitamin E appears to protect the cell membranes from deterioration caused by peroxides and free radicals formed from fats. This ability of vitamin E to protect membranes has been related to ageing, which is also characterized by cell membrane deterioration.

Deficiency: A deficiency of vitamin E can be produced in young animals and is manifested by a variety of symptoms that are different for different species. Specific clinical symptoms can be observed in human adults but the changes noticed are the enhanced fragility of red blood cells and thus increased urinary excretion of creatine, thus indicating muscle damage.

Vitamin E is absorbed in the same way as the other fat-soluble vitamins. However, it is stored primarily in fatty tissues and not in the liver, unlike the other fat-soluble vitamins. Compared with vitamin A and vitamin D, vitamin E is relatively nontoxic. However, it is suggested that high levels of vitamin E might interfere with vitamin K activity in some individuals.

The vitamin E activity of foods may be considerably reduced in processing, storage and packaging. About 80 per cent or more of activity is lost when whole wheat is converted to white bread. Dehydrated foods are particularly susceptible to changes resulting in decreased vitamin E activity, because of their propensity to undergo oxidation. Freezing of vegetables is also known to cause some destruction of vitamin E.

According to the original international standards, 1 IU of vitamin E is the activity of 1 mg of α-tocopherol acetate. The activity of 1 mg of naturally occurring α-tocopherol is 1.49 IU. Now vitamin E activity is referred to in terms of milligrams of α-tocopherol equivalents.

The recommended daily allowance of vitamin E for infants is 3–4 mg α-tocopherol equivalents (α-TE), for children and adolescents, 10 mg α-TE and for adult males and females 7–13 mg α-TE. During pregnancy and lactation, an additional 2–3 mg α-TE is recommended.

5.1.4 Vitamin K

Two forms of vitamin K occur naturally—vitamin K_1, (phylloquinone) in green plants and vitamin K_2 (menaquinone) which is formed as a result of bacterial action in the intestinal tract. Water-soluble forms of K_1 and K_2 are available for use by individuals unable to absorb the fat-soluble form. The K vitamins are naphthoquinone derivatives and differ from one another in the length and type of their side chains

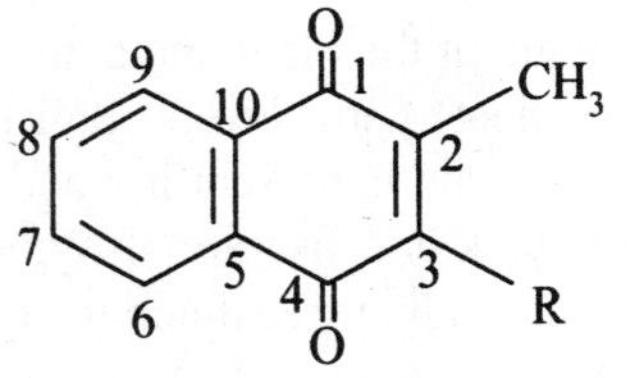

Vitamin K

$$K_1, R = -CH_2\text{-}CH = \overset{CH_3}{\overset{|}{C}}\text{-}CH_2\text{-}(CH_2CH_2\text{-}\overset{CH_3}{\overset{|}{C}H}\text{-}CH_2)_3\text{-}H$$

$$K_2, R = -(CH_2\text{-}CH = \overset{CH_3}{\overset{|}{C}}\text{-}CH_2)_n\text{-}H$$

Menadione (2-methyl-l, 4-naphthoquinone, vitamin K_3) is a fat-soluble synthetic compound and is about twice as potent biologically as the naturally occurring K_1, and K_2 on a weight basis because it lacks the long side-chain of the natural vitamin. Menadione is a provitamin and a side-chain in position 3 is to be introduced before it becomes biologically active and this takes place in the body.

The best sources of vitamin K are green leafy vegetables, especially spinach, cabbage and lettuce. Fruits, cereals, dairy products and meat provide lesser amounts. An average mixed diet provides 300-500 μg of vitamin k daily. Half of the vitamin K in man is of intestinal origin synthesized by the gut flora and half is phylloquinone. Deficiency of this vitamin is uncommon in adults. New-born infants before establishment of intestinal floraes show a deficiency.

Vitamin K is an anti-haemorrhagic vitamin. It is necessary for the synthesis of prothrombin and other proteins involved in the clotting of blood. Vitamin K deficiency prolongs blood clotting time which may lead to internal haemorrhage and uncontrolled bleeding.

Because of the synthesis of vitamin K by intestinal bacteria in normal individuals, no specific recommended allowance is made for this vitamin. To be safe, a daily allowance of 12–20 μg for infants, 20–40 μg for children, 50–100μg for adolescents, and 70–400 μg for adults, is recommended.

5.2 Water-Soluble Vitamins

Water-soluble vitamins are not normally stored to any extent in the body and the ingested vitamins in excess of requirement are excreted through the kidney. For the body to carry out its normal functions the daily supply of these vitamins is necessary. Most of the water-soluble vitamins are components of essential enzymes. These vitamins are extensively lost by leaching, during the cooking operations. The principal food sources of the B complex vitamins are liver, yeast and bran of cereal grains. Some vitamins of the B group result from bacterial activity in the small intestine. Many are easily synthesized and used as food additives.

B complex vitamins: One important reason for grouping the B vitamins together is that they all occur together in nature. Therefore, a diet lacking in one B complex vitamin usually lacks in others of the group. As a result, single discrete deficiency of a B group vitamin is seldom seen. Deficiency diseases involving the vitamins are multiple in nature, although the signs and symptoms of the deficiency of a particular member of the group may predominate. In general, the B group vitamins function as coenzymes and thus they play an essential role in the metabolic processes of all living cells.

5.2.1 Thiamine (Vitamin B-1)

This vitamin is widely distributed throughout the plant and animal kingdoms. The best sources of this vitamin are cereal grain (particularly wheat) germ layers. Polished cereal grains and refined wheat flour are deficient in the vitamin. The vitamin is present in good quantity in pulses (peas, beans) and in nuts. Liver, lean meats, poultry, egg-yolk and fish are also good sources of the vitamin. Thiamine can exist in foods in a number of forms including free thiamine, the pyrophosphate ester, and bound to respective apoenzymes (see Sec. 10.1).

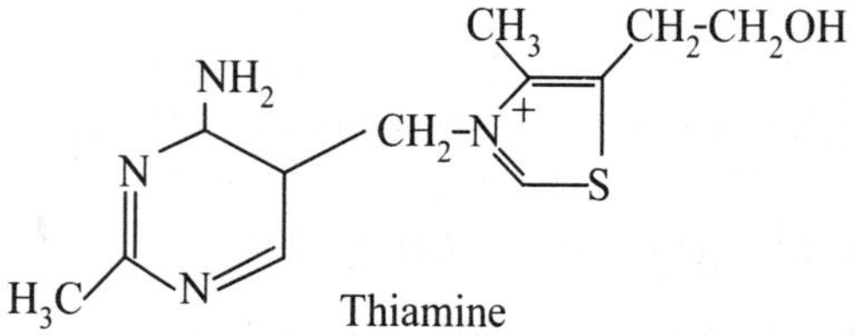

Thiamine

Thiamine is readily soluble in water and insoluble in fat solvents. The dry vitamin is fairly stable but solutions of it are unstable in the presence of heat or alkali. Temperature is an important factor in thiamine stability. Thermal destruction of thiamine results in many degradation products and leads to the formation of a characteristic odour which is involved in the development of "meaty" flavour in cooked foods. Thermal destruction is pH dependent. In acidic of pH, the vitamin is heat stable, but the coenzyme form of the vitamin is more sensitive to pH than thiamine. Starch and/or the protein components of cereal products exert a protective action against the destruction of the vitamin in some pH ranges.

Thiamine is also destroyed by oxidation and reduction. It is particularly sensitive to sulphur dioxide and sulphite, and so these should not be used to preserve thiamine-containing foods. Loss of thiamine can occur in raw fishery products because of thiaminase activity. This does not seem to be a significant human problem.

Thiamine is one of the least stable vitamins. Extensive losses occur in cereals as a result of cooking or baking, and in meats, vegetables and fruits as a result of various processing operations and during storage. Freezing has little or no effect on the thiamine content of foods.

Deficiency: Mild thiamine deficiency may result in fatigue, emotional instability, depression, irritability, retarded normal growth, loss of appetite and lethargy. Severe thiamine deficiency of long duration causes beriberi which is characterized by disturbances of the neurological and cardiovascular systems and of the gastrointestinal tract. Thiamine deficiency occurs most frequently in areas where the diet consists of unenriched white rice and white flour. Thiamine deficiency occurs among alcoholics. Decreased consumption, increased requirement and decreased absorption all appear to play a role in the development of the deficiency in alcoholics. Individuals consuming large amounts of tea, which contains a thiamine antagonist (a compound whose structure is similar to the specific nutrient), may have an increased risk of developing a deficiency.

Functions:. The most important function of thiamine is its role as a coenzyme. It combines with phosphoric acid to form thiamine pyrophosphate (TPP) which functions as a coenzyme: TPP is the coenzyme of carboxylase which is required for oxidative decarboxylation of pyruvate during the biological oxidation of glucose. The oxidation of other α -keto acids and 2-keto acids derived from amino acid metabolism also requires thiamine. TPP is also the coenzyme of transketolase, another enzyme involved in carbohydrate metabolism.

Thiamine is necessary throughout life for release of energy from fuel molecules. The amount required is related to body weight, calorie intake, and the small amount of vitamin synthesized in the intestinal tract. On the basis of these considerations, a thiamine allowance of 1.2–1.5 mg/day for males and 1.0–1.2 mg/day for females is recommended. The requirement of thiamine increases during pregnancy and lactation; an additional allowance of 0.3 mg is recommended in these cases.

5.2.2 Riboflavin (Vitamin B-2)

This vitamin is widely distributed in plant and animal foods in small amounts. Relatively good dietary sources of the vitamin are milk, cheese, liver eggs and leafy vegetables. Dried yeast is also a rich source of the vitamin. Pulses and lean meats contain appreciable amounts of riboflavin.

Riboflavin belongs to a group of yellow fluorescent pigments called flavins. The flavin ring is attached to an alcohol related to ribose (ribitol).

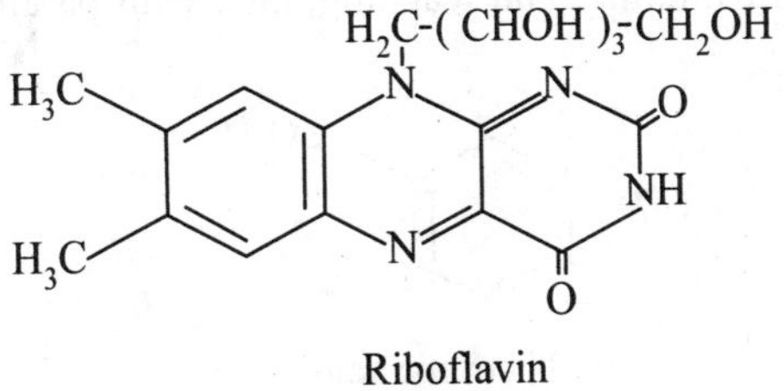

Riboflavin

Riboflavin is orange yellow in colour. On reduction, it changes into a colourless form. It is less soluble in water than thiamine but is more stable to heat in acid and neutral media. It is destroyed by heating in alkaline solution. Owing to heat stability and limited water solubility, very little of the vitamin is lost during the cooking and processing of food. Baking soda used for faster cooking destroys much of the riboflavin content of the food.

On exposure to light, riboflavin readily loses its vitamin activity due to the photochemical cleavage of the ribitol moiety of the vitamin, forming lumiflavin. Lumiflavin is a stronger oxidizing agent than riboflavin and can catalyze the destruction of a number of other vitamins, particularly ascorbic acid. When milk is sold in glass bottles, there is 50-70 per cent loss of riboflavin potency in two hours due to the effect of direct sunlight. With the advent of paper or plastic milk containers this problem has disappeared.

Deficiency: Riboflavin is essential for growth and is thought to have multiple functions in production of corticosteroids, formation of red blood cells, synthesis of glucose from non-carbohydrate materials and the thyroid enzyme regulating activity. Its deficiency in man results in reddened, denuded areas on the lips, with cracks at the corners of the mouth (cheilosis); swollen and reddened tongue (glostitis), and scaly, greasy dermatitis of the face, ears and other parts of the body. The vitamin deficiency also results in eye disorders such as itching, burning, lacrimation, dimness of vision and cataract. Symptoms of general debility and behavioural changes may also be associated with a deficient intake of riboflavin.

Function: Free riboflavin, such as is found in some foods, must be phosphorylated in the intestinal tract before it can be absorbed. On combining with phosphoric acid, it becomes part of the structure of two flavin coenzymes—flavin mononucleotide (FMN) and flavin adenine dinucleotide (FAD). These coenzymes are attached to some enzymes (flavoprotein enzymes). Most of these enzymes catalyze many oxidation and reduction reactions in the cells,

The recommended daily allowance for riboflavin is 1.5–1.8 mg for men and 1.1–1.4 mg for women with an additional 0.3 mg during pregnancy and 0.5 mg during lactation. It is reported that women using oral contraceptives have increased riboflavin requirements.

5.2.3 Niacin

The term "niacin" includes both nicotinic acid and nicotinamide, both natural forms of the vitamin with niacin activity. In foods, both these forms of the vitamin and their coenzyme forms occur. Good sources of the vitamin are lean meat, yeast, fish, poultry, groundnuts, pulses and whole grain cereals. Vegetables and fruits are poor sources. Niacin can be synthesized by the bacteria of the intestinal flora and is formed in the tissues from the amino acid tryptophan, which has niacin sparing activity. This explains why some foods rich in tryptophan, e.g., milk and egg, have a far greater niacin potency than would be expected from their actual content of niacin.

Niacin is one of the stablest vitamins, being relatively resistant to heat, light, acids and alkalis. Its loss from foods occurs via trimming, and leaching, etc., with parallel loss of other water-soluble vitamins.

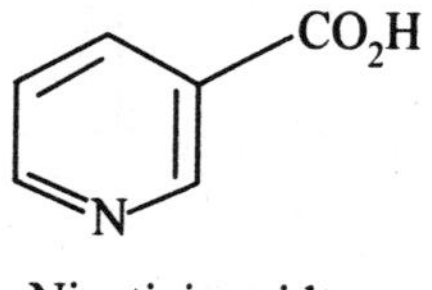

Nicotinic acid

In man, deficiency of niacin results in weakness and indigestion followed by ulcerated mouth and tongue. Prolonged deficiency leads to pellagra, and this results in dermatitis, diarrhoea and depression or dementia. Skin lesions are aggravated by exposure to sunlight; neurological symptoms and mental changes occur in more advanced cases.

The chief function of niacin in the body is to form the active part of the coenzymes that play an important part in biological oxidations. Nicotinamide is the component of two coenzymes—nicotinamide adenine dinucleotide (NAD), and its phosphate; nicotinamide adenine dinucleotide phosphate (NADP), known as pyridine nucleotides. These coenzymes are components of enzymes involved in reactions that release energy from carbohydrates, fats and proteins, also participate in fat synthesis. Also, pyridine nucleotides in the reduced form reduce the riboflavin containing coenzymes in the electron transport reactions involved in the release of biological energy.

As tryptophan has niacin sparing action, the niacin requirement of the body is expressed as niacin equivalent. It is assumed that 60 mg of tryptophan in the diet is equivalent to 1 mg of niacin. The recommended daily allowance of niacin is 16–20 mg for men and 13–16 mg for women. During pregnancy an increase of 2 mg and during lactation 4 mg of niacin is recommended.

5.2.4 Pyridoxine (Vitamin B–6)

There are 3 chemical compounds found in foods which have vitamin B–6 activity. They are pyridoxine, pyridoxal and pyridoxamine.

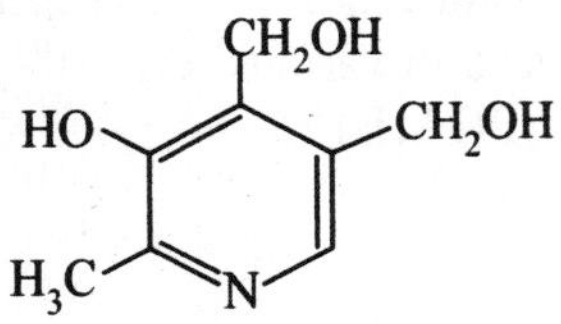

Pyridoxine

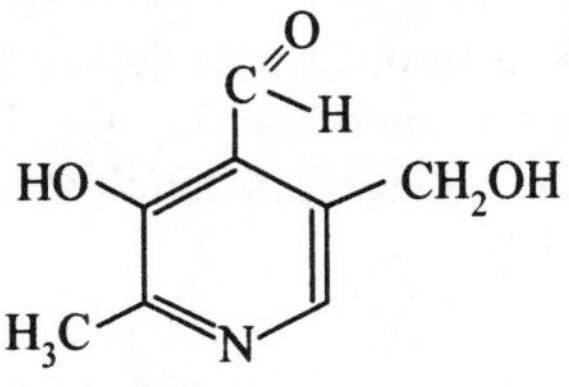

Pyridoxal

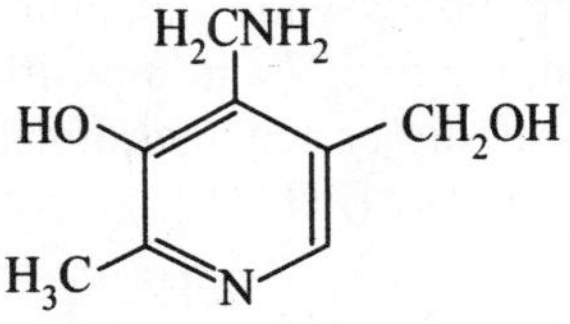

Pyridoxamine

The term B–6 or pyridoxine is used to designate this group of substances. This vitamin is widely distributed throughout the plant and animal kingdoms. The best sources are meat, especially liver, some vegetables and grain cereals with bran.

Pyridoxine (pyridoxol) is the most stable form of this vitamin and is the form used for the fortification of foods. The vitamin is stable in an acid medium and relatively stable in alkaline solution. It is very unstable to light. The product formed by photoconversion is biologically inactive.

Deficiency: Deficiency of vitamin B–6 in infants may result in epileptic form of convulsions, loss of weight and abdominal distress, vomiting and hyper irritability. In adults, deprivation of vitamin B-6 may cause depression, confusion and convulsions. Administration of vitamin B–6 antagonist (deoxypyridoxine) to subjects receiving a diet low in vitamin B–6 results in greasy (seborrheic) dermatitis around the eyes, in the eyebrows have and at the angles of the mouth, along with soreness of the mouth and a smooth red tongue, that, responded to pyridoxine but did not respond to thiamine, riboflavin and niacin. Vitamin B–6 deficiency has been shown to increase urinary oxalate formation and has been indicated in renal calculi formation.

Pregnant women on a normal diet have shown B–6 deficiency. It is also reported that women taking oral contraceptive agents have increased urinary excretion of tryptophan and impaired glucose tolerance, and these are rectified by vitamin B–6 supplementation.

Function: Pyridoxine is found in cells in the active form, pyridoxal phosphate (PLP). This is the coenzyme of many enzymes involved in carbohydrate, fat and protein metabolism, being required in transamination, deamination, desulphuration and decarboxylation reactions. The vitamin is the cofactor of enzymes involved in the conversion of tryptophan to niacin, the essential fatty acid linoleic acid to arachidonic acid, and release of glucose from glycogen.

Vitamin B–6 requirement for both men and women is 1.6 to 2.0 mg per day. The need increases to 2.5 mg per day in the case of pregnant and lactating women.

5.2.5 Folic Acid

The name folic acid comes from the Latin word for foliage or leaf (folium), because the vitamin was first isolated from spinach leaves and was known to be widely distributed in green leafy plants. Nutritionists use the term "folacin" for folic acid. There is no single compound with the name folacin. The word represents a number of related compounds exhibiting the biological properties of folic acid.

Yeast, kidney, liver and green leafy vegetables, especially spinach, asparagus and broccoli, are rich sources of folic acid. Dried beans and the whole wheat bread are good sources of the vitamin. The folic acid content of processed milk, highly milled cereals, eggs, root vegetables and most fruits is low.

Folic acid belongs to a group of compounds known as pterins. It consists of three components, a pteridine ring attached to p-aminobenzoic acid, which, in turn, is coupled to glutamic acid. Its chemical structure is pteroyl-glutamic acid (PGA). In many foods, folic acid contains more than one glutamic moiety with glutamates linked through peptide bonds involving the ϒ-carboxyl group. In addition, the 5, 6, 7 and 8 positions of the pteridine ring may be reduced in various forms to yield a variety of di- or tetrahydrofolates, i.e., 5, 6, 7, 8 tetrahydrofolate ($PGAH_4$), 5, 6–, 5, 8–, or 7. 8-dihydrofolate ($PGAH_2$).

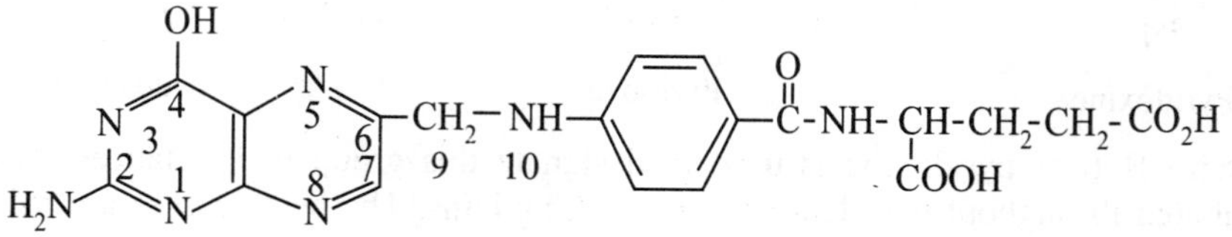

Folic acid (Pteroylmonoglutamic acid,PGA)

A variety of chemical forms of PGA have vitamin activity. The essential subunit structure should remain intact for activity. If the parent molecule is broken into its constituents, the nutritional activity is lost. Different members of the folic acid group vary in nutritional effectiveness, stability and availability. For example, N^5-methyl $PGAH_4$, N^5-formyl $PGAH_4$ and N^{10}-formyl PGA are heat stable, whereas others like unsubstituted $PGAH_4$ are rapidly destroyed by heat. PGA itself is unstable to heat in acid medium but stable to sunlight when in solution.

Loss of folic acid occurs when foods are processed and stored; vitamin activity is lost in processed and stored milks. Primarily, the inactivation is due to oxidation. The destruction of folate runs parallel to that of ascorbate and added ascorbate can stabilize folate.

Folacin deficiency in man results in poor growth, megaloblastic anaemia and other blood disorders, gastrointestinal tract disturbances arising from impaired absorption, and metabolic derangement. The vitamin controls macrocytic anaemias of pregnancy. In pernicious anaemia, folic acid gives some initial response but the disease is cured only after administration of vitamin B–12.

After absorption, folic acid is converted into many active coenzyme forms, the parent being tetrahydrofolic acid. The principal function of, PGA-containing coenzymes is the transport of one-carbon groups (specially, the formyl and hydroxymethyl groups) from one compound to another. Many of the steps catalyzed by folate-containing enzymes are essential for the synthesis of nucleic acids and for the normal metabolism of certain amino acids. This explains the important role of folate in cell division and protein synthesis.

The recommended daily allowance of folacin is 400 μg of total PGA activity for nonpregnant, nonlactating adults and adolescents. The requirement during pregnancy is 800 μg/day and during lactation 500 μg/day.

5.2.6 Biotin

Biotin is widely distributed in nature and is essential for the health of many animal species including man. Good sources include liver, kidney, egg yolk, groundnuts and some vegetables. Cereal grains, fruits and meat are regarded as poor sources. Wide differences exist in the bioavailability of biotin-bound vitamin is unavailable for nutritional purposes. Biotin of maize and soyabean meal is completely available to test animals, whereas the biotin of wheat is almost unavailable.

Biotin is a water-soluble, sulphur–containing vitamin. It is stable to heat and light but unstable in strong acid or alkali. Its optimum stability is in the pH range 5–8. As it contains a sulphur atom, it is susceptible to oxidation.

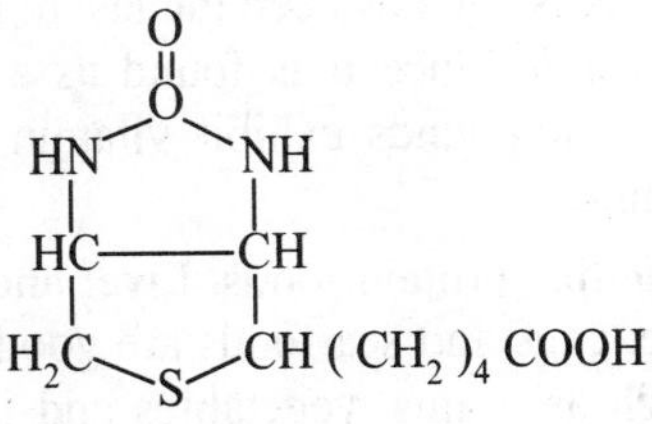

Biotin

Deficiencies of biotin are unlikely in man due to its extensive synthesis in the intestinal tract. Deficiency manifestations can be induced by feeding large amounts of the biotin binding protein, avidin, present in raw egg-white. Symptoms of biotin deficiency in man include anorexia, nausea, vomiting, mental depression, and a dry scaly dermatitis.

Biotin is the coenzyme required by several carboxylating enzymes (carboxylases) which have the capacity to add or remove carbon dioxide. The vitamin plays an extremely important role in the metabolism of both carbohydrates and fats.

The dietary allowance for biotin cannot be established easily. The daily recommended quantities are: 0.4 mg for adults, 0.8 mg in pregnancy and 0.6 mg in lactation.

5.2.7 Pantothenic Acid

Pantothenic acid is widely distributed in foods and is particularly abundant in animal tissues, whole grain cereals and pulses. It also occurs in lesser amounts in milk, vegetables and fruits. It is reported that it is synthesized by intestinal microflora.

Pantothenic acid is more stable in solution than in the dry form. It is stable in the pH range 4–7. It is decomposed by alkali and dry heat. It is stable in moist heat in neutral solutions.

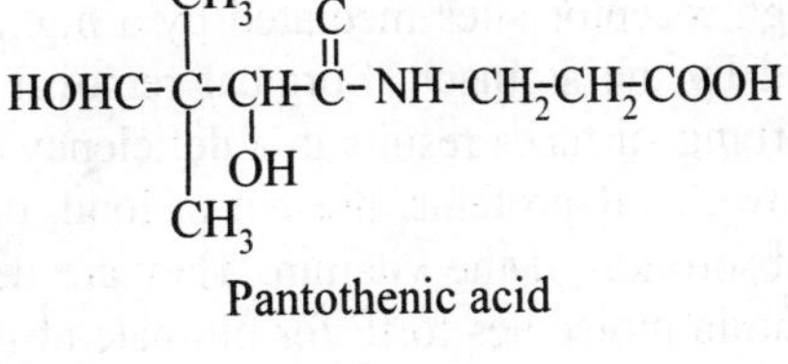

Pantothenic acid

As the vitamin is widely distributed in foods, a deficiency disease due to lack of it has not been observed in man. Deficiency symptoms have been produced by the administration of metabolic antagonists (ω-methylpantothenic acid). Pain and sensation in the arms and legs, loss of appetite, nausea and indigestion have been noticed in these conditions. Pulse rise, fainting attacks, and increase in susceptibility to infection, have also been observed.

The physiological role of pantothenic acid is primarily as a component of coenzyme A which is involved in acetylation and other acylation reactions. These reactions are important in the release of energy from carbohydrates, in glucose synthesis, in the synthesis and degradation of fatty acids and in the synthesis of steroids and steroid hormones.

An intake of 4–7 mg per day of pantothenic acid would be adequate for adults. A higher intake may be needed during pregnancy and lactation.

5.2.8 Cobalamin (Vitamin B-12)

This is the most complex of the vitamins and has been the last to have its structure elucidated. Vitamin B–12 is known by the name cobalamin since it is found as a co-ordination complex with cobalt. Several of the different cobalamin compounds exhibit vitamin B–12 activity. There are, however, some nutritionally inactive cobalamins.

Vitamin B-12 is present in animal protein foods. Liver and kidney are excellent sources of this vitamin. Milk, muscle meat, cheese, eggs and sea-foods are good sources of this vitamin. There is no vitamin B-12 in plant products such as grams, vegetables and fruits. Strict vegetarians may not get sufficient vitamin B–12 from their dietary source. However, human requirements are very low and this is met by intestinal bacterial synthesis. The coenzyme form of vitamin B-12, which is the major part of vitamin present in foods, is very unstable to the heat used in processing procedures and to light. Up to 10 per cent of the vitamin is lost when milk is pasteurized and 40-90 per cent is lost in the preparation of evaporated milk.

Vitamin B-12 is water-soluble and heat-stable. Approximately 70 per cent of the vitamin activity is retained during cooking. The region of optimal pH stability of the vitamin in food is 4–6. At higher pHs or in the presence of reducing agents, such as the ascorbic acid or sulphite, there is loss of the vitamin on heating.

Vitamin B–12 is converted to nutritionally active forms for man when given either orally or parenterally. The vitamin is a red crystalline material and the compounds exhibiting this vitamin activity are called corrinoids because of their porphyrin structure. The cobalt present in the vitamin molecule occupies the centre of the molecule and may be attached to various chemical groups. When attached to the cyanide group, the compound is called cyanocobalamin and when attached to the hydroxyl group, hydroxycobalamin. The former is the most stable form of the vitamin and is present in the body in very small amounts.

Deficiency: Vitamin B-12 deficiency in man is not usually dietary in origin, but results due to a lack of its absorption in the intestines, no matter how much is eaten. The intestinal absorption of vitamin B-12 takes place through receptor sites mediated by a highly specific binding glycoprotein, the intrinsic factor (IF) secreted by the stomach. Surgical removal of the intrinsic factor secreting portions of the stomach or absorbing surfaces results in a deficiency of vitamin B-12. There are other cobalamin binding proteins, known as R-proteins, present in food, milk, plasma and saliva but these do not facilitate the intestinal absorption of the vitamin. They are degraded by pancreatic proteases, permitting the transfer of cobalamin molecules to IF for ultimate absorption by the intestine. A small percentage of absorption (1–3 per cent) may also occur by simple diffusion.

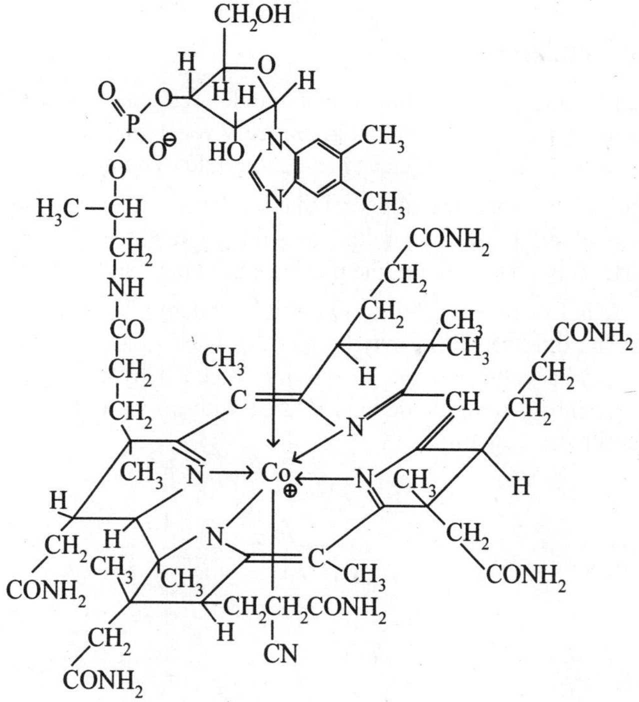

Vitamin B-12

The biological half-life of vitamin B-12 is high. This is because there is an effective enterohepatic circulation that recycles the vitamin from bile and other intestional secretions. Anaemia caused by a deficiency of vitamin B-12 occurs most commonly about five years after total gastrectomy (surgical removal of stomach). The capacity of the body to reutilize the vitamin and replenish its stores after an interval of days makes it unnecessary to consume vitamin B–12 everyday either as food or as a dietary supplement.

A long-term deficiency of vitamin B-12 results in an anaemia known as pernicious anaemia. The red cells enlarge but do not mature properly and the red cell count decreases. If the anaemia is not reversed in time, degenerative changes take place affecting the spinal cord, leading to sensory disturbances, general weakness and paralysis.

Function: Cobalamin is necessary for normal functioning in the metabolism of all cells, especially for those of the gastrointestinal tract, bone marrow and nervous tissue and for growth. Cobalamin containing coenzymes play an important role in the transfer of methyl groups. They are linked to nucleic acid metabolism through the regeneration of folic acid from the 5–methyl $PGAH_4$ pool. The vitamin also plays a role in the synthesis of polyglutamyl forms of PGA.

The recommended allowances of vitamin B-12 for adults is 3.0 μg per day and 4.0 μg per day for pregnant and lactating women.

Other B vitamins: Other factors listed among the B–complex vitamins are choline, inositol and p–aminobenzoic acid (PABA). These are not vitamins for man. Choline is required in the diet of young animals. Inositol is a growth factor for certain yeasts and PABA is an important growth factor for lower animals.

5.2.9 Ascorbic acid (Vitamin C)

Vitamin C is an antiscorbutic substance which prevent and cures scurvy. Excellent sources of vitamin C are citrus fruits, berries, guava, capsicum and green leafy vegetables. Canned or frozen citrus fruits and tomatoes are also good sources. Milk, eggs, meat and poultry contain little or no ascorbic acid.

Ascorbic acid is a highly soluble compound that has both acidic and strong reducing properties. It is the most unstable of all known vitamins. In solution it easily gets oxidized, especially on exposure to heat. Oxidation is accelerated in the presence of copper and with alkaline pH.

Ascorbic acid is a hexose derivative. On mild oxidation ascorbic acid is converted into dehydroascorbic acid. The oxidized form may be reduced back to ascorbic acid. Both ascorbic acid and dehydroascorbic acid have the vitamin C activity. When dehydroascorbic acid is treated with weak acid it is converted into diketogulonic acid (DKG) with no vitamin C activity and it cannot be reduced to dehydroascorbic acid again.

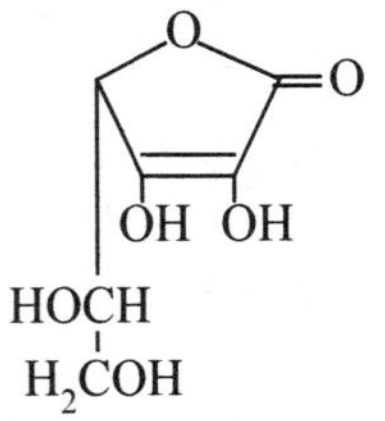

Ascorbic acid

Since ascorbic acid is soluble in water and easily oxidized it is susceptible to loss during the cooking and processing of food. It is readily lost via, leaching from the cut or bruised surface of the food. Prolonged cooking at high temperature and undue exposure to oxygen, copper and iron result in a loss of the vitamin. Factors influencing degradation during processing include temperature, salt and sugar concentration, pH, oxygen, enzymes, metal catalysts, amino acids, oxidants or reductants also initial concentration of ascorbic acid and the ratio of ascorbic acid to dehydroascorbic acid. However, in processed foods, the most significant losses result from chemical degradation. In foods which are particularly high in ascorbic acid, such as fruit products, loss is usually associated with nonenzymic browning.

Deficiency: Many species of animals are able to synthesize ascorbic acid and do not require it in the diet. When deprived of a dietary source of vitamin C for sufficient length of time (about a month), man, along with other primates and several other species, develops scurvy. It is a fatal disease characterized by a weakening of the collagenous structure, and this results in widespread capillary haemorrhaging. Other symptoms include weakness, poor appetite and growth, anaemia, tenderness to touch, swollen and inflamed gums, loosening of teeth bone and joint diseases.

Function: Specific biochemical functions of vitamin C have not been well defined. Vitamin C has been implicated in the hydroxylation of proline to form the hydroxyproline required in the formation of collagen. It helps in the healing of wounds, fractures, bruises and bleeding gums, and reduces liability to infections. Ascorbic acid is involved in the metabolism of some amino acids, such as tyrosine, in drug and folic acid metabolism, and in the synthesis of epinephrine and anti-inflammatory steroids in the adrenal glands. The absorption of iron is increased by dietary ascorbic acid when the two nutrients are ingested simultaneously. Enhancement of iron absorption takes place when the ascorbic acid content of meal is 25-75 mg or more.

A number of factors determine the requirement of vitamin C. Acute emotional or environmental stress requires high levels of the vitamin. Other factors like age, sex, drugs, smoking and oral contraceptive agents also determine the magnitude of the vitamin required. Taking all aspects of vitamin C requirement, an allowance of 45 mg/day for children, 60 mg/day for adults of both sexes, an additional 20 mg/day for pregnant women and additional 40 mg/day for lactating women is recommended.

Pharmacological effects of vitamin C: Intake of ascorbic acid in excess of nutritional requirements (1 g/day or more) has been reported to have some effect in reducing in frequency and severity of common cold and other winter illness. It is now believed that the benefits of large doses of ascorbic acid are too small to justify the recommendation of a routine intake of large amounts.

Large amounts of ascorbic acid have also been reported to lower serum cholesterol in some hypercholesterolemic subjects. Ascorbic acid supplement can prevent the reduced platelet and plasma concentration of ascorbic acid in aspirin treated rheumatoid arthritis patients and has been reported to increase the human serum level of some immunoglobulins. Thus, ascorbic acid in large doses may have some pharmacological or drug-like effects that are not related to the normal functioning of the vitamin.

Large doses of ascorbic acid have generally been considered non-toxic. However, a number of adverse effects of excessive intake of the vitamin have been reported. Thus, routine consumption of large amounts of ascorbic acid is not recommended without medical advice.

CHAPTER

6

Minerals

Minerals are inorganic components of food that leave ash as residue when burned. They occur in foods and tissues as inorganic salts (sodium chloride, calcium phosphate), in combination with organic compounds (phosphoproteins, phospholipids, haemoglobin) and chiefly in their ionic form (Na^+, K^+ Ca^{2+}, Cl^- and $H_2PO_4^-$). Some mineral content of foods is lost through leaching and much is lost during processing and storage.

Depending upon their amounts in the adult's body, the minerals are classified as macronutrient and micronutrient elements. The former are present in amounts greater than 0.005 per cent of body weight, while the latter are present in less than 0.005 per cent of body weight. The macrominerals are required in the adult human diet in amounts of over 100 mg per day. These include calcium, phosphorus, sulphur, potassium, chlorine, sodium and magnesium. The microminerals or trace minerals are required in amounts of less than 20 mg per day and they are iron, fluorine, zinc, copper, iodine, chromium and cobalt. There are also other microminerals required in much smaller quantities by man.

Minerals have various functions in the body. About 4–6 per cent of the human body weight consists of minerals, 4/5 of this being in the skeleton and the rest in other organs. Minerals, as salts, are constituents of bone and teeth. As ions in body fluids, minerals regulate the metabolism of many enzymes, maintain the acid-base balance and osmotic pressure, facilitate the membrane transport of essential compounds, and maintain nerve and muscular irritability. However, trace elements are toxic when consumed in excessive amounts.

6.1 Macronutrients

6.1.1 Calcium

Calcium is the most abundant mineral in the body. The body of an adult male weighing 70 kg contains approximately 1,200 g of calcium which comprises 39 per cent of the total minerals present. About 99 per cent of calcium is present in the skeleton. In the bones, calcium occurs as calcium phosphate within a soft, fibrous, organic matrix. The unique structure of this matrix is required for normal calcification. Calcium phosphate is present in bones mostly in crystalline form (hydroxyapatite) and also in non-crystalline form. The amorphous form is predominant in early life and is superseded by crystalline apatite in later life. Despite the seeming permanence of mineral deposits, bone is constantly being formed and resorbed. In an adult man, it has been estimated that about 700 mg of calcium enter and leave the bones each day.

About 1 per cent of the body's calcium is found in the body fluids and soft tissues. This calcium is mostly in the ionic form. This is essential for certain enzyme activities, blood clotting, excitability of peripheral nerves and muscle, myocardial function and muscle contraction.

Usually 20–30 per cent of ingested calcium is absorbed by the body. The calcium-phosphorus ratio has been said to influence the absorption of calcium. There are, however, different opinions regarding this. There are a number of factors which increase or decrease calcium uptake. Vitamin D, low pH, presence of lactose, fat in low concentration and high protein intake increase calcium absorption. Lack of vitamin D, high fat intake, oxalic acid present in some fruits and vegetables, phytic acid present in cereals, alkaline medium and emotional instability decrease absorption of calcium.

Most ingested calcium (65-70 per cent) is excreted in urine and faeces. Changes in urinary excretion of calcium with changes in calcium intake are only slight; in contrast, faecal excretion is related to calcium intake. There is also some loss of calcium (about 15 mg per day) in sweat.

Calcium deficiency in children leads to rickets, while in adults it may result in osteomalacia. Sometimes there is a gradual demineralization of bony tissues; this disease is characterized by porosity, thinness and fragility of the bones, and is known as osteoporosis. This is due to decreased calcium absorption with age.

FAO/WHO recommends an intake of 400–500 mg per day of calcium for adults. The need for calcium during pregnancy and lactation is increased. An additional 400 mg per day is required during these periods. For children from 1 to 10 years of age, recommended calcium allowance is 800 mg per day. During the rapid growth period (10–18 years), a higher intake of 1,200 mg per day is recommended.

Among common foods, milk and milk products are the richest sources of calcium. The calcium in milk is assimilated readily because of the lactose and vitamin D that are also present in milk. Other foods rich in calcium are molasses, nuts, sesame seeds and millets (ragi). Meat, poultry and fish are poor in calcium. The calcium content of many fruits and vegetables is also poor.

6.1.2 Phosphorus

Phosphorus, in combination with calcium, contributes to the supporting structures of the body. Second to calcium in abundance, it comprises 22 per cent of the total minerals of the body. About 80 per cent of phosphorus is present as calcium phosphate in the bones. The remaining 20 per cent is present in the blood and other cells as soluble phosphate ions and also in lipids, proteins and carbohydrates. Phosphorus is a component of nucleic acids and the cell membrane.

Phosphorus, in addition to its structural role, is involved in a great variety of chemical reactions in the body. Substances, such as glucose and fats, become highly reactive in tissue metabolism and are more readily transported in body fluids by combination with the phosphate radical. In the stepwise anaerobic oxidation of glucose, most of the components are phosphorylated compounds. Energy transfer compounds contain phosphate residues.

Phosphorus is present in nearly all foods and dietary deficiency is extremely unlikely to occur in man. Intake of this mineral in the ordinary diet is almost always, if not invariably, higher than that of calcium. The recommended daily allowance of phosphorus in milligrams per day is the same as that for calcium. Phosphorus deficiency, when it occurs, results in weakness, anorexia, malaise and pain in the bones.

Rich sources of phosphorus in foods are meat, poultry, fish and egg. Milk and its products, nuts and pulses are good sources. Cereals are good sources but availability of phosphorus as well as its effect on calcium absorption is poor due to the presence of phytic acid.

6.1.3 Sulphur

While other minerals take care of dietary needs in inorganic forms, sulphur is required principally in the form of the sulphur containing amino acids such as cystine, cysteine and methionine. Sulphur is present in all proteins but is more prevalent in the keratin of skin and hair. Sulphur is also a component of glutathione. Sulphur can exist in the reduced sulphydryl form as in cysteine and oxidized disulphur form as in cystine. This is important in the specific configuration of some proteins and the activity of some enzymes. Sulphur is also a component of the vitamins like thiamine and biotin.

6.1.4 Magnesium

Magnesium has many essential biological functions in plants and animals. It is a component of chlorophyll and is absolutely essential for plants to synthesize carbohydrates. The human body contains 20–28 g of magnesium, more than half of which is stored in the bones. The element is an essential part of many enzyme systems, particularly those involved in the liberation of energy. Magnesium is important in maintaining the electrical potential of nerve and muscle membranes.

Magnesium deficiency is an important complication in Kwashiorkor. Hypomagnesemia occurs in alcoholics. There seems to be a relationship between the levels of serum magnesium and occurrence of tremor and convulsion in infants and children.

Because magnesium occurs widely in foods, particularly those of vegetable origin, a dietary deficiency of magnesium is rare. Animal products, including meat and milk, are poor in magnesium. Processing of foods leads to loss of magnesium.

An allowance of 50 mg per day for young infants and 70 mg per day for older infants is recommended. Based on the estimated magnesium content of an average diet, the allowance recommended for adult males is 350 mg per day and for adult females 300 mg per day. During pregnancy and lactation, an additional allowance of 150 mg per day is recommended.

6.1.5 Sodium, Potassium and Chlorine

Sodium, potassium and chlorine constitute 2, 5 and 3 per cent respectively of the total mineral content of the body. They are distributed throughout the body fluids and tissues, but sodium and chlorine are principally extracellular elements, while potassium is mainly an intracellular element. These elements are involved in maintaining the body fluid volume, osmotic equilibrium, and acid-base balance. Sodium and potassium are primarily responsible for the potential differences existing across the membranes of nerve and muscle cells, which facilitate the conduction of nerve impulses.

Sodium and chlorine, in the form of table salt, have been in use in the diet of man since early times. We consume about 6 to 8 g of sodium chloride as a food additive. About 0.6 to 3.5 g is an adequate daily intake. Deficiency of sodium occurs during hot weather or as a result of heavy work in hot climate, owing to excessive sweating. An extra intake of salt is necessary in such conditions. The sodium and chloride ions are also important in digestive fluids; as sodium bicarbonate in bile and pancreatic juice, and as hydrochloric acid in gastric juice.

Potassium is a nearly constant component of lean body tissue. Therefore, when there is growth and development of lean tissue an adequate supply of potassium is essential. Potassium is lost whenever muscle is broken down. Deficiency of potassium results in muscular weakness or paralysis.

A potassium deficiency from inadequate intake is unlikely since potassium is widely distributed in foods. Meat, milk, many fruits and dark green leafy vegetables are good sources of this mineral.

6.2 Micronutrients

Some elements which are present in trace amounts in diets are as important as those found in largest amounts. Their absence leads to the occurrence of deficiency diseases. Many plant foods, such as grains, pulses, fruits and vegetables are reasonably good sources of these elements. Animal foods, such as eggs, milk, meat and fish also contain these elements in small quantities. The processing of foods, such as blanching or the removal of the endosperm of grains, results in loss of trace elements. These elements function as components of enzymes and of important organic compounds, such as haemoglobin and thyroxine.

6.2.1 Iron

About 3–5 g of iron is present in a healthy adult. Of this, about 70 per cent is in a functional form as a constituent of haemoglobin, myoglobin, and a number of enzymes which catalyze oxidation and reduction processes in the cell. The remaining 30 per cent is storage iron. It is stored in the liver, bone marrow and spleen as ferritin and haemosiderin.

Iron, as a component of haemoglobin, plays an important part in the transport of oxygen from the lungs to the tissues and of carbon dioxide from the cells to the lungs. The iron present in pigments and enzymes in the tissues serves to bring about the transfer of oxygen within the cell in much the same manner (cellular respiration). Iron also plays a role in the conversion of β-carotene to vitamin A, the synthesis of purines, the clearance of blood lipids and the detoxication of drugs in the liver.

Iron deficiency results first in the reduction of stored iron and after it is depleted, a reduction in haemoglobin concentration and size occurs (microcytic hypochromic anaemia). Some 250 million women in the developing world, in the 15 to 49 age-group, are estimated to be suffering from iron-deficiency anaemia, according to a WHO report. In India, between 60 to 80 per cent of pregnant women are anaemic. India probably shows one of the highest prevalences of nutritional anaemia in women. Anaemia is caused due to diets deficient in iron, protein and the vitamins folate, B–12, B–6 and C, or due to poor absorption over long periods. Loss of blood through illness, injury or haemorrhage and excessive loss of blood during menstrual periods also results in iron deficiency.

The absorption of iron is a complex process influenced by the intestinal mucosa, the amount and chemical nature of the iron in the ingested food, and a variety of factors that increase or decrease the availability of iron. Ferrous salts are more easily absorbed than are the ferric salts. Ascorbic acid, acid medium, presence of calcium, and physiological states such as growth and pregnancy, enchance iron absorption. It is estimated that on an average only 10 per cent of the iron in food is absorbed by adults with normal haemoglobin values. However, this needs to be corrected as the actual amount absorbed depends upon the haeme and nonhaeme iron of the food.

Only very small amounts of iron are normally excreted from the body. The average loss of iron in the healthy adult is approximately 1 mg per day. In adult women, there is a loss of 0.5 mg per day of iron in the menstrual blood flow averaged over one month. In order to provide the retention of 1 mg per day of iron in adult males and post-menopausal females an allowance of 10 mg per day is recommended. The allowance for women of childbearing age is 18 mg per day.

The iron absorbed is stored in the body as ferritin and haemosiderin. The stored iron can be mobilized for haemoglobin synthesis. When the red blood cells disintegrate, the non-protein portion of haemoglobin is split into an iron-containing substance (haematin) and then to a pigment (bilirubin).

Almost all the iron and much of the pigment are saved, to be used over again in the synthesis of new red corpuscles.

Organ meats, such as liver, kidney and heart, are rich in iron. Lean meats, eggs, pulses, nuts, dried fruits, whole grains and green leafy vegetables, are good sources. Milk and milk products are practically devoid of iron.

6.2.2 Fluorine

Fluorine (fluoride) is present in small but widely varying concentrations in practically all soils, water supplies, plants and animals. It is therefore a constituent of normal diets. Because of its ubiquity, a severe fluoride deficiency is rare.

Fluoride is incorporated into bone and tooth enamel. It protects against dental caries, on an intake of 1.5 mg per day or more. A higher intake (water containing 2 or more mg per litre of fluoride) produces mottling of the teeth in children. A still higher intake (4 mg of fluoride per litre of water) may afford protection against osteoporosis in adults. Chronic fluoride toxicity, fluorosis, is seen only in persons consuming more than 20 mg per day over an extended period. A total intake (from food and drinking water) of 1.5–4 mg per day is safe and adequate for adults. This range is obtained when water used contains at least 1 mg per litre of fluoride.

6.2.3 Zinc

Zinc is an essential element for plants, animals and man. It is a constituent of the enzymes involved in most major metabolic pathways. Zinc-containing enzymes are involved in nucleic acid synthesis and degradation. Large amounts of zinc are stored in bones. Signs of deficiency of zinc in man are loss of appetite, failure to grow, skin changes, impaired regeneration of wounds and decreased taste activity.

The turnover of body zinc has been calculated at 6 mg per day. There is about 40 per cent absorption of dietary zinc. Phytate and fibre affect zinc availability adversely. Thus, an intake of 15 mg per day of zinc is recommended for adults, with an additional 5 mg per day during pregnancy and 10 mg during lactation. The recommended allowance for pre-adolescent children is 10 mg per day and that for infants 3 mg per day.

The biological availability of zinc in different foods varies widely. Animal meats and seafoods are much better sources of available zinc than vegetable products.

6.2.4 Copper

Copper is an essential element for all vertebrates and some lower animal species. It is present in combination with a plasma protein, ceruloplasmin, which is the transportable form of copper. The deficiency of copper results in anaemia due to the improper mobilization of iron from iron storage sites. In animals, copper deficiency leads to a variety of abnormalities including anaemia, skeletal defects, defects in pigmentation and structure of hair or wool, reproductive failure and cardiovascular diseases. Copper is a constituent of some enzymes.

A daily copper intake of 2–3 mg is recommended for adults and this is met by the normal daily diet. Copper is widely distributed. The richest food sources are oysters, followed by nuts, liver, kidney and dried pulses. Cow milk is a poor source of copper.

6.2.5 Iodine

Iodine is an important micronutrient for all animal species including man. It is an integral part of the thyroid hormones, thyroxine and tri-iodotyronine, which have important metabolic roles. Iodine deficiency, among other causes, leads to the enlargement of the thyroid gland (goitre). The body normally contains 20 to 30 mg of iodine, 60 per cent of which is in the thyroid gland and the rest diffused throughout all the tissues.

An intake of 150 μg is recommended for adolescents and adults of both sexes. An additional 25 to 30 μg are required for pregnant and lactating women. Among man's foods, seafoods are excellent sources of iodine. In the absence of food containing iodine, use of iodized salt can rectify iodine deficiency.

6.2.6 Chromium

In the absence of chromium, there is disturbed glucose metabolism in man. Chromium levels in human tissues decline with age. A chromium intake of 50-200 μg per day is recommended for adults. Brewer's yeast, meat products, cheese, whole grains and spices are good sources of available chromium, whereas leafy vegetables contain the element in a poorly available form.

6.2.7 Cobalt

Strangely cobalt deficiency has never been described for man. In its absence, ruminants develop anaemia, muscular atrophy and eventual death. The major role of cobalt in the body is to serve as a part of vitamin B–12. Inorganic cobalt is necessary for the microbial synthesis of vitamin B–12 in the gut of animals. To some extent, human beings also have this ability to obtain vitamin B–12 from cobalt due to synthesis by micro-organisms. This explains why true vegetarians can live for many years without vitamin B–12 in the diet.

6.2.8 Other Micronutrients

There are a number of other micronutrients essential for man. Some of them are silicon, vanadium, tin, selenium, manganese, nickel and molybdenum. The amounts of these nutrients required for human beings have not yet been estimated.

CHAPTER

7

Water

Water, next to oxygen, is the most important constituent of life. A person can live for a few weeks without food but only for a few days without water. It is an integral part of animal and vegetable tissues. Water is the medium through which all cellular reactions occur. It functions in digestion, absorption, circulation and excretion Water helps maintain the electrolyte balance of the body and plays a role in the maintenance of body temperature. Water is not only a solvent but it also participates in several reactions, either as a reactant or as a product.

Water is the most widely distributed compound in the world as liquid, solid and vapour. It is one of the most important chemicals in foods and drinks. Fruits and vegetables contain more than 90 per cent water. Milk is 87 per cent water, and meat 60 to 75 per cent water. Even dried foods such as figs and raisins contain 20 per cent water. Foods, such as dried pulses, cereals and flour, also contain appreciable quantities of water.

Water influences the appearance, texture and flavour of food. Water is involved in most of the changes that take place when food is cooked. Food spoilage also is related to the presence of water in food. Some of the desirable and undesirable changes that take place when food is cooked are due to the properties of water as a food solvent. The characteristic flavour of coffee and tea is due to the ability of water to dissolve the flavour materials present in tea leaves and coffee powder. The loss of water-soluble vitamins during cooking is due to their high solubility in water. Water is also the dispersion medium in foods. Too much water in foods can be a danger as it favours the growth of undesirable bacteria and other micro-organisms. The aim of modern food technology is to keep the water content of many foods as low as possible to increase shelflife.

7.1 Physical Properties of Water

The physical constants of water are very different when compared with molecules of similar molecular weight and atomic composition, such as hydrogen sulphide, hydrogen fluoride, ammonia, etc. Water has unusually large values for melting point, boiling point, surface tension, specific heat, and dielectric constant. Its heats of fusion, vaporization and sublimation are also high. Another unusual property of water is that it has maximum density at 4°C and not at 0°C, its freezing point. The thermal conductivity of ice at 0°C is approximately four times that of water at the same temperature, indicating that ice conducts heat energy at a much faster rate than immobilized water. Also, in a given environment, thermal diffusion of ice is greater than that of water. These differences account for the more rapid freezing of tissues than their thawing.

7.2 Structure of Water Molecule

The properties of water are closely related to its structure. Its unusual properties suggest the existence of strong attractive forces among water molecules. The observed differences between the properties of water and ice also indicate that the structure of water and ice are not common. A molecule of water is formed by two hydrogen atoms forming covalent bonds (see subsection 11.3.3) with an oxygen atom. The bond angle is 104.5°. Though water is an electrically neutral molecule, there is an imbalance of charge, because of the arrangement of the atoms. The oxygen atom of the water molecule on one side is slightly more electronegative and the sides where the hydrogen atoms are located are slightly more positive. This polar nature of the water molecule results in each hydrogen atom being attracted to the oxygen atom of another molecule and the oxygen atom to the hydrogen atom. This type of attraction leads to multiple hydrogen bonding (see subsection 11.3.5) on a three-dimensional basis. Each water molecule is able to hydrogen bond with a maximum of four other molecules (Fig. 7.1). Water's ability to form three-dimensional hydrogen bonding provides a logical explanation for its unusual properties. For example, its large values for heat capacity, melting point, boiling point, etc., are related to the extra energy needed to break intermolecular hydrogen bonds.

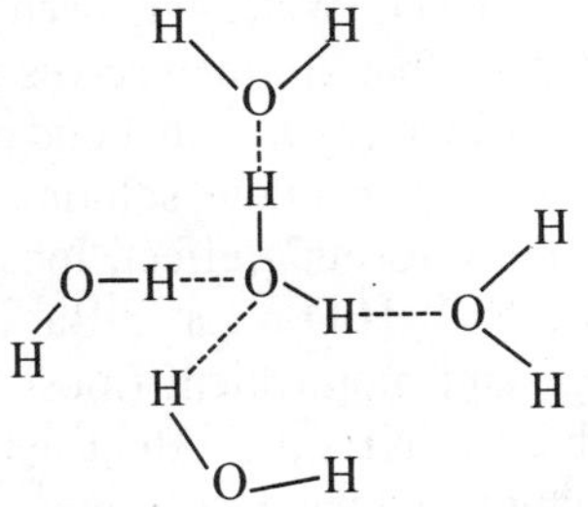

Fig. 7.1 Hydrogen bonding of water molecules; hydrogen bonds are represented by dotted lines

Theories of water structure are often classified into two major categories: the homogeneous and mixture models. According to the former, intermolecular hydrogen bonds are distributed uniformly throughout water, so that each water molecule has essentially the same environment. According to the mixture model, the intermolecular hydrogen bonds are concentrated, at any given moment, in localized multimolecular clumps or clusters of water molecules. The most widely accepted model appears to be the mixture model.

The hydrogen bonding in water also determines the structure of ice. When water freezes into ice, a regular hexagonal pattern of molecules results (Fig. 7.2). This structure of ice accounts for its properties. In most substances the solid form is more dense than the liquid. This is not true of water. The crystal structure of ice contains a large proportion of empty space; so ice at 0°C is actually less dense than liquid water at 0°C. The transition to an open structure increases appreciably below 4°C, so that maximum density occurs at 4°C, even though the freezing point is 0°C. It is difficult to visualize what our world would be like if ice did not float on the warmer water beneath it; the fish population that presently thrives under the insulating blanket of ice in the winter time would clearly be the first victims if water's unusual properties were not the rule.

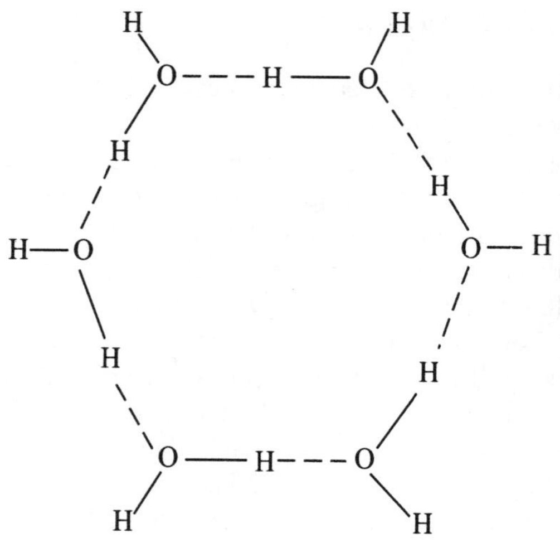

Fig. 7.2 Structure of ice

Effect of solutes on structure of water: Water has been called the "Universal solvent" with considerable justification; for, substances that are themselves polar or ionic are readily soluble in water. The normal structure of pure water (hydrogen bonded arrangement) is disrupted by the addition of dissociable solutes. Some ions in dilute solution break the hydrogen bonds of pure water whereas others have a net structure forming effect. Ions which are small and/or multivalent (mostly positive ions), such as Li^+, Na^+, H_3O^+, Ca^{2+}, Ba^{2+}, Mg^{2+}, Al^{3+}, F^- and OH^- are not structure formers. Ions that are large and monovalent (most of the negatively charged ions and large positive ions), such as K^+, Rb^+, Cs^+,NH_4^+,Cl^-, Br^-,I^-,NO^-_3, are net structure breakers. In a concentrated salt solution, the structure which is common in the vicinity of ions is likely to predominate.

Solutes capable of forming hydrogen bonds, such as urea, may be expected to enhance or at least not disturb the normal structure of water. However, the distribution and orientation of the solute's hydrogen-bonding sites may be geometrically incompatible with the normal hydrogen bonded clusters of water, resulting in the disruption of the latter. But the total number of hydrogen bonds per mole of solution, will not be substantially altered as the disrupted water-water hydrogen bonds are replaced by water-solute hydrogen bonds.

The newly formed water-solute bonds are of particular importance when macromolecules are involved. If hydrogen bonding sites are properly distributed on the surface of macromolecules, it is conceivable that a structured zone of water exists at the macromolecule – water interface. A considerable number of carbohydrates, proteins and steroid hormones appear to have hydrogen-bonding sites.

Inert solutes, such as hydrocarbons and the non-polar groups of compounds like fatty acids, amino acids and proteins have a structure forming action when introduced into water. Solutes of this nature situate themselves at the boundary of the bulky hydrogen-bonded clusters of water molecules and thereby encourage the formation of the more extensive water-to-water hydrogen bonding. This causes the solute to become partly surrounded by water with a greater than normal amount of structure. In most proteins, about 40 per cent of the total amino acids have non-polar side chains. These non-polar groups have a structure-forming action on the adjacent water and the interaction between the water and non-polar groups has an important influence on the reactivity of proteins and on their native tertiary conformations.

7.3 Bound Water

Food and living systems contain bound water molecules due to their biological structures or the presence of solutes. The intensity of binding varies but only those molecules of water that are mobile and bound least firmly determine the observed water activity. Bound water behaves differently from that of pure water. The bound water is grouped into four types. Distinct boundaries do not, however, exist between the four types of bound water. There are intermediate stages of boundness.

Type IV water is one with full activity, and does not exist except in the free state. The other types of water are present in biological matter. Type III activity is found in water physically entrapped in tissue matrix and in solutions. This type of water represents the majority of water forms in plant and animal food tissues. The activity of this type of water is only slightly reduced than water in the free state. This type of bound water is available for the growth of micro-organisms, enzymic activity (hydrolytic and oxidative) and non-enzymic browning. Type III water can easily be reduced to a moisture content of 12–25 per cent.

Type II water is more firmly bound and its activity is reduced substantially. It permits enzymic activity (only hydrolytic) and non-enzymic browning. Removal of this type of water reduces the water level to 3 to 7 per cent and eliminates the possibilities of microbial growth and greatly reduces most kinds of chemical reactions. Type I water is much more firmly bound than Type II and the water activity is further reduced. Partial removal of this type of water can be accomplished by conventional dehydrations but not by freezing. The degree of binding is such that any reaction depending on solution is so slow as to be immeasurable. At this stage, there is an acceleration of lipid phase reactions, such as oxidative rancidity.

CHAPTER

8 Pigments and Colours

The first impression of a food is usually visual and a major part of our willingness to accept a food depends upon its colour. The colour of food may vary considerably, from place to place, and from season to season, depending upon numerous factors. Nevertheless, colour can serve as a useful criterion of quality. Furthermore, it can be an indicator of the many types of deteriorative changes undergone by the food. The change of colour during the preparation of food is a useful index of the required degree of cooking. Colour also provides a useful guide to quality control and is used by the food processor as a criterion for selecting raw materials.

The characteristic colour of raw food is due to the natural pigments present in the plant and animal materials. Sometimes, artificial colour matter is added in the preparation of foods and in their processing. Therefore, to achieve the desirable colour and acceptability, an understanding of pigments and colour is necessary.

8.1 Chlorophylls

Chlorophylls are green pigments involved in photosynthesis in plants and some micro-organisms. These also include other photosynthetic pigments of similar structure. There are a number of chlorophylls, **such as chlorophylls *a*, *b*, *c* and *d*; bacteriochlorophylls *a* and *b*, and chlorobium chlorophylls.** In foods only chlorophylls *a* and *b*, found in higher plants, are important. They are present in the leaves in chloroplasts, normally in the ratio 3:1, emdedded between a layer of protein and lipid with carotenoids alongside.

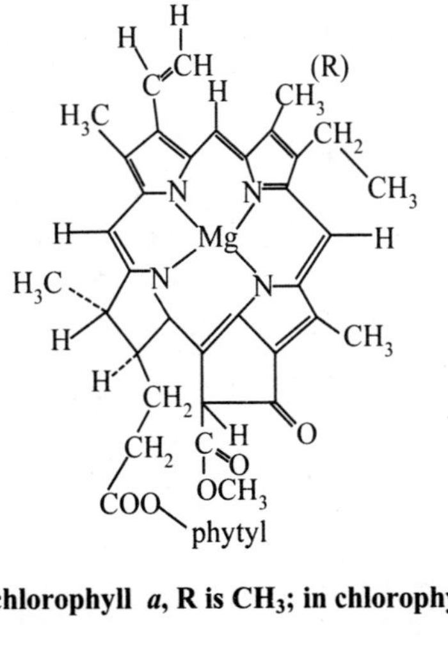

Chlorophyll. In chlorophyll *a*, R is CH_3; in chlorophyll *b*, R is -CHO

Chlorophylls are complex molecules containing four pyrrole rings with magnesium in the centre. The conjugated tetrapyrroles are known as porphyrins. Chlorophyll *a* has four methyl groups at positions 1, 3, 5 and 8; vinyl at 2; ethyl at 4; propionate esterified with phytol at 7; keto at 9; and carboxyl at 10. Chlorophyll *b* has the same structure as chlorophyll *a* except that in position 3 there is a formyl group instead of a methyl group. The chlorophylls have characteristic absorption and fluorescence spectra, which are useful in the analysis of the pigments.

In the presence of an acid, the central magnesium of the chlorophylls is replaced by hydrogen giving pheophytins, with a dramatic change in colour from green to dull olive brown. The phytol group present in chlorophylls is removed by the enzyme chlorophyllase resulting in the formation of chlorophillides, which are green compounds. If the magnesium in the chlorophillides is removed, the corresponding pheophorbides are formed which have a colour similar to pheophytins:

$$\begin{array}{ccc} \text{Chlorophylls} & \xrightarrow{\text{-phytol}} & \text{Chlorophillides} \\ \downarrow \text{-Mg} & & \downarrow \text{-Mg} \\ \text{Pheophytins} & \xrightarrow{\text{-phytol}} & \text{Pheophorbides} \end{array}$$

The above reactions are responsible for the deterioration of the chlorophyll pigments in the processing and storage of foods. Green vegetables subjected to heat processing and subsequent storage turn from bright green to a dull olive brown colour due to the conversion of chlorophyll to pheophytin. Chlorophyll-containing vegetables also show colour changes upon freezing and subsequent storage. The colour change in this case is influenced by the time and temperature of blanching before freezing. The formation of pheophytin from chlorophyll is related to the amount of acids produced within the system during heating and storage. For example, frozen raw peas lose more colour than beans because of the greater acidity of the former.

A number of attempts have been made to preserve the green colour of heat-processed green vegetables. Chlorophyllides are more stable than chlorophylls. Therefore, chlorophylls are converted to chlorophyllides by means of the naturally occurring chlorophyllase. However, this enzyme functions at a temperature in the range of 65-75°C. Because of the high temperature used, products processed by this method lose colour on standing. Another method is the use of alkalizing agents to produce a higher pH in the system and thus minimize pheophytin formation. High-temperature-short-time (HTST) processing has also been used to stabilize the molecule during heat processing. However, there is always some deterioration of chlorophylls with storage, whatever the processing method used.

8.2 Myoglobin and Haemoglobin

The colour of fresh muscle is due predominantly to myoglobin. Muscle pigments also include cytochromes, some haemoglobin, vitamin B-12, and yellow coenzymes associated with cytochromes in the electron transport system in the cell; these pigments contribute little or nothing to the total colour of muscle. Haemoglobin is the red pigment of blood. Both myoglobin and haemoglobin serve to complex with the oxygen required for the metabolic activity of the animal.

Myoglobin and haemoglobin are complex proteins, consisting of the protein moiety globin and the non-protein part called haem. Haem, like the chlorophylls, is a porphyrin made up of four pyrrole units and contains an atom of iron in the reduced state (Fe^{2+}) in the centre of the molecule. Myoglobin contains one globin moiety attached to a haem group. Haemoglobin contains four globins attached to four haem groups.

The iron atom in haem, in addition to the four nitrogen atoms of the pyrrole rings, is attached to the protein and has a sixth position open for complexing with water or other compounds. It is this complexing that is, in part, responsible for differences in the colour of meat. It unites reversibly with oxygen, thus converting myoglobin which is pink red in colour to oxymyoglobin which is bright red. On prolonged exposure to oxygen, the reduced form of iron of myoglobin gets oxidized (Fe^{3+}), resulting in the formation of metmyoglobin which is brown in colour. The haem moiety undergoing complexation and the changes it undergoes on combining with oxygen are shown below:

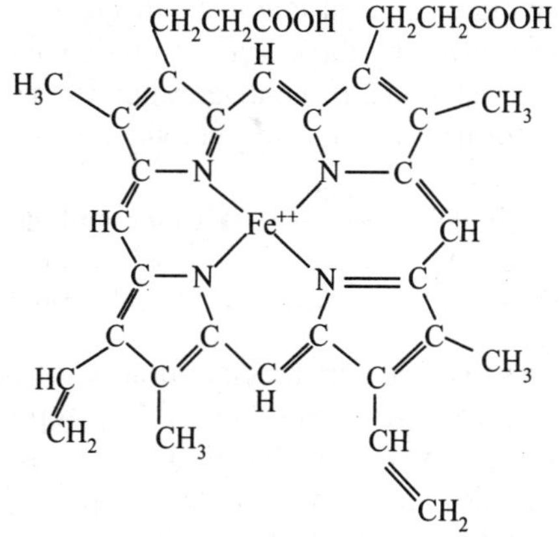

Structure of haem

The red oxymyoglobin, once formed, is stabilized by the formation of a highly resonant structure, and as long as haem remains oxygenated, no further changes take place. But the oxygen is continually associating and dissociating. When this happens the reduced myoglobin is oxidized to metmyoglobin. The formation of brown metmyoglobin is accelerated by high temperature, oxygen, pressure, fluorescent and incandescent light, salts and the presence of metals. In fresh meat, the production of indigenous reducing substances constantly reduces metmyoglobin to myoglobin.

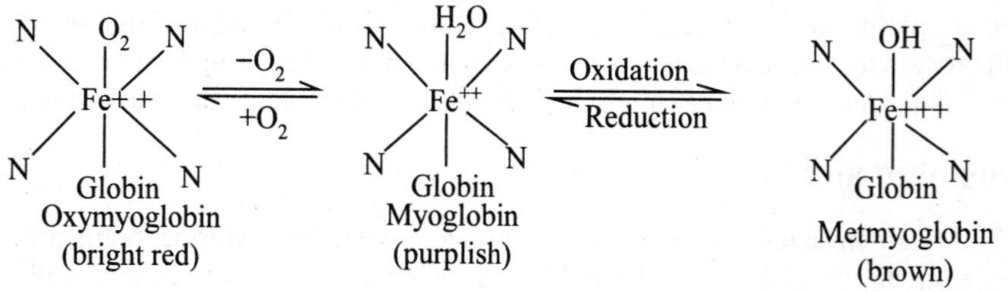

Myoglobin also combines with nitric oxide when nitric oxide myoglobin (or nitroso-myoglobin) is formed, which is a stable red-pink pigment. When meat is cured with nitrite, the latter is coverted to nitric oxide and nitrosomyoglobin is formed. When the nitrite-cured meat is heated there is a thermal denaturation of globin, and nitric oxide myochrome, which has a more intense pink colour, is formed. The iron in this complex is still in the ferrous state.

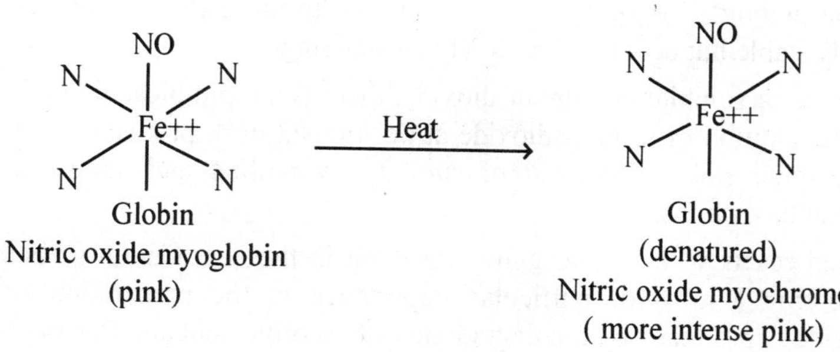

8.3 Anthocyanins

These pigments are responsible for the red, purple and blue colour of fruits, vegetables and flowers. These are water-soluble compounds occurring in the cell sap. All anthocyanins are derivatives of the basic flavylium cation structure.

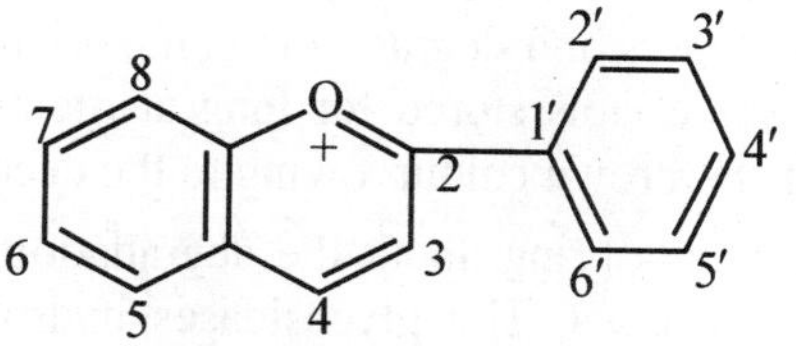

Flavylium cation

Anthocyanins are polyphenols containing hydroxyl groups in positions 3, 5 and 7. Generally, a sugar moiety is linked to position 3 and sometimes to the 5 or 7 position. Some contain two sugars, with either both on the 3 position, or one each on the 3 and 5 positions. When three sugars are present, usually two of them will be in position 3 with one in 5. No anthocyanin contains more than three sugars. The sugars found, in order of relative abundance, are glucose, rhamnose, galactose, xylose and arabinose. The presence of the sugar moiety in the anthocyanin molecules is responsible for their high solubility in water.

The aglucone of an anthocyanin is an anthocyanidin. A number of anthocyanidins are known. Six of them are important in foods. They are pelargonidin, cyanidin, delphinidin, peonidin, petunidin and malvidin:

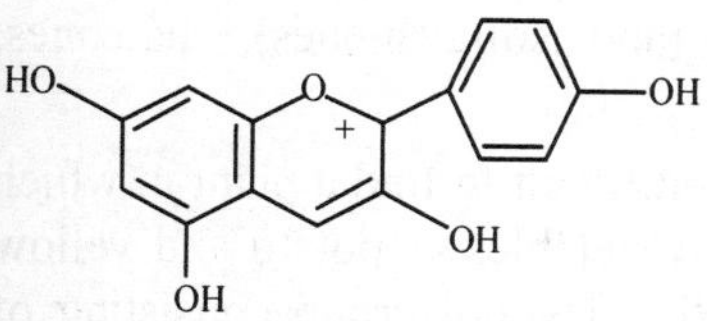

Pelargonidin

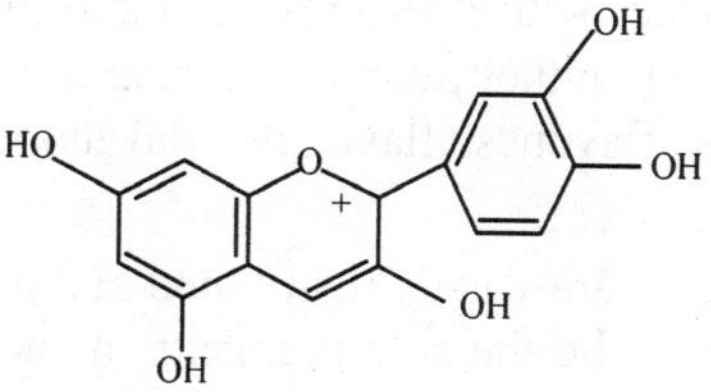

Cyanidin

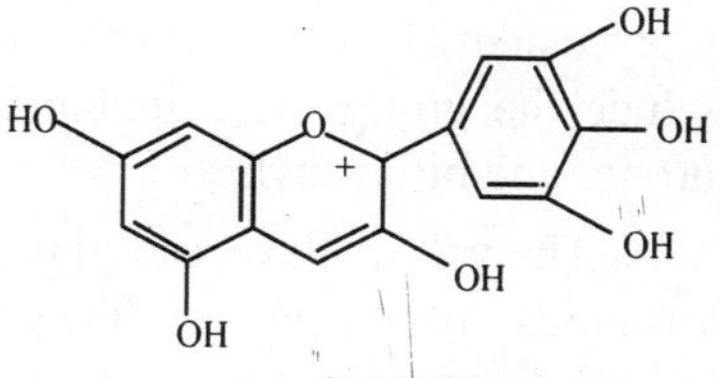

Delphinidin

In the other three anthocyanins, there are respectively in positions 3′, 4′ and 5′, OCH_3, OH, H in peonidin, OH, OH, OCH_3 in petunidin, and OCH_3, OH. OCH_3 in malvidin.

Because of the presence of the flavylium nucleus, anthocyanins are highly reactive. The reactions they undergo result in decolouration and this is pH and temperature dependent. At low pH, the colour of anthocyanins is intense red. As the pH value rises, the colour changes through orange and red to blue or purple. These colour changes are due to changes in the molecular structure of anthocyanins to the quinoidal or anhydro bases and then to the carbinol base. The carbinol base is colourless and fairly stable but decomposes slowly on standing.

In the presence of sulphite or sulphur dioxide, there is a rapid bleaching of anthocyanins. This is on account of the addition of sulphur dioxide at positions 2 or 4, producing compounds which are colourless but are quite stable. Removal of sulphite by boiling and acidification results in the regeneration of the anthocyanins.

Ascorbic acid reacts with anthocyanins, resulting in the degradation of both the compounds. The effect of ascorbic acid is of particular importance in the preparation of fruit juices. An intermediate peroxide is produced by the degradation of ascorbic acid and this may be responsible for the reaction with anthocyanins. Oxidation of ascorbic acid is catalyzed by copper and iron compounds and this results in a greater oxidation of anthocyanins.

Sugars also influence the stability of anthocyanins. Decolouration is not due to the sugar itself but is brought about by its degradation products, such as furfural and 5-hydroxymethyl furfural. Accelerated instability of anthocyanins in the presence of sugar derivatives, ascorbic acid, amino acids and phenols, may be due to the actual condensation reaction of these compounds or their degradation product with the pigment. The polymers and degradation compounds produced in these reactions are complex and are brownish red. Some jams stored for long at room temperature have no detectable anthocyanins but still have a reddish– brown colour, owing to the decomposition of the compounds.

Many enzymes present in plants bring about the degradation of anthocyanins. These include glycosidases, phenolases and peroxidases. The glycosidases hydrolyze the protective 3-glycosidic linkage to yield unstable aglycones. The phenolases oxidize the O-dihydroxy phenol and catechol to O-quinone, which then oxidizes the anthocyanins non-enzymatically to colourless breakdown products. The peroxidases bring about decolouration of anthocyanins by oxidation.

Leucoanthocyanins are colourless compounds which, during processing and handling, are converted into coloured products. When heated in an acid solution, leucoanthocyanins are converted into anthocyanidins. Some canned fruits develop colour with time. This is due to the acid present in fruits converting leucoanthocyanins to anthocyanidins, which then complex with metals discolouring the food. Leucoanthocyanins contribute to the enzymic browning in fruits and vegetables through their orthohydroxy groups and to haze formation in beer and wine.

8.4 Flavonoids

These are also polyphenolic substances with structures similar to those of anthocyanins and also occur as glycosides. Flavonoids differ from anthocyanins in having a carbonyl group in position 4. These include the groups of compounds, flavones, flavonols, flavanones (and isoflavanones), chalcones, aurones and biflavanyls.

The yellow flavonoid pigments are widely distributed and it is difficult to find a plant in which flavonoids are not present. They may be the sole pigments in such vegetables as potato and yellow skinned onion. The major group of flavonoids found in nature is the flavonol group consisting of kaempferol, quercetin and myricetin. Less common than flavonols are flavones, such as apigenin, luteolin and tricetin. The other groups occur to a limited extent.

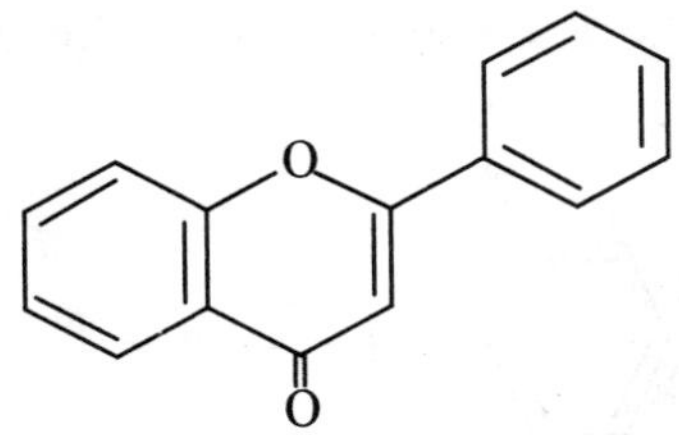

Flavone

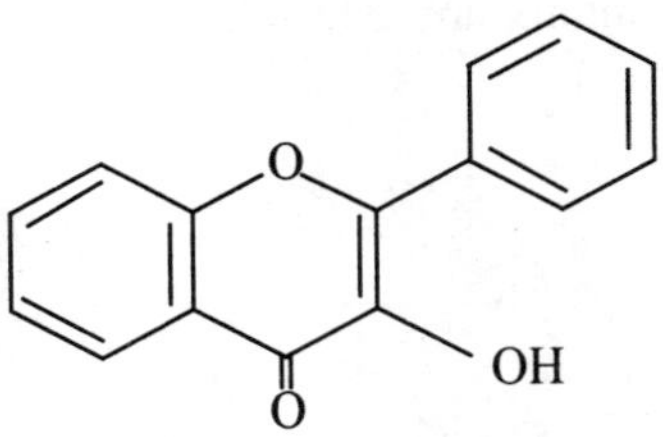

Flavonol

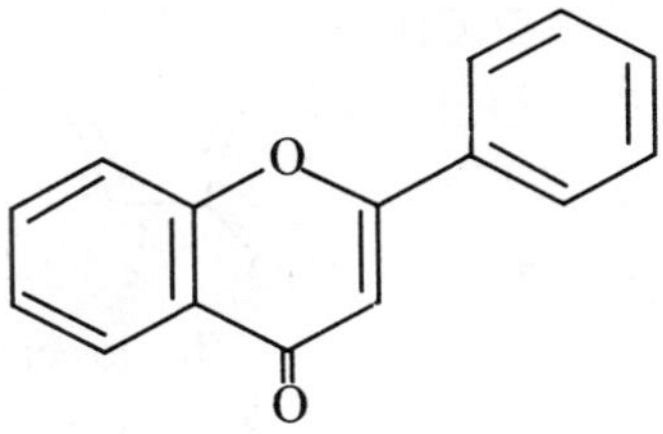

Flavanone

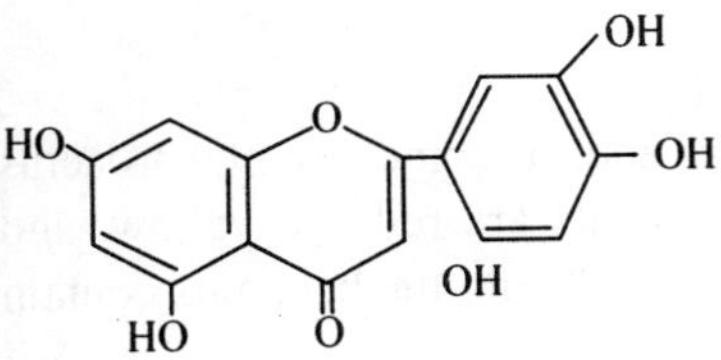

Quercetin
(Flavonol)

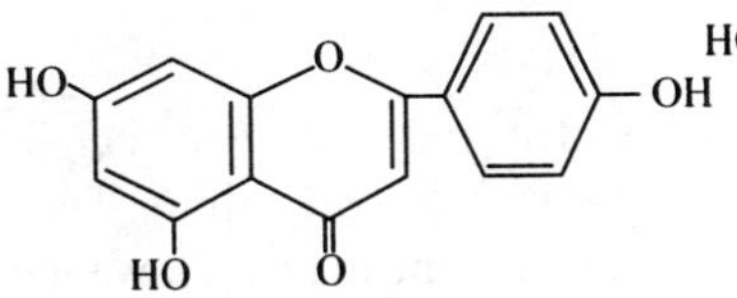

Apigenin
(Flavone)

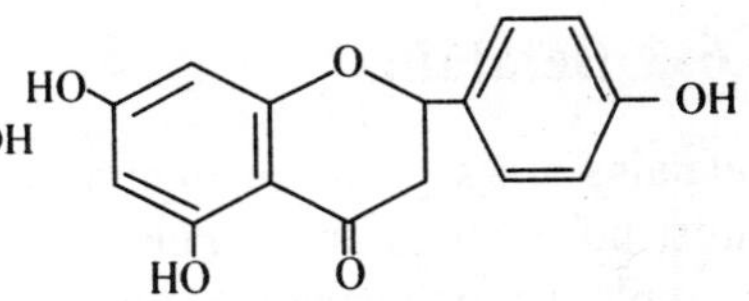

Naringin
(Flavanone)

The other flavonols and flavones differ from quercetin and apigenine respectively in the number of hydroxyl groups present in position 3', 4' and 5'. The above aglucones exist as glycosides with sugar substituted in the 7, 5, 4 and 3, positions. In contrast to the anthocyanins, the position 7 is the most frequent site of substitution. The flavonoid compounds are usually more stable to heat and oxidation than the anthocyanins.

The three flavonol aglucones, quercetin, kaempferol and myricetin, are found in considerable amounts in tea. In green tea, the three compounds and their glycosides comprise as much as 30 per cent of the dry weight. One flavonoid, rutin (quercetin 3-rhamnoglucoside), complexes with iron to cause dark discolouration of canned foods (as in asparagus). The tin complex, in contrast, produces a desirable yellow colour.

The flavanones are found mainly in citrus plants and they can be used as synthetic sweeteners. Naringin with neohesperidose (disaccharide of rhamnose and glucose in α-1.2-linkage) in position 7 is intensely bitter, whereas an isomer of the above compound with ratinose (rhamnose and glucose in α-1,6-linkage, is tasteless. A compound synthesized from naringin has a sweetness nearly 2,000 times that of sucrose.

8.5 Tannins

Tannins (also known as tannic acid or gallotannic acid) are complex mixtures of polymeric polyphenols. Gallnut contains 50–70 per cent tannin. Tannins are divided into two groups: condensed tannins and hydrolyzable tannins. The former are compounds in which the nuclei are held together by carbon-carbon or ether linkages. The catechins and related compounds belong to this group. The other group of tannins are ester-like and are the polymers of gallic acid (gallotannins) and ellagic acid (ellagitannins):

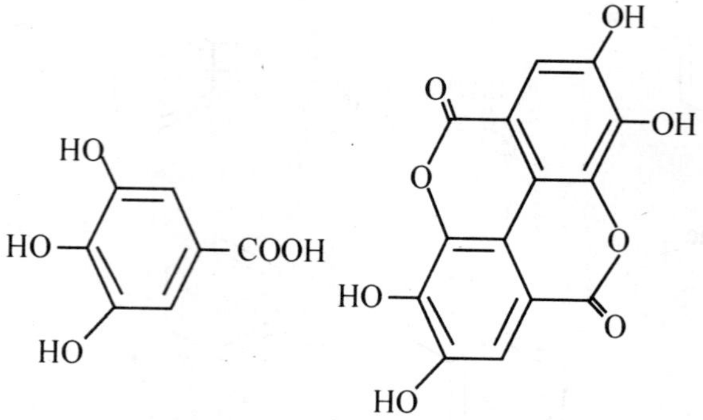

Gallic acid Ellagic acid

The appearance of tannins ranges from colourless to yellow or brown. Tannins contribute to the astringency of foods and also to enzymic browning reactions.

8.6 Betalains

Betalains are a group of pigments found in red beet *(Beta vulgaris)* and, to some extent, in cactus fruits, pokeberries and a number of flowers (bougainvillia). The pigments are red and yellow, and resemble the anthocyanins and flavonoids in appearance. However, unlike them, the betalains contain nitrogen. The basic structure of betalains is as given:

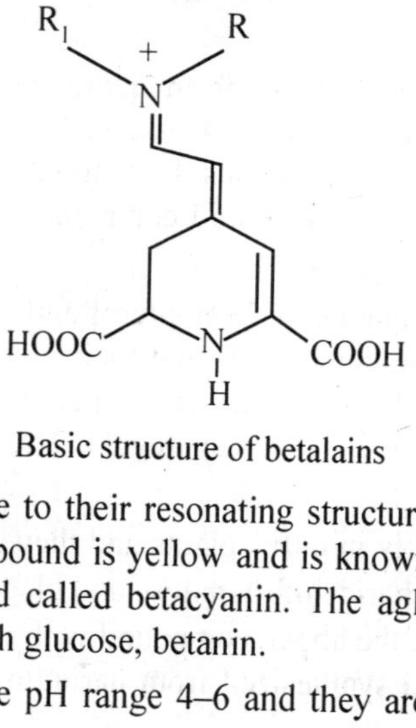

Basic structure of betalains

The colour of betalains is due to their resonating structure. If R or R_1 in the above structure does not extend resonance, the compound is yellow and is known as betazanthin. If R or R_1 extends resonance, the compound is red and called betacyanin. The aglucone of betacyanin in red beet is called betanidin and its glucoside with glucose, betanin.

The betalains are stable in the pH range 4–6 and they are subject to degradation by thermal processing as in canning.

8.7 Quinones and Xanthones

A large group of pigments found in the cell sap of flowering plants, fungi, bacteria and algae, are derivatives of anthraquinone, naphthoquinone and benzoquinone. A number of synthetic dyes also are derivatives of quinones. The natural quinones range in colour from pale yellow to almost black.

Anthraquinone derivatives are the largest group of natural quinone pigments, followed by those of naphthoquinone and benzoquinone.

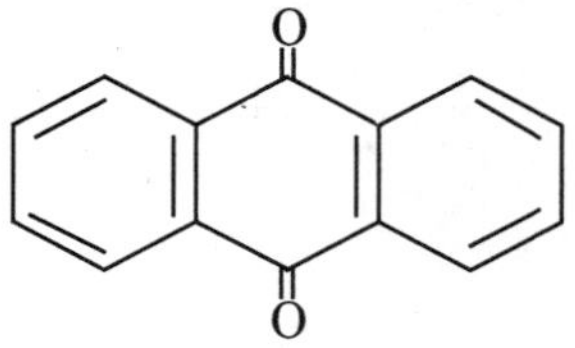

Anthraquinone

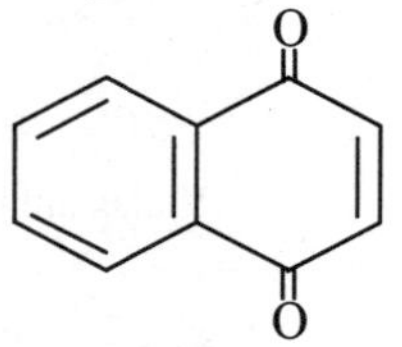

Naphtoquinone

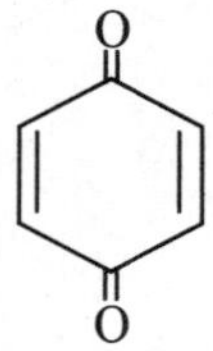

Benzoquinone

Xanthones are a group of yellow pigments. One well-known member is mangiferin, which occurs as a glucoside in mangoes.

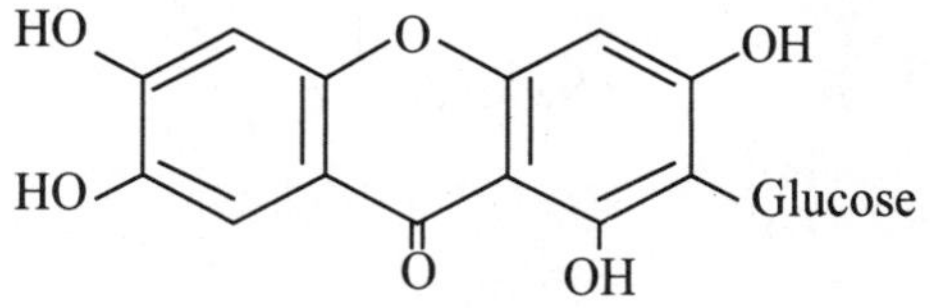

Mangiferin

8.8 Carotenoids

Carotenoids, also called carotenes, are a group of lipid-soluble hydrocarbons and their oxygenated derivatives are called xanthophylls. They derive their name from the principal colouring matter of carrot roots, namely carotene. They are widely distributed in the plant world. They are found in all green leaves, in most yellow and red fruits, and many roots. The colour of egg-yolk and some fish is due to carotenoids. The most widely distributed are the carotenoids found in green leaves, lutein, violaxanthin and neoxanthin. Others found in small quantities, but occurring widely, are β-carotene and zeaxanthin. Other pigments, like lycopene in tomatoes, capsanthin in red pepper and bixin in annatto, predominate in certain plants.

Carotenoids consist of eight isoprenoid units joined in such a manner that the arrangement of isoprene units is reversed in the centre of the molecule. The basic carbon structure, shown below for lycopene, indicates the symmetrical arrangement around the central pair of carbons. This structure cyclized at the ends is β-carotene. Other carotenoids, have different end groups with the same central structure.

Carotenoids exist in nature in the free state in plant tissues as crystalline or amorphous solids, or in solution in lipid media. They also occur as esters or in combination with sugars and proteins. The alternate double bonds in their structure are responsible for the colour of carotenoids. Compounds with double bonds can exist in two isomeric forms, the *cis* and *trans*, depending on the disposition of atoms or groups at the double bonds. In nature, carotenoids, having only the *trans* configuration, which are stable structures, are found.

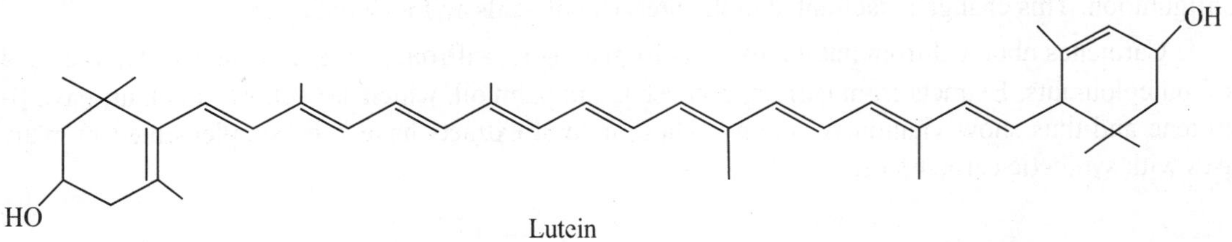

Lutein

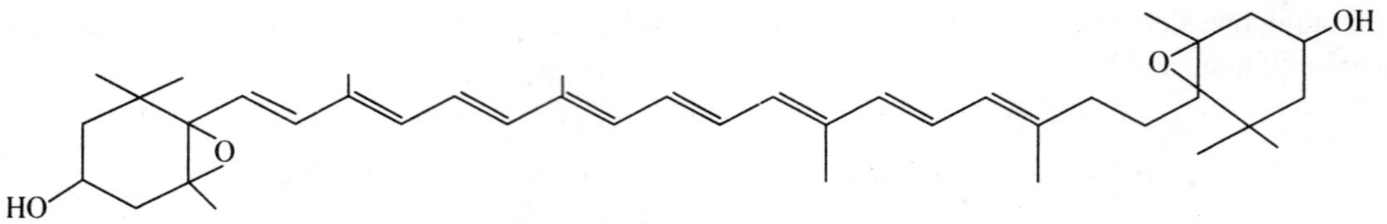

Violaxanthin

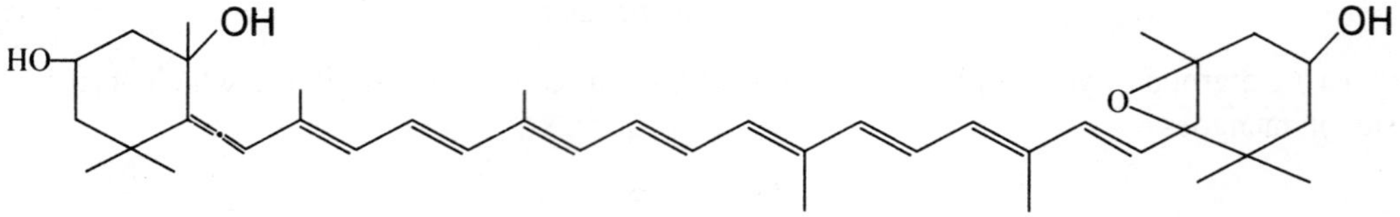

Neoxanthin

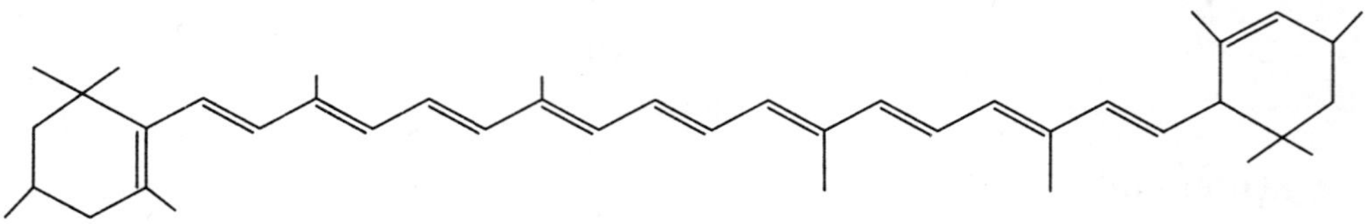

β -Carotene

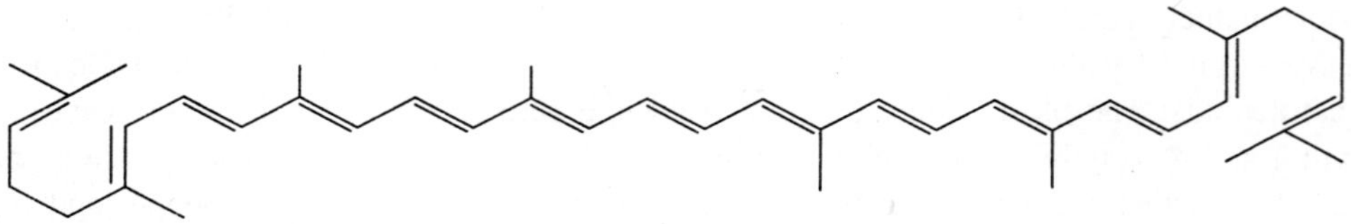

Lycopene

β-carotene is the precursor of vitamin A; it yields two molecules of vitamin A by a cleavage at the centre of the molecule. Compounds, such as α-carotene, which have half of their structure identical to β-carotene, function as precursors of one molecule of vitamin A.

The stability of carotenoids varies widely in foods. As the compounds are unsaturated they are susceptible to oxidation, with concurrent loss of colour. Oxidation takes place both in the presence of enzymes and non-enzymatically. The pigments may auto-oxidize by reaction with atmospheric oxygen at the rates dependent on light, heat and presence of pro- and anti-oxidants. In the presence of unsaturated fatty acids, lipoxygenases bring about the oxidative degradation of carotenes.

Carotenes can also change colour by undergoing isomerization from *trans* to *cis* configuration. The orange–red colour of *trans* compounds changes to lemon–yellow with the change in configuration. This change is facilitated in the presence of acids and with the temperature.

Carotenes obtained from natural extracts from annatto, saffron, paprika, tomatoes, etc., are used as food colourants. Extracts from carrots, butter fat, and palm oil, which are yellow in colour, have β-carotene and thus show vitamin A activity. These natural extracts have been supplemented in many cases with synthetic carotenoids.

8.9 Synthetic Colours

A number of synthetic colourants are widely used in food materials. It is not possible to completely do away with the addition of synthetic colourants. There is, however, the question of health hazard in their use. Some of the formerly accepted colourants have now been disallowed as a safety measure. This raises the question as to what should be used in the place of the disallowed colours and dyes. Some of them can be replaced by natural pigments. However, this cannot solve the problem regarding the use of synthetic colours as natural colours cannot be obtained in quantities required to replace the synthetic ones. Most natural colours are also vital part of the host material. For example, the removal of anthocyanins from strawberries or carotenoids from tomatoes makes them unacceptable as foods. An account of synthetic colourants used in foods is given under food additives in Chap. 29

CHAPTER

9 Flavours

Appearance of a food is important, but it is the flavour that ultimately determines the quality and acceptability of foods. No matter how safe, nutritious, inexpensive and colourful a food may be, if the flavour is undesirable, it is rejected. Even hungry and nutritionally deprived populations reject food that does not have the flavour of their choice. Flavours have insignificant nutritive value but they exert a great influence on food acceptance.

Flavour is a sensory phenomenon depending upon taste, odour or aroma, appearance, temperature—sensation of heat and cold, and texture or "mouthfeel" affecting the sense of touch. Some of the constituents of foods contribute to these sensations. But most food flavours have some common characteristics. Flavour is the result of a number of components, some of which may be present in a high proportion but most are present in low proportions. Flavours are minor constituents of foods, usually non-nutritive, exerting their influence at very low concentrations. They are highly specific to the molecular configuration of the receptive molecules. They are labile and heat unstable compounds.

Natural flavouring materials, such as spices, essential oils and fruit concentrates, have been used for long in food preparations. Owing to the increase in the world population and the consequent use of foods from non-traditional sources, the need for flavouring materials has been increasing. As the supply of flavours from natural sources is diminishing with consequent rise in their cost, natural flavours have been duplicated with synthetic flavourings. Thousands of synthetic flavours are now being used as food additives.

9.1 The Sensation of Taste

Sensory evaluation of flavours for analytical purposes is limited to the sensations of taste and smell.

The sense of taste refers to the ability of the taste organs to perceive and recognize the four basic tastes—sweet, sour, salty and bitter. These taste qualities are independent of one another and are analogous to the skin senses (touch, warmth, cold and pain). The taste sensation is therefore responsible for chemical stimulation. The components of food responsible for taste are non-volatile compounds. They must be in solution or dissolve in saliva to produce the taste response. Taste is sensed by the buds which lie mostly in grooves around little projections on the upper surface of the tongue. The taste buds consist of sensitive cells, in bundles, from which slender hair-like structures emerge through the pore of the taste bud and make contact with the stimulating substance. The message is then sent back through one of the nerves of taste to the brain.

The total number of taste buds is greatest in new-born infants and gradually diminishes with age and this is related to the reduction in the activity of sense of taste as one gets older. The sensitivity to different tastes is not uniform all over the tongue. The anterior portion of the tongue (tip of the tongue) is more sensitive to sweet stimuli, the posterior (back of the tongue) to bitter substances, and the lateral portions (edges) to salty and sour stimuli. However, there is a considerable overlap.

9.1.1 Substances with Taste

In general, saltiness is produced by inorganic salts. Sodium chloride is the only compound that gives a pure salty taste. Other salts have additional tastes, e.g., some iodides and bromides are bitter and some inorganic salts of lead and beryllium are sweet. Sweetness is stimulated by a number of organic compounds. Aliphatic hydroxy compounds, such as carbohydrates, are sweet substances. Diverse compounds, such as saccharin, peptides and cyclamates, are also sweet. Sourness is caused by proton donors. This does not, however, entirely account for sourness; at the same pH, acetic acid tastes more sour than hydrochloric acid. Aliphatic long-chain fatty acids are more sour than short-chain acids. Compounds with quite different structures are bitter. One group of bitter substances are alkaloids like quinine, strychnine and nicotine. Caffeine, a constituent of coffee and tea, is bitter. Phenolic compounds like tannin and some flavonoid compounds contribute to bitterness and astringency.

9.1.2 Taste Factors

A number of factors influence the sense of taste. Taste is affected by temperature. Thus, a sugared drink appears sweeter when hot than when cold. Similarly, a lemon drink tastes more sour when it is hot than when cold. Coffee and tea appear to be more bitter when cold than when hot. These effects are due to the variations in the sensitivity of taste buds to temperature. If a food is sufficiently hot to "burn" the tongue, it destroys the sensitivity of the taste buds to taste stimuli.

Some substances taste different to different individuals. The inability of persons to taste some substances is a genetic one. Depending upon one's ability to taste phenylthiocarbamide (PTC), persons are classified as "tasters" and "non-tasters". The inability to taste PTC is dependent, in part, on differences in the saliva of tasters and non-tasters.

When substances with different taste qualities are mixed, the intensities of their tastes change even if no chemical reactions occur. For example, bitterness and sweetness interact and tend to counteract each other. Sugar lessens the impact of sourness in lemon. The addition of salt to food not only adds a salty taste but also changes the perceived intensities of other tastes in the food. Generally, suppression of individual taste occurs between pairs of substances with different taste qualities, while simple additivity or synergism occurs between pairs of substances with similar taste qualities. In the latter case, however, the increase in taste may not be directly proportional to the concentration of the added substances.

The sensitivity of different tastes also depends upon the concentration of the substances. The lowest concentration of hydrochloric acid, sugar, sodium chloride and quinine that can be perceived is 0.003 M HC1,0.03M sucrose, 0.001 M NaCl, and 0.00001 M quinine hydrochloride. Time is also one of the factors that determines taste sensitivity. Salt on the tongue is sensed in a fraction of a second, whereas a bitter substance may require a full second after it contacts the tongue before it is sensed by the taste buds.

9.1.3 Taste Modifiers

Some substances interfere with taste sensitivity by desensitizing the taste buds. Chewing of the leaves of the tropical plant *Gymnemna sylvestre* destroys the ability to taste sweet substances (sugar and non-sugar sweeteners) for several hours, and decreases the bitter sensation, but the sensitivity to salt and sourness is untouched. The active principle (gymnemic acid) of the plant blocks the taste of sweet substances by reacting with the receptor site. The berries of another plant, *Synsepalum dulcificum* (miracle fruit), grown in West Africa, abolishes sour sensation after being chewed for a few minutes. Some foods like lemon, lime, rhubarb and beer taste sweet after chewing the berries. The active principle in miracle fruit is a glycoprotein which binds to the taste membrane near the sweet receptor site. The globe artichoke *(Cynara scolymus),* eaten as a salad course, induces a sweet taste in water. This is due to the potassium salts of cyananin and chlorogenic acid found in artichoke. The taste of water after eating artichoke is, however, dependent on the nature of the substance that precedes it on the tongue. For example, water tastes sweet when it follows a variety of acids and bitter substances including caffeine and quinine, while it tastes bitter when it follows sucrose, and salty when it follows urea.

Some substances intensify the taste flavours. These substances have no flavour of their own, but a small addition to a food modifies its flavour, usually in a desirable manner. Two groups of compounds that have been used as flavour potentiators are certain L-amino acids and 5'-nucleosides. The best known of these is monosodium glutamate (MSG), which is largely added to meat and soup to produce enhanced flavour. MSG enhances the desirable flavour while minimizing the undesirable ones, like the sharpness of raw onions, vegetables, etc. The 5'-nucleosides are a group of substances obtained by the enzymic hydrolysis of ribonucleic acid having the same flavour-enhancing properties as MSG, but are more powerful. Both these substances appear to affect all the four kinds of taste buds in the mouth.

9.1.4 Perception of Sweet Taste

All compounds that taste sweet are viewed to have a unit consisting of two electronegative atoms A and B, with a hydrogen atom covalently bonded to A. AH is a proton donor group, while B is a proton acceptor group. The distance between AH and B is about 3 Å. The sweetness of a compound is due to the concerted intermolecular hydrogen bonding phenomenon, as shown below, using the adjacent sugar hydroxyl groups as a compound's AH-B unit and making them interact with a geometrically commensurate AH-B unit on the receptor site. On the receptor site, an amino acid residue (probably lysine) of a sweet sensitive protein provides the AH-B unit. The differences in sweetness of sugars is due to the stereochemical position of the -OH groups in the sugar molecule. If the effective distance between the two OH groups in sugar (constituting AH-B) is too great, they are unable to bond effectively to the taste bud, and if too close, they form intramolecular bonds. In either case, sweetness is diminished.

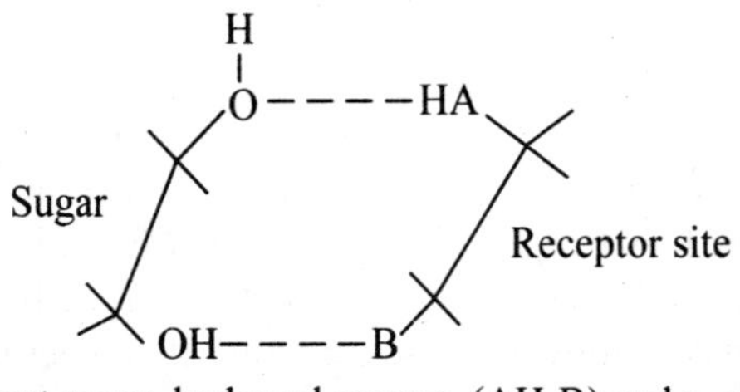

Interaction of adjacent sugar hydroxyl groups (AH-B) and a geometrically commensurate unit at the receptor site.

The chemical interaction with the receptor site described above is a bipartite AH-B interaction. This bipartite interaction is associated with the quality (sweetness) of the compound. The intensity of sweetness is associated with a tripartite AH-B-γ interaction. There is a primary AH-B unit for each sugar and, in addition, a third component unit, known as γ, is involved in tripartite interaction. For example, the γ-group in glucose is the methylene C-6 carbon atom. The tripartite interaction results in hydrophobic and lipophilic characters which determine the relative sweetness of a compound. Thus, a tripartite fit may result in a stronger interaction with the receptor site or may activate an otherwise inert or relatively inert AH-B unit on the compound.

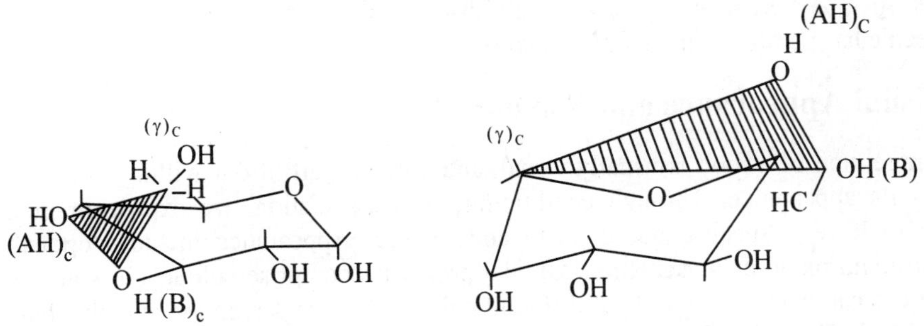

The relationship between AH-B and γ superimposed on glucose and fructose

Bitterness resembles sweetness in that it results from the stereochemistry of stimulus molecules. When sugar molecules are chemically modified the resulting derivatives are almost bitter, sweet or bitter-sweet. Sucrose octa-acetate, for example, is as bitter as quinine sulphate. In chemical modification of sugars, one "end" of the molecule (the third and fourth OH groups of the glucopyranoside type of structure) elicits sweetness and the other end (the first and second hydroxyl groups, ring oxygen atoms and primary alcoholic group of the glucopyranoside type of structure) elicits bitterness. In the case of bitter-sweet compounds, the sweet eliciting AH-B systems are not involved in modification. Such compounds may be polarized on taste receptors in such a way that one end elicits sweetness and the other bitterness. There are evidences for the proximity of both sweet and bitter sites.

9.2 The Smell Sensation

Odour or smell plays a prominent role in most flavours. One can experience thousands of odour sensations. Like taste, smell is recognized by receptor cells called olfactory cells. There are many millions of them, mostly in the cleft on each side of the septum in the upper part of the nasal cavity. They lie in a yellow-coloured area and are slender, spindle-shaped cells ending in a bunch of fine hairs (cilia) projecting into the surface layer over the mucous membranes. When an odorous molecule passes over the mucous membrane, it stimulates the sensitive hairs of the olfactory cells, which send the message through the olfactory nerve to the brain.

The sensitivity of olfactory reception by man is very great and that of animals is even greater. Man can detect the smell of some sulphur-containing substances at a level of one part in 30 billion and of vanillin at a concentration of 1 part in 10 million. The critical duration for olfaction in man is about 0.18 sec. It is estimated that experienced judges can distinguish as many as 10,000 different odour qualities and each quality can be distinguished at about 20 different levels of intensity. There are differences in odour sensitivity with age and sex, and on an average, there is a decrease of one per cent per year, after birth, of the primary olfactory fibre.

Theories of olfaction: In order for an odour to be perceived, the odorous molecule must be transported to the olfactory receptors. The adsorption of the odour molecule to the receptor surface causes electrical depolarization of the olfactory cells which initiate nerve impulses and these are transmitted to the brain. This depends upon the molecular structure of the molecule as well as on the functional groups. The correlation of odour quality with chemical structure is not conclusive. Some compounds with completely different functional groups have similar odours, whereas closely related compounds, such as stereoisomers, have totally distinct odours. With other compounds, the chirality of the molecule has no effect on the odour quality.

9.3 Visual Appearance and Flavour

The first impression of a food is usually visual, and a major part of our willingness to accept a food depends on its appearance. Through conditioning and association, we expect an item of certain appearance to have a specific odour, taste and texture. Appearance includes optical properties, physical form and mode of presentation. Optical properties comprise colour, gloss and translucency. The human eye can detect thousands of different colours. Colour perception is a phenomenon unique to the individual. The colour of an object changes with illumination. Colour, gloss and translucency could be standardized to relate to the psychological response of the observer. Physical form consists of shape and size, surface, texture, and visual viscosity.

9.4 The Texture Sensation

In addition to appearance, taste and smell, the textural aspects of food contribute to flavour. Primary textural aspects, such as hardness, cohesiveness, viscosity and elasticity, and secondary characteristics, such as brittleness, chewiness and gumminess, all contribute to food acceptability and taste. Confectionery made from the same syrup differ in taste because of their differences in texture. Ice creams made from the same ingredients have different flavours depending upon whether the frozen product is coarse or fine.

Interaction of taste, odour, texture and flavour: Even though the colour, odour and texture contribute individually to the flavour of a food, the composite flavour sensation depends upon the interaction of all these sensations in the mouth (mouthfeel). The tissues of the mouth, throat and nasal cavity are so interrelated and innervated that any or all of the sensory systems operate simultaneously. The skin sensibilities of the mouth react to texture, tingle and astringency, as well as to chemical burning, biting or cooling. Temperature of food by itself is an important aspect of quality. In addition, temperature influences the volatility of compounds which elicit odour and affect the ability of the taste buds to pick up taste sensation. Taste sensations are less intense when the temperature of food is below 20°C and raised above 30°C. Olfaction furnishes the most elaborate experiences associated with the flavours. When the intensity of any stimulus, be it visual, tactile, thermal or olfactory, becomes too strong, it results in pain.

9.5 Flavour Compounds

Many thousands of flavour compounds have been found in foods, and in any one food there may be hundreds of different flavour compounds. Some of the flavour compounds of food are considered below.

9.5.1 Terpenoids

Terpenes or terpenoids are ubiquitous in plant foods. These are formed by the linking of the five-carbon unsaturated hydrocarbon isoprene to yield monoterpenes (C_{10}), sesquiterpenes (C_{15}), diterpenes (C_{20}), etc. Terpenes are the major compounds in citrus oils and contribute to the flavour of citrus fruits. Lemonene, a monoterpene hydrocarbon possessing a lemon-like odour, accounts for approximately 90 per cent of most citrus oils. In addition to terpene hydrocarbons, oxygenated terpenes occur naturally and these are mainly alcohols, aldehydes and ketones. These oxygenated terpenes provide the characteristic flavour of individual citrus species. Of these, neral and geranial contribute to the distinctive flavour of lemons and the bicyclic sesquiterpene nootkatone contributes to the flavour of grapefruit.

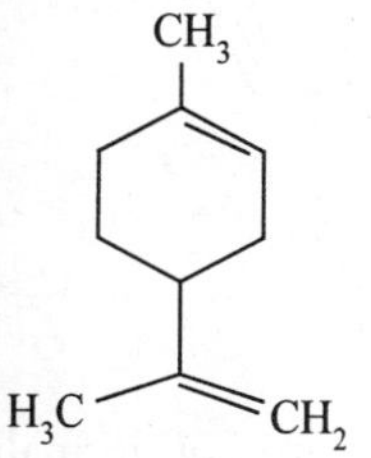

Lemonene

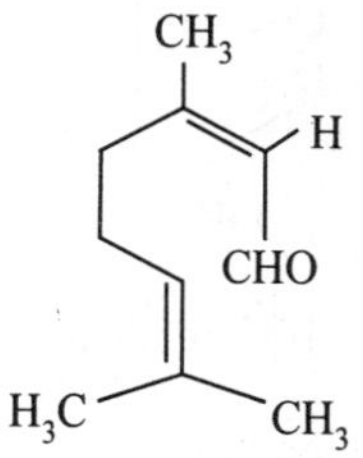

Neral

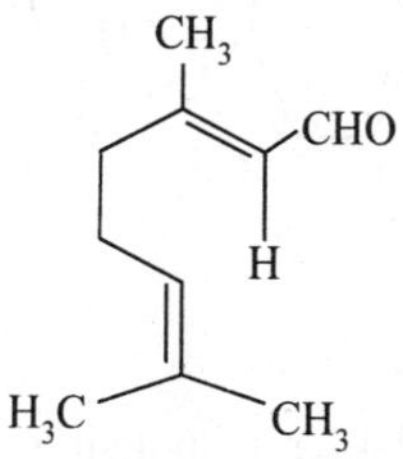

Geranial

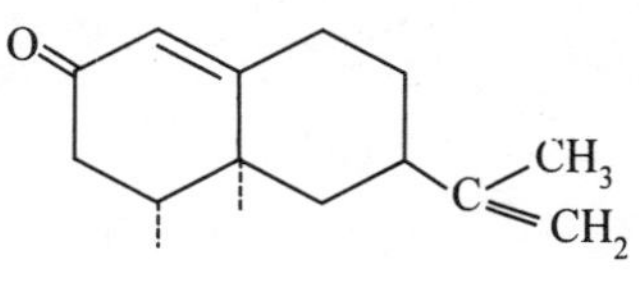

Nootkatone

Terpenoids undergo structural changes and hydration in the presence of air or dissolved oxygen. This explains why citrus juice concentrates prepared by low-temperature vacuum evaporation techniques are superior in flavour to those processed at high temperatures.

Juices of certain varieties of oranges and grapefruits become bitter when held at room temperature for some time. The delayed bitterness is due to the terpene limonin, which is formed from its non-bitter precursor (limonin monolactone) by the action of the acids present in the juice. The formation of the bitter compound can be prevented by exposing the fruits to ethylene before juice extraction, which removes the precursor of limonin, or by the addition of its specific enzyme to the juice to degrade limonin.

9.5.2 Flavonoids

Some flavonoids present in citrus fruits contribute to their flavour (see Sec. 8.4). Peels of oranges, lemons and grapefruits contain a wide range of flavanone glycosides. The most common of these is hesperidin, present in oranges and lemons, and naringin present in grapefruits. Hesperidin is quite tasteless whereas naringin has an extremely bitter taste. Both hesperidin and naringin are glycosides with a disaccharide of glucose and rhamnose in position 7. In hesperidin the linkage between the sugars is α-(1→6), while in naringin it is α-(1→2). Conversion of naringin into its chalcone changes the intensely bitter compound to an intensely sweet one.

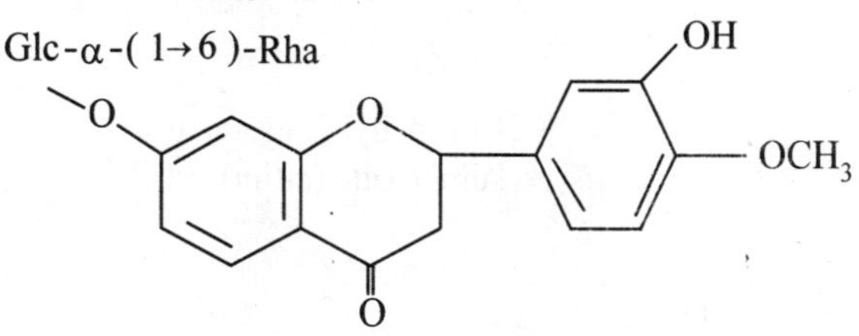

Hesperidin (tasteless)

9.5.3 Sulphur Compounds

Sulphur compounds possess powerful and distinctive odours which contribute to both the pleasant and unpleasant characters of many foods. The aroma of vegetables belonging to the genus *Allium* (onion, garlic) and *Brassica* (cabbage, cauliflower, brussel's sprouts, broccoli) is due to a variety of volatile sulphur compounds present in them. The flavour of the vegetables of the *Brassica* family are milder than those of the members of the *Allium* family.

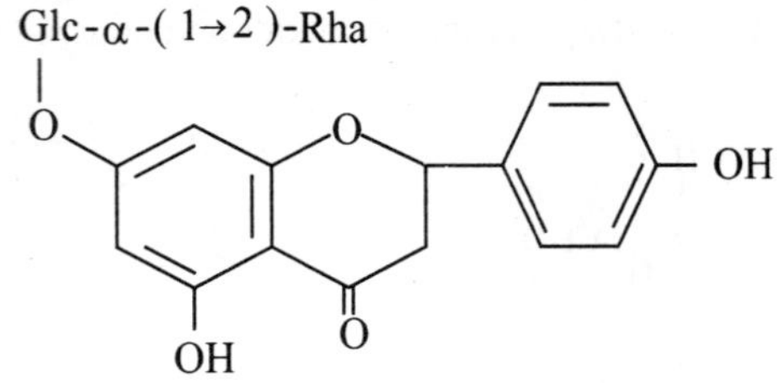

Naringin (bitter)

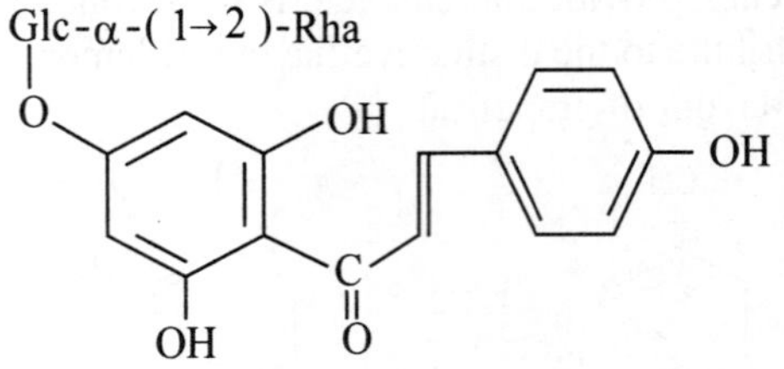

Naringin Chalcone (sweet)

Alliums: The sulphur volatiles responsible for the odour of these vegetables are not normally present in the intact vegetable tissue, but appear rapidly when the vegetable is disrupted or during chewing. The flavour compound is formed from a precursor by the action of an enzyme. The precursor and the enzyme are present in different compartments of the tissue and they come into contact when the cellular system is disrupted. The flavour precursors of allium are cysteine sulphoxide derivatives which undergo enzymic decomposition in the following way:

$$\underset{\text{Cysteine sulphoxide}}{R-\overset{O}{\overset{\|}{S}}-CH_2-\underset{NH_2}{\underset{|}{CH}}-COOH} \xrightarrow{\text{Enzyme}} \underset{\text{Flavour compound}}{\text{S - Volatile}} + NH_3 + CH_3-CO-COOH$$

where R is the methyl (CH_3,-), S-1-propenyl (CH_3-CH =CH-) or S-2 propenyl (CH_2, = CH-CH_2-) group. These flavour compounds, then undergo non-enzymatic degradation to more volatile compounds, such as sulphides, disulphides, trisulphides and thiosulphates.

The characteristic odour of garlic is due to allicin, which is formed from the odourless allicin, S-2-propenyl (allyl) cysteine sulphoxide by the action of the enzyme allinase. The allicin then undergoes non-enzymic decomposition to disulphide and thiosulphinate. The disulphide further decomposes to give a complex mixture of monosulphide and trisulphide.

$$2CH_2=CH-CH_2-\overset{O}{\overset{\|}{S}}-CH_2-\underset{NH_2}{\underset{|}{CH}}-COOH + H_2O \xrightarrow{\text{Allinase}}$$

S-2- Propenyl-L-cysteine
sulphoxide (alliin)

$$CH_2=CH-CH_2-\overset{O}{\overset{\|}{S}}-S-CH_2-CH=CH_2 + 2NH_3 + 2CH_3-CO-COOH$$

Allicin

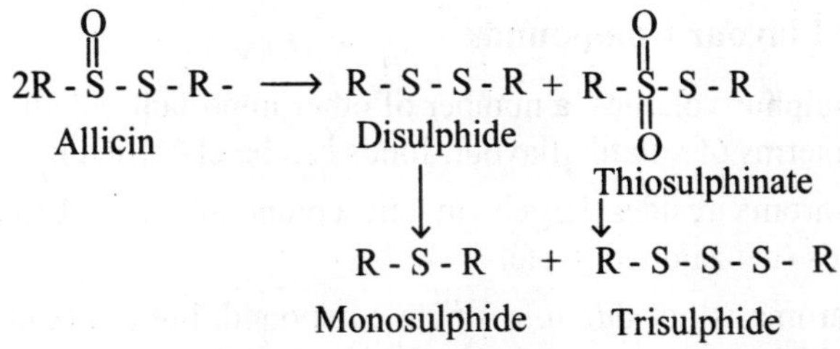

The production of volatile flavour from onion is similar to that of garlic, except that S-1-propenyl cysteine sulphoxide is the flavour precursor. This precursor is enzymatically cleaved to give propenyl-sulphenic acid which is unstable and undergoes rearrangement to form thiopropanal-S-oxide, the lachrymatory factor in onion.

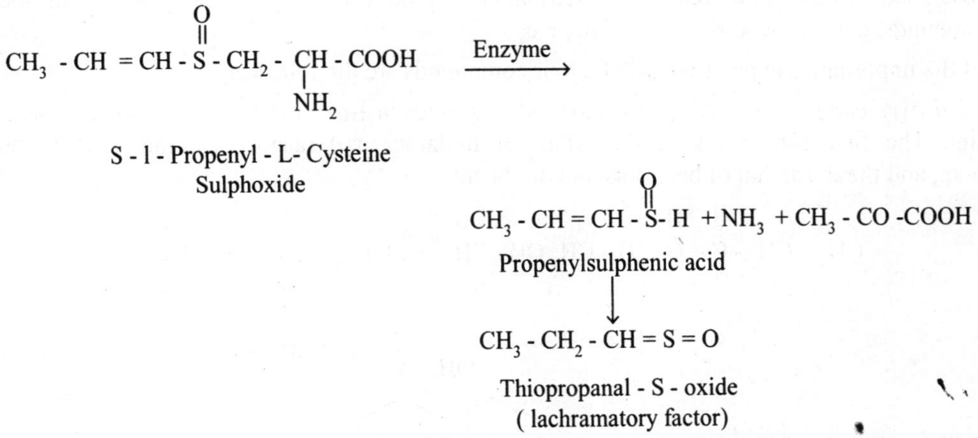

The flavour components of the vegetables of the *Brassica* family are due to the sulphur compounds S-methyl-cysteine sulphoxide and thioglucosides. The former is converted into dimethyl sulphides on cooking the vegetables, which are responsible for flavour. However, the prominent flavour of this family of vegetables is due to the formation of isothiocyanates from thioglucosides by enzymatic hydrolysis. This reaction occurs only after cellular disruption because the enzyme and substrate are compartmentalized separately within the intact cells. The reaction occurs in two steps. The first product formed (thiohydroxamic-O-sulphate) is unstable and undergoes spontaneous degradation to form isothiocyanate.

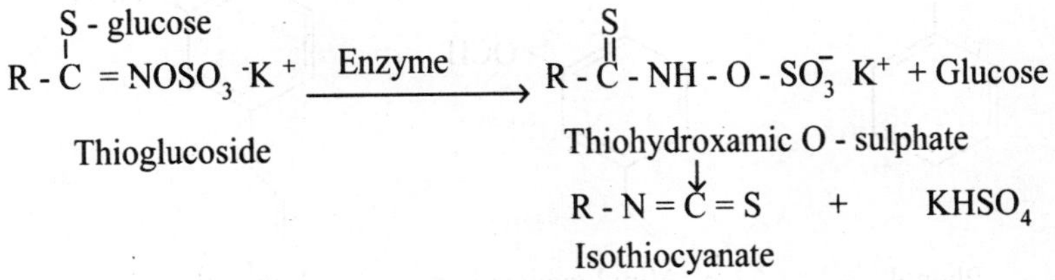

9.5.4 Other Volatile Flavour Compounds

In addition to the above sulphur volatiles, a number of other important volatile components contribute to the flavour of foods. In terms of volatile flavour, foods can be classified into four groups:

1. Those foods whose aroma resides largely in one compound, e.g., banana (isopentyl acetate), lemon (citral), almonds (benzaldhyde), etc.
2. Those foods whose aroma is not due to a single compound, but a mixture of a small number of compounds, one of which may be a major component. For example, the major flavour component of apple is 2-methylIbutyrate and it contains four other minor components.
3. Those foods whose aroma can be reproduced faithfully by the use of a large number of compounds, such as pineapple, walnut, etc.
4. Those foods whose aroma cannot be reasonably reproduced by a complex mixture of specific compounds, e.g., strawberries, chocolate, etc.

Some of the important groups of volatile flavour compounds are the following:

Hydroxy compounds: Among alcohols, cis-3-hexen-I-ol, l-octen-3-ol and geosmin are important. The first contributes to the odour of tomatoes and raspberries; the second, that of mushroom, and the third, that of beetroots and dry beans.

$$CH_3 - CH_2 - \overset{H}{\overset{|}{C}} = \overset{H}{\overset{|}{C}} - CH_2 - CH_2OH \qquad CH_3 - (CH)_2)_4 - \underset{OH}{\underset{|}{CH}} - CH = CH_2$$

cis - 3 - Hexen-1 -ol   1 - Octen - 3 -ol

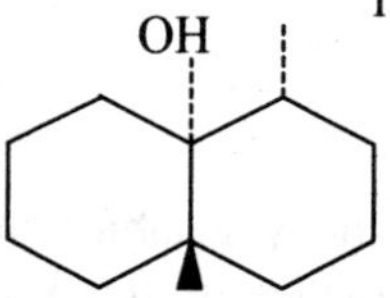

Geosmin

Among the phenols, phenol itself contributes to the flavour of some cheeses. Vinylguaiacol is present in many foods and eugenol is widely distributed but is an important compound of oil of cloves. l-(p-hydroxy-phenyl)-3-butanone is present in the raspberries, and thymol is an important contributor to the flavour of tangerines.

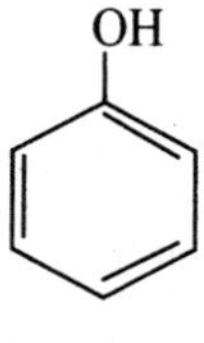

Phenol

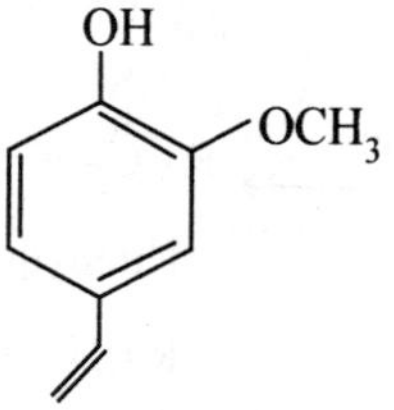

p - Vinyl guaiacol

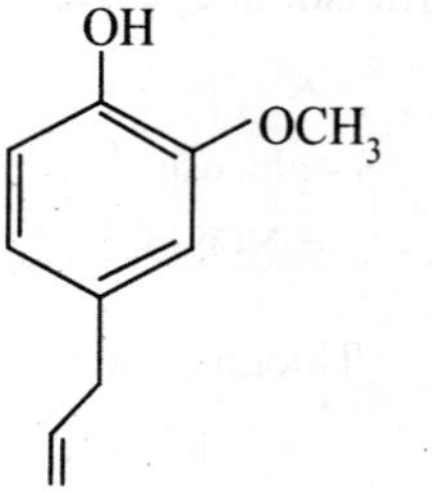

Eugenol

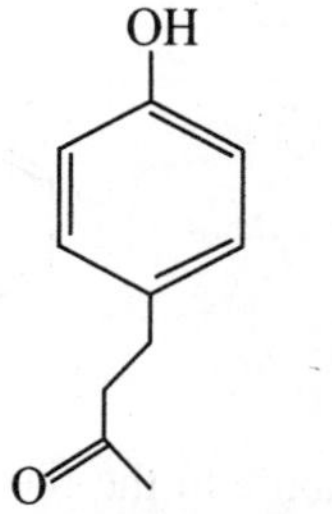

1 - (p- Hydroxyphenyl - 3- butanone)

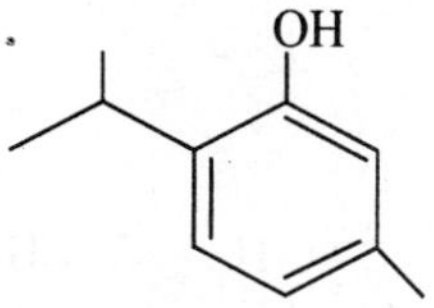

Thymol

Carbonyl compounds: A large number of aldehydes are responsible for the flavour of foods. Acetaldehyde contributes to the flavour of butter, hexenal to that of apples and *trans*-2-hexenal to those of apples, some berries and cucumber. Benzaldehyde is the flavour component of almonds, cherries and peaches. *cis*-4-heptenal is the flavour compound of cream and *trans*-2-*cis*-6-nonadienal of cucumber. 2,4-decadienal is present in many foods. Geranial is the important component of lemon flavour. 5-Methyl-2-phenyl-2-hexenal is a contributor to the flavour of chocolate.

$CH_3 - CHO$

Acetaldehyde

$CH_3\,CH_2 - CH_2 - CH_2 - CH_2 - CHO$

Hexenal

$CH_2\,CH_2 - CH_2 - \overset{H}{C} = \underset{H}{C} - CHO$

trans - 2 - Hexenal

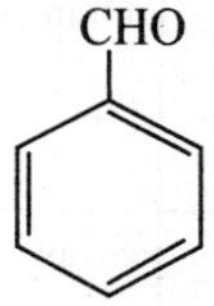

Benzaldehyde

$CH_3 - CH_2 - \overset{H}{C} = \overset{H}{C} - CH_2 - CH_2 - CHO$

cis 4 - Heptenal

$CH_3 - CH_2 - \overset{H}{C} = \overset{H}{C} - CH_2 - CH_2 - \overset{H}{C} = \underset{H}{C} - CHO$

trans -2, *cis* - 6 - Nonadienal

$CH_3 - (CH_2)_4 - \underset{H}{C} = \overset{H}{C} - \overset{H}{C} = \underset{H}{C} \cdot CHO$

trans - 2, *trans* - 4 - Decadienal

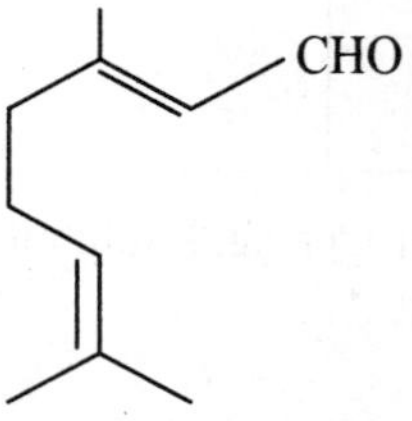

Geranial

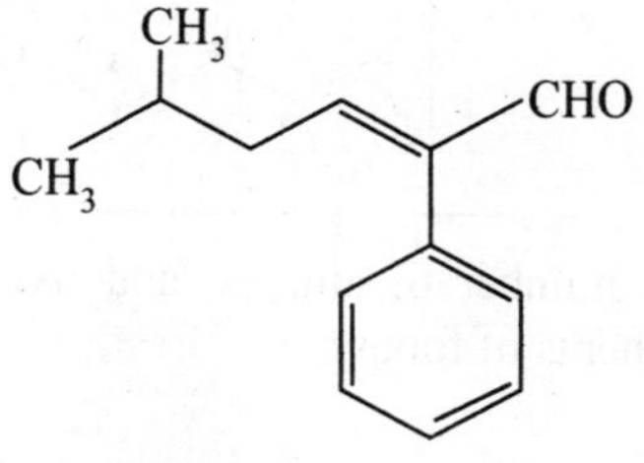

5 - Methyl - 2 - phenyl - 2 - Hexenal

Among ketones, 2,3-butanedione contributes to the flavour of butter, celery and many other foods. 2-heptanone and 2-nonanone are flavour compounds of blue cheese. Acetophenone contributes to the flavour of many foods.

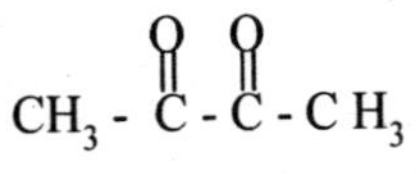
2, 3- Butanedione

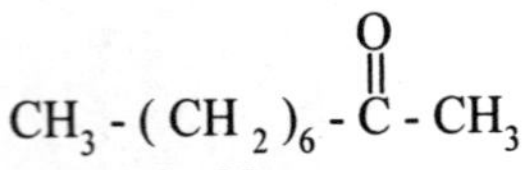
2 - Nonanone

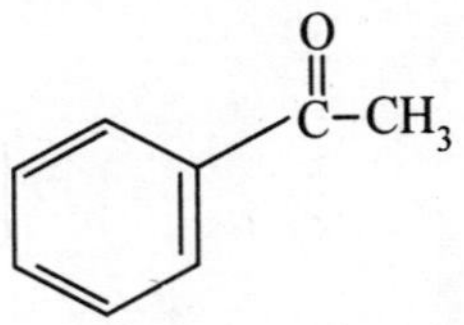
Acetophenone

Acids: Some acids have powerful odours and contribute to the flavour of many foods. Acetic acid is the flavour component of vinegar, and 2-methyl-butyric acid that of cranberries. Many branched-chain and unsaturated acids contribute to the odour of mutton.

Esters: The flavour of fruits is due to esters. Some of the esters responsible for the flavour of some fruits are the following;

Ester		**Fruit Flavour**
Pentylacetate	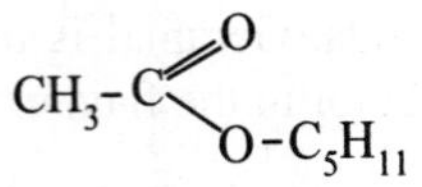	If C_5H_{11} is branched, banana
Butylacetate	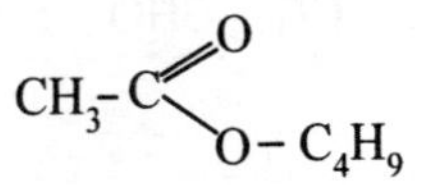	If C_4H_9 is straight chain, raspberries If C_4H_9 is branched, strawberries
Octylacetate	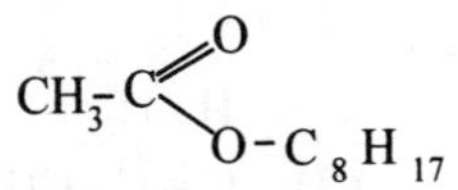	Orange
Ethylbutyrate	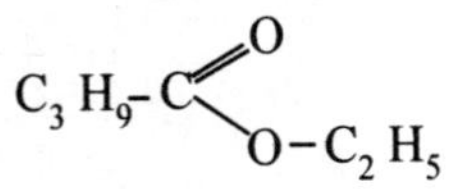	Strawberries
Pentylvalerate	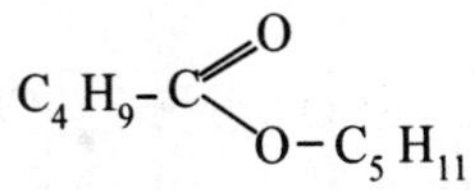	Apple
Methyl salicilate	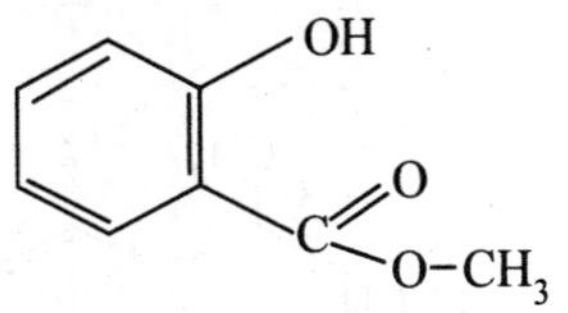	Grapes, Oil of Winter Green

In addition to these a number of amines, and oxygen, nitrogen and sulphur heterocyclics are the volatile flavour components of foods.

CHAPTER

10 Enzymes

Enzymes are biological catalysts. A catalyst is an agent affecting the velocity of a chemical reaction without appearing among the final products of the reaction. Unlike general catalysts, enzymes functioning in the living system have to operate at a temperature of approximately 37°C and pH close to neutrality. Yet, the chemical versatility and ability of enzymes are superior to those of chemical catalysts by a factor of 10^5 to 10^8.

Use of enzymes to accomplish certain desirable changes in food has been practised from antiquity. Use of malted barley in brewing, yeast in the production of alcoholic beverages, and wrapping of meat in the bruised leaves of papaya tree for tenderizing meat, are techniques that have been used for centuries. In bread and cheese making also enzymes have been used from generation to generation. Thus, enzymes have been exploited without knowing the nature of enzyme catalysts and the reactions involved. However, it is only recently that a knowledge of the nature of enzyme action has bean known and its importance to food science realized.

Enzymes are distributed among the cells and tissues of plants and animals. Some cellular enzymes are present in solution in the cytosol, while most exist bound to the subcellular organelles. Some subcellular enzymes are characteristic of the organelle, while others occur at different subcellular and tissue locations, catalyzing the same reaction.

Some terms often encountered in the study of enzymes need definition. Enzymes are proteins with catalytic properties due to their power of specific activation. It is the protein nature of enzymes that is responsible for their characteristic behaviour and properties. Many enzymes (but not all) depend on the co-operation of non-protein substances called cofactors for their activity. The complete active enzyme, consisting of both the protein and the cofactor, is called the holoenzyme. The protein component without its cofactor is termed apoenzyme. The substance on which the enzyme acts is termed the substrate. Isoenzymes or isozymes are multiple forms of an enzyme occurring in the same species. They catalyze the same reaction and arise from genetically determined differences in the primary structure of the enzyme protein.

The cofactors are of two categories—the inorganic cofactors which include simple inorganic ions, such as Zn^{2+}, Mg^{2+}. Mn^{2+}. Fe^{2+}, Cu^{2+}, K^+, Na^+, etc., and the organic cofactors consisting of about a dozen substances of diverse structure. The organic cofactors are usually called coenzymes. Coenzymes are derived from vitamins as indicated in Chap. 5.

10.1 Nomenclature and Classification

Since the isolation of the first enzyme in a pure state (urease) in 1926, about 2,500 different enzymes have been isolated from all types of organs. Many of these have been obtained in a pure state. Some enzymes were given non-descriptive names such as trypsin, pepsin, rennin and lysozyme as and when they were isolated. Later, they were named with the addition of "ase" to the stem of the substrate, e.g., maltase, urease, etc. This type of nomenclature is not satisfactory. Based on the recommendations of the Enzyme Commission of the International Union of Biochemistry, the enzyme nomenclature has now been systematized. Accordingly, the enzymes are named with an "ase" ending as per the type of reaction they catalyze, together with the name of the substrate, e.g., the enzyme that oxidizes ethyl alcohol to yield acetaldehyde is named alcohol oxidoreductase. Similarly, the enzyme transferring the amino group of aspartic acid to an acceptor is known as aspartic amino-transferase. In addition to the systematic name assigned to the enzymes, a trivial name is also recommended for common use.

Table 10.1 Main classification of enzymes

Main group	Class	Type of reaction catalysed
1	Oxidoreductases	Oxidation –reduction of all types
2.	Transferases	Transfer of a group from a donor to an acceptor
3	Hydrolases	Hydrolytic cleavage of bonds (with water participating)
4	Lyases	Cleavage of bonds by means other than hydrolysis or oxidation
5	Isomerases	Interconversion of various isomers
6	Ligases	Bond formation due to condensation of two different substances with energy provided by ATP (adenosine triphosphate)

All known enzymes are categorized into six main groups on the basis of the general type of reaction they catalyze. The main groups and the types of reaction they catalyze are given in Table 10.1. In each main group, enzymes are further grouped into subgroups and sub-subgroups. The subgroup identifies the enzymes in more specific terms, the sub-subgroup precisely defines the reaction that is catalyzed. Finally, each enzyme is recognized by a numerical code consisting of four numbers, such as 2.1.3.4; the first number specifies the main group, the second and third numbers correspond to the specific subgroup and sub-subgroup of the enzyme and the final number represents the serial listing of the enzyme in the sub-subgroup. Thus, a number 1.1.1.1 denotes an oxidoreductase with alcohol as a donor of hydrogen and NAD^+ as an acceptor of hydrogen with serial number 1. The systematic name of this enzyme is alcohol: NAD^+ oxidoreductase and its trivial name is alcohol dehydrogenase. Similarly, 2.6.1.1 represents aspartate aminotransferase.

10.2 Specificity

Unlike nonbiological catalysts, enzymes are very selective in their action. In a great majority of cases, an enzyme catalyzes only one reaction. This is known as absolute specificity, e.g., urease acts only on urea, hydrolyzing it to carbon dioxide and ammonia. Similarly, maltase acts only on maltose, hydrolyzing it to two molecules of glucose. This property is a very important biological phenomenon and is also of significance in industrial processes. In some cases, enzymes show a lower order of specificity, e.g., trypsin hydrolyzes a peptide bond which involves the carboxyl group of lysine or arginine. In this case, the enzyme is specific only towards the chemical bond and a specific group on one side of the linkage. This is known as the group specificity or relative specificity.

In some other cases, enzymes are specific only towards the linkage which is split, and the nature of the group on either side of the linkage is immaterial. For example, lipases hydrolyze any triglyceride and esterases any ester. This is a case of low specificity.

In the case of substances which are optically active or which occur as *cis-trans* geometrical isomers, the enzymes act on only the one of the isomers, e.g., lactic dehydrogenase from animal sources oxidizes only L-lactic acid to pyruvic acid and not the D-isomer. Similarly, fumarase acts on fumaric acid, which has a *trans* configuration and not on the isomeric maleic acid, which has a *cis* configuration. In these cases, the enzymes exhibit stereochemical specificity.

The basis of enzyme specificity is the existence of an active site in the enzyme. This is the region where the substrate comes into contact with the enzyme. The active site is the three-dimensional region consisting of side-chains contributed by amino acids situated for part in the linear sequence of the polypeptide chain. The side chains constituting the active site are involved in the binding of the substrate and in bringing about catalysis.

One of the theories put forward to account for the specificity of the enzyme is the lock-and-key hypothesis of Emil Fischer. According to this concept, there is a structural complementarity between the active site of the enzyme and the substrate. This concept has proved to be correct in accounting for the absolute specificity exhibited by many enzymes. However, a major limitation of the lock-and-key hypothesis is the implication that the entire conformation of the enzyme is rigid. However, proteins are not rigid structures. They are capable of undergoing slight and subtle changes in their configuration. Therefore, Koshland has proposed an induced-fit theory of enzyme action. According to this theory, the complementarity of the active site conformation to the substrate structure is obtained only after the substrate is bound to the enzyme.

10.3 Factors Affecting the Rate of Enzyme Catalyzed Reactions

A number of factors influence the rate of enzyme catalyzed reactions. The most important factors are enzyme concentration, substrate concentration, temperature, pH, electrolytes and the presence of inhibitors. The study of the effect of these factors on the rate of enzyme action is referred to as kinetic studies.

10.3.1 Effect of Enzyme Concentration

For any enzyme, if the temperature, pH and substrate concentration (saturating level) are held constant and if the enzyme concentration *[E]* is varied, plots of initial velocity (V_o) versus the enzyme concentration are linear (Fig. 10.1). In enzymic reactions, the rate of reaction decreases with time. To minimize errors due to this factor, in enzyme kinetic studies, only initial velocity measurements are made. The straight line relationship between enzyme concentration and initial velocity indicates that the reaction rate is proportional to enzyme concentration.

10.3.2 Effect of Substrate Concentration

If, in the above case, the enzyme concentration is kept constant and the substrate concentration is varied, the velocity versus substrate concentration plots are hyperbolic (Fig. 10.2). This shows that the reaction velocity is proportional to substrate concentration only at low concentrations of the substrate and is independent of it at high concentration. To explain this, it is proposed that the enzyme *(E)* reversibly combines with the substrate (S) to form an intermediate complex of enzyme and substrate *(ES)* which then decomposes to yield the product *(P)* and the free enzyme in its original form.

From the concept of *ES* formation, it follows that at low substrate concentration, not all enzyme molecules are saturated with the substrate and as the substrate concentration increases the enzyme gets saturated with respect to the substrate. Once all the enzyme is in the form of *(ES)* any further increase in substrate concentration will not increase the rate of reaction, as there will be an equilibrium between *[E]*, *[S]* and *[ES]* (or more appropriately as *[ES]* reaches a steady state). The velocity of the reaction at the saturating condition of the substrate is the maximum velocity (V_{max}).

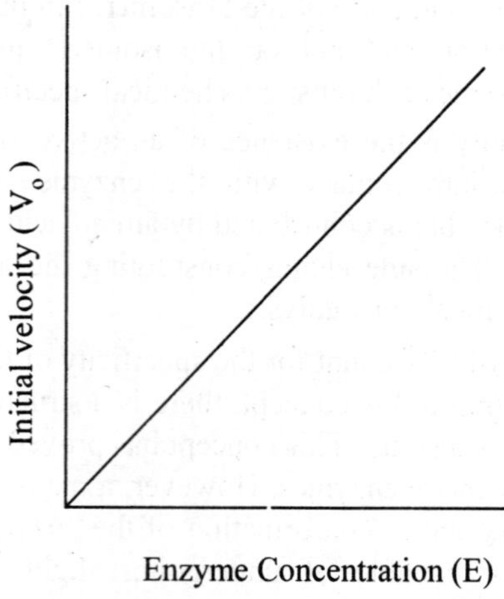

Fig. 10.1 Effect of enzyme concentration on reaction velocity . [E] represents concentration in molarity

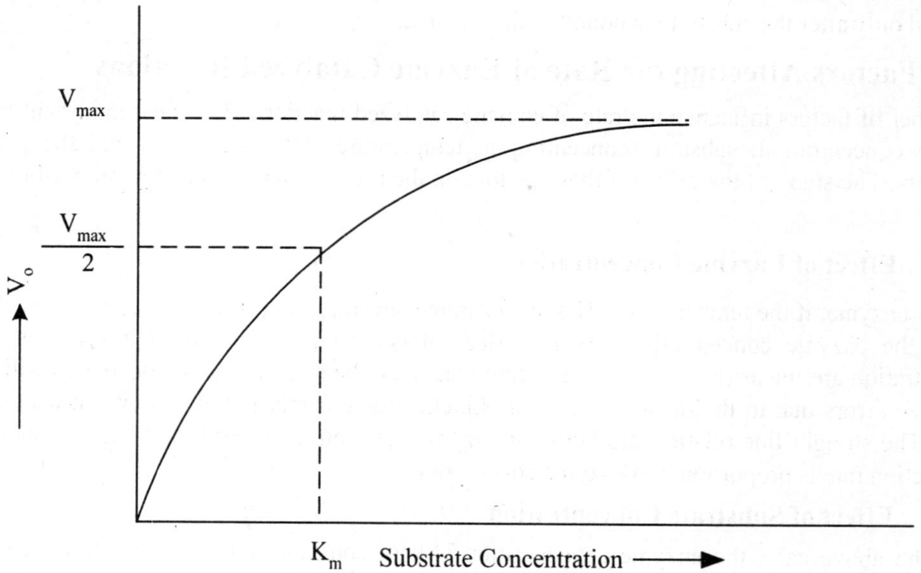

Fig. 10.2 Effect of the substrate concentration on reaction velocity

Based on the equilibrium concept, Michaelis and Menten, in 1913, derived the following rate equation, which shows the relationship between initial velocity and substrate concentration:

$$v_o = \frac{V_{max}[S]}{K_s + [S]}$$

where K_s is the equilibrium constant.

This equation was subsequently modified on the basis of steady-state kinetics to:

$$v_o = \frac{V_{max}[S]}{K_m + [S]}$$

where K_m is the Michaelis constant.

From the above equation it is seen that when $v_o = V_{max}/2$, $K_m = [S]$. Thus, K_m is equal to substrate concentration when the reaction proceeds at half the maximum velocity, K_m and V_{max} are characteristic and important parameters for an enzyme reaction. The smaller the value of k_m, the greater is the affinity of the enzyme for the substrate.

10.3.3 Effect of Temperature

Enzyme activity proceeds very slowly at low temperatures. As the temperature increases, the rate of the enzyme-catalyzed reaction increases, as is true of chemical reactions in general. The reaction rate doubles itself for every 10° rise in temperature. However, since enzymes are proteins, thermal denaturation of the apoenzyme sets in as temperature increases, resulting in inactivation of the enzyme. Thus, the temperature effect is the result of two processes, namely, increase in the reaction rate and increase in the rate of denaturation of the enzyme above a critical temperature.

If the enzyme activity versus temperature is plotted, a curve of the type shown in Fig. 10.3 is usually obtained. The temperature of maximum activity is not fixed, i.e., there is no optimum temperature characteristic of an enzyme. The temperature of maximum activity depends on time, when other conditions of experiment are constant.

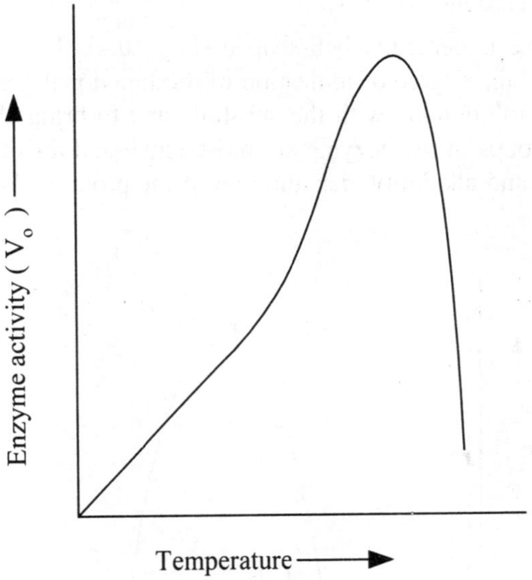

Fig. 10.3 Effect of temperature on enzyme activity

A great majority of enzymes have a temperature of maximum activity between 30-40°C. Inactivation then sets in and is complete above 50 -55°C. There are, however, a few enzymes such as peroxidases which can withstand higher temperatures.

Thermolability of enzymes is of great importance in the food industry. In food preservation it is desirable to prevent or control enzyme activity, as otherwise the food product would be of undesirable flavour, poor appearance, altered texture or lowered nutritive value. By the application of heat to food to about 70°C for a few minutes these undesirable effects can be overcome. For example, pasteurization of milk involves exposure of milk to 63°C for 30 minutes. This treatment is sufficient to inactivate the enzymes (or destroy the organisms containing the enzymes), thus retarding milk spoilage.

Similarly, blanching of fruits and vegetables by subjecting them to boiling water or live steam for a short period inactivates all the enzymes present in them. Thus, the activity of enzymes such as phenolase, lipoxygenase, chlorophyllase and ascorbic acid oxidase are destroyed, and the deterioration of fruits and vegetables during storage is prevented.

The effect of low temperature on enzymes is important from the point of view of food preservation. Many enzymes exhibit significant activity in partially frozen systems. At temperatures from 0 to –10°C, enzyme activity can increase or decrease, depending on the enzyme and the system. A further decrease in temperature results in decreased activity. The behaviour of enzymes in a partially frozen condition depends upon the composition of the medium, rate and extent of freezing, concentration effects on the freezing, viscosity and complexity of the sample (see Chap. 30).

10.3.4 Effect of pH

The activity of an enzyme depends on the pH of the reaction medium. All enzymes are active only within a narrow pH range and for every enzyme there is a pH of maximum activity known as optimum pH. Most enzymes are active in the pH range of 4.5 to 8.0. There are exceptions: pepsin has a pH optimum of 1.8 and arginase around 10.

The pH activity curve is generally bell-shaped (Fig. 10.4). The effect of pH on the enzyme molecule is the alteration of the degree of ionization of the functional groups in the active site of the enzyme, normally required to combine with the substrate and to bring about catalysis. At one ionic condition, the functional groups of the enzyme are most active and thus the enzyme has an optimum pH. At extremes of acidity and alkalinity, denaturation of the protein takes place with a concomitant loss of enzyme activity.

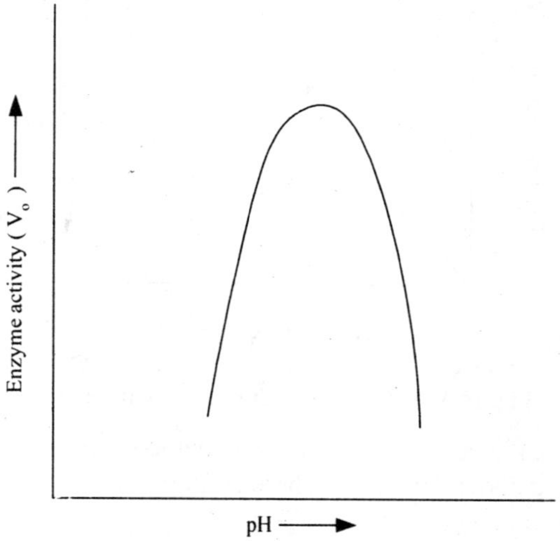

Fig. 10.4 Effect of pH on enzyme activity

10.3.5 Effect of Electrolytes

Some enzymes require certain ions for their activity. Ionic effects vary from enzyme to enzyme; a given ion may be an activator for one enzyme but an inhibitor for another. Further, a given ion may be an inhibitor of an enzyme at one level but may activate the same enzyme at another level. Some ions are required as components of the active site.

Anions are fairly non-specific in their action on enzymes, while the cation requirement of an enzyme is sometimes specific. Cations activating enzymes include Na^+, K^{+f}, NH^+_4, Mg^{2+} Ca^{2+}, Zn^{2+}, Mn^{2+}, Co^{2+}, $A1^{3+}$ and others. Heavy metal ions, like Hg^{2+}, Pb^{2+}or Ag^+, are usually poison enzymes.

Ions bring about the activation of enzymes by a number of methods; this may include the ion becoming an integral part of the active site, forming a link between the enzyme and the substrate, removing the inhibitor of the reaction, and displacing an ineffective metal ion from the active site or from the substrate. It may also act by bringing about a change in the equilibrium constant of the enzyme reaction, changing the surface charge on the enzyme protein and shifting the equilibrium from a less active to a more active form of the enzyme.

10.3.6 Enzyme Inhibition

A substance which reduces the velocity of an enzyme catalyzed reaction is an inhibitor. Enzyme inhibitors have practical importance in food science and other diverse fields such as toxicology and pharmacology. Inhibitors are also of great importance in understanding the mechanism of enzyme catalyzed reactions.

There are two types of inhibitions, irreversible and reversible. In the former case, the enzyme will combine with the inhibitor (*I*) forming a stable enzyme inhibitor complex (*EI*).

$$E + I \longrightarrow EI$$

Irreversible inhibition is progressive and becomes complete when all the enzyme is combined with the inhibitor. Removal of excess of the inhibitor does not reactivate the enzyme. Alkylating agents, such as iodoacetate or iodoacetamide, cause irreversible inhibition by forming covalent linkages with essential -SH groups. Nerve gases also act as irreversible inhibitors. This type of inhibition also results when the enzyme is irreversibly denatured by heat and extremes of pH. Irreversible inhibition is of great importance in food industry.

Reversible inhibition is one in which the inhibitor reacts with an enzyme in a reversible manner. The enzyme activity is restored when the inhibitor is removed

$$E + I \rightleftharpoons EI$$

Reversible inhibitors can be divided into two types based on their kinetic behaviour: competitive and non-competitive.

Competitive inhibition: A competitive inhibitor competes with the substrate for the active site of the enzyme. This means that the inhibitor has a structure similar to that of the substrate, e.g., malonic acid is the competitive inhibitor of the enzyme succinic dehydrogenase, which converts succinic acid to fumaric acid. This is because both succinic acid and malonic acid have two carboxyl groups each, which are separated by an equal distance.

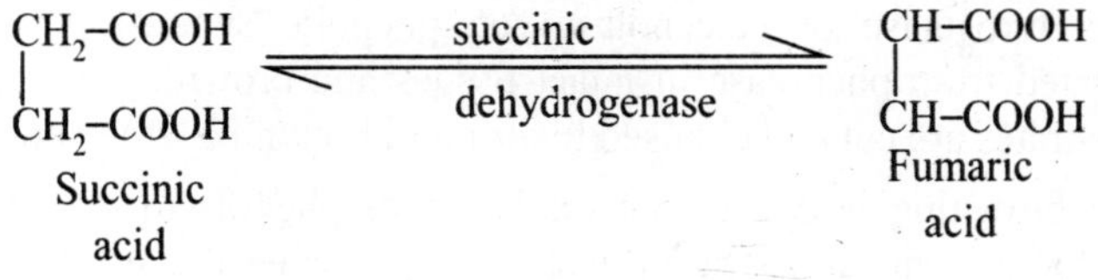

The degree of inhibition depends upon the relative concentration of the inhibitor and the substrate. In the presence of the excess of substrate concentration competitive inhibition can be eliminated. Competitive inhibition affects the apparent K_m.

Non-competitive inhibition: Non-competitive inhibitors interact with enzymes in a number of ways. The inhibitory effect cannot be reversed by increasing the substrate concentration. Non-competitive inhibition largely affects V_{max}. The degree of inhibition is affected by inhibitor concentration. Examples of non-competitive inhibitors are heavy metal ions, such as Ag^+, Hg^{++}, Pb^{++}, which react reversibly with the thiol groups of an enzyme, and chelating agents, which combine with essential metal ions of the enzyme.

10.4 Enzyme Inhibitors

Enzyme inhibitors used in food materials are limited because of their flavour, odour and toxicity problems. The most frequently employed techniques of enzyme inhibition in food are heat, variation of pH, use of sulphur dioxide and other compounds like diethyl pyrocarbonate which decomposes leaving no toxic residue.

A variety of naturally occurring enzyme inhibitors are found in plant and animal tissues. Plant enzyme inhibitors inhibit both mammalian and plant enzymes. Enzyme inhibitors from plants are found in all leguminosae, in grains such as wheat, rice and corn, and in potatoes and beet roots. Enzyme inhibitors thus have nutritional significance.

Inhibitors from soyabean have been extensively investigated. About eight protease inhibitors are present in soyabean and they act on trypsin and chymotrypsin. Unheated soyabean meal fed to rodents retards growth. The growth inhibitory effect may not be just due to the impairment of protein digestion but also due to the endogenous loss of essential amino acids via the secretion of a hyperactive pancreas responding to the trypsin inhibitor. Most plant protein inhibitors including the soyabean trypsin inhibitor are destroyed by heat, with a concomitant increase in the nutritive value of the protein. Other inhibitors of specific enzymes found in plants are those that inhibit the action of amylase, invertase, phosphorylase and polygalacturnase.

Enzyme inhibitors from animal sources have been reported in a variety of body secretions, beef pancreas, blood and egg-white from various avian species. The two inhibitors found in egg-white are ovomucoid and ovoinhibitor. The latter inhibits human trypsin. It is not destroyed by ordinary cooking. Yet, egg-white protease inhibitors are of little nutritional significance as their presence has no effect on nitrogen retention by man.

10.5 Enzymic Browning

Foods undergo non-enzymic and enzymic browning reactions. The former type of browning has been considered under carbohydrates (Subsection 2.4.1). Browning can be observed on the cut surfaces of light coloured fruits and vegetables, such as apples, bananas and potatoes, and this is due to enzymic action. The formation of brown colour is due to the action of the enzyme phenolase (also known as polyphenol oxidase, tyrosinase or catecholase) on phenolic substances. Normally, the phenolic substrates are separated from phenolase in intact tissues and browning does not occur. When foods containing such substrates are cut and exposed to air rapid browning of the cut surface takes place.

The enzymic browning is due to the oxidation of phenols to orthoquinones, which in turn rapidly polymerize to form melanin, the brown pigment. When the substrate is a phenol, it is first converted by hydroxylation into O-diphenol and then oxidized to orthoquinone. Tyrosine is the major phenol substrate for phenolase action in foods. Other phenolic substances, such as caffeic acid, protocatechuic acid and chlorogenic acid, also serve as substrates.

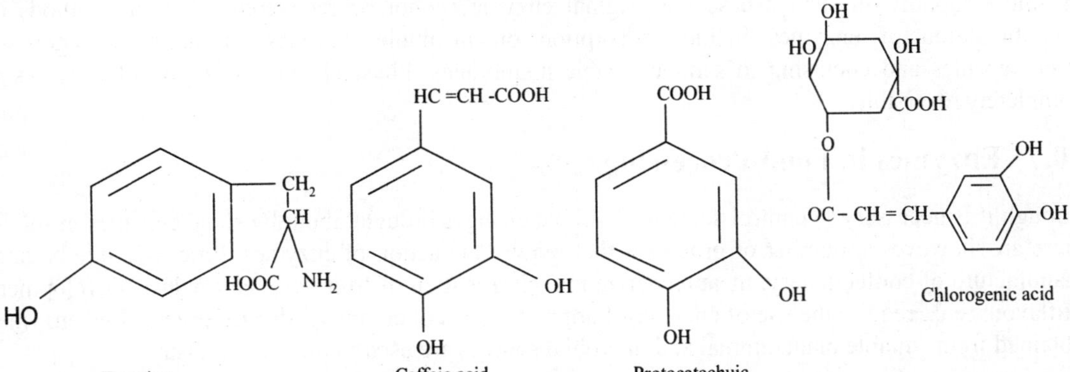

Tyrosine Caffeic acid Protocatechuic acid Chlorogenic acid

The formation of melanin from tyrosine takes place in the following manner.

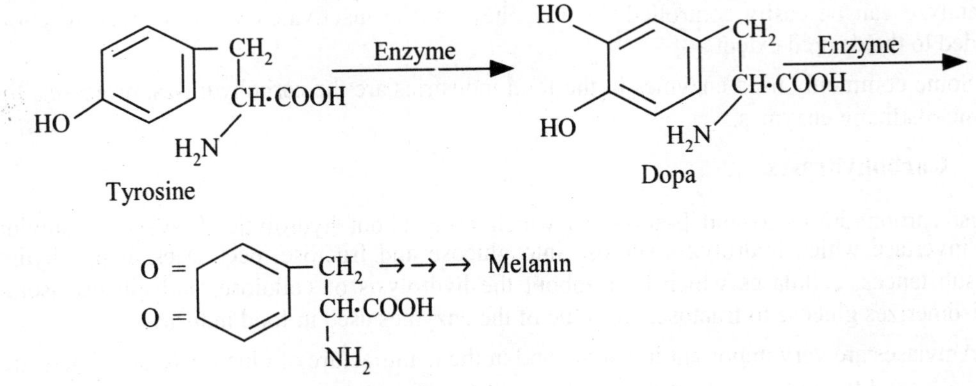

Tyrosine Dopa Dopaquinone

Melanin formation is undesirable during the processing of fruits and vegetables. Pigment formation can be eliminated by inhibiting enzyme action. Heat treatment and application of sulphur dioxide or sulphites are the commonly used methods of inactivating phenolase. The enzyme is irreversibly inactivated at pH values of 3 or less and this can be achieved by the addition of sufficient acidulants, such as citric, malic or phosphoric acids. Browning can also be prevented by excluding oxygen from the reaction site or protecting the phenolic substrates. The former is achieved by immersing the tissues in brine or syrup, or by processing under vacuum and the latter by the use of certain enzymes which modify orthophenolic substrates.

10.6 Immobilized Enzymes

In recent years immobilized enzymes have proved to be of value in food processing. Ordinarily, added enzymes are inactivated after they serve the desired purpose. Also, in analytical applications, a sample of enzyme is to be employed for each analysis. Immobilized enzymes can be used repeatedly or continuously and permit the automation of analytical procedures.

An immobilized enzyme is chemically or physically restricted in movement so that it can be physically reclaimed from the reaction medium. The enzymes are immobilized by binding them, by a chemical or physical method, to some sort of an insoluble support. Chemical methods of immobilization involve the formation of a covalent bond between a residue of an enzyme and the insoluble support. In such a case the original enzyme cannot be recovered. Physical methods of immobilization of enzymes include adsorption on insoluble matrices, entrapping in gels or microcapsules and enclosing in semipermeable membranes. Physical immobilization of enzymes is completely reversible.

10.7 Enzymes in Food Processing

Though it is necessary to control some undesirable changes brought about by some enzymes in foods, there are, however, a number of processes that require the action of enzymes. Processes like baking, manufacture of confectionery, meat tenderization, clarification of fruit juices and wines, development of flavour, etc., require the use of enzymes. Large quantities of commercial, partially purified enzymes obtained from suitable plant, animal and microbial sources are used in the food industry.

There are a number of advantages of using enzymes in food processing. They are natural non-toxic substances that catalyze a given reaction without causing unwanted side reactions. They are active under mild conditions of temperature and pH, active at low concentrations and the reactions they catalyze can be easily controlled. Finally, they can be inactivated when a given reaction has proceeded to the desired extent.

Some commonly used enzymes in the food industries are the carbohydrases, proteases, lipases and some oxidizing enzymes.

10.7.1 Carbohydrases

Amongst carbohydrases, α-and β-amylases which bring about hydrolytic cleavage of amylum or starch, invertase which hydrolyzes sucrose into glucose and fructose, pectinases, which hydrolyze pectic substances, cellulases which bring about the hydrolysis of cellulose, and glucose isomerase which isomerizes glucose to fructose, are some of the enzymes used in food industries.

Amylases are very important in baking and in the manufacture of glucose syrups. There are two amylases: α- and β-amylases, α-amylase hydrolyzes the α-1, 4 bonds of amylase and amylopectin in a random manner liberating maltose. β-amylase also hydrolyzes the α-1, 4 bonds in starch fractions but it acts in an orderly way, removing successive maltose units form the nonreducing end. The α- and β-amylases do not hydrotyze α-1, 6 linkages which occur in amylopectin. The enzyme amylo α-1, 6 glucosidase can hydrolyze these bonds. By the combined action of α- and β-amylases, in flour used in bread-making, dextrins and maltose are formed and this provides the fermentable sugar for the yeast cells. These enzymic reactions continue in the baking process till the enzyme activity is destroyed as the oven temperature rises. The type and extent of changes due to carbohydrases in the flour determine the softness, crust colour, volume and texture of the baked products.

Enzyme preparations, consisting of α- and β-amylases, amylo-1, 6-glucosidase, and glucoamylase from microbial sources, can carry out the hydrolysis of starch paste to near completion and are used in the preparation of glucose or glucose syrups (chocolate syrup). By the combined action of acid and enzyme hydrolysis, sugar syrups of the required flavour and consistency can be obtained. Amylases also find use in brewing industry in the conversion of starch to maltose for fermentation. They are also used for the removal of starch turbidity in jellies to increase sparkling properties.

Invertase is the enzyme that hydrolyzes sucrose to glucose and fructose. While sucrose is dextrorotatory (positive optical rotation), the mixture of equimolar amounts of glucose and fructose is levorotatory (negative optical rotation) due to the highly levorotatory property of fructose. This product of hydrolysis is called invert sugar and the enzyme is thus named invertase. Invert sugar is much sweeter than sucrose and is widely used in the confectionery industry.

Pectic enzymes play an important part in fruit ripening, maintaining the viscosity of processed foods and in textural changes. They also find use in the food industry. The haziness noticed in fruit juices and wines is due to pectic substances. While in some cases, as in fruit juices, the haziness is desirable, in other cases it is objectionable. When clarified fruit juices are required, the colloidal pectic substances can be hydrolyzed by the enzyme pectinase when the cloud-forming particles settle down. Clear juices can be obtained by decantation or centrifugation. Similarly, wines can be clarified using pectinases. If, on the other hand, cloudiness is required in juices, the pectinase is to be destroyed by pre-heating the juice, before it is processed. Pectinases are also used in the digestion of mucilagenous material in coffee manufacture.

Glucose isomerase converts glucose to fructose. Corn syrup treated with this enzyme gives high-fructose syrup, which is 50 per cent more sweet than sucrose. High fructose syrup is used in the manufacture of aerated drinks.

10.7.2 Proteases

Proteases are enzymes that cleave a protein molecule by the hydrolysis of peptide bonds. They find important uses in many food industries, such as baking, meat tenderization, cheese manufacture and beer manufacture.

The main constituents of wheat flour are starch and protein. In the baking industry, to obtain a product of required volume, texture, flavour and better storage properties, it is necessary that both starch and the protein gluten of wheat flour undergo some degradative changes. The required changes in the properties of gluten in the preparation of bakery products are brought about by the use of proteases from fungal sources.

A number of proteolytic enzymes from plant, animal and microbial sources are employed in tendering meat. The enzymes hydrolyze one or more of the muscle components of meat resulting in increased tenderness. The enzymes commonly used in tenderizing meat are trypsin, papain, bromelin and ficin, and also other enzymes from fungal sources.

Rennin is the major proteolytic enzyme of the fourth stomach of the suckling calf. This enzyme plays an important role in the production of cheese. The casein of milk is an aggregate of many caseins. Rennin cleaves one peptide bond of one of the caseins (K-casein), resulting in the curdling of milk. Curdling of milk by rennin yields a firm curd, which is the initial step in the manufacture of cheese.

One of the problems in the production of beer is haze in beer. This could be due to the proliferation of the infecting micro-organisms in beer or to the combination of proteins and tannins in the beer. Proteolytic enzymes can successfully prevent the latter type of haze. By reducing the size of the protein molecules by partial hydrolysis, the protein-tannin reaction is eliminated. The enzymes papain, pepsin, ficin, bromelin and bacterial proteases are used to prevent beer haziness, the most commonly used enzyme being papain.

10.7.3 Lipases

Lipases are enzymes that hydrolyze ester linkages in glycerides. The fatty acids produced from the hydrolysis of triglycerides can lead to characteristic off-flavour in foods. Lipases are also involved in the manufacture of cheese. During cheese ripening there is extensive hydrolysis of butter fat resulting in the formation of various fatty acids responsible for the characteristic flavour of cheese. For the production of milk with a slightly cured flavour, for use in milk chocolate, lipases are used.

10.7.4 Oxidoreductases

In addition to hydrolytic enzymes discussed above, a number of oxidoreductases are of importance in food science. Some of the important ones are the following:

Glucose oxidase: Glucose oxidase is an enzyme which oxidizes glucose to gluconic acid in presence of oxygen, and in the process, hydrogen peroxide is formed. The commercial preparation of glucose oxidase contains catalase which quickly decomposes hydrogen peroxide to water.

Glucose oxidase is commercially used to remove traces of glucose and oxygen in a variety of food products, such as beer, cheese, carbonated beverages, dried eggs, fruit pies, wines, etc., to prevent deterioration during storage by oxidation and/or browning.

$$\text{Glucose} \xrightarrow[\text{Oxidase}]{\text{Glucose}} \text{gluconic acid} + H_2O_2$$

$$2H_2O_2 \xrightarrow{\text{Catalase}} 2H_2O + O_2$$

Peroxidases: Peroxidases are enzymes which oxidize H_2O_2 or organic peroxides (e.g. methyl hydrogen peroxide) in the presence of an oxidizable substance.

$$AH_2 + ROOH \longrightarrow A + H_2O + R\cdot OH$$

where AH_2 is the hydrogen donor or oxidizable substance and ROOH is a peroxide. This enzyme is quite heat stable. About 50 per cent of enzyme activity remains even after the enzyme is heated at 85°C for over 30 min. Because of this property the activity of this enzyme is used to detect effectiveness of blanching. The loss of peroxidase activity in a blanched food product is taken to indicate the inactivation of the deteriorative enzymes.

Ascorbic oxidase: Ascorbic acid gets easily oxidized in the presence of ascorbic oxidase. It also gets oxidized by atmospheric oxygen without the involvement of the enzyme. The enzymic oxidation reactions are significant in the processing and storage of citrus fruit juices and concentrates, and vegetable products. The oxidation results in a browning reaction and loss of vitamin C activity.

Lipoxygenases: These enzymes bring about the oxidation of essential fatty acids resulting in the development of off-flavour. The intermediate products of lipoxygenase action on lipids damage vitamins and proteins in foods. Lipoxygenases are present in legumes like soyabean, mung bean, green beans and peas, and in cereals such as wheat, oats, barley and corn. The off-flavour and odour noticed sometimes in foods are due to the action of lipoxygenases on lipids present in them.

Lipoxygenases are used in some countries in the production of bread. The enzyme brings about bleaching by oxidation of the natural pigments of the flour to produce a very white crumb.

A number of enzymes other than those mentioned above are also of importance in food science.

CHAPTER

11 Properties of Foods

Foods are generally complex materials. The properties of their components determine the quality of food. The food components are in the form of solids, in solution, or in the form of colloidal sols or emulsions. These undergo various physical and chemical changes when exposed to various conditions. A knowledge of the scientific principles of these changes is necessary to understand and control the changes occurring in foods during the various aspects of their handling. The scientific principles governing the physical and chemical properties of foods are discussed in this chapter.

11.1 Physical Properties

Many of the foods consumed, such as milk, fruit juices and other beverages, are liquids. The liquid portion of foods like canned fruits, soups, etc., are solutions. Eggs and lean meats contain some ingredients in solutions. Hence, certain physical properties of solutions are considered below.

11.1.1 Solutions

A solution is a homogeneous mixture of two or more different substances. This means that the molecules of the dissolved substances (solutes) and the medium in which they are dissolved (solvent) are uniformly distributed throughout the whole of the solution. Solubility is the amount of solute that can be dissolved in a given amount of solvent at a given temperature. The effect of temperature on solubility varies with solutes. Increasing temperature increases the solubility of some solutes but has less effect on the solubility of others.

The extent to which a solute will dissolve in a solvent depends upon the attractive forces between the solute and solvent molecules, and the solvation of the solute, i.e., the attachment of the molecules of the solvent to solute molecules or ions, either by electrical attraction or chemical bonding. The strongest attractive forces between the solvent and solute molecules are between ions and polar solvent molecules, where the electrical attraction is so strong that the ions, when in solution, have molecules of the solvent attached to them. The water molecule is highly polar therefore water is an excellent solvent for ionic substances. The solvation that takes place in this case is known as hydration. If both solvent and solute consist of polar molecules, there is also strong electrical attraction in this case between the two dipoles. This results in solvation and good solubility. The solvation of molecules is often increased by the formation of hydrogen bonds. Therefore, polar solvents like water are good solvents for polar molecules and for ionic substances.

The concentration of a solution is the amount of the solute dissolved in a specified amount of solvent or solution. When the concentration reaches a point when no more solute can dissolve in a solvent at a particular temperature, the solution obtained is said to be saturated. If a saturated solution of a solid is prepared at or near the boiling point of the solvent, on cooling, the solid crystallizes out.

Sometimes, when a saturated solution is carefully cooled, crystals may not separate out. Such a solution holds more solute than could normally be present at the same temperature. This solution is said to be supersaturated. Supersaturated solutions are unstable and become more unstable as the degree of supersaturation increases. Crystals do form ultimately, when the solution becomes fairly cool. This phenomenon is of importance in sugar cookery.

Several properties of solutions are particularly important in food preparation. Amongst these are the colligative properties, such as vapour pressure, and certain properties are directly connected with vapour pressure, namely boiling point, freezing point and osmotic pressure.

11.1.2 Vapour Pressure

The intermolecular forces in a liquid prevent most molecules from escaping from the surface. However, due to molecular collisions, some molecules have sufficient kinetic energy to escape from the liquid. This causes the evaporation of these molecules into a gaseous state. Any liquid, therefore, has above its surface, a certain amount of material in the form of vapour. Vapour molecules move in all directions. Some of the vapour molecules that strike the surface of the liquid get condensed. When the rate of evaporation and condensation are equal, an equilibrium is established. The pressure exerted by the vapour above the liquid when equilibrium exists is vapour pressure. The vapour pressure is temperature dependent.

When a solid is dissolved in a volatile solvent, the vapour pressure of the solution is less than the vapour pressure of the pure solvent because of the presence of solute molecules. In a solution, the number of solvent molecules at the surface is reduced and therefore the rate of evaporation is less than for the solvent. The extent of lowering, is proportional to the number of molecules of solvent compared with the total number of solvent plus solute molecules. For example, when equal quantities of sucrose and sodium chloride are dissolved in a known amount of water at constant temperature, the lowering of the vapour pressure of water by sodium chloride is twice as much as that of sucrose, because sodium chloride contains twice the number of ions than the number of sucrose molecules in the solution. Properties of a solution which depend on the relative number of molecules present and not on their chemical nature are known as colligative properties. These properties hold good if the solution is dilute.

11.1.3 Boiling Point

A liquid boils when its vapour pressure is equal to the external pressure. The boiling point is thus constant for any external pressure. The normal boiling point (BP) refers to an external pressure which is equal to the atmospheric pressure (760 mm Hg), which for water is 100°C. With an increase in pressure the boiling point increases, e.g., the boiling point of water at 770 mm is 100.37°C. In a pressure cooker, a greater external pressure is to overcome and that the boiling point is elevated. At 103 kg/kilo Pascal, water boils at 121°C. Conversely, at a reduced atmospheric pressure, as at high altitudes, the boiling point is lowered. For each 290 m increase in altitude above sea level, the boiling point of water is lowered by 1°C

As already stated, dissolved substances reduce the vapour pressure of a solvent resulting in a higher temperature being required for a solvent to boil, i.e., dissolved substances, elevate the boiling point. One mole of a non-volatile non-ionizing solute raises the boiling point of a litre of water by

0.52°C. Ionic materials elevate the boiling point to a much higher extent than non-ionizing substances. For example, sodium chloride forms two ions and calcium chloride three ions in solution and, if they undergo complete ionization, one mole of them could raise the boiling point of a litre of water by 1.04° and 1.56°C, respectively.

A knowledge of elevation in boiling point is useful in the processing of foods, such as jams, jellies, syrups, confectionery, etc., they are liquids at higher temperatures, to determine the concentration of sugars and the properties the materials will have upon cooling.

11.1.4 Freezing Point

The freezing point of a material is the temperature at which it changes from a liquid to a solid. A liquid freezes when its vapour pressure is equal to the vapour pressure of its solid. The freezing point of water is 0°C.

The freezing point of a solvent is depressed when a solute dissolves in it. A mole of non-ionizing solute in a litre of water depresses its freezing point by 1.80°C. A mole of sodium chloride or calcium chloride could depress it by 3.72°C and 5.58°C for reasons given under boiling point. The practical importance of this, is that a mixture of ice, water and salt gives freezing mixtures. Ice and water alone are in equilibrium at 0°C, but if the salt is added some ice will melt in order to reduce the temperature to the new equilibrium position. Ice, salt and saturated salt solution (29 parts of salt to 71 parts of ice) give a freezing mixture with a temperature of 21°C and, therefore, this is used in making home-made ice cream.

The freezing point of milk is 0.53°C. Its freezing point is determined by its soluble constituents, lactose and salts present in it. Since these soluble components vary in milk only slightly, the freezing point remains almost constant. This makes it possible to determine any dilution of milk. Addition of 1 per cent by volume of water to milk raises the freezing point by approximately 0.0055°C.

Freezing is a means of preservation of food. This is considered in Chapter 30.

11.1.5 Osmotic Pressure

Osmosis is the flow of a solvent into a solution, or from a more dilute solution to a more concentrated solution, when the two liquids are separated from each other by a semi-permeable membrane. The membrane contains minute pores through which the solvent molecules can travel. The phenomenon of osmosis causes a change in the relative volume of the two liquids separated by the semi-permeable membrane. The volume of the solution that becomes more dilute increases. Osmotic pressure is the pressure required to prevent that increase in volume or osmosis.

The phenomenon of osmosis occurs in food. In fruit cooking, when the fruits are cooked in water, the fruit increases in size as the water flows into the fruit tissues where the sugar concentration is higher. If, on the other hand, fruits are cooked in syrups having a sugar concentration higher than that of the fruit, the fruit will shrivel, because of passage of water through the skin of the fruit into the syrup. Osmosis is also a very important process in living organisms.

11.1.6 Viscosity

Viscosity is associated with fluid flow. It is the internal friction which tends to bring to rest portions of fluids moving relative to one another. This is measured in relation to some standard viscosity, generally of water at 25°C. A number of factors affect the viscosity of a fluid; for instance, large changes take place due to temperature. In the case of a colloidal system, factors in addition to temperature, such as the particle size distribution, nature of the particle surface, particle shape and volume of dispersed phase, etc., affect the viscosity of the fluid.

Viscosity determination is useful in the study of consistency of foods. Viscometric measurements are made in the food industry for the study of food structure. Viscosity has an effect on heat transfer, during pasteurization in the preparation of certain food materials, such as fruit juices. Hence, viscosity and the rate of change of viscosity with change in temperature, are factors of importance in the food industry.

11.1.7 Surface and Interfacial Tensions

The boundary between a liquid and a gas or vapour is termed "surface," whereas that of a liquid-liquid or a solid-liquid junction is termed "interface." There is an attractive force between molecules in a liquid. For a molecule in the body of the liquid, these forces tend to cancel each other according to directions so that there is no net force. Molecules at the surface or interface are not surrounded completely by other molecules of the same type and the same physical state. This results in a net attractive force for each molecule directed towards the interior of the phase in which the molecule resides. This inward attraction tends to reduce the number of molecules at the surface or interface and, as a result, the surface or interfacial area is reduced to a minimum. For example, a drop of oil in water will always tend to assume a spherical shape since the forces cause the surface to contract to the smallest possible size. A drop of water on a greasy surface behaves in a similar way. The forces causing a reduction in the surface or interfacial area are referred to, respectively, as surface tension and interfacial tension.

Intermolecular attractions like hydrogen bonding (Subsection11.3.3) and Van der Waal forces (weak attraction forces between molecules) are responsible for surface and interfacial tensions. With polar compounds like water both these forces are important, whereas only Van der Waal forces (London forces) are operative in non-polar liquids, such as triglycerides.

A number of factors affect surface tension. Increase in the temperature of a liquid phase decreases the surface tension; the decrease with water is greater than with triglycerides. Since water and triglycerides are the most important food liquids, the marked difference in the surface tensions of these two liquids is important in food preparations. The interfacial tension between edible oils and water is of particular importance in the creation and stability of many food emulsions.

The presence of a solute influences the surface tension of water. With solutions of inorganic salts and compounds with a large number of hydroxyl groups (e.g., sucrose), surface tension increases slightly as the concentration of the solute increases. Many organic compounds, including hydrophilic colloids like proteins, are surface acting agents (surfactants) which rapidly decrease surface tension. Surface active agents which have a balance of both polar (hydrophilic) and non-polar (hydrophobic) groups are adsorbed at the surface of a solution. This results in a reduction of surface tension. Lipids, such as phospholipids, salts of fatty acids and monoglycerides, have surface active properties.

11.1.8 Specific Gravity

The density of a substance is defined as mass per unit volume. The density of a substance is a characteristic property and has a definite value at a given temperature and pressure. The density of one substance in relation to the density of another material (e.g., water), is known as specific gravity. Therefore, specific gravity is the weight of a given substance referred to the weight of an equal volume of the water at a definite temperature.

The specific gravities of foods depend upon their components. The specific gravity of milk, for example, is greater than that of water since its constituents, except fat, have specific gravities higher than that of water. The average specific gravity of milk is 1.032 (at 15.5°C); it ranges from 1.027 to 1.035. If the fat content of milk increases, the specific gravity decreases (up to 0.93), and if the nonfat components increase, the specific gravity increases. The actual specific gravity is a function of the two. Similarly, the specific gravity of fats is the resultant specific gravity of the component triglycerides.

Considerable use of specific gravity is made in the sale of products like syrups, foams, jellies, milk, cream, ice cream and alcoholic beverages. It is also useful in the control of processing during the production of these compounds. Specific gravity indicates the amount of air incorporated into products (lightness of products), such as whipped cream, egg-white foam, creamed shortening and cake batter.

11.2 Acids, Bases and Buffers

Foods are complex physicochemical systems consisting of electrolytes like acids, bases, salts and proteins, and non-electrolytes like carbohydrates, lipids and other substances. The properties of the ionizable components of foods, such as acids, bases, and buffer systems, are considered here.

11.2.1 Acids and Bases in Foods

Both organic and inorganic acids occur in foods and serve a variety of roles. Acids are also added to foods to provide the benefits of their natural action. Organic acids commonly used in foods are acetic, lactic, citric, malic, fumaric, succinic and tartaric. Phosphoric acid is the only inorganic acid employed as a food acidulate.

The most important function of acids in foods is the contribution of sour taste. Acids also have the power of intensifying and modifying the taste perception of other flavour agents. Hydrogen ions are believed to trigger the sour taste response. Short-chain free fatty acids contribute significantly to the aroma of foods such as cheese and butter. In higher concentrations they contribute to the characteristic flavour of hydrolytic rancidity.

Another important function of acids in foods is participation in buffering systems. Acids and acid salts are used as chemical leavening agents to impart a characteristic porous, cellular structure to baked foods (see Subsection 16.2.3). Acids act as microbial inhibitors in food preservation (e.g., benzoic acid). They also help achieve the sterilization of fruits and vegetables under less severe thermal conditions. Acids are also important in the setting of pectin gels, in defoaming and bringing about emulsification. Acids induce coagulation of milk proteins in the production of cheese and other dairy products.

Bases or alkaline substances find a number of applications in foods and food processing. Alkaline agents are used to neutralize excess acid in the production of butter from fermented milk. The reduction of acidity improves churning efficiency and retards the development of oxidative off-flavours. Basic substances like sodium carbonate and bicarbonate are used, along with acids, for the production of carbon dioxide during baking. Basic compounds are also used for the enhancement of colour and flavour of foods. For example, treatment of ripe olives with dilute sodium hydroxide solution aids the removal of the bitter principal and development of dark colour. Use of sodium bicarbonate during cocoa processing produces dark chocolate. Strong bases are employed for peeling a number of fruits and vegetables.

11.2.2 Concept of Acids and Bases

Acids, bases and the salts dissociate in aqueous solutions into positively charged and negatively charged atoms or groups of atoms called ions. This process is known as ionization. In an electric field, the positively charged ions move towards the negative electrode (cathode) and the negatively charged particles, towards the positive electrode (anode). The current is thus carried across the solution by ions and not by electrons as in the case of metals. Liquids, in which this type of electric conductance takes place, are known as electrolytes.

According to the classical definition (Arrhenius), a substance which on ionization in aqueous solution yields hydrogen ions (H^+,proton) is an acid and one that yields hydroxyl ions (OH^-) is a base. As there is a strong affinity between hydrogen ions and water molecules, they produce hydronium ions ($H^+ + H_2O \rightarrow H_3O^+$). A substance which undergoes complete ionization (100 per cent) is a strong acid or base, while that which undergoes partial ionization (i.e., considerably less than 100 per cent) is a weak acid or base.

$$HCl + H_2O \rightarrow H_3O^+ + Cl^-$$

Strong acid — Hydronium ion — Chloride ion

$$CH_3 \cdot COOH + H_2O \rightarrow H_3O^+ + CH_3 \cdot COO^-$$

Weak acid — Acetate ion

$$NaOH + H_2O \rightarrow Na^+ + OH^-$$

Strong base — Sodium ion — Hydroxyl ion

$$NH_3 + H_2O \rightarrow NH_4^+ + OH^-$$

Weak base — Ammonium ion

Water is a very weak conductor of electricity which shows that it is ionized to a very small extent. To conduct electric current, however tiny the conduction is, water must dissociate to a very small extent forming hydrogen or hydronium and hydroxyl ions.

$$H_2O + H_2O \rightarrow H_3O^+ + OH^-$$

The equilibrium constant (K_a) for the reaction is:

$$K_a = \frac{[H_3O^+][OH^-]}{[H_2O]^2}$$

Since the ionic concentrations of H_3O^+ and OH^- are small, the concentration of water molecules may be taken as constant and equal to unity. Thus, the equilibrium constant becomes

$$K_a = [H_3O^+]\ [OH^-] = K_w$$

where K_W is the ionic product of water.

By definition, pure water is neutral, and thus the concentrations of hydronium ions and hydroxyl ions are equal, i.e.,

$$[H_3O^+] = [OH^-]$$

At 25°C, the concentration of each of these ions is 1×10^{-7}. Thus, the product non-conduct of the two ions is:

$$K_w = [H_3O][OH^-]$$
$$= [1\times10^{-7}]\,[1\times10^{-7}]$$
$$= 1\times10^{-14}\ \text{mole}^2\ \text{litre}^{-1}$$

(units are usually omitted)

This constant applies to all aqueous solutions. If the hydronium ion concentration increases, the hydroxide ion concentration decreases and vice-versa.

The classical definition of acids and bases has been found to be neither sufficient nor accurate. For example, hydrogen chloride (HC1) dissolved in the non-aqueous solvent, benzene, gives no evidence of the presence of ions, yet it shows the reactions of acids. Again, liquid ammonia ionizes, $NH_3 \rightarrow H^+ + NH_2^-$; the amide ion is a strong base akin to the OH^- ion. To account for these, Bronsted and Lowry, gave a more general definition of acids and bases. According to them, an acid is any substance that donates a proton to another substance and a base is any substance that can accept a proton.

From this point of view, in the ionization of acetic acid

$$\underset{\text{Acid}_1}{CH_3\cdot COOH} + \underset{\text{Base}_1}{H_2O} \rightleftharpoons \underset{\text{Acid}_2}{H_3O^+} + \underset{\text{Base}_2}{CH_3\cdot COO^-}$$

$CH_3 \cdot COOH$ is an acid for it gives up a proton. Water is a base because it accepts a proton. In the reverse reaction, $CH_3.COO^-$ is a potential proton acceptor, and hence the ion is a base. H_3O^+ ion is an acid, because it is now a potential proton donor. Acid_2 resulting from base is said to be the acid conjugate of base_1. Similarly, base_2 is the conjugate of acid_1. Thus, most substances called acids or bases are according to the classical definition, are also acids and bases when the Bronsted-Lowry definition is used. The new definitions are much broader and can be applied to non-aqueous systems.

The strength of an acid depends upon the percentage of its ionization. An acid that is 50 per cent ionized will yield a greater amount of H^+ than one that is 5 per cent ionized. At constant temperature, the extent of ionization is a constant value and is characteristic of an acid. Table 11.1 lists the relative strengths of a number of acids and their conjugate bases. It is noticed from the table that the conjugate base of a strong acid is weak and, conversely, the conjugate base of a weak acid is strong.

Another definition of acids and bases, which is even more general than that given by Bronsted and Lowry, has been proposed by Lewis. He defines an acid as an electron pair acceptor and a base as an electron pair donor. Thus, any molecule or ion with an incomplete electron group around one of its atoms can accept a pair of electrons from another molecule or ion called the Lewis base. This definition extends the usefulness of the acid-base concept. According to the Lewis concept, even a simple metal ion, such as $A1^{3+}$, can act as an acid since it can accept electrons from the oxygen atom of H_2O molecules, as in the hydrated ion $Al(H_2O)_6^{3+}$.

The pH scale: Since hydrogen ion concentrations, vary widely in solutions of acids and bases, and are nearly always less than unity, it is more convenient to use a logarithmic scale in the following way:

Table 11.1 Relative strength of acids and their conjugates

Acid (Strong acid ↑ Weak acid)	Conjugate base (Weak base ↓ Strong base)
HCI	Cl^-
HNO_3	NO_3^-
H_2SO_4	HSO_4^-
H_3O^+	H_2O
HSO_4^-	SO_4^{2-}
H_3PO_4	$H_2PO_4^-$
$CH_3 \cdot COOH$	$CH_3 \cdot COO^-$
H_2CO_3	HCO_3^-
NH_4^+	NH_3
HCO_3^-	CO_3^{2-}
H_2O	OH^-
NH_3	NH_2^-

$$PH = -\log_{10}[H^+]$$

i.e. the pH of a solution is the negative logarithm of the hydrogen ion concentration. Since $[H^+] = 10^{-7}$M is in a neutral solution at 25°C, it follows that for such a solution

$$pH = -\log_{10}[10^{-7}] = -[-7] = +7$$

if $[H^+]$ is greater than that of pure water (that is the solution is an acid), then the negative logarithm of $[H^+]$ will be smaller than 7; in a basic or alkaline solution, $[H^+]$ will be less than 10^{-7} and the pH will be greater than 7.

11.2.3 Buffers

Control of pH is a very important step in food industries and in food preparations. In the manufacture of bread, the control of pH (between 4.5. and 5.0) is required for the action of amylases on wheat starch. In the processing of fruits and vegetables, if pH is not controlled, browning occurs and there may be change in the colour of green vegetables. The stability of jellies is pH dependent. The activity of enzymes in the manufacture of products like vinegar and cheese is regulated by pH control.

The pH stability is achieved through a buffer system. Buffer solutions have the ability to maintain a relatively constant pH when small amounts of acids or bases are added to them. Strong acids and bases are unsuitable for this purpose. A buffer solution contains a week acid and a salt of that acid or a week base and one of its salts. For example, a solution of acetic acid and sodium acetate contains a large excess of both undissociated acetic acid and acetate ions. When a small amount of base is added, the undissociated acetic acid reacts with the hydroxide ions to form water and more acetate ions.

$$OH^- + CH_3COOH \rightarrow H_2O + CH_3COO^-$$

The addition of a small amount of acid produces a reaction with some of the excess acetate ions.

$$H_3O^+ + CH_3COO^- \rightarrow H_2O + CH_3COOH$$

Both of these reactions go virtually to completion because the reverse reaction has very little tendency to take place, water being very weak both as an acid and as a base. The result is that the solution can resist pH change by removing both the acids and bases (in reasonable amounts) that are added to the solution.

The pH of a buffer solution can be calculated from the dissociation constant of the weak acid. In general, for a weak acid HA, the dissociation constant K_a is expressed as follows:

$$HA \rightleftharpoons H^+ + A^-$$

$$K_a = \frac{[H^+][A^-]}{[HA]}$$

$$\text{or}\,[H+] = K_a \frac{[HA]}{[A^-]} = K_a \frac{[\text{acid}]}{[\text{salt}]}$$

Since the salt in solution is almost completely dissociated, it is assumed equal to the concentration of the conjugate base A^-. The negative logarithm of the above term yields

$$-\log\,[H^+] = -\log K - \log \frac{[\text{acid}]}{[\text{salt}]}$$

By substituting pH for $-\log H^+$ and pK_a for $-\log K_a$ the equation becomes

$$pH = pk_a + \log \frac{[\text{salt}]}{[\text{acid}]} = pK_a + \log \frac{[A^-]}{[HA]}$$

This equation is known as the Henderson - Hassel Bach Equation.

For each buffer mixture there is a pH range over which it acts most effectively. For combinations of common acids and salts, these are: pH 2.1–4.7 for citric acid-sodium citrate, pH 3.0–5.6 for acetic acid-sodium acetate and pH 2.0–3.0, 5.5–7.5 and 10–12, respectively, for the three anions of phosphoric acid. In foods, proteins, organic acids and phosphate salts participate in pH control and buffering systems.

11.3 The Chemical Bond

All matter is composed of atoms. Most substances, however, are not found as independent atoms but exist as groups of atoms, e.g., chlorine (Cl_2), nitrogen (N_2) phosphorus (P_4) and sulphur (S_8), in the form of neutral molecules or as charged species called ions. Ions can be monoatomic, i.e., consisting of only one charged atom, such as a sodium ion (Na^+) and chloride ion (Cl^-), or can be polyatomic (consisting of a group of atoms) with an overall charge such as an ammonium ion (NH^{4+}) and sulphate ion (SO_4^{-2}). The superscript represents the net charge. The molecular or ionic species have properties quite different from those of the individual constituent atoms.

The forces holding together the atoms or ions in a species constitute a chemical bond. The formation of the chemical bond is a result of the electronic structure of the atoms and the minimum potential energy principle. Any object spontaneously tends towards a state of minimum potential energy consistent with its surroundings.

The value of the potential energy of species, such as atoms, ions, electrons and protons, varies with the charge on the species. The species are subject to electrostatic forces (attraction of unlike charges and repulsion of like charges). Thus, the positively charged nuclei of atoms strongly attract their own negatively charged electrons and also attract the electrons of nearby atoms, ions or molecules. There are also repulsive forces when two or more atoms approach one another, due to the positive charges of the nuclei or the negatively charged electrons. If the attractive forces exceed the repulsive forces, the atoms can combine to form a stable molecule, at a state of lower potential energy. Then the atoms are said to have formed a chemical bond. For example, as two hydrogen atoms (H and H) approach one another, attractive forces between unlike charges predominate over repulsive forces between like charges and a stable H_2 (H-H) molecule is formed, with the chemical potential energy at its minimum value.

In an isolated atom, each electron is under the influence of the nucleus and the other extra-nuclear electrons. When two or more atoms come together there is an interaction between the electrons, particularly the valence electrons, of the different combining atoms, and a rearrangement in the orbital occupancy of the valence electrons takes place, giving rise to a more stable state. This re-arrangement, results in bond formation and lowering of the chemical potential energy.

11.3.1 Octet Rule

One group of elements, however, has essentially no tendency to gain or lose electrons. These extremely unreactive elements are the noble gases. The noble-gas structure consists of eight electrons in the outermost orbit for all elements except helium, which consists of only two electrons. Where possible, atoms interact to change the number of electrons in their outer electronic shells to achieve a noble-gas structure. This is known as the octet rule. Although there are exceptions to this simple rule, it accounts for the formation of most known molecules and ions.

A simple way to represent the number of valence electrons of an atom is by an electron dot structure (Lewis structure). It is formed around the standard symbol for the element by writing a dot for each valence in the highest major energy level as indicated below:

H•, Mg:, Äl•, •C̈•, •N̈:, •S̈:, •C̈l:, :N̈e:

The octet rule can be well illustrated with respect to sodium and chlorine atoms. The sodium atom readily loses one electron in the outermost orbit. The resultant sodium ion is a very stable species and has an electronic structural arrangement exactly similar to the stable octet valence electron structure of the noble gas neon.

Na	⟶	Na^+	+	1e
Sodium atom		Sodium ion		Electron

Chlorine gains an electron to complete its outer orbit to a stable configuration of eight electrons.

:C̤̈l:	+	1e	⟶	:C̤̈l:$^-$
Chlorine atom				Chloride ion

According to the octet rule, an atom can achieve a lower potential energy state by gaining, losing or sharing electrons to obtain a stable structure, similar to the nearest noble gas atom. Thus, the octet rule is the basis of three models of chemical bonding—the ionic bond, the covalent bond and the metallic bond. In ionic bonding, one or more electrons are transferred from one atom to another. In the covalent form, electrons are shared between atoms to achieve a noble-gas atomic structure. Actually, most bonds fall somewhere between the two extremes of electron transfer and sharing. Such bonds will be either principally ionic or principally covalent. The metallic bond, which is a bond between atoms of metallic elements, has its own characteristics. Metal and non-metal ions form ionic bonds, non-metals and non-metal atoms form covalent bonds, and metal and metal atoms or ions form metallic bonds.

11.3.2 The Ionic Bond

When one or more electrons are transferred from a metal atom (electron donor) to a non-metal atom (electron acceptor), a positively charged metal ion and a negatively charged non-metal ion are formed. The electrostatic attraction between the two ions results, in an ionic or electrovalent bond. For example, as already explained under the octet rule, a sodium atom can donate an electron and a chlorine atom can accept one. The resulting ions can then interact to form an ionic bond:

$$Na \longrightarrow Na^+ + e^- \qquad E_1$$

$$Cl + e^- \longrightarrow Cl^- \qquad E_2$$

$$Na^+ + Cl^- \longrightarrow Na^+Cl^- \qquad E_3$$

$$Na + Cl \longrightarrow Na^+Cl^- \quad E_1 + E_2 + E_3$$

where, E_1 is the energy required to remove an electron from sodium atom, E_2 is the energy associated with the acceptance of an electron by a chlorine atom, and E_3 is the energy involved in the formation of the chemical bond resulting from electrostatic attraction. The total balance of energy, $E_1 + E_2 + E_3$, is such, that heat is given off; the reaction is exothermic. The product Na^+Cl^- is in a lower energy state than the reactants; hence, a stable compound is formed as a result of the formation of the chemical bond.

Different units of the sodium chloride formed can then join until a lattice or orderly repeating pattern of units is built up to form an ionic solid.

The crystalline structure of most ionic species is a result of strong electrostatic forces of attraction, Because of the strength of these forces, ionic compounds are very stable and have high melting points. Ionic solids do not conduct electricity in the solid state, but in the molten state or in solution they are very good conductors. Ions are not free to move in the solid state.

11.3.3 The Covalent Bond

The bond formed through the sharing of one or more pairs of electrons between two atoms is known as a covalent bond

$$H\cdot + H\cdot \longrightarrow H:H \text{ or } H-H$$

Hydrogen molecule

$$:\ddot{\underset{..}{Cl}}\cdot \quad + \quad :\ddot{\underset{..}{Cl}}: \longrightarrow \ddot{\underset{..}{Cl}}:\ddot{\underset{..}{Cl}}: \text{ or } Cl-Cl$$

Chlorine atom   Chlorine atom   Chlorine molecule

Each atom of the chlorine molecule effectively has eight electrons; because two electrons are shared between two atoms. Often the dots representing a shared pair of electrons (covalent bond) are replaced by a dash. Frequently, the unshared electrons are not shown and only the shared pair or dash is used to represent the covalent bond. In this abbreviated form Cl_2 would be represented as C1:CI or Cl-Cl.

Oxygen and nitrogen molecules are formed through multiple covalent bonds:

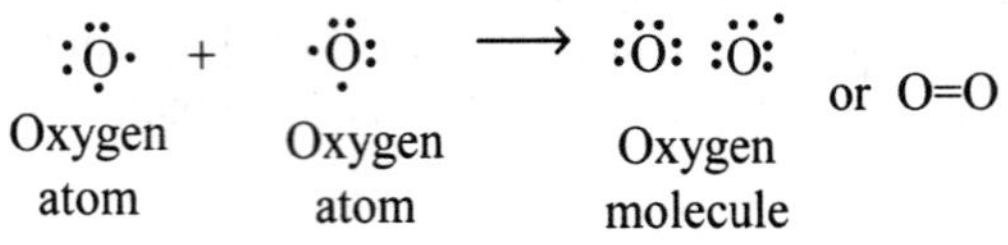

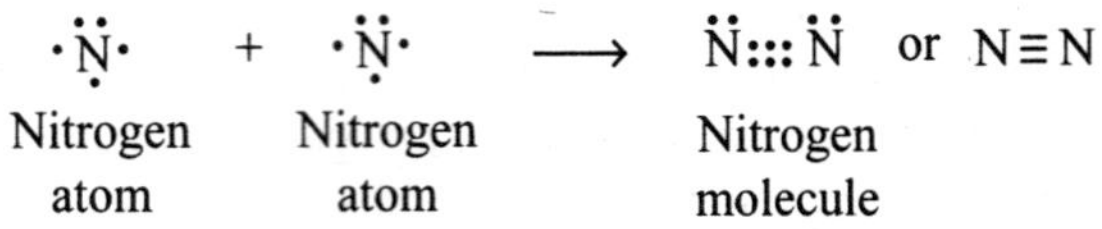

The properties of purely covalent compounds differ in many respects from those of electrovalent compounds. This is because they exist as molecules. The attractive forces between molecules are weaker than the electrostatic forces between ions, since molecules carry no electric charge. Because of the definite length and direction of the bonds, molecules have a definite shape. The melting and boiling points are much lower than those of ionic compounds. Solubility varies widely, but in general they are soluble in non-polar solvents. Solutions are non-ionic and therefore do not conduct electricity, except in cases where reaction occurs with the solvent, e.g., acids and bases.

11.3.4 Polar and Non-polar Molecules

Pure covalent and ionic bondings do exist. However, in a majority of substances there is a blend of the two types of bonds. In metal-non-metal compounds the ionic character tends to predominate. In non-metal-non-metal compounds the covalent bond outweighs the ionic bond. This partial ionic and partial covalent character can be described by the concept of bond polarity and electronegativity.

When two identical atoms share one or more pairs of electrons, as in hydrogen-chlorine or nitrogen molecules, each atom exerts the same attraction for the shared electron pair or pairs. Thus, the electrons are shared equally between the two atoms and the molecule is non-polar and the bond is a non-polar covalent bond.

When two different atoms share one or more electron pairs, as in hydrogen chloride or hydrogen fluoride, one atom will have a greater attraction for electrons than the other owing to the differences in the nuclear charge and the electronic structure of the two atoms. This tendency of each atom to attract, a shared pair of electrons is known as electronegativity. The uneven distribution or sharing of electrons, produces a slightly negative partial charge (represented by δ) on one end of the molecule and a slightly positive charge (represented by δ^+) on the other end of the molecule. But the overall charge of the molecule will be zero. This uneven distribution of charges is known as a dipole and the resulting unsymmetrical covalent bond is a polar covalent bond. The polar covalent molecule with a small negative charge on one atom and a small positive charge on the other can be represented as $^{\delta}H{-}Cl^{\delta-}$.

The polarity of a molecule depends upon the polarity of each bond. For example, carbon dioxide has two separate polar double bonds between carbon and each oxygen atom, O=C=O. The molecule is non-polar because the carbon dioxide molecule is linear and thus the two polar bonds are equal within the molecule and pulling symmetrically in opposite directions. As a result, the two dipoles cancel one another out and there is no net molecular polarity for carbon dioxide. In the case of water, the molecule is bent or angular, and the two dipoles do not cancel one another out. Thus, water has net molecular polarity and is a polar covalent molecule.

11.3.5 The Hydrogen Bond

Molecules that contain -F-H, -O-H or >N-H bonds show a strong tendency to associate, that is, to link up to form larger molecules. This tendency occurs both in the solid form and in solution in certain solvents. The hydrogen attached to a F, O or N atom of one polar covalent molecule is strongly attracted to the F, O, or N atom in another molecule. Water, ammonia and hydrogen fluoride molecules have bonds between them as shown below for water.

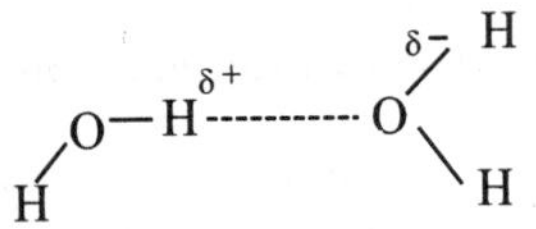

In the above structure, since the hydrogen atom appears to form a linkage between two oxygen atoms, this is known as a hydrogen bond, i.e., the hydrogen atom is attached to two other atoms. But, a hydrogen atom, with only one electron for bond formation, cannot form two covalent bonds. In a molecule such as H_2O, the electron pair in the O-H bond is displaced towards the oxygen nucleus and away from the hydrogen nucleus. This partial ionic character of the O-H bond lends to the hydrogen atom some positive character, permitting an electron from another atom to closely approach the proton even though the proton is already bonded, resulting in a second weaker bond. The hydrogen bond is represented by a dotted line.

A hydrogen bond can not only be intermolecular as shown above with water, it could also be intramolecular (in the same molecule) in such a position that a ring can be formed without disturbing the normal bond angles (e.g., the folding or coiling of starch to form a loop). Hydrogen bonds are comparatively weak, with bond energies of 3–7 Kcal/mole, while that of covalent bonds are about 100 Kcal/mole.

Hydrogen bonds play an important part in determining physical properties, such as solubility, melting point and boiling point, and in effecting the form and stability of crystal structures. Their role in water and the resultant effect on foods has been discussed in Chapter.7. Water can attach itself by hydrogen bonding, either by providing the proton, as in

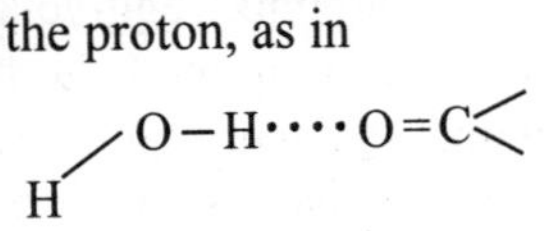

or in accepting the proton, as in

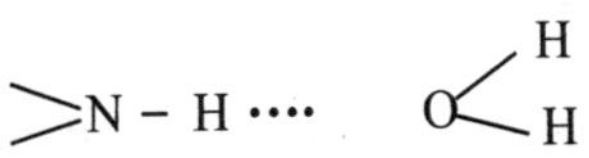

Furthermore, intramolecular hydrogen bonding is one of the chief factors that determine the structure of such important biological substances as proteins, DNA and RNA.

11.4 Colloids

Some categories of foods consist of one or more dispersed or discontinuous phases in a continuous phase. The types of dispersed particles in food include crystals, amorphous solid matter, cell fragments, cells, liquid droplets and gas bubbles. In most cases, the continuous phase is water or an edible oil.

Dispersions are classified on the basis of the size or physical state of dispersed particles. In a solution, the particles are dispersed throughout the solvent in the form of molecules or ions (molecular dispersion) and it is a one-phase system with molecules having dimensions below 1 nm. If the particles range in size from 1 nm to 0.5 μm, they can remain dispersed for a long time without precipitation and constitute a colloidal system. When the size of the dispersed particles is more than 0.5 μm it is termed coarse dispersion or suspension. These systems consist of two or more phases.

Colloidal systems are not restricted to the dispersion of a solid in liquid. Each of the three states of matter can be dispersed in a medium which may be gaseous, liquid or solid. Systems with two phases can occur in eight different combinations and five of them are important in foods (Table 11.2).

Table 11.2 Types of diphasic colloidal dispersion in foods

Dispersed phase	Continuous phase	Name of dispersion	Example
Solid	Liquid	Sol	Skimmed milk, Starch suspension
Liquid	Liquid	Emulsion	French dressing
Gas	Liquid	Foam	Meringue
Gas	Solid	Solid foam	Foam confectionery
Solid	Gas	Aerosol	Smoke for flavouring food

Dispersions involving a solid and a liquid may be either a sol or gel. In a gel, the dispersed solid forms a three-dimensional network in whose interstices the liquid dispersion medium is retained.

Many foods consist of two or three dispersed phases in a continuous phase. For example, whipped cream and mayonnaise are tetraphasic systems with oil droplets, protein particles and gas bubbles as dispersed phases and water as the continuous phase. This system can be termed as emulsion-sol-foam. Depending upon the relative affinity of the dispersed phase for the dispersion medium, colloidal dispersions are divided into two classes. If the affinity between the dispersed phase and the medium is high, the dispersed phase is said to be lyophilic (solvent loving) or hydrophilic in the case of aqueous dispersion. Biopolymers, such as seaweed gum, pectic substances and proteins, and hydrophilic complexes found in skimed milk, egg-yolk and brewed coffee are hydrophilic colloids. If the affinity of the dispersed phase to go into or to remain in colloidal dispersion is slight, the dispersed phase is said to be lyophobic (solvent repelling) or hydrophobic when the medium is water. Lyophobic colloids are mainly aqueous dispersions of inorganic substances rarely encountered in food systems.

11.4.1 Sols

Sols exhibit characteristic optical properties. They may have an opaque or clear appearance to the naked eye and when viewed under a microscope, but the dispersed particles are sufficiently large to scatter and polarize the incident light to some extent. This is, known as the Tyndall effect. The effect is more pronounced in lyophobic sols than in lyophilic sols.

When viewed through an ultramicroscope, colloidal particles appear to be in a state of rapid and irregular motion called the Brownian movement. The movement is caused by the constant bombardment of the dispersed particles by the molecules of the dispersion medium. The smaller the size of the colloidal particles, the more vigorous is its Brownian motion.

In a sol possessing a continuous aqueous phase, the colloidal particles have an electrically charged surface. The ionized groups of proteins and phospholipids can be the sources of these charges. In the presence of a small quantity of dissolved electrolyte, sol particles selectively adsorb ions of one type from the solution. The surface of the particle thus becomes covered with a layer of ions and acquires the charge of the adsorbed ions. This results in an electrical double layer consisting of approximately a single layer of oppositely charged ions adsorbed to the surface of each particle and a diffuse layer of ions distributed in solution near the interface. The resulting potential difference between the surface of the particle and the solution is known as the zeta potential.

The adsorption of ions by colloidal particles is a major factor in stabilizing a colloidal dispersion. Since the colloidal particles in a given system have the same charge, they repel each other, and hence the tendency to coalesce is reduced. Addition of salts to a sol causes precipitation. Salts affect hydrophilic sols by reducing the zeta potential on the particles. Charged particles have strong attraction for the polar water molecules and therefore are hydrated, probably having a complete envelope of water molecules. Addition of salt also helps the withdrawal of water from the hydrated surfaces of the particles and thus helps precipitation.

Sols, unlike solutions, have low osmotic pressure. Thus, they cannot pass through animal membranes or through cellulose walls in plants. In lyophobic sols, there is little interaction between the dispersed phase and the dispersion medium. Consequently, properties like viscosity and surface tension of such sols are the same as those of the dispersion medium at the same temperature. In lyophilic sols, owing to the solvation of the dispersed phase, there is difference in properties. The viscosity of lyophilic sols is greater than that of the dispersion medium and is increased markedly by a decrease in temperature or an increase in particle concentration. At particle concentrations greater than 20 per cent, sols may exhibit elasticity.

11.4.2 Gels

Sols that have a fairly high concentration of dispersed solids change spontaneously into gels. During sol-gel transformation a three-dimensional network is formed by the interlocking of dispersed particles. The liquid phase is entrapped in the interstitial areas of this structure. When this happens, the sol loses its fluidity and becomes a gel. The rigidity of the gel depends on the nature of the links at the sites of junction of dispersed particles. Bonds in the junction zones are electrostatic, hydrophobic, covalent and hydrogen bonds.

The concentration of the jelling agent, the salt content, the pH and temperature, determine the strength, elasticity and brittleness of the gel. Polysaccharides, proteins or colloidal complex particles, such as caseinate micelles, form gels at levels of 10 per cent or less. Gums, pectins and gelatin form firm gels at levels of 1 per cent or lower. Salts and pH influence gel formation adversely or favourably depending upon their concentration. By the reduction in the number of charged particles, by the adjustment of pH or addition of salt, a sol can be transformed into a gel. Addition of sugar which competes with the water of the continuous phase helps gel formation when used in the proper proportion. Change in temperature has an effect on gel formation; a cooler temperature reduces the mobility of the colloidal molecules in the sol, and increases viscosity. This condition facilitates gel formation.

The rigidity of a gel changes with time leading to syneresis, which involves release of water and contraction of gel volume. The amount of liquid released varies with the type of gel and the conditions under which it is prepared.

11.4.3 Emulsions

An emulsion is a colloidal dispersion of one liquid in another immiscible liquid. A food emulsion is basically a two-phase system consisting of a liquid, such as oil, wax or essential oil and water. Most of the dispersed droplets in food emulsions have diameters between 0.1 and 10 μm. There are two types of food emulsions, the oil in water (O/W) and water in oil (W/O). The former type consists of lipid droplets dispersed in water (e.g., milk, cream, ice cream, mayonnaise, salad dressing); the latter is made up of water droplets dispersed in a continuous oil phase (e.g., butter, margarine).

Food emulsions must have the appropriate appearance (colour and opacity), texture (viscosity, plasticity and oiliness) and flavour, for acceptance. Some features of food emulsions are of importance from the point of view of food quality. Oil in water emulsions helps the incorporation of fat-soluble flavouring and colouring matter or vitamins. The opacity of a fluid product can be created by dispersing droplets of very small size (0.05 to 1.0 μm) in the continuous phase. A high degree of plasticity can be achieved, by raising the concentration of the dispersed liquid to about 60 per cent or above. Oil can be introduced into a system without imparting an oily sensation.

Formation of emulsions: The most common method of preparing an emulsion is by mechanically dispersing one liquid phase in another. Formation of small droplets takes place from a beater blade or from passage of the coarse emulsion through a homogenizer. A stable emulsion is not formed by a mere mixing of the liquids. When the emulsion is left to stand, droplets in the dispersed phase coalesce due to surface tension. An emulsifier added to the system would reduce the interfacial tension, enhance the formation of small droplets, and reduce the rate at which droplets coalesce.

Properties of emulsions: The opacity of an emulsion is determined by droplet size, droplet concentration and difference in the refractive indices of the two phases. An emulsion is transparent, when the refractive indices of the two liquids are the same or when the droplet diameter is 0.05 μm or less. An increase in the size of the droplets results in opaqueness which reaches a maximum when the size is 0.05 to 1.0μm.

The viscosity of the continuous phase is a major factor in governing the properties of an emulsion. In many food emulsions, gums are added to the continuous phase to enhance the viscosity and stability of the emulsion. Gum stabilizes an emulsion by being adsorbed at the oil-water interface to form a hydrated film and by increasing the viscosity of the continuous phase.

Since, small droplets of the dispersed phase in an emulsion behave like rigid spheres, their influence on viscosity is slight. The viscosity of an emulsion is usually similar to that of the continuous phase, if this phase constitutes the major portion of the emulsion. However, when the dispersed phase is increased to a volume greater than that of the continuous phase, the viscosity of the emulsion increases. When the volume of the dispersed phase exceeds 74 per cent of the emulsion, the droplets are distorted and the emulsion has a high degree of plasticity.

Stability of emulsions; Emulsions can be stabilized by the use of emulsifiers, finely divided particles adsorbed at the interface, and water-dispersible hydrocolloids.

Food emulsifiers are surface active agents consisting of hydrophilic and hydrophobic moieties. There are both ionic and non-ionic compounds. Some ionic emulsifiers used are salts of fatty acids (sodium stearoyl-2-lactate), phospholipids and proteins. The non-ionic emulsifiers used are mono- and di-esters of propylene glycol and sorbitan esters (prepared by heating sorbitol with fatty acids).

Ionic emulsifiers can react with ions (hydrogen ions, inorganic ions or oppositely charged emulsifier ions) to form complexes which may have reduced emulsifying power and low solubility in both the liquids. In contrast, non-ionic emulsifiers are generally soluble in one of the phases and do not react with ions. For this reason, non-ionic emulsifiers are extensively used in foods.

Many finely divided solids, which do not ordinarily exhibit surface activity, can act as stabilizing agents for emulsions. Hydroxides of magnesium; aluminium and calcium, as well as pumice, silicates, coagulated proteins and plant cell fragments, adsorb at the oil-water interface and function to prevent coalescence.

Hydrocolloids, such as plant gums and gelatin, act as stabilizers in oil-in-water emulsions by increasing the viscosity of the continuous phase and sometimes by forming a strong interfacial film around droplets of the dispersed phase. Pectin, alginates, plant and seed gums, and cellulose derivatives, such as carboxymethyl- , hydroxypropyl- and methylcellulose gums, are used as stabilizers.

11.4.4 Foams

Foams are dispersions of gas bubbles in a liquid, which is the continuous phase. The gas bubbles are separated from each other by liquid walls (films or camellae) that are elastic. The diameters of the foam bubbles range from about 1 μm to several centimetres. Depending on the bubble size and wall thickness, dense or light foams are formed. Whipped cream, ice cream, cake, bread and meringues, are typical food foams. Food foams contain large amounts of entrapped gas. They have an extensive surface area between the gaseous and liquid phase, have a higher concentration of the solute at the surface than in the bulk liquid, have walls which are rigid and elastic, and reflect light so that they have an opaque appearance.

Formation of foam: For the formation of a foam there must be a foaming agent in the continuous phase prior to dispersion of gas. The foaming agent must be adsorbed at the surface to reduce surface tension and provide a distinct surface layer, which resists the coalescence of gas bubbles. Surface active lipids, glucosides, cellulose derivatives and proteins, are used as foaming agents.

Foams are formed by injecting gas into the foaming solution through orifices or by introducing gas while beating the solution. They are also prepared by dissolving the gas under pressure in the solution that is to be foamed. On release of pressure, since dissolved gas leaves and the rest of the gas in the system expands, foam is created.

Foam stability: The collapse of a foam occurs due to the diminishing of liquid in bubble walls. This is caused by gravitational force, a suction effect at the periphery of the walls due to the high curvature, evaporation of the solvent, or by movement of gas bubbles from small bubbles to larger ones.

Foam stability can be enhanced by increasing the elasticity (related to the surface tension) of the bubble wall, by increasing the viscosity of the solution or by introducing particulate matter. Viscosity of the solution can be markedly increased by gums and proteins, such as gelatin. Sometimes sugars are used in the foam to increase viscosity as well as act as sweetening agents. The viscosity of the surface layers can be increased by adding polar foam stabilizers (such as primary alcohols and glycerol ethers) to a solution containing a foaming agent. Surface viscosity is also increased by denaturing of proteins. The denatured proteins orient themselves with their hydrophobic groups directed towards the air phase and their hydrophilic groups towards the water phase. Protein coagulum has a high water-binding capacity and thus contributes to a decrease in the rate of drainage from the foam. Finely divided materials, such as spices and cocoa, with sufficient hydrophobic character can migrate to the foam surface, increase surface viscosity, and enhance foam stability.

Anti-foaming agents: In food industries undesirable foams may be formed. In the concentration of fruit juices, coffee extracts, vegetable oils and syrups, or in fermentative processes, foaming occurs. Excessive foaming leads to the loss of a product and reduced rate of processing. Anti-foaming agents cause the collapse of a foam and retard the formation of additional foam. Water-insoluble dimethyl polysiloxanes (silicon oils) are used as anti-foaming agents in food industries. An anti-foaming agent in a foam spreads as a monolayer and displaces the stabilizing foam film, resulting in the thinning of the bubble walls, and causing bursting.

CHAPTER

12 Beverages

Many liquids or liquorous foods, such as coffee, tea, cocoa, soft drinks and alcohol-containing drinks, are considered beverages. These contain stimulants or flavouring agents that perform some useful functions but are not essential for the proper functioning of the body. Soft drinks are non-alcoholic beverages containing syrup, essences or fruit concentrate that are mixed with water or carbonated water. The basis of all alcoholic drinks is ethyl alcohol, or simply alcohol.

12.1 Coffee (*Coffea*)

Coffee is an evergreen shrub or small tree indigenous to Central Africa and Asia. There are many species of coffee, but three species are of commercial importance: *Coffea arabica*, which supplies the largest and best quality of coffee beans; *Coffea robusta* (*C. canephora*), which yields beans of lower quality; and *Coffea liberica*, whose beans are of still lower quality. *C. arabica* is indigenous to Ethiopia and was introduced to India through Arabia. It is cultivated in South India, mainly in the states of Karnataka, Kerala, and Tamil Nadu. It is best grown in the American tropics, where Brazil is by far the largest producer and exporter of *Arabica* coffee.

Considerable quantities of *C. robusta* are also produced in India because the plant can be cultivated at a lower elevation, is longer living and disease resistant, and the yield of coffee beans is greater than from arabica. The robusta variety gives thick, strong decoction. *C. liberica* has not been popular in India as the plant is susceptible to diseases and the beans have not found favour in the market. Caffeine is present in coffee, tea, soft drinks, chocolates and some nuts. Whether high caffeine intake increases the risk of coronary heart disease is still under study.

12.1.1 Production

The world production of coffee is estimated at 11,064,205 tonnes and 11.1 million tonnes in 2023; 352,000 tonnes in India. In India, Karnataka state produces 0.248 million tonnes and contributes 70.5% to total Indian production. Kerala produces 0.0728 million tonnes and contributes to 20.6% of total India's production. Followed by Tamil Nadu's 0.0187 million tonnes production. For the year 2024 post- blossom estimate is 0.35 million tonnes. India is at sixth place in coffee production; first is Brazil followed by Vietnam, Indonesia, Colombia, Ethiopia, as per 2023.

Coffee flowers are white and sweet-smelling, producing green berries that turn red when ripe. The berry contains a mucilaginous pulp with two greenish-grey seeds or beans, each covered by a thin membrane, a silvery skin, and both are enclosed in a common husk-like membrane or parchment. Sometimes a single bean fills the berry instead of two, when the seed is called a peaberry, since it is like a pea. The berries are picked when ripe. Unripe berries give defective beans (triage) and overripe ones are difficult to beat to a pulp.

12.1.2 Processing

Coffee processing consists of removing the skin, pulp, parchment, and silvery skin. The quality of the final product depends upon the manner of processing. Two methods are employed for processing, viz., the dry and the wet (washed coffee process) methods. In the former method, the berries are sun-dried by spreading them out on drying floors, and the coverings are removed by hulling. The beans are later cured in curing sheds. The product obtained is known in the trade as "cherry" or "native coffee". In the wet method, the ripe fruits are squeezed in a pulping machine which removes the soft outer pulp, leaving a slippery exposed layer of mucilage. The mucilage is removed by spontaneous fermentation. This is sometimes facilitated with added enzymes. The seeds separating from the pulp are washed and subsequently dried to a moisture content of 12 per cent. The wet method gives better quality coffee with a bluish-green colour (green coffee). The green seeds are then graded and packed. Green coffee may be stored for prolonged periods with no adverse effects.

Each variety of coffee has its own flavour and other characteristics. Generally, marketed coffee is a blend of different varieties of coffee beans. The blends are controlled for flavour, aroma, colour, and strength or body of the beverage from the roasted bean.

Roasting: Raw or green coffee has no flavour or aroma and has an unpleasant taste. For use as a beverage, it is roasted, powdered, and brewed, and the aqueous extract is taken as a drink with or without the addition of milk, sugar and other substances. During roasting, many physical and chemical changes occur. The beans swell in size to almost double their original size, the dull-green colour changes to brown and the characteristic coffee aroma develops. The beans lose their hard, horny structure and become brittle, with the outer surface still smooth and firm. During roasting, pressure develops in the beans and this appears to be necessary for the proper emergence of coffee flavour. It is said that pressure holds the initial breakdown products together until the proper stage of roasting is reached, when they react with each other to produce coffee flavour. The flavour is due to a mixture of numerous components rather than that of a definite chemical entity and is produced during roasting. Some moisture is lost during roasting and carbon dioxide is produced in a comparatively large quantity, some of it escaping and some being absorbed within the texture of the roasted bean. Carbohydrates decompose, caramelize and, perhaps in combination with other substances, contribute to the aroma of the beverage produced from the roasted beans. Fatty constituents are also affected, volatile fatty acids are driven off, and complex fats and waxes are cracked to form simple ones. Proteins may be hydrolyzed and give cleavage products. There is little change in the caffeine content of coffee during roasting.

The flavour of roasted coffee, to a large extent, depends upon the manner and extent of roasting. The flavour, and aroma of coffee are best when it is freshly roasted but deteriorate on standing. Coffee exposed to air changes more rapidly than coffee not exposed. The staleness of coffee exposed to air is due to the oxidative changes that take place within certain coffee constituents. This is prevented by the presence of carbon dioxide in roasted coffee. In storage, carbon dioxide is lost and so are the flavour and aroma. Moisture also has a profound effect on the flavour of the coffee. Coffee exposed to moisture loses all its flavour in a relatively short time. The loss of flavour in vacuum-packed coffee or coffee packed under pressure using carbon dioxide is less. Since the loss of flavour and aroma is more in ground coffee than in beans, the roasted beans should be freshly ground to obtain quality coffee. Despite many investigations, it has not been possible to clearly understand the many complex physical and chemical changes taking place during the roasting of coffee beans.

12.1.3 Chemical Composition of Coffee

The constituents of coffee that are important in making a good beverage are the flavour substances, the bitter substances, and caffeine which, is responsible for the stimulating effect of the drink.

Caffeine is present in the coffee bean in both the free and combined states. Its content in the bean varies in different species—*C. arabica* contains 1.0–1.2, *C. robusta* 1.5–2.5 and *C. liberica* 1.4–1.6 per cent. There is a variation in the amount of caffeine in the seeds of the same species from different parts of the world. Caffeine, in addition to stimulation, also contributes to the bitterness of the coffee. The caffeine content of a cup of coffee (150 ml) is about 100 mg. Most people consume three cups of coffee a day and thus 300 mg of caffeine. While caffeine is a stimulant, its excessive use causes undesirable effects on the mental and physical health. It is as much a health hazard as alcohol and nicotine. Chronic caffeine intoxication results in several symptoms (caffeinism), which include sleep disturbance, frequent urination, muscular tension, jitteriness, anxiety, etc. Thus, many people who like the taste of coffee but are afraid of the adverse health effects of caffeine use decaffeinated coffee. By chemical methods, most of the caffeine can be removed from green coffee. Decaffeinated coffee retains most of the characteristic aroma of coffee. The average composition of green and roasted *C. arabica* beans is given in Table 12.1.

Table 12.1 Composition of green and roasted *C. arabica* beans (g for 100 g coffee)

	Moisture	Protein	Fat	Sugar	Dextrose	Ash	Caffeine	Chlorogenic acid
C. arabica (green)	8.98	9.87	12.60	9.55	0.87	3.74	1.08	8.46
C. arabica (roasted)	0.63	11.23	13.59	0.43	1.24	4.56	0.82	4.74

Source: *Wealth of India*, Vol. II, Council of Scientific and Industrial Research (CSIR), New Delhi, India, 1988.

Several organic acids are present in the aqueous extract from green coffee beans, the predominant one being chlorogenic acid and the least predominant acetic acid. During roasting, formic and acetic acid contents are increased and chlorogenic and other acids like citric and malic are partially destroyed. The pH of the coffee brew comes down. Acidity affects coffee flavour, the more acid-tasting the coffee, the better its flavour and aroma. *Robusta* beans produce coffee beverage that is less acid-tasting than the *arabica*-coffee beverage and is generally less desirable so far as taste is concerned.

As already indicated, the flavour of roasted coffee is due to several components to which the name "coffeol" has been given. More than 600 volatile compounds have been identified in roasted coffee. Low-boiling sulphur compounds in coffee are the main flavour contributors. Chlorogenic acid contributes to the body and astringency of the coffee beverage, and its decomposition products contribute to the aroma of coffee. The decomposition products of sucrose contribute much to the colour of the beverage and also, to some extent the aroma, bitterness, and sourness of coffee. Protein decomposition compounds seem to be the major precursors of coffee aroma.

Polyphenolic substances (tannins) present in coffee contribute to the bitterness of the coffee beverage. They are readily soluble at the boiling temperature of the water. There are also other substances present, extracted on boiling, that contribute to the bitter taste and combine with certain metallic salts to give a metallic flavour to the beverage.

12.1.4 Coffee Making

Coffee, fresh from the roaster and ground fresh, makes a good beverage. If it is not possible to roast fresh, it is better to buy small quantities of the powder and keep it covered to exclude air and moisture. The beverage is at its best when freshly brewed. If it is cooled and reheated, it becomes bitter and unpleasant.

Coffee is ground and marketed to suit a range of brewing methods. The basic grinds are fine, medium, and coarse. A variation can be found within each of these categories. Fine grind is used in vacuum coffee makers; medium or drip grind is used for making coffee in a drip pot or by steeping; and coarse grind is used in a percolator. It is always best to match the grind to the coffee-making equipment to obtain a good-quality beverage.

Preparation of coffee beverage of high quality requires that the extraction of caffeine and flavouring materials be maximum and that of tannin minimum. Different methods are used to obtain this object. The methods differ in the type of utensils used and the nature of ground coffee, but they are all based on the principle of bringing ground coffee in contact with hot water to extract the soluble constituents. Whatever the method employed, the vessels used to prepare coffee must be very clean. The material used for coffee making is important. Some metals influence the flavour of the beverage. Stainless steel, glassware and enamelware are preferred. Water used in coffee-making should be soft or of low hardness. A temperature between 85° and 95°C is optimum for preparing coffee. If the water is heated to a boiling point, it over-extracts soluble solids and the beverage is bitter, and there is also a loss of flavour substances. However, pouring boiling water on the coffee powder is permissible, as the temperature drops as soon as the water comes in contact with the grind.

Vacuum coffee: Vacuum coffee is made in a two-part container. The upper compartment holding the coffee has an open tube that extends to the bottom of the lower compartment containing water. By heating water in the lower compartment, sufficient pressure is created in the bottom container to force water through the coffee grind into the upper compartment. When the water and grounds are in contact for about 3 min., the heat is reduced on the lower compartment resulting in reduced pressure and the brewed coffee is pulled down to the bottom compartment. Powdered coffee is usually prevented from pouring into the lower compartment by the use of a cloth-covered disk, held in place over the tube opening. The advantage of vacuum coffee is its convenient preparation; its disadvantage is that the coffee prepared thus is slightly bitter because the water and grounds are in contact for a few minutes at a high temperature.

Drip coffee: Drip coffee is made in a dripolator (coffee filter) consisting of an upper compartment that is perforated and a lower compartment that receives the filtered coffee. The perforation of the upper compartment is covered with a thin cheesecloth or a perforated disc with a stem to prevent the passage of the grind into the beverage. Drip-grind coffee is placed in the upper compartment, and boiled water is poured into the compartment. The water drips or flows through the grind into the lower compartment. The drip method is easy and is used by a majority of people. This method extracts fewer bitter substances and retains more flavour constituents than other methods.

Percolator coffee: Percolator coffee is made by placing coarse ground coffee in a basket suspended on a stem near the top of the percolator and then inserted into it. Cold water is placed in the lower part of the percolator and heated. The heated water is forced up the tube of the percolator and sprays on the grounds, extracting the soluble materials. The usual percolation time is 6 to 8 min. Percolator coffee is likely to be somewhat bitter because very hot water goes through the grounds several times. Also, the constant aeration of the brew as the liquid is forced up and sprayed over the grounds results in the loss of flavour.

Steeped coffee: This coffee (misnamed as boiled coffee) is made by heating water and medium-ground coffee without allowing it to boil. If coffee is boiled, it becomes bitter. Steeping time is about 6–8 min. During steeping, the coffee pot should be lightly covered to prevent loss of volatile flavouring compounds. The coffee is then passed through a strainer. This method of making coffee is convenient since no special equipment is required. If care is taken not to boil it, the beverage will have a good aroma and desirable flavour and will not be bitter.

Espresso coffee: This is made by a special machine that brews the beverage a cup at a time. It is derived from brewing finely ground coffee with a mixture of steam and hot water.

Cappuccino: Cappuccino is made by topping one-third espresso, with one-third steamed milk and one-third frothed milk.

French drip: This is another form of drip coffee-making but without the paper filter. A porcelain coffee serving pot has a separate top that acts as the strainer for coffee grounds after hot water is poured onto them. The coffee liquid then trickles through this top section into the lower receptacle.

French press: This method utilises coffee infusion. Ground coffee is placed in the glass beaker, hot water is added and allowed to steep down. The tightly attached fitting and plunging device is then pushed to the bottom of the beaker, where the grounds are trapped, and above this sits the coffee.

Cold water method: This very simple method creates a coffee liquid by soaking the coffee grounds in cold water for 10-20 hours, depending on the strength. The coffee and grounds are strained, and the concentrated liquid is then stored in a refrigerator for several weeks.

Iced coffee: This is made by pouring a freshly made strong coffee infusion over crushed ice. The infusion is obtained by using more coffee grounds per cup. This offsets the dilution that takes place as the ice melts in the hot beverage, resulting in a pleasing beverage with a distinctive flavour.

12.1.5 Soluble Coffee

Soluble coffee is a dry, powdered, water-soluble solid made from a very strong coffee brew. It is marketed as "instant" and "freeze-dried" coffee. Instant coffee is made by the vacuum spray drying of the brew from ground coffee obtained from the percolation method. Freeze-dried coffee is made by first freezing the strong brewed coffee and then drying by vaporization in a vacuum. Instant coffee has a flavour similar to freshly brewed coffee but lacks the aroma of the fresh beverage. Attempts are being made to improve aroma by using additives. Freeze-dried coffee is available in granulated form, the particle size being roughly that of ground coffee. Attempts to recover the volatile aromatic substances lost during the processing of the coffee brew and add them to freeze-dried coffee to obtain a product with an aroma similar to that of freshly brewed coffee have been fairly successful. Though India is producing and exporting instant coffee, we have not yet made freeze-dried and granulated coffee. The world export of soluble coffee amounts to around 3,00,000 tonnes of green coffee equivalent.

Chicory (*Cichorium intybus*) is a well-known substitute for coffee, often used for blending (up to 50 per cent) with the latter in liquid coffee extracts. It gives bitterness to the beverage, which some people find it refreshing. The part of the plant used is the root which is chopped, roasted and ground.

12.2 Tea (*Camellia sinensis*)

Camellia is an evergreen shrub or tree, that grows wild from India to China. There are about 45 species of Camellia of which *Camellia sinensis*, considered native to India, is the important one from which tea of commerce is made. Commercial tea is obtained from plants propagated by seed sown in a nursery; cuttings can also be rooted. Trees for plucking are regularly pruned to obtain a bush shape, which encourages maximum leaf production. Among cultivated *C. sinensis,* there are two types: "China" and "Indian". The former type is a slow-growing, smaller tree with narrow leaves, while the latter is fast-growing with large, drooping leaves. The yield from the Indian type is higher than that of the China type. The important tea-growing countries are India, China, Sri Lanka, Japan, and Kenya.

Tea leaves are usually plucked by hand. The average interval between pluckings is about a week. In India, about 5–6 pluckings are made in a season. Usually, the terminal bud and two terminal leaves from the end of each shoot are plucked. In some cases, the bud and three leaves are taken giving a higher yield and it is a poorer quality product. Some of the best teas come from high-altitude areas, such as Darjeeling, while teas from the plains are often of common quality. The yield at high elevation is poor compared to that at lower elevation for the same kind of plant.

12.2.1 Production

Tea is indubitably Chinese, and both the world *teh* and *cha* are of Chinese origin. Cultivation of tea has been practiced for 2000 years.

The world production of tea is estimated at 6.8 million tonnes and India produced 1.365 million tonnes in 2023; China is the largest tea producer in the world with 3.181 million tonnes in 2023. India imported 1.8 million kg of tea into India during 2023. India ranked second in the world production of tea next to China in the year 2023.

12.2.2 Processing

Commercial tea is available mainly in three forms; black tea, green tea, and oolong tea. The three forms of tea differ only in the method of processing the leaves. Black tea is by far the most popular among the three.

Black tea: The various processing steps in the manufacture of black tea are withering, rolling, fermentation, drying, grading, and packing. Withering is carried out by spreading tea leaves thinly on racks or shelves to dry the leaves partially. Generally, withering is allowed till the water content in the leaf is lowered by about 40 per cent. The withered leaves are then rolled to break open the cells and release the juices and enzymes. Various rolling techniques are employed and the flavour characteristics inherent in various teas partially depend on the technique used. After rolling, the leaves are shifted and spread out thinly on suitable platforms and allowed to ferment for 2–6 hours at temperatures between 21° and 27°C. During this process, the enzymes bring about the oxidation of the various polyphenols present in the juices, resulting in the change of colour from green to reddish copper. Two of the important polyphenols that undergo oxidative changes are catechin and gallocatechin.

When the fermentation has proceeded to the desired degree, further change is arrested by drying or firing. This comprises the passing of the fermented leaves through a chamber in which hot air is circulating. At the entrance of the chamber, the temperature is 93°C which drops to about 49°C near the exit. The time required for this process is about 30–40 minutes and the dried product contains 3–4 per cent moisture. Besides halting the fermentation process, firing causes some caramelization to occur, resulting in the characteristic colour of black tea leaves.

The aroma of tea is believed to develop during the fermentation and firing processes. Although a large number of volatile compounds have been identified from tea leaves, none has been found to make any significant contribution to the tea aroma.

The dried product is cleaned and sorted into various grades of tea for commerce. The quality of black tea is related to the polyphenol and enzyme content of the leaves used in processing. They are maximum in the buds and the first and the second leaves (28, and 27 per cent respectively) and teas obtained from these are the most desirable. On this basis, tea is categorized as "leaf" grade and "broken" grade. The broken grade comprises the smaller sizes sifted from bulk or those obtained by cutting the longer leaf grades to desirable sizes. Both leaf grade and broken grade are further categorized as orange pekoe and pekoe souchong. Orange pekoe and pekoe refer to the size of the leaf only. Orange pekoe has the largest leaves, followed by pekoe souchong in decreasing order. Orange pekoe is perhaps the best quality.

Other things being equal, the broken grades usually give a stronger tea than the leaf grade. Besides the above grade, there are the waste products—fannings and dustings.

Tea is generally blended before it reaches the consumer. In India, the blended tea is packed in plywood boxes lined with aluminium foil and parchment paper. During packing, tea absorbs moisture. If the moisture content increases to 6–7 per cent, tea is to be subjected to a second firing before packing. India is also exporting tea in consumer tea packs instead of bulk tea chests.

Green tea: Green tea is made in the same manner as black tea, but the withering and fermentation steps are omitted. The leaves are heat-treated, rolled, and dried. The heat treatment consists of pan-firing or steaming to inactivate the enzymes. The aroma, flavour and colour of green tea are significantly different from those of black tea. Green tea is a light, yellow-green beverage when brewed correctly. The Japanese mainly produce and consume green tea.

Oolong tea: Oolong tea is an intermediate between black and green tea in colour and taste characteristics. Its production method is similar to that employed for green tea, except that the leaf is slightly withered and light fermentation is allowed before the leaf is dried.

White tea: White tea is made from young leaves that have not undergone oxidation. The buds may be shielded from sunlight to prevent the formation of chlorophyll. White tea is produced in lesser quantities than most of the other types.

Yellow tea: Either used as a name of high-quality tea served at the Imperial Court of Japan or of special tea processed similarly to green tea but with a slower drying phase.

Kukicha: Also called winter tea, kukicha is made from twigs and old leaves pruned from the tea plant during its dormant season and dry roasted over a fire. It is popular as a health food in Japan and in macrobiotic diets.

12.2.3 Composition of Tea

The important constituents of tea contributing to the flavour of the tea beverages are caffeine, polyphenols, and essential oils. Analysis of fresh leaves of Indian tea gives the following values: Polyphenols, 22.2;

protein, 17.2; caffeine, 4.3; crude fibre, 27.0; starch, 0.5 and ash, 5.6 per cent. Fresh tea leaf also contains carotenes, B-vitamins and ascorbic acid. During the manufacture of black tea, ascorbic acid is lost.

The maximum amount of caffeine is present in the bud and the first two leaves. Small quantities of compounds related to caffeine, viz., theophylline, theobromine, xanthine and hypoxanthine are also present.

The important polyphenols present in tea leaves are catechins and gallocatechin. These undergo changes during fermentation in black tea manufacture. Enzymes involved in fermentation are polyphenol oxidases.

No change takes place in green tea as its manufacture does not involve fermentation. During fermentation, polyphenols undergo oxidation and the oxidized products polymerize and part of them combine with caffeine. The caffeine-polyphenol complexes are soluble only in hot water and this accounts for the "creaming" observed when hot tea infusions are cooled.

Tea leaves contain a volatile oil consisting of alcohols, aldehydes, phenols and some fatty acids. On steam distillation, black tea gives an essential oil. The characteristic aroma and flavour of tea are due to the essential oil.

Tea, like coffee, has no nutritive value. The proteins present in tea leaves are rendered insoluble in the processing. Tea infusion contains negligible quantities of carbohydrates and fat. Whatever nutritive value tea has, comes from added milk and sugar. Tea as a beverage is consumed mainly for its stimulating value.

12.2.4 Preparation of Tea

A good cup of tea will be sparklingly clear and not have a surface film. It should have maximum flavour with minimum polyphenol compounds, which contribute to bitterness. In order to obtain this, the water used in making tea should be fresh and soft. If water is hard, the dissolved salts form an undesirable precipitate with polyphenols and this will be present as an unattractive film that floats on the surface of tea. The water should be freshly boiled but still contain sufficient oxygen to give the tea a fresh and pleasant odour. Metallic teapots impart a metallic flavour. It is best to use China, glass or enameled ware. Water heated to 85°C boiling should be added to the appropriate amount of tea (generally one teaspoonful for 150 ml contained in the pot). The pot should be covered with a lid that helps retain the heat and prevents the escape of volatile compounds. Flavour substances and caffeine are readily extracted by short infusion periods. Generally, a steeping period of about 3 min. gives a stimulating, but not astringent, beverage.

A very convenient method of making tea is by the tea-ball or bag method. In this method, water at the boiling temperature is poured over tea contained in a cheesecloth or paper bag or a silver ball. The bag or ball is allowed to remain in contact with water till the desired strength is obtained. Milk or lemon may be added to the tea infusion for body and flavour, and sugar for taste.

Iced tea: Iced tea is popular in some countries. Hot tea is prepared in the usual way by using twice as much tea leaves. The hot tea is thoroughly chilled before pouring it over ice. It may also be poured over ice while it is still hot. This will result in a beverage that dilute to normal strength as ice melts. Cloudiness is generally a problem with iced tea, as tannins precipitate when tea cools.

12.2.5 Instant Tea

Instant tea (soluble tea) products have become popular in recent times. These products are hot and cold water-soluble, iced tea concentrates, carbonated tea, etc. In the preparation of hot water-soluble instant tea, the fermented tea leaves are extracted with hot water, centrifuged, and dried in a drum dryer or freeze dryer. For the manufacture of cold water-soluble tea, the aqueous extract is cooled to 5°C, the separated caffeine-polyphenol compound is removed by centrifugation and then it is dried. Iced tea concentrate is cold water-soluble and contains sugar, citric acid and essences. Ready tea is instant tea with sugar and milk powder. India produces all these varieties of instant tea, and sizeable quantities are exported. The export in 2021–22 was 201 million kg.

Instant tea is largely used in making iced tea because of its solubility in cold water. However, the flavour, and aroma of instant tea are less full than those of the beverage freshly prepared from tea leaves.

12.2.6 Herbal Tea

It is a herbal infusion not made from leaves of the tea bush but from fresh or dried flowers, leaves, seeds or roots, generally by pouring boiling water over the plant parts and letting them steep for a few minutes.

12.2.7 Tea Bags

Tea bags were invented way back in 1908. Tea leaves are packed into small (usually paper) tea bags. It is easy and convenient, making tea bags popular for many people nowadays.

12.2.8 Tea Sticks

One of the modern forms of tea consumption, an alternative to the common tea bags, is tea sticks.

12.2.9 Blended and Unblended Varieties

Various blended and unblended teas that have achieved fame for their characteristic flavours include Assam, Darjeeling, and Keemun, also known as English breakfast tea. Popular blended teas include Irish breakfast, Russian style and Earl Grey.

12.3 Cocoa (*Theobroma cocoa*)

The cocoa plant is a small tree native to the American tropics. It is now grown in all tropical regions of the world. The chief cocoa-producing countries of the world are Ghana, Nigeria, Ivory Coast and Brazil. Cocoa was introduced to India from Sri Lanka and is a comparatively new crop. Its production is fast picking up, and it is grown in Kerala, Karnataka, and, to some extent, in Tamil Nadu.

The cocoa tree has the unusual habit, like the jackfruit tree, of bearing its flowers and, subsequently, its pods on the main trunk as well as on the branches. Cocoa pods, when mature, are yellow in some varieties and red in others. The pods are 10 to 18 cm in diameter, having thick leathery rinds containing 20–50 beans inside in rows. The seeds are embedded in white or pinkish pulp. Seeds are the principal source of cocoa or cocoa powder, highly prized as a nutritious beverage and as chocolate used as a food supplement the world over.

12.3.1 Production

Both the terms "cocoa" and "chocolate" derive from words in the Maya language of South America. While the equatorial slopes of the Andes were home to theobroma cacao, the center of civilization, about 2000 years ago, was Central America. The types of beans are recognised; criollo-large, plump beans, round in cross-sections, forastero-flattened bean the third variety of coca has a crossed ancestry, yields a fine cocoa. The world production of cocoa is estimated at 5.6 million tonnes and India is 0.03 million tonnes in 2023; India produced 0.03 million tonnes. Côte d'Ivoire is the largest cocoa producer in the world, with 2.377 million tonnes in 2023.

12.3.2 Processing

Cocoa pods, after harvesting, are cautiously opened. The beans and mucilage are scooped out and subjected to natural fermentation either in heaps, wooden boxes (sweat boxes), or baskets. Fermentation generally takes five to ten days. At the end of fermentation, the pulp breaks down, and there is a change in the colour of the seeds from pale yellow or violet to brown. The endogenous enzymes, activated by the heat of fermentation, bring about changes in proteins and polyphenols in the kernel, and there is also a reduction in the astringency of the kernel. The beans are then dried to six to eight per cent moisture level in the sun or in artificial dryers. The bean is then ready for export or further processing to manufacture cocoa products.

The dried beans are cleaned, sorted, and roasted. Roasting develops the characteristic flavour of cocoa. Although a large number of compounds have been identified in cocoa and chocolate, no single constituent is found responsible for the characteristic subtle aroma. Roasting also causes changes in the chemical structure of polyphenols, producing less astringent compounds. While roasting, the beans are passed through corrugated rollers to break their shells and removed by winnowing. The cotyledons are known as "nibs." Usually, some blending of the nibs from different varieties of cocoa is done before they are processed further.

The nibs are used for the manufacture of cocoa and chocolate. The nibs are ground in stone mills or other suitable mills to a fine paste or liquor. The heat produced during grinding causes cocoa fat to melt and the melted fat carries with it, in suspension, finely ground particles of cocoa. This is known as "cocoa mass," "chocolate liquor", or "bitter chocolate." This mass solidifies at about 30°C.

Cocoa mass is very rich (50–55 per cent) in fat and cannot be used directly for the preparation of any beverage. It is subjected to filter-pressing to separate out a major part of the fat (cocoa butter). The amount of fat left in the pressed cake can be varied by changing the conditions of pressing. The pressed cake is used for producing cocoa powder. The fat content of cocoa used for beverages is fixed by law. According to Indian Standards Institution (ISI) specifications, cocoa used for beverage should contain 20 per cent cocoa fat. Medium-fat cocoa, containing between 10 and 20 per cent fat and low-fat cocoa, containing less than 10 per cent fat, are both made. Flavouring substances like vanilla and cinnamon are generally incorporated into cocoa powder.

The pressed cake, after the removal of cocoa butter, contains 1.8–11.3 per cent free acids. In one of the methods of cocoa processing, the acid is neutralized with the addition of a requisite amount of alkali. This is known as the "Dutch process" because it originated in Holland. Cocoa processed by this method is dark in colour and the flavour will be somewhat more bitter and astringent than the same material not treated with alkali.

Chocolate: Cocoa mass not treated with alkali is generally used for the manufacture of chocolate. There are many types of chocolate depending upon the level of cocoa mass, added cocoa butter, sugar, milk, and other ingredients. Plain chocolate (sweet chocolate) is cocoa mass processed with cocoa butter and sugar. Milk chocolate contains, in addition to these ingredients of plain chocolate, milk solids. Plain chocolate contains 40–55 per cent sugar and 32–42 fat, while milk chocolate contains 35–55 per cent sugar, 28–39 per cent fat and 12 per cent milk solids. Plain and milk chocolate are extensively used in confectionery and ice cream.

12.3.3 Composition

An analysis of cocoa beans (processed) gives the following values: moisture, 2.13 per cent; fat, 54.68 per cent; total nitrogen, 2.16 per cent; starch, 6.14 per cent; pentosans, 11.19 per cent; and tannins, 6.15 per cent. The total nitrogen includes protein, theobromine, and related alkaloids. The theobromine content of cocoa is high (about 2.8 per cent). Cocoa is the natural source of theobromine. There is some loss of theobromine content during fermentation and roasting. Cocoa also contains caffeine (about 0.6 per cent). The proteins of the cocoa bean are present in combination with polyphenols. Unlike coffee and tea, which are strained forms of beverages, cocoa and chocolate remain in the beverage and contribute to the nutritive value of the beverage. Because of their high content of fat, cocoa products are a good source of energy. Milk, the usual constituent of cocoa and chocolate drinks, adds to the nutritive value of the beverage. The theobromine and caffeine contribute to the stimulating effect of the beverage.

Cocoa butter: Cocoa butter, which accounts for more than 54-58 per cent of the cocoa bean, is a valuable by-product of the cocoa industry. The world trade in 2023 in cocoa butter was 0.252 million tonnes. The butter is mostly used in the manufacture of chocolate.

The butter is a pale yellow liquid with a characteristic odour and the flavour of chocolate. It is brittle at temperatures below 25°C, softens in the hand and melts (34°C) in the mouth. It is not greasy to touch. It is rich in saturated fatty acids (palmitic and lower acids 26.21 per cent, stearic and higher acids 34.4 per cent). Oleic and linoleic acids are present to the extent of 37.3 per cent and 2.1 per cent, respectively. The butter keeps well due to the presence of fat-soluble antioxidants in it.

12.3.4 Cocoa Beverages

Cocoa and chocolate, apart from their many uses in foods, find extensive use in the preparation of beverages. When chocolate is used, it sticks to the container and gets scorched when heated. This can be eliminated by heating chocolate over hot water or by heating it at a low temperature. The melted chocolate is then blended with other ingredients. Owing to its high starch content, cocoa will lump if put directly into a hot liquid. It should be mixed with a small amount of cold liquid before being combined with other ingredients. Cocoa and chocolate thus treated are heated to boiling and held at that temperature for some time to gelatinize the starch. This gives body and flavour to the beverage and reduces the amount of sediment that settles from either of the beverages.

Apart from coffee, tea, and cocoa, several branded preparations are available in the market, such as Ovaltine, Bournvita, Boost, etc., which are consumed as hot drinks. While the former group of beverages are stimulants, the latter are energy foods and are consumed as supplementary to a regular diet. They contain mainly malted cereals, creamy milk, sugar, and artificial flavours, and sometimes are fortified with nutrients and minerals. Some preparations also contain cocoa. The drink is prepared by stirring the material in warm water or milk and is generally consumed as a hot drink, but it could also be used as a cold drink.

12.4 Soft Drinks

In recent years, there has been a growing demand for alternatives to sugar-heavy soft drinks. "Diet soft drinks" are sweetened with chemicals, usually aspartame, saccharin, and acesulfame potassium. These artificial sweeteners are, however, of a controversial nature, as many of them are claimed to cause cancer or other disorders.

Some scientists have pointed out that a range of foods in India contains pesticides and that the problem is not specifically with soft drinks as such but with the lack of proper controls on pesticide use in the food chain generally. They say many Indian foods and beverages have high levels of pesticides because intensive use of these chemicals by farmers has contaminated the groundwater. They are asking the government to focus on the wider issue of pesticide proliferation.

The average amount of pesticide residues found in all the samples of soft drinks tested in 2006 was 11.85 parts per billion (ppb)—24 times higher than the BIS standards for total pesticides in soft drinks (0.5 ppb).

Following international trends, consumer preferences in India shifted towards healthier drinks during the review period. Carbonates began to decline as consumers switched to fruit/vegetable juice and bottled water. The lingering effects of the discovery of pesticides in carbonates in 2003 took its toll while consumers began to look for healthier alternatives. Furthermore, an increase in school and college awareness about the alleged harmful effects of carbonates was caused by the pesticides controversy, and this is also encouraging people to switch to healthier alternatives.

As carbonates took a beating, so did overall soft drinks, as total volume growth for 2005 came down to single digits for the first time in almost a decade. Various soft drinks and other healthy alternatives are eroding sales of carbonates, including flavoured milk drinks, fruit/vegetable juice, and bottled water. The improved distribution of bottled water and a wider availability of juice drinks at entertainment centres has attracted customers previously addicted to carbonated colas.

Sales of fruit/vegetable juice were also boosted in 2005 by the changing lifestyles of the Indian middle-income group. More women going to work and having to travel long distances prefer readily available packaged fruit/vegetable juice rather than preparing their own juice for breakfast.

Soft drinks are, however, expected to see a robust volume growth over the forecast period. This will occur despite a total volume and constant value decline for carbonates. Growth will be led by bottled water and, from a smaller base and with slower growth, fruit/vegetable juice. Health and convenience are predicted to be the two most important factors affecting buying behaviour, as carbonates and concentrates play second fiddle to healthier bottled water and fruit/vegetable juice. The important thing to remember is that over-consumption of soft drinks should be avoided because of their numerous harmful effects, such as obesity, osteoporosis, nutritional deficiencies, and tooth decay. It is important to be aware of the harmful effects of such deleterious beverages.

Soft drinks constitute one of the largest food industries in the world today. Tremendous advances have taken place in process technology in the soft drink industry in the past one or two decades.

In India, in the organized sector alone, the annual production of soft beverages is about 45 million cases. The flavoured component of most of the well-known brands of soft drinks is a well-guarded secret. The most popular soft drinks sold throughout the world today are "cola" (an extract from the cola tree), orange, root beer, ginger, lemon, and lime. Most of the cold drinks sold in the country belong to this class.

Soft drinks are divided into three classes: carbonated, fruit-flavoured (still) and sparkling (soda water). The carbonated beverages, in turn, are divided into two groups: those with artificial flavour and those with natural fruit juice.

12.4.1 Ingredients

The major ingredients of soft drinks are (i) sugar and sugar substitutes, (ii) flavour emulsion and cloudifiers, (iii) colouring agents, (iv) acids and preservatives, (v) water and (vi) carbon dioxide. A quality soft drink should have a balanced blend of flavour at the proper intensity leaving a clean mouth taste with no lingering flavour or unpleasant aftertaste, and should have proper carbonation to impart zest and sparkle to the drink.

The process of manufacturing carbonated beverages consists of several steps: Syrup is prepared from sugar or substitutes and water. To the syrup, acids, colour and flavouring agents are added as required.

The components are blended. A suitable aliquot of the mixture is diluted with chilled carbonated water and bottled. Alternatively, the ready syrup is diluted, chilled, carbonated, and then filled in the bottle. The bottles are then capped, labelled, and marketed.

Sugars: The sugar and sugar substitutes contribute the sweetness necessary to balance the various ingredients, give body and mouthfeel, and also act as carriers to distribute the flavour components uniformly throughout the drink. The sugar component also contributes to the food value of the beverage and, to some extent, to the flavour. Sucrose is the most widely used sweetening agent. Some sweetening agents, like cyclamates, which were being used formerly, are now banned as they are found to be harmful. Because of the high cost of crystalline sugar, sugar syrups are used as sweeteners. Fructose syrup (processed from cornstarch) or high-fructose corn syrup (HFCS) is used these days. 55 per cent fructose corn syrup has approximately the same sweetness as sucrose, while 90 per cent fructose syrup is approximately 50 per cent sweeter than sucrose. Use of fructose syrup in soft drink manufacture has other advantages; it permits a substantial reduction in the calorie content of the drink and also reduces the cost of the drink. Fructose syrup is not yet available in India.

Flavouring materials: Three types of flavouring materials are used in soft drinks: those obtained from natural sources, such as fruit concentrates or extracts from natural flavour materials; synthetic compounds identical to those obtained from natural products; and synthetic chemicals not found in nature. Most flavours, however, are wholly natural or a blend of natural and synthetic materials identical to those found in nature. The flavouring agents should have complete solubility, compatibility, a clean mouthfeel without an aftertaste, resistance to acid and heat, and stability to light. Flavours are used generally emulsified in vegetable gums. This prevents the flavour substances (particularly oils) from separating out in the beverages.

Colouring materials: These are used in soft drinks in order to maintain a uniform colour in the beverage from batch to batch. In some cases, colour is derived from the flavouring substances used. Generally, synthetic food colours and natural colouring ingredients like caramel are used. Caramel in beverages gives them a dark to light brown colour and is usually associated with flavour of the type derived from roots, leaves, herbs and berries.

Acids and preservatives: Acids, in addition to taste, enhance the flavour of soft drinks. The acid most widely used is citric acid. Other acids used in considerable quantities are tartaric and phosphoric acids. Lactic and malic acids are also used in lesser amounts. Citric acid (present in citrus fruits) adapts itself well to nearly all light and fruity flavours. Phosphoric acid is used in beverages with leaf, root, nut, or herbal flavours. Tartaric acid (present in grapes) is used in grape flavours.

The acids, besides giving taste and flavour, also act as mild preservatives. However, to ensure against spoilage, sodium benzoate is commonly used as a preservative.

Water: Water constitutes the largest (about 92 per cent) component of soft drinks. Water used in beverage manufacture must be free from suspended matter and colouring matter. It should not contain minerals that would interfere with the flavour and colour of the beverage. It should also be free from objectionable odours. Thus, water used should conform to the specification set for beverages.

Carbon dioxide: Carbon dioxide is an important constituent of soft drinks. The gas used must be absolutely pure. It enhances the flavour of the beverage and gives it its sparkle. It also extends the life of the drink. The level of carbonation is determined by the flavour component and quality of flavour.

Carbonated beverages are mostly packaged in bottles. In some countries they are also packed in cans with a pull-ring top. Besides glass bottles and cans, plastic containers (polyethylene terephthalate, PET) are coming into use. Glass bottles are covered with crowns lined with PVC or cork. In recent times, glass containers are being covered with a foil lid.

12.5 Fruit Beverages

There has been a considerable increase in the consumption of fruit and vegetable juices in the world during the last few years, and there are possibilities of its further increase. The export of fruit juices from developing countries has been increasing steadily. In India, foreign exchange earnings from fresh and processed fruit pulps and juices amounted to US $986.32 million in 2023-24.

The beverage industry is by far the largest outlet for fruit juice and concentrates, absorbing over 80 per cent of production. In India a little over 60 per cent of the fruit produced is used in fruit-based beverages. Many different types of beverages, such as fruit juices, fruit drinks, squashes, cordials, and fruit punches, are available. They are broadly defined as follows:

Fruit juice: This is a natural juice pressed out of fruit. This is unaltered in its composition during preparation and preservation.

Fruit drink: This is made by liquefying the whole fruit, and at least 10 per cent of the volume of undiluted drink must be whole fruit. It may be diluted before being served.

Fruit squash: This consists essentially of strained juice containing moderate quantities of fruit pulp to which sugar is added for sweetening, e.g., orange squash, lemon squash, mango squash, etc.

Fruit cordial: This is fruit squash from which all suspended material is completely eliminated and is perfectly clear, e.g., lime juice cordial.

Fruit punches: These are made by mixing the desired fruit juices at the time when they are served.

Fruit juice concentrate: This is fruit juice that has been concentrated by the removal of water either by heat or by freezing.

Sherbets: This is a cooling drink of sweetened and diluted fruit juice.

Fruit juices are valuable from the nutritional point of view; they are rich in minerals, vitamins, and other nutritive factors. Besides, fruit juices are delicious and have a universal appeal. In developed countries, fruit juices commonly form part of the breakfast and are produced in very large quantities. (In the USA, the annual production of juices is more than 50 crore kilolitres.) Fruit juices do not form the normal diet in our country, and the fruit juice industry is in its infancy in India. Preparation of the juice is limited mostly to home-scale production. The fruits generally used for making juice are orange, grape, apple, pomegranate, melon, mango, etc. Of late, the manufacture of squashes on a commercial scale has made some progress.

Fruit juices are best in taste, aroma, and colour, when freshly expressed. The most important problem, therefore, in the fruit juice industry is to use such methods as would help retain these properties to the maximum extent. The steps involved in the processing of juice are selection of fruit, extraction of juice, deaeration, straining, and preservation.

Freshly picked, sound, and suitable varieties of fruits are selected and thoroughly washed. The juice is extracted by crushing and pressing the fruits; while extracting the fruit juice, fruit components other than sacs or cells in which juice is present are to be avoided as far as possible. Further, the juice should not be unduly exposed to air. The juice (particularly pure orange juice, which is susceptible to the action of air) is immediately deaerated by subjecting it to a high vacuum. After deaeration, the vacuum is released with nitrogen gas, and the juice is transferred into containers that are hermetically sealed and frozen. Fruit juices in sealed containers keep well for about 2 years in the frozen condition. In the alternative, the fruit juice is spray-dried.

When clear juice is required, the juice is strained and complete removal of all suspension is effected by filtration and clarification. Clarification needs the removal of colloidal suspensions of the fruit juice. This can be brought about by freezing, heating, use of enzymes or of finning agents. The fining agents produce a voluminous flocculent precipitate which gradually settles, carrying down with it colloidal suspensions. The clarified juice, as in the case of whole fruit juice, is preserved by freezing, pasteurization or the addition of chemical preservatives, such as sodium benzoate or bisulphite.

12.6 Alcoholic Beverages

Alcoholic beverages have been known since antiquity. These are judged in terms of flavour and stimulant effect and hardly at all as sources of calories. However, the calorific value of alcohol is 7 kcal/g and excess alcohol consumed could add to the total calorie intake of a person. In the case of distilled liquors (whisky, brandy, gin and rum), the calorific value is only due to alcohol and consumption of 100 ml of these beverages would yield about 230 kcal of energy. Beer and wine contain some nutrients present in the original malted barley and the fruit juice used in their preparation and naturally, their energy value would be higher than that of distilled liquors; 350 ml of beer gives about 150 kcal and 100 ml of wine about 80 kcal.

Alcohol is absorbed without prior digestion but the body has limited capacity to oxidize it. That is the reason why alcoholic beverages are to be sipped instead of gulped. As a drug the effects of alcohol vary from mild stimulation, when small amounts are consumed, to loss of co-ordination and even death when large amounts are consumed.

There are three main classes of alcoholic beverages: wines, malted beverages (beer), and distilled liquors. Different starting materials and different methods are used in their manufacture. But there is one common characteristic in all of them, namely, they are made by the process of fermentation. The essential step in all the fermentation processes is the conversion of glucose into alcohol by yeast. The enzymes present in yeast catalyze the breakdown of glucose.

$$C_6H_{12}O_6 \xrightarrow{\text{Yeast enzymes}} 2C_2H_5\,OH + 2CO_2$$

12.6.1 Wines

Wine is the oldest of the alcoholic beverages made by the fermentation of grape juice. Wine, strictly speaking, is a product of the grapevine, but often includes all fermented liquors obtained from different fruit juices (fruit wines). Wines differ greatly in their character, because grapes grown in different regions differ in their composition, particularly with respect to their volatile components which contribute to flavour and bouquet and in the method used for wine making.

There are different varieties of wines and in many cases they are named by reference to their place of origin, e.g., champagne is produced in the district of Champagne in France. Most of the wines produced in the world are natural and still (without excess of carbon dioxide). Sparkling wines, such as champagne, contain an excess of carbon dioxide due to the secondary fermentation that occurs after bottling. The carbon dioxide generated is stored within the liquid under its own pressure and gives the wine a "sparkle" Some wines, like port and sherry, are fortified wines and differ from natural wines in that some alcohol (grape brandy) is added to them before the completion of fermentation. Vermouth is also a fortified wine prepared by the addition of spice mixtures or their extracts at various stages during fermentation.

Wines also differ in their colours. The colour of the wine may be white or red. However, the colour does not depend on the colour of the grapes from which it is made; in fact, white wines may easily be made from black (dark b!ue) grapes by using only the juice. In making red wines both juice and skin are used; the pigment giving colour to the grapes lies just under the skin and is extracted from it during fermentation. Researchers are examining the potential benefits of components in red wine such as flavonoids and other antioxidants in reducing heart disease risk. Some of these components may be found in other foods such as grapes or red grape juice. Wines may be either "dry" or sweet depending upon the extent to which the fermentation has taken place. If fermentation has taken place until all the sugars are used up, the resulting wine will be dry; whereas if it is stopped while some sugar remains, it will be sweet. Yeast cannot tolerate an alcohol content greater than 16 per cent. Most of the natural wires contain 8–10 per cent alcohol. Fortified wines contain about 20 per cent alcohol, which is sufficiently high to kill the micro-organism that attack natural wines. Wines containing less than 14 per cent alcohol are table wines while those which contain more are dessert wines.

In the manufacture of wine, grapes are picked at the proper time when the sugar and acid contents are in the right proportion. The composition of the grapes varies according to the climatic conditions prevailing during their cultivation and thus the quality of wine varies from one year to another. Therefore, there is the practice of "vintage dating" the wine with the year of the crop from which it is made. Immediately after picking, in the case of red wines, the grapes are crushed and the juice together with the skin, pulp and seeds are transferred to the fermenters. After fermentation is completed, the fermented juice is pressed out. In the case of white wines, pressing takes place before fermentation.

"Wild" yeast and other micro-organisms are present on the skin of the grapes and these pass into the juicy pulp (known as "must") when the fruit is crushed. These are destroyed by adding sulphur dioxide (or potassium metabisulphite) in the required quantity. If the sugar content is low, sucrose is added to the desired strength and the pH is adjusted to 3.2–3.4 by the addition of tartaric acid. Next, the "must" is inoculated with a pure culture of actively growing yeast (*Saccharomyces ellipsoideus*). The temperature and duration of fermentation depend upon whether dry or sweet wine is required. Fermentation usually lasts 4 to 10 days.

When fermentation is complete, the clear wine is syphoned from the yeast sediment into barrels (raking) and the wine allowed to age. During this period secondary fermentation takes place and the wine also loses its raw and harsh flavour and mellows down. During this period of maturation, clarification takes place in the natural way. It can also be achieved by fining and filtration. Next, the wine is bottled and allowed to mature; the time of this maturation extends to several years depending upon the quality desired.

Wines are also made from the juices of other fruits and berries. Cider is fermented apple juice. The method of fermentation with fruit juices other than grapes is almost similar to that of preparation of grape wine. The world production of wine was 27.4 million tonnes in 2022.

12.6.2 Beer

Beer, next to wine, is the oldest alcoholic beverage to have been made. There are evidence to show that fermented beverages from barley existed in the Indus Valley civilization about 5,000 years ago and in China, Egypt and other cultures even earlier. The first brewery in India was started in 1860, and in 2005 there were 56 breweries and the beer production was about 121,6 million hectolitres, which is very insignificant compared with a world production of 120 billion hectolitres. It is projected that world consumption will be approximately 187.9 billion litres in 2023. The chief beer producing countries in the world are China, the United States, Brazil, Mexico, and Germany.

In 2022, the United States was the second-largest country in beer production from barley, with an output of about 20.45 million tonnes, following China. The world production of barley-based beer was 35.69 million tonnes and India produced 3.9 million tonnes in 2022. Asia is the largest producer with regional output of around 35.69 million tonnes in 2022.

The term "beer" is normally applied to a beverage made by the fermentation of barley malt. However, terms like "ale", "stout", "lager" and "porter" are also used for beer, the difference between them being the method of production. The materials used in the manufacture of beer are barley malt, cereal adjunct, hops, water and yeast. The principal operations involved in the production of beer are malting, mashing and fermentation.

The starting material for the production of beer is barley malt. (For malting of barley see subsection 15.10.4.)

Starchy materials that are cheaper than malt are used as "adjuncts" to replace some malt. The most commonly used cereal adjunct is maize in the form of grits or flakes. Other adjuncts suitable for brewing are broken rice, wheat, raw barley, tapioca, starch and sorghum. Such adjuncts should not impede the fermentation process or have an undesirable effect on the quality of the product. The entire starch of the adjunct is to be converted into sugar. Thus, the percentage of adjunct that can be added is restricted by the amount of enzymes in the malt. The introduction of the microbial enzymes has increased the flexibility of varying adjunct proportions, as these enzymes supplement malt enzymes. They also reduce the cost of raw materials and maintain the quality of beer. Liquid syrup adjuncts can alsc be used, but they are yet to enter the brewing field in India.

Hop (*Humulus lupulus*) is a vine native to Europe and Western Asia. During the early 1970s, hop growing had been introduced to Kashmir and successfully cultivated. Varieties grown in Kashmir have satisfactory brewing quality regarding bitterness but are low in flavour. From about the 15th century, beer has been flavoured with hop. The part used in brewing is the female "cone" consisting of a cluster of pale, yellowish-green bracts and bracteoles enclosing the flowers and later the fruits. Hop contains essential oils and resins that impart the characteristic bitter flavour and pleasant aroma to beer. It also destroys the enzymes and helps sterilize the brew before fermentation.

Suitability of water for brewing is of great importance in beer making. Water should be hard; if soft, salts are added to get the required hardness. If the water is too hard, it may have to be boiled to remove most of the temporary hardness.

The yeast used depends upon the type of beer to be manufactured. For the production of ale, "top fermentation" systems are used with the yeast *Saccharomyces cerevisiae*. In top fermentation, the yeast is carried to the top of the fermenting vats by rapidly evolving bubbles of carbon dioxide. For the production of lager, the "bottom fermentation" system is employed with *Saccharomyces carlsbergensis*. During fermentation, the yeast settles at the bottom of the vats.

In the manufacture of beer, the malt is "mashed", i.e., the ground malt is steeped in hot water in vessels called mash tun. Two mashing methods are generally employed: infusion mashing, followed in India, and decoction mashing. In infusion mashing, hot water at 65.5°C is mixed with ground malt to the consistency of porridge. Cereal adjuncts (gelatinized) are added to the malt grit. Sugar syrups, if desired, are also added at this stage. The period of infusion is about 2 hours and the temperature is maintained at 65.5°C. During this period, malt amylases degrade starch in aqueous solution to produce sugars approximately in the following ratios: 7–10 per cent monosaccharides, 48–55 per cent disaccharides, 12–15 per cent trisaccharides and 20–30 per cent dextrin. By regulating the mashing conditions, the proportion of various carbohydrates can be varied to suit the requirement of the beer to be brewed. When steeping is complete, the extract, known as "wort" is filtered off through barley husks which settle on the perforated false bottom of the mash tun.

The wort is then boiled with hops. This boiling destroys the malt enzymes and sterilizes the wort. The essential oil and bitter substances of hops are extracted and the proteins are coagulated. The coagulation of protein assists in clarifying the beer. The liquor is filtered through spent hops which retain the precipitated materials. The liquor, when cold, is seeded with yeast and allowed to ferment for a few days during which time sugars are converted into alcohol. When the fermentation is complete, the beer is allowed to stand for 1 or 2 days when the yeast settles down.

After fermentation, the beer is run off to storage tanks for maturing when secondary fermentation takes place and the flavour and bouquet of the beer develop. The maturing process varies from only a few days for mild beer to several months for strong beer. Next, the beer is pasteurized or sterile filtered and bottled or canned, with the introduction of carbon dioxide under pressure.

Variation in the quality of beer, such as the strength of alcohol, colour and extractives, depends upon the quality of malt, malt adjuncts used, mashing method, amount of hops added and the condition of fermentation. Beer, ale, porter and stout are beverages produced by top fermentation, while lager beer is a product of bottom fermentation. Ale is made like lager but is usually stronger in hop character and contains a higher alcohol content. Porter is a heavier and darker drink made with longer dried, roasted, or caramelized malt with less hops. Stout is like porter except that it has heavier malt flavour and is much darker than any other malt drink. It has a stronger hop taste than porter. The alcohol content of various beers varies from 2.5 to 7 g per cent. Beers produced in India contain 4–5 per cent alcohol and have a calorific value of about 30 kcal per 100 ml.

Saki is Japanese beer, that is made entirely from rice. Whole grain rice is soaked until it is quite soft and then steamed. The steamed rice is partially dried by spreading it on straw mats. It is then inoculated with a yeast-like mould and after 30–14 days, the completely fermented material is filtered. This fluid is placed in barrels to settle. After a few days, the clear liquid is withdrawn and pasteurized giving Saki. It contains about 17 per cent or more alcohol by volume.

For toddy see Subsection 18.3.2.

12.6.3 Distilled Spirits

Distilled spirits are made by distilling fermented liquors. Whisky is made by the fermentation and distillation of fermented cereal grains, brandy from wine and rum from fermented molasses. Gin is a distilled spirit flavoured with juniper (*Juniperus communis*) berries or some other aromatics. Distilled liquors usually have 40 per cent alcohol and thus have excellent keeping qualities. Usually, distilled liquors, other than gin, are allowed to mature before consumption, e.g., whisky is matured in wooden casks for 5–15 years to become smooth and mellow.

An essential stage in making spirits is distillation. The liquid obtained by fermentation from different materials contains dilute alcohol and is concentrated by distillation. Originally, distillation was carried out in a pot still. To obtain a concentrated alcoholic liquor, the distillation in a pot still has to be repeated several times. To overcome this disadvantage, continuous distillation stills have been developed. In spite of this development, pot still distillation is still used for making the finest whiskeys, brandies and other renowned spirits. Pot still allows many of the volatile components which contribute characteristic and subtle flavours to the drink to pass over with the alcohol during distillation. The best of brandy, cognac, is made by distilling twice in a pot still.

For the preparation of gin and vodka, and for fortification of any other beverage with alcohol, a colourless and tasteless spirit is required and this can be obtained by distillation in a continuous still. Dilute alcohol from any source when distilled in a continuous still can give 95 per cent alcohol. Such alcohol is very pure and has only the odour and flavour characteristic of alcohol. Such alcohol is known as neutral spirit (silent spirit).

Whiskey is made using different cereals. Scotch malt whisky, the original whisky, is made from malted barley and Scotch grain whisky from barley malt and other unmalted cereal grains. US whiskeys are generally made from rye (straight rye whisky) and maize (straight maize whisky). Canadian whisky is made from maize, wheat, rye or barley. Irish whisky is made from malted barley alone or with a mixture of unmalted barley, wheat, rye and oats.

In the manufacturing process, the grain is converted into beer except for the omission of hops and is distilled to obtain a distillate containing 80 per cent alcohol by volume. It is then diluted with water and stored in charred barrels. After the desired period of aging, the whisky is adjusted to the required alcohol strength and bottled. The characteristic flavour of Scotch whisky is said to be due to the fumes from the peat used for firing malt kilns and the characteristics of the water used.

Brandy can be made from any fruit. Generally, "brandy" refers only to the distillate from grape wine. Grape wine obtained from selected grapes is completely fermented using pure cultures of yeast and distilled. The brandy obtained is stored in oak casks and is allowed to age in a damp storage building for as long as 20 years.

Rum is an alcoholic beverage distilled directly from fermented sugarcane products, such as sugarcane juice, syrup or molasses. The rum obtained by distillation is stored in either charred, plain or reused barrels or vats. Rum readily improves in character and flavour with aging. After aging, the strength of alcohol is adjusted to 40 per cent and bottled.

Gin is produced by diluting neutral spirit with distilled water so that the alcohol content is 60 per cent. This is distilled in a pot still in the head of which are placed juniper berries and other aromatics. During distillation, the alcohol-water vapour extracts the flavouring principles. The distillate is then reduced to the required alcohol strength by the addition of water and bottled. No aging is required for gin; in fact, it may be harmful as the essential oils in gin may decompose with time.

For arrack and feni see Subsections 18.3.1 and 18.3.2.

Vodka is a distilled liquor without any identifying characteristics except that of dilute alcohol. It is free from all traces of colour and flavour. Vodka is made by diluting neutral spirit obtained from wheat or other cereal grains or potatoes.

Liqueurs are products obtained by steeping herbs, fruits, flowers or plants in neutral or distilled spirits and distilling the resulting produce. To the distillate, sugar is added to the extent of 2.5 per cent. As a rule, liqueurs are sweet, and caramel colour or other colouring may be added. Liqueurs like Benedictine, Drambuie and Creme-de-Menthe are obtained this way. The recipes of most liqueurs are closely guarded secrets.

CHAPTER

13 Fruits

The parable of Adam eating the "forbidden fruit of heaven" and Vedas emphasize fruit being offered to God has immortalised usage of fruits.

A fruit is the edible, and more or less juicy, a product of a tree or plant and consists of the matured ovary, including its seeds and adjacent parts. Usually, fruits are sweet, with a wide range of flavours, colours and textures.

India's diverse climate ensures availability of all varieties of fresh fruits & vegetables. It ranks second in fruits and vegetable production in the world, after China. As per National Horticulture Database published by National Horticulture Board, during 2023-24 India produced 112.62 million metric tonnes of fruits. The area under cultivation of fruits stood at 7.04 million hectares.

13.1 Composition

Fruits contain a high range of water, ranging between 80 to 90 per cent. They have only a small amount of protein and are also less in fat, with a few exceptions like avocado or butter fruit (*Persea americana*) which contains up to 14 per cent fat. The polysaccharides, cellulose, hemicellulose and pectic substances, form the structural components of fruits.

They provide all the nutrients such as carbohydrates in the form of dextrose, glucose, fructose, maltose. The fruits maturity and ripening determine the contents of the sweetening property. Fruits make up in minerals. These make fruits important sources of roughage or bulk in the diet. Various sugars are found in them, whose content varies in different fruits. Fruits also contain some free organic acids. Malic and citric acids occur in most of the fruits, but tartaric acid is a prominent constituent of grapes. Oxalic acid, when present, usually combines with calcium to form calcium oxalate.

Fruits are good sources of vitamins. Some fruits are very valuable as sources of ascorbic acid, citrus fruits being excellent sources of this vitamin. About 100 g of orange juice will meet the recommended daily allowance of ascorbic acid (50 mg per day). Strawberries, melons and tropical fruits (guava contains 200 mg of the vitamin per 100 g) are also good sources of ascorbic acid. Yellow fruits contain carotenoid pigments which are precursors of vitamin A. The B vitamins occur in relatively low concentration in fruits.

They contain minerals such as calcium, phosphorus, iron, sodium, potassium, sulphur, magnesium, chloride, and copper. Similarly, vitamin A, as carotene, all water-soluble B complex are life-giving and sustaining nutrients are rich. Their aromas are due to the volatile aromatic acids like citric, malic, acetic, tannic, and tartaric. These enhance appetite, improve digestion and also act as antiseptic. Their acid salts counteract alkaline based in protein metabolism. Their pectin content leaches itself to make jam, jellies, fruit preserves, given that they have high contents of water and fibre that keeps regular bowel movements. Table 13.1 lists the composition of some commonly consumed fruits.

Various pigments are present in fruits. The yellow and orange carotenoids, as well as the red, purple and blue anthocyanins, predominate in fruits. Some fruits contain a combination of various pigments; oranges, for example, in addition to carotenoids, contain some chlorophyll. Some oranges also contain anthocyanins. Carotenoid pigments are almost insoluble in water and are not much affected by acids or alkalis. Anthocyanins, on the other hand, are water-soluble and change their colour with alkali. So fruits are protective foods as their anabolism function improves the resistance for diseases. Some fruits like orange, lime keep the gum healthy. Fruits lower initial acidity and they also act as diuretic. Some fruits are to be had with caution in kidney problems, digestive problems and diabetes. Salts from fruit have basic reaction because fruit consumption maintains acid-salts equilibrium in the blood. The colour of fruits containing these pigments ranges from deep blue (certain varieties of grapes) to bright red (strawberries). Thus, in a combination of fruit juices, often undesirable colour changes occur. The colour of fruit mixtures may also change when they come in contact with metals. The flavonoids, when they come in contact with the metals aluminium, iron and tin, as happens in canned fruits, form a complex with metals and undesirable colour shifts occur.

The surface of some fruits (apples and peaches), when pared or cut and exposed to air, becomes brown. This is owing to the oxidation of phenolic substances by the enzyme phenol-oxidase. This can be prevented by the addition of some sugar to the fruit, which forms a film on its surface, and prevents air from reaching the surface, or by the addition of a small amount of lemon juice, which changes the pH and inhibits the action of the oxidizing enzyme. Browning can also be prevented by the addition of ascorbic acid that acts as an antioxidant or by keeping the fruit refrigerated until it is used, thus retarding the action of enzymes.

Flavouring compounds of fruits are many and quite varied. The flavour characteristic of a fruit, in many cases, is due to the characteristic blending of several compounds. Acids contribute to the flavour of fruits in free or combined form as salts and esters. Many aldehydes, ketones and esters contribute to the flavour of fruits. Sugar and phenolic compounds present in fruits also contribute to flavour. Some fruits contain essential oils which are also important flavour contributors.

13.2 Fruit Ripening

Among the important constituents of fruits are enzymes. These bring about changes, such as the softening of the edible tissues, changes in colour, carbohydrates and flavours, during the ripening of fruit. The enzymatic changes continue to take place even after the fruit has reached its full maturity and thus fruits are to be used before these changes set in. Alternatively, the changes have to be prevented by appropriate methods of fruit preservation.

Pectic substances are cementing agents holding the cells of the fruits together. In immature fruit, most of the pectin will be present as protopectin. As the fruit ripens this changes to pectin and pectic acid. These changes are partially responsible for the softening of fruit tissue during ripening. Starch content is relatively high in unripe fruit but it changes to sugar in ripe fruits. The acid content of most fruits decreases as the fruit ripens resulting in changes in the pigment of some fruits. Ripening also brings about changes in the flavour components with the development of a characteristic pleasant sweetness. There is no appreciable change in the content of protein, fats and minerals during ripening. In some cases, the vitamin content increases as the fruit matures.

13.3 Fruit Storage

Fruits are consumed fresh and are a perishable commodity. In advanced countries, fruit storage technology and transportation methods have developed so well that fresh fruits, grown not only in the country concerned but also in widely scattered parts of the world are available throughout the year. In our country,

Table 13.1 : Composition of Fruits (per 100 gms of edible portion)

Name of fruits	Moisture	Protein	Total Fat	Total Fiber	Carbohydrate	Energy		Calcium	Phosphorous	Iron	β-Carotene	Thiamine	Riboflavin	Niacin	Vitamin C
	g	g	g	g	g	KJ	Kcal	mg	mg	mg	µg	mg	mg	mg	mg
Apple, big (*Malus domestica*)	83.01 ± 0.94	0.29 ± 0.08	0.64 ± 0.04	2.59 ± 0.15	13.11 ± 0.76	261	62	13.68 ± 3.20	10.44 ± 1.18	0.26 ± 0.02	2.41 ± 2.13	0.03 ± 0.017	0.01 ± 0.011	0.25 ± 0.07	3.57 ± 0.58
Apple, green (*Malus domestica*)	85.54 ± 0.98	0.46 ± 0.07	0.50 ± 0.05	2.54 ± 0.26	10.65 ± 1.00	214	51	6.53 ± 2.48	7.48 ± 0.11	0.20 ± 0.04	2.20 ± 0.93	0.01 ± 0.023	0.02 ± 0.016	0.21 ± 0.06	2.90 ± 0.32
Apple, small (*Malus domestica*)	82.91 ± 0.48	0.31 ± 0.05	0.53 ± 0.05	2.06 ± 0.12	13.95 ± 0.48	267	64	5.39 ± 0.82	8.39 ± 1.20	0.25 ± 0.06	2.08 ± 0.82	0.01 ± 0.001	0.01 ± 0.000	0.09 ± 0.01	4.00 ± 0.72
Apple, small, Kashmir (*Malus sylvestris*)	82.79	0.27	0.6	2.07	13.99	269	64	4.72	10.72	0.21	2.11	0.01	0.01	0.09	4.24
Apricot, dried (*Prunus armeniaca*)	16.68 ± 0.59	3.17 ± 0.29	0.74 ± 0.03	3.32 ± 0.13	72.63 ± 0.27	1321	316	28.57 ± 4.32	72.02 ± 6.39	2.50 ± 0.26	1806 ± 106	0.04 ± 0.011	0.04 ± 0.006	1.66 ± 0.12	0.42 ± 0.14
Apricot, processed (*Prunus armeniaca*)	85.75 ± 0.81	1.47 ± 0.15	0.64 ± 0.04	0.59 ± 0.01	10.93 ± 0.88	236	56	5.42 ± 0.41	27.33 ± 1.29	1.12 ± 0.23	1372 ± 198	0.25 ± 0.011	0.04 ± 0.007	1.07 ± 0.07	7.98 ± 1.75
Avocado fruit (*Persea americana*)	73.56	2.95	13.86	6.69	1.75	604	144	28.48	63.14	0.81	12	0.07	0.08	0.9	9.36
Bael fruit (*Aegle marmelos*)	61.36	2.63	0.57	6.31	28.21	569	136	47.95	37.29	0.23	2.5	0.03	0.04	0.25	7.5
Banana, ripe, montham (*Musa x paradisiaca*)	70.13	1.25	0.32	2.21	24.95	463	111	6.77	20.85	0.4	53.06	0.01	0.04	0.48	8.06
Banana, ripe, red (*Musa x paradisiaca*)	70.28	1.29	0.29	1.98	25.21	467	112	9.56	23.27	0.24	51.52	0.01	0.02	0.46	6.74
Banana, ripe, poovam (*Musa x paradisiaca*)	71.32	1.49	0.35	2.33	23.41	445	106	8.73	33.63	0.35	57.33	0.01	0.03	0.43	6.74
Banana, ripe, robusta (*Musa x paradisiaca*)	71.93 ± 0.85	1.23 ± 0.08	0.33 ± 0.01	1.94 ± 0.07	23.63 ± 0.74	440	105	5.07 ± 0.94	24.32	0.28 ± 0.05	56.78 ± 11.56	0.01 ± 0.000	0.03 ± 0.005	0.47 ± 0.04	4.76 ± 1.34
Boysenberries, frozen, unsweetened*	85.9	1.1	0.26	5.3	12.19	209.1	50	27		0.85	67**	0.053	0.037	0.767	3.1
Black berry (*Rubus fruticosus*)	82.94 ± 0.42	0.92 ± 0.10	0.63 ± 0.02	4.35 ± 0.25	10.64 ± 0.35	227	54	23.81 ± 2.70	20.08 ± 4.50	0.28 ± 0.05	52.32 ± 2.65	0.01 ± 0.002	0.02 ± 0.005	0.40 ± 0.09	19.45 ± 1.54

Cherries, red (*Prunus cerasus*)	83.61 ± 0.21	1.49 ± 0.22	0.46 ± 0.05	2.12 ± 0.12	11.87 ± 0.31	250	60	23.88 ± 5.01	25.31 ± 8.43	0.63 ± 0.21	40.78 ± 1.15	0.07 ± 0.006	0.02 ± 0.004	0.19 ± 0.01	8.82 ± 0.57
Currants, black (*Ribes nigrum*)	83.27	1.51	0.53	4.07	9.93	227	54	40.32	78.8	0.36 ± 0.10	62.48	0.03	0.03	0.35	182
Custard apple (*Annona squamosa*)	71.55	1.62	0.67	5.1	20.38	414	99	28.2	40.81	0.031		0.13	0.09	0.69	21.51
Dates, dry, pale brown (*Phoenix dactylifera*)	11.14 ± 0.73	2.45 ± 0.24	0.35 ± 0.03	8.95 ± 0.23	74.91 ± 0.52	1340	320	71.20 ± 4.51	73.02	0.42	2700 ± 345	0.03 ± 0.012	0.03 ± 0.008	1.47 ± 0.07	4.42 ± 0.54
Dates, dry, dark brown (*Phoenix dactylifera*)	13.13	2.38	0.35	9.1	72.67	1301	311	66.13	70.26	3.20 ± 0.45	2705	0.02	0.03	1.09	3.84
Dates, processed (*Phoenix dactylifera*)	22.01	1.18	0.41	6.52	67.95	1197	286	15.73	33.88	4.79	2781	0.05	0.02	0.51	15.51
Dragon fruit*	93	3.57	0	1.8	82.14	309.468	74	107		0	0				6.4
Durian*	64.99	1.47	5.33	3.8	27.09	271.83	65	6		0.43	44	0.374	0.2	1.074	19.7
Fig (*Ficus carica*)	75.60 ± 1.16	2.03 ± 0.22	0.37 ± 0.06	4.64 ± 0.41	16.28 ± 1.13	341	82	78.52 ± 16.48	21.62 ± 1.97	0.89	2.40 ± 0.59	0.04 ± 0.020	0.02 ± 0.008	0.27 ± 0.08	16.92 ± 4.26
Goosberry (*Emblica officinalis*)	87.02 ± 0.78	0.34 ± 0.03	0.16 ± 0.04	7.75 ± 0.64	4.39 ± 1.09	99	24	20.14 ± 2.51	21.85 ± 1.87	0.69 ± 0.06	1.58 ± 0.09	0.01 ± 0.009	0.03 ± 0.012	0.12 ± 0.02	252 ± 30.4
Grapefruit juice, white, raw*	90	0.5	0.1	0.1	9.20	163.098	39				10**	0.04	0.02	0.2	38
Grapes, seeded, round, black (*Vitis vinifera*)	83.88 ± 0.56	0.76 ± 0.13	0.32 ± 0.02	1.35 ± 0.14	13.23 ± 0.60	254	61	10.57 ± 2.03	21.04	1.25 ± 0.08	29.36 ± 8.37	0.03 ± 0.009	0.03 ± 0.005	0.14 ± 0.03	18.30 ± 2.32
Grapes, seeded, round, green (*Vitis vinifera*)	85.07 ± 0.29	0.77 ± 0.12	0.29 ± 0.03	1.25 ± 0.04	12.19 ± 0.20	235	56	11.16 ± 2.02	19.5	0.22 ± 0.04	30.77 ± 11.10	0.03 ± 0.005	0.02 ± 0.004	0.13 ± 0.02	17.10 ± 5.63
Grapes, seeded, round, red (*Vitis vinifera*)	84.46 ± 1.60	0.95 ± 0.11	0.29 ± 0.04	1.28 ± 0.10	12.55 ± 1.38	244	58	11.27 ± 3.54	27.91	0.24 ± 0.10	19.94 ± 1.29	0.04 ± 0.027	0.03 ± 0.018	0.10 ± 0.03	20.59 ± 3.45
Grapes, seedless, oval, black (*Vitis viniféra*)	75.30 ± 1.55	1.41 ± 0.26	0.46 ± 0.11	1.64 ± 0.15	20.48 ± 0.97	395	94	15.26 ± 3.03	29.02	0.33 ± 0.04	19.73 ± 1.76	0.03 ± 0.021	0.02 ± 0.015	0.15 ± 0.04	27.32 ± 5.18

Grapes, seedless, round, black (*Vitis vinifera*)	76.90 ± 1.40	1.24 ± 0.25	0.35 ± 0.03	1.15 ± 0.19	19.86 ± 1.58	374	89	18.75 ± 5.41	26.68	0.23 ± 0.33	25.46 ± 6.66	0.03 ± 0.019	0.03 ± 0.029	0.13 ± 0.05	22.79 ± 3.45
Grapes, seedless, round, green (*Vitis vinifera*)	85.55 ± 1.70	0.62 ± 0.13	0.26 ± 0.02	1.28 ± 0.05	11.81 ± 1.52	224	54	14.22 ± 2.14	20.27	0.16 ± 0.03	25.8 ± 7.90	0.04 ± 0.023	0.03 ± 0.019	0.12 ± 0.04	16.47 ± 2.06
Guava, pink flesh (*Psidium guajava*)	81.22 ± 0.45	1.19 ± 0.19	0.25 ± 0.03	7.39 ± 0.38	9.14 ± 0.27	195	47	14.22 ± 2.92	29.93 ± 7.85	0.32 ± 0.07	267 ± 88.2	0.03 ± 0.010	0.03 ± 0.005	0.59 ± 0.07	222 ± 27.0
Guava, white flesh (*Psidium guajava*)	83.79 ± 0.30	1.44 ± 0.09	0.32 ± 0.03	8.59 ± 0.05	5.13 ± 0.33	135	32	18.52 ± 2.10	23.54 ± 3.12	0.39 ± 0.07	298 ± 32.8	0.05 ± 0.006	0.04 ± 0.008	0.60 ± 0.04	214 ± 13.6
Jack fruit, ripe (*Artocarpus heterophyllus*)	78.56 ± 0.34	2.74 ± 0.47	0.15 ± 0.02	3.62 ± 0.17	14.01 ± 0.56	302	72	35.03 ± 4.50	23.03	0.40 ± 0.14	23.53 ± 1.24	0.05 ± 0.004	0.01 ± 0.004	0.42 ± 0.08	6.73 ± 1.59
Jambu fruit, ripe (*Syzygium cumini*)	83.33	0.82	0.17	3.07	12.30	235	56	25.36	9.6	0.36 ± 0.16	1.55	0.02	0.02	0.14	16.47
Karonda fruit (*Carissa carandas*)	86.04	1.15	1.67	7.25	2.87	141	34	10.81	32.62	0.33	15.64	0.01	0.02	0.25	135
Lemon, juice (*Citrus limon*)	91.59 ± 0.53	0.41 ± 0.05	0.75 ± 0.02		6.97 ± 0.56	153	37	22.68 ± 2.90	9.86 ± 0.52	0.87	2.62 ± 0.34	0.04 ± 0.007	0.01 ± 0.000	0.10 ± 0.01	48.16 ± 4.35
Lime, sweet, pulp (*Citrus limetta*)	91.32 ± 0.33	0.76 ± 0.09	0.20 ± 0.06	2.07 ± 0.11	5.18 ± 0.37	114	27	25.79 ± 5.02	20.55 ± 1.27	0.12 ± 0.05	2.54 ± 0.30	0.06 ± 0.005	0.01 ± 0.003	0.17 ± 0.02	46.96 ± 7.64
Litchi (*Nephelium litchi*)	85.56 ± 0.27	0.99 ± 0.09	0.26 ± 0.02	1.34 ± 0.05	11.41 ± 0.20	225	54	5.77 ± 0.80	23.32 ± 3.13	0.11 ± 0.02	1.47 ± 0.21	0.02 ± 0.003	0.06 ± 0.008	0.23 ± 0.02	33.82 ± 5.24
Kiwi*	149.53	2.05	0.94		26.39	255.102	61	61		0.56	87	0.027	0.025	0.341	92.7
Kumquat, raw*	80.85	1.88	0.86	6.5	15.90	296.922	71	62		0.86	290**	0.037	0.09	0.429	43.9
Logan Berry *	84.61	3.57	39.29			230.01	55	36		0	536**				
Longan, raw*	82.75	1.31	0.1	1.1	15.14	250.92	60	1		0.13		0.031	0.14	0.3	84
Mango, ripe, banganapalli (*Mangifera indica*)	88.44 ± 0.55	0.54 ± 0.10	0.55 ± 0.03	1.88 ± 0.15	8.18 ± 0.49	175	42	15.77 ± 1.64	11.07	0.79 ± 0.21	1168 ± 141	0.03 ± 0.005	0.04 ± 0.004	0.26 ± 0.03	32.97 ± 7.14
Mango, ripe, gulabkhas (*Mangifera indica*)	86.65	0.52	0.53	1.67	10.32	209	50	19.33	10.66	0.51 ± 0.17	666	0.03	0.04	0.23	27.65

Mango, ripe, himsagar (*Mangifera indica*)	88.04 ± 0.10	0.46 ± 0.04	0.54 ± 0.02	1.55 ± 0.13	9.03 ± 0.26	187	45	15.54 ± 1.84	12.25	0.38	1181 ± 136	0.03 ± 0.005	0.03 ± 0.004	0.27 ± 0.04	49.09 ± 23.24
Mango, ripe, kesar (*Mangifera indica*)	85.07 ± 0.59	0.54 ± 0.05	0.57 ± 0.03	2.02 ± 0.20	11.36 ± 0.49	231	55	15.74 ± 0.89	12.36 ± 0.38	0.29 ± 0.05	1264 ± 172	0.03 ± 0.007	0.04 ± 0.006	0.26 ± 0.02	29.08 ± 4.61
Mango, ripe, totapari (*Mangifera indica*)	84.14	0.41	0.49	1.73	12.75	248	59	13.34	9.87	0.51	602	0.02	0.05	0.27	25.26
Mangosteen (*Garcinia mangostana*)	85.52	0.63	0.24	1.87	11.41	219	52	4.69	7.18	0.28	1.8	0.01	0.01	0.58	26.33
Mango, ripe, neelam (*Mangifera indica*)	88.41	0.68	0.55	1.77	8.21	178	43	11.36	11.63	0.43 ± 0.19	1291	0.03	0.04	0.23	29.93
Mango, ripe, paheri (*Mangifera indica*)	87.69	0.68	0.58	1.97	8.67	188	45	15.11	15.18	" 0.36 0.36 "	1061	0.03	0.04	0.28	30.75
Manila tamarind (*Pithecellobium dulce*)	74.54	3.56	1.14	4.4	13.54	342	82	8.51	73.53	0.28	2.2	0.18	0.14	0.4	55.78
Mulberry*	122.75	2.02	0.55		13.72	250.92	60	55		2.59	35	0.041	0.141	0.868	
Musk melon, orange flesh (*Cucumis melon*)	92.97 ± 0.38	0.42 ± 0.06	0.35 ± 0.02	1.51 ± 0.28	4.24 ± 0.40	97	23	9.80 ± 2.14	17.28	0.71	771 ± 96.4	0.01 ± 0.000	0.01 ± 0.003	0.41 ± 0.05	22.76 ± 3.42
Musk melon, yellow flesh (*Cucumis melon*)	91.84 ± 0.93	0.53 ± 0.05	0.26 ± 0.02	1.49 ± 0.10	5.40 ± 1.04	116	28	9.02 ± 2.95	13.09	0.18 ± 0.04	6.87 ± 0.36	0.01 ± 0.018	0.02 ± 0.013	0.43 ± 0.08	21.32 ± 1.19
Nectarians, raw*	87.59	1.06	0.32	1.7	10.55	184.008	44	6		0.28	332**	0.034	0.027	1.125	5.4
Orange, pulp (*Citrus aurantium*)	89.61 ± 0.19	0.70 ± 0.12	0.13 ± 0.02	1.29 ± 0.05	7.92 ± 0.27	156	37	19.52 ± 1.48	12.90 ± 4.47	0.21 ± 0.06	31.94 ± 2.12	0.07 ± 0.009	0.02 ± 0.005	0.28 ± 0.04	42.72 ± 4.81
Palm fruit, tender (*Borassus flabellifer*)	91.93	0.5	0.12	2.4	4.92	101	24			0.81 ± 0.04		0.01		0.46	0.25
Papaya, ripe (*Carcia papaya*)	91.47 ± 0.76	0.42 ± 0.05	0.16 ± 0.01	2.83 ± 0.26	4.61 ± 0.48	100	24	15.02 ± 1.47	17.73 ± 3.53	0.23 ± 0.02	694 ± 84.5	0.03 ± 0.009	0.11 ± 0.008	0.33 ± 0.03	43.09 ± 7.02
Passion fruit*		0.67	0.18	0.2	14.45	250.92	60	4		0.36	943**	0	0.101	2.24	18.2
Peach (*Prunus communis*)	88.31	0.86	0.37	2.13	7.82	168	40	6.98	19.08	0.35		0.06 ± 0.045	0.02	0.29	5.49

Pear (*Pyrus sp.*)	86.49 ± 0.18	0.36 ± 0.04	0.27 ± 0.04	4.48 ± 0.08	8.09 ± 0.23	157	38	6.55 ± 1.39	6.74 ± 1.79	0.28 ± 0.10	13.16 ± 1.78	0.02 ± 0.005	0.02 ± 0.008	0.13 ± 0.03	3.31 ± 0.90
Persimmons*	16.1	0.2	0.1	2.4	8.38	133.824	32	7		0.62					16.5
Phalsa (*Grewia asiatica*)	77.48	1.66	0.14	4.54	15.09	299	71	153	23.65	2.01	1.71	0.03	0.06	0.4	5.11
Pineapple (*Ananas comosus*)	86.06 ± 1.19	0.52 ± 0.09	0.16 ± 0.02	3.46 ± 0.12	9.42 ± 1.15	180	43	10.88 ± 1.91	13.56 ± 4.36	0.28 ± 0.11	31.21 ± 4.33	0.11	0.03 ± 0.011	0.12 ± 0.02	36.37 ± 3.65
Plum (*Prunus domestica*)	84.44 ± 1.25	0.64 ± 0.13	0.40 ± 0.16	2.07 ± 0.36	12.10 ± 1.47	238	57	7.61 ± 0.94	13.83	0.25 ± 0.09	1.32 ± 0.22	0.01 ± 0.001	0.02 ± 0.001	0.44 ± 0.02	2.26 ± 0.00
Pomegranate, maroon seeds (*Punica granatum*)	83.55 ± 0.39	1.33 ± 0.07	0.15 ± 0.02	2.83 ± 0.06	11.58 ± 0.43	229	55	10.65 ± 1.82	27.2	0.31 ± 0.06	2.05 ± 0.58	0.06 ± 0.005	0.01 ± 0.004	0.20 ± 0.03	12.69 ± 1.36
Pummelo (*Citrus maxima*)	86.97 ± 1.52	0.68 ± 0.06	0.42 ± 0.01	0.80 ± 0.04	10.64 ± 1.54	210	50	14.03 ± 4.73	13.99 ± 1.75	0.06 ± 0.01	1.55 ± 0.35	0.06 ± 0.045	0.02 ± 0.011	0.23 ± 0.08	48.89 ± 1.52
Raisins, dried, black (*Vitis vinifera*)	19.69 ± 0.59	2.57 ± 0.20	0.34 ± 0.02	3.92 ± 0.23	71.29 ± 0.48	1279	306	73.24 ± 5.48	77.62 ± 8.95	6.81 ± 0.91	3.71 ± 1.08	0.09 ± 0.013	0.04 ± 0.017	0.48 ± 0.04	2.05 ± 0.14
Raisins, dried, golden (*Vitis vinifera*)	21.50 ± 0.51	2.76 ± 0.26	0.35 ± 0.03	4.56 ± 0.50	68.79 ± 1.00	1241	297	51.83 ± 5.26	93.30 ± 7.18	4.26 ± 0.60	2.53 ± 0.63	0.09 ± 0.012	0.04 ± 0.006	0.64 ± 0.05	1.85 ± 0.27
Rambutan (*Nephelium lappaceum*)	80.87	0.68	0.16	1.02	16.84	306	73	8.67	6.98	0.37	2.9	0.11	0.01	0.26	65
Raspberry*	85.75	1.2	0.65	6.5	11.94	217.464	52	25		0.69	33**	0.032	0.038	0.598	26.2
Rose Apple (*Syzygium aqueum*)*	84.21	0.6	0.3		5.70	104.55	25	29		0.07	339**	0.02	0.03	0.8	22.3
Salmonberry*	88.21	0.85	0.33	1.9	10.05	196.554	47	13		0.4	496**	0.041	0.062	0.466	9.2
Sapota (*Achras sapota*)	73.64 ± 1.01	0.92 ± 0.07	1.26 ± 0.02	9.60 ± 0.57	13.90 ± 1.13	307	73	17.87 ± 3.38	22.26 ± 1.34	0.49 ± 0.33	80.70 ± 5.96	0.01 ± 0.001	0.03 ± 0.005	0.24 ± 0.02	20.96 ± 4.62
Soursop (*Annona muricata*)	80.85	0.74	0.94	4.95	11.94	260	62	10.05	25.83	0.29	2.2	0.03	0.04	0.85	59.54
Star fruit (*Averrhoa carambola*)	91.18	0.79	0.39	2.81	4.51	110	26	4.97	11.67	0.45	1.4	0.08	0.02	0.34	33.55
Strawberry (*Fragaria ananassa*)	92.03 ± 0.64	0.97 ± 0.10	0.56 ± 0.02	2.50 ± 0.03	3.40 ± 0.64	103	25	15.28 ± 3.37	26.31 ± 2.09	0.36 ± 0.03	2.19 ± 0.17	0.06 ± 0.063	0.01 ± 0.003	0.48 ± 0.11	50.20 ± 4.97

Tamarind, pulp (*Tamarindus indicus*)	20.83 ± 0.57	2.92 ± 0.22	0.15 ± 0.02	5.31 ± 0.27	67.35 ± 0.45	1207	289	149 ± 13.9	113 ± 18.1	9.16 ± 1.71	1.54 ± 0.42	0.34 ± 0.039	0.07 ± 0.004	1.56 ± 0.16	3.62 ± 0.85
Tangerines, (*mandarin oranges*), raw*	85.17	0.81	0.31	1.8	13.34	221.646	53	37		0.29	681**	0.058	0.036	0.376	26.7
Water melon, dark green (*sugar baby*) (*Citrullus vulgaris*)	94.54 ± 0.63	0.60 ± 0.06	0.16 ± 0.01	0.70 ± 0.14	3.86 ± 0.59	85	20	5.29 ± 1.09	11.33	0.22 ± 0.14	605 ± 121	0.02 ± 0.004	0.02 ± 0.003	0.28 ± 0.03	13.26 ± 2.66
Water melon, pale green (*Citrullus vulgaris*)	95.33 ± 0.22	0.59 ± 0.03	0.16 ± 0.01	0.78 ± 0.11	3.02 ± 0.21	70	17	4.35 ± 0.88	8.09	0.16 ± 0.07	576 ± 119	0.02 ± 0.003	0.02 ± 0.002	0.30 ± 0.04	11.45 ± 2.09
Wood Apple (*Limonia acidissima*)	79.36 ± 0.17	3.14 ± 0.30	3.62 ± 0.03	5.21 ± 0.38	7.52 ± 0.58	327	78	55.71 ± 7.46	84.32 ± 4.00	0.45 ± 0.06	3.81 ± 1.28	0.04 ± 0.009	0.01 ± 0.001	0.55 ± 0.05	22.17 ± 7.49
Zizyphus (*Zizyphus jujube*)	84.39	1.34	0.35	3.73	9.40	204	49	46.55	32.38	0.4	1.5	0.01	0.02	0.33	60.93

IFCT, NIN, ICMR, Hyderabad, 2017

*https://ndb.nal.usda.gov

**Vitamin A, IU

due to lack of facilities, there is considerable wastage of fruits, and fresh fruits are not available except during the season. Only 0.5 per cent of fruits and vegetables produced are being processed.

In the large-scale preservation of fruits, the control of humidity is very important. It should be maintained such that mould formation, dehydration and shriveling of fruit do not take place. A relative humidity in the range of 85 to 90 per cent promotes the retention of water in the fruit cells.

Fruits continue to respire after harvesting. This should be reduced to prolong storage life. Cold storage and controlled atmosphere help achieve this. Low temperatures reduce the metabolic rate. A low oxygen level (about 2 to 3 per cent, instead of the normal 21 per cent) and high carbon dioxide (about 5 per cent) level decrease spoilage by retarding the ripening process. Apples and pears can be stored for a long period by this process.

Some fruits like ripe banana cannot be stored at a low temperature, because of a colour change in the skin when they are later removed to the room temperature. Some berries also do not stand extended cold storage periods.

The colour of the fruit is important so far as its acceptance is concerned. Ethylene gas has been used for many years as a means of hastening the ripening and the accompanying colour development of fruits. Ethylene when decomposes the chlorophyll which obscures the pigment of fruits.

Classification: Fruits are divided into groups depending upon the shape, cell structure, type of seed or natural habitat. One system classifies them into the following groups: berries, citrus fruits, drupes, grapes, melons, pomes, tropical and subtropical fruits.

13.4 Berries

Berries, are fruits with layers of pericarp (fruit coat) which are often homogeneous, except for the skin on the outside. The pericarp layers are pulpous and juicy, and contain seeds embedded in the pulp mass. The fruits have a fragile cell structure that is damaged by rough handling or freezing. Some important berries are strawberry, gooseberry, currant, blackberry, raspberry, blueberry, cranberry, etc. Most of the berries are native to Western countries and acclimatized to cold climate. However, some of these are grown in our country in places where climatic conditions are favourable. The berries are high in acid (citric, malic and benzoic) and have high pectin content, rich flavour and colour. Berries are dessert fruits. They are largely used in the preparation of jams, jellies and various baked products such as pies.

Bramble, is the name given to range of berries belonging to genus Rubus. The main two types are Raspberries and cultivated blackberries. When Raspberries ripens, it comes out from the plug or torus where as blackberry the plug stays with the fruit when ripe. Hybrid blackberries are *Rubus* subgenus *Eubatus*, the wild blackberries *Rubus fructicosus*. The other barries are Blacksatin, Murrindindi, Loch Ness, thornfree, Dirkum, Chester are all thornless. Boysenberry can be with thorn or thornless. Silvan is thorny. All these berries mature around December, January and February. Most of the berries are named after the person who created by grafting different berries together.

The world production of berries is 957 million tonnes and India produced 114 million tonnes.

13.4.1 Blackberry (*Rubus frucicosus*)

The blackberry (*Rubus frucicosus*) is a fruit produced by many species in the genus *Rubus* in the family *Rosaceae*, hybrids among these species within the subgenus *Rubus* and hybrids between the subgenera *Rubus* and *Idaeobatus*. The barriers are 1–3 cm in diameter, changing colour from green to red to black as it

Blackberry

ripens; each berry an aggregate of many single-seeded juicy segments (drupelets). Fruit develops from late December until April.

It contains numerous phytochemicals including polyphenols, flavonoids, anthocyanins, salicylic acid, ellagic acid, and fibre. Anthocyanins in blackberries are responsible for their rich dark colour.

The fruit is used in desserts, jams, seedless jelly, and sometimes wine. It is often mixed with apples for pies and crumbies. Blackberries are also used to produce candy.

13.4.2 Blueberries and Cranberries (*Vaccinium corymbosum*)

Blueberry (*Vaccinium corymbosum*) is a native of North America where the blueberry pie is a traditional dessert. The fruit is smooth surfaced, blue-black in colour and is also used in the preparation of jams, jellies and juices. Cranberry (*Vaccinium oxycoccus*) is a native of Europe and North America. The berry is red throughout and is nearly spherical or oblong. The fruit is extensively used for making sauce and jelly and juice.

Blueberry

Blueberries have been found to be the number one source of antioxidants among fruits and vegetables.

13.4.3 Loganberries (*Rubus loganobaccus*)

It is a hybrid produced from crossing a blackberry and a raspberry. The canes or vines are very large without the thorns of blackberry bushes, but have very fine soft spines much like those of raspberry bushes. The fruit is as large as the largest size blackberry. It has the same shape and colour, which when fully ripe is dark bright red. It has the combined flavour of both berries, pleasant, mild and delightful to taste.

Longanberry

Loganberries are eaten fresh as fruit, juice, jams, muffins, pies, fruit syrups and wines. It is interchangeably used in place of raspberries and blackberries.

13.4.4 Boysenberry (*Rubus ursinus* var/*oganobaccus*)

Boysenberry, scientific name, *Rubus ursinus* var/*oganobaccus* cv Boysenberry, is actually a hybrid aggregate fruit that was cultivated by cross-pollinating the flowers of three other berries: raspberry, loganberry and the blackberry. Ironically, the loganberry itself is also a cross between the raspberry and the blackberry. The fruit is named after its originator, Charles Rudolf Boysen. Boysenberry is normally 3 cm long and from 2 to 3 cm in width, an aggregate of several succulent drupelets, each containing a single seed. Fruit is usually green when young changing to straw-yellow, amber, orange, red, reddish-black, or glossy purplish-black as they ripen. The fruit has soft, glossy, thin skin. They have a rich, complex, and sweet flavor with just a hint of acid. Normally fruit weighs 8.0 gram (0.28 σz). It has tangy taste, can be eaten fresh or made into jams, jellies, syrups, sauces, and pie fillings. They can also add a touch of sweet tartness to dessert offerings, yogurt, and smoothies.

Boysenberry

13.4.5 Salmon Berry (*Rubus spectabilis*)

A member of the rose family, the salmon berry plant (*Rubus spectabilis*) is related to the raspberry, nagoonberry, wild strawberry, thimbleberry and cloudberry. One should not confuse salmon berries with cloudberries, occasionally referred to as low bush salmon berries. The plant is native to the west coast of North America. Salmon berries were normally picked and eaten raw or mixed with meat or dried salmon. Other parts of the plant, including the young shoots and the bark, were collected and eaten or used for medicinal purposes. Fruits are normally yellow to orange to deep red colored and are harvested from June to August. The ripe fruit, offers a delectable aroma and sweet to slightly sour taste which is favorable to several food items. Traditionally, the berries were eaten with salmon. Today the berries are frozen, canned, made into jams and jellies, used for flavoring candies, for making wine and other alcoholic beverages.

Salmon Berry

13.4.6 Raspberries (*Rubus idaeus*)

Raspberry (*Rubus idaeus*) is grown in the Northern Hemisphere. The fruits have a red and yellow colour. A black-fruited raspberry is also cultivated. Raspberries are delicious, fresh or cooked. Both raspberries and blackberries are used for jams, jellies and juices. They can be canned and frozen.

Fruit can be consumed raw, used in pies and puddings can be cooked, used in ice creams, tarts, trifles, cheesecakes, candies, and preserves–jams, jellies and as liqueur. Its leaves are used to make tea. It is rich in Vitamin C. Red Raspberries, Black Raspberries, Golden or yellow Raspberries, and Pumple Raspberry are the varieties of raspberries available.

The world production of raspberries is 9,47,852 tonnes, 2022.

Raspberry

13.4.7 Silvan Blackberry (*Rubus fruticosus silvan*)

Hybridized in Australia, this berry is a cross between Marion berry and a seedling cross of Pacific and Boysenberries. The fruit is purple-black with excellent flavor and great for processing. These plants are long living (15 to 20 years) perennials, hardy and cold tolerant, easy to grow, and prolific spreaders. The fruit is very large, dark red, glossy blackberries that are extremely high in vitamin C borne off of thorny vines. Silvan berry, plants are vociferous producers. Harvests early-December to mid-January. Fruit is glossy, red-black to fully black at ripe; upto 35 mm long × 20 mm diameter. Soft and easily damaged when fully ripe. Excellent aromatic/acidic flavour and is the nearest flavour to the wild weed blackberry. It freezes beautifully.

Silvan Blackberry

13.4.8 Black Mulberry Fruit (*Morus nigra*)

It is dark purple in colour and gives an impression of being black. They are very juicy and refreshing, subacid and has saccharine taste. It has numerous health benefits, rich in vitamin C, also in iron and the fruit, is used for premature greying of hair. The bark is anthelmintic and a purgative used to expel tapeworms. The bark is diuretic used to treat hypertension, asthma and cough.

Mulberry

13.4.9 Strawberries (*Fragaria virginiana*)

Strawberries (*Fragaria virginiana*) are greatly valued fruits of temperate climates and are delicious but perishable. Many species of strawberries are grown but the cultivated strawberry is of American origin. The juicy strawberry fruit is an enlarged receptacle (the end of the flower stalk on which the parts of the flower are borne). Numerous achenes or seeds are embedded in the surface of the juicy receptacle. Many strawberries arc heart-shaped, others are spherical. The fruits are firm, red-fleshed and sweet.

Strawberry

More than 50 per cent of the sugar in strawberries is glucose. The fruits contain mostly citric acid and some malic acid. The red colour of the fruits is due to anthocyanin. Many volatile esters responsible for the flavour of the fruit, are present in it. The fruits are a rich source of vitamin C but the vitamin is rapidly lost when the fruit is injured, cut or juiced. Strawberries are mainly dessert fruits; they are also canned, frozen and made into jams. They are a favourite in ice cream making and confectionery.

Strawberries have been identified by research as most effective in fighting against cancer cells.

The world production of strawberries is 10.5 million tonnes in 2023. China is the largest producer with 4.21 million tonnes in 2023. India's production is 0.2 tonnes in 2023.

13.4.10 Gooseberries and Currants

Both these fruits belong to the genus *Ribes*. Their fruits are round, with a thin, often translucent skin enclosing a number of seeds in juicy flesh.

The gooseberry, *Ribes uva-crispa, syn. R. Grossularia* is a species of Ribes, native to Europe, north-western Africa and south-western Asia. It is often of good flavour; it is generally hairy, and colour is usually green, but there are red variants and occasionally deep purple berries occur. The flavour of the fruit is said to improve with increasing latitude. In most northern parts of Scotland, it is commonly known as a "grozet", in Norway it is named as "*stikkelsbear*" or "*prickly berry*".

Gooseberries (Green)

Gooseberries (Red)

Currants (White)

Currants (Black)

Currants (Red)

Culinary uses

Gooseberries are edible and can be eaten as-is, or used as an ingredient in desserts, such as pies and crumbles. They are also used to flavour beverages such as sodas, flavoured waters, or milk, and can be made into fruit wines and teas. Gooseberries can be preserved in the form of jams, dried fruit, or as the primary or a secondary ingredient in pickling, or stored in sugar syrup.

There are different kinds of gooseberries. The European variety (*P. grossularia*) varies in size, colour of the skin, flavour and shape of the fruit. A yellowish type with hairy skin is the most predominant, but varieties with reddish, dark green and pale whitish-green skins are known. The American varieties *R. divaricatum*, which is black, and *R. hirtellum*, which is red, are small, smooth and spherical berries. Gooseberries are also rich in pectic material, and like currants, are used for jams and jellies.

The world production of gooseberries in 2022 was 95,420 tonnes. In India it was 1.9 million tonnes in 2022.

The currants are grouped into three groups based on colour: black current (*R. nigrum*), red currant (*R. sativum*) and white currant which is the seedling from red currant and lacks red pigment. Though white currants are closely related to the red kind, they have a distinct flavour and less acid than the latter. Black currant is a different species and is a true berry growing in clusters. Currants are rich in vitamin C, contain high-grade pectic substances and are extensively used in the preparation of jams, jellies and preserves. The world production of currants is 9,59,440 tonnes in 2022.

13.5 Citrus Fruits

These fruits belong to the genus *Citrus* which consists of about 16 species of evergreen aromatic shrubs and trees mostly with thorny branches, distributed throughout the tropical and subtropical regions of the world. The genus as a whole originated in China and South-East Asia, apart from lime which is native to India. Most of the species are cultivated in India. In addition to the cultivated varieties, a few wild varieties with several unusual characteristics also occur in India. Some hybrid varieties of citrus fruits have been developed in various parts of the world.

Citrus fruits are one of the largest and most important groups of fruits produced on an enormous scale.

The common citrus fruits are orange, grapefruit, lemon and lime, and some of the lesser-known members of this family are tangerine, citron and kumquat. Their bright colour, pleasing flavour and sweetness make them favourite fruits. They are served as juice or slices. The fruit juice on a dry matter basis contains 80–90 per cent sugar and acids. Sugar predominates in most species, but in lemon and lime acids predominate, so they are used in different ways. The richness of vitamin C in all citrus fruits makes them valuable from the nutritional point of view. Citrus fruits have high pectin content in the white portion of their skin (albedo) which makes them one of the principal sources of commercial pectin and also of citrus marmalades. All species of fruits contain essential oils in the skin of the fruit, and often in the flowers and leaves, which are extracted and used in perfumery. Citric acid, at one time, was being prepared from citrus fruits; at present, however, it is being produced by microbiological methods.

13.5.1 Sweet Oranges (*Citrus sinensis*)

Sweet orange (*Citrus sinensis*) or *Musambi* is native to China and nowadays grown on the largest scale in the warmer regions of the world. The best known areas producing sweet orange for the world market are Florida and California in the USA, Spain, Israel and South Africa. In almost every country with a warm climate oranges are grown for domestic purposes. In India, sweet oranges are grown in different parts of the country and some are exported.

Sweet Lime

Sweet orange is almost spherical and golden yellow or orange when ripe. In the tropics, the fruit often fails to develop the typical orange colour and ripens with the skin still green, which makes it less attractive in the export market. However, the orange colour can be developed with suitable gas treatment. The fruit contains a large amount of pulp which is yellow, orange or reddish in colour and held in varying numbers of segments loosely joined together and tightly adhering to the fairly thick rind. Many oranges contain light coloured seeds in the segments.

There are many varieties of sweet oranges. Some of the well-known types are "Jaffa" whose fruits are large, juicy and seedless, "Valencias" with a long fruiting season and "Washington Navel," so named because of an umbilical mark at the apex of the fruit. This is caused by the formation of a second small fruit. Navels are almost seedless. Oranges with a red pulp (or blood oranges) include the well known varieties "St. Michael" and "Maltese" The popular Indian types are "Musambi" (Mozambique) and "Sathgudi" (Chinese oranges). Blood-red Malta is also cultivated in India.

Sweet oranges are flavorous and juicy, and their pulp is sweet. They are mostly consumed as fresh fruits or used in the preparation of orange juice which is sold fresh, canned or as frozen concentrate. It is used for flavouring pastry products and in making marmalades. The essential oils, obtained from sweet orange flowers and leaves, are used in the preparation of essences and perfumes. Orange peels are used for making spiced spirits and to obtain pectin.

The world production of oranges is 47.4 million tonnes and India's 10.2 million tonnes, 2023-24. Andhra Pradesh in India produced, 2258 million tonnes, 2023–24, followed by Maharashtra, 973.3 million tonnes and Telangana, 395.3 million tonnes, 2023–24.

13.5.2 Tangerine (*Citrus reticulata*)

Tangerine (*Citrus reticulata*) is also known under several other names, one of which is "mandarin" denoting its origin in the Far East. Some have attempted to discriminate between tangerine and mandarins as different varieties, the former having deeper coloured skins than the latter, but the nomenclature, has become so confused that they are practically used as synonyms. There are a very large number of varieties of tangerines in India, known by the names "Santra," "Kamala," "Kinnow" and others.

Orange

Tangerines are the most valued commercial oranges in India. The fruit has the shape of a slightly flattened sweet orange. It has a thin, loose rind that can be easily detached from the fruit. The pulp of the fruit is sweet, juicy and has a characteristic and attractive flavour. The fruits are mostly eaten as a fresh dessert fruit and are used in the production of orange juice. The fruit is cultivated in the North-Eastern parts of India, Sikkim, Punjab, in Nagpur area of Maharashtra and the Coorg (Kodagu) district of Karnataka.

The world production is 44.2 million tonnes and Madhya Pradesh 2060.6 million tonnes, 2021–22, Punjab and Maharashtra produced 1177.5 million tonnes and 987.5 million tonnes respectively.

13.5.3 Sour Orange (*Citrus aurantium*)

Sour orange or *Khatta* (*Citrus aurantium*), also known as bitter orange, is indigenous to India. The fruit is round, rather rough and orange in colour. The pulp is juicy but is sour and bitter, and this makes it unattractive for eating raw. The fruit is largely used in the preparation of marmalades, and also in confections, liqueurs and other drinks. In India, it is used to prepare pickles.

13.5.4 Lime (*Citrus aurantifolia*)

Lime or *Nimbu* (*Citrus aurantifolia*) is a native of India. It is mainly cultivated in tropical countries. The fruits are small (smaller than most kinds of citrus), round and smooth with yellow or greenish-yellow skin. The fruits vary in size and the pulp is very acidic in taste. Lime is extensively used, for culinary purposes. It is used for squeezing the juice over other foods to bring out their flavour. It is used for preparing beverages, such as lemonade and as an additive in drinks, such as gin and rum. Lime cordial and pickles are the important commercial products of lime.

Lime

13.5.5 Lemon (*Citrus limon*)

Lemon or *Baranimbu* (*Citrus limon*) is cultivated in India. It is very widely grown in the Mediterranean and subtropical countries. The fruits are oblong or ovoid and terminate in a nipple-like end, the rind is thick and yellow, while the pulp is nearly white and the juice is the most acidic of the citrus juices. It is used for cookery and other purposes, in the same way as limes. Lemon juice with added sugar (lemonade) is a very refreshing drink. Lemon is also used in baking and confectionery. Lemon peels are used in the preparation of lemon oil.

Lemon

The world production is 10.1 million tonnes and India's being 3.79 million tonnes, 2023-24. In India, Andhra Pradesh is the highest producer of lime and lemons with 905.9 million tonnes, followed by Gujarat and Maharashtra 636.4 million tonnes and 429.4 million tonnes respectively, 2023-24. India ranked first in world production in the year 2023-24.

13.5.6 Pummelo (*Citrus maxima*)

Pummelo or *Chakotra* (*Citrus maxima*) is not a cultivated crop; it is mostly a home yard fruit. The fruits are large, oval shaped, yellow and sometimes crimson, with a thick rind. The pulp is white or red, and the cells are large and separated from each other. Chakotras, are distinguished from grapefruits, mainly from their larger size, thicker rind, tough and solid pulp, and the tree bears fruit singly. The fruits are an esteemed dessert fruit; they are also made into jam and marmalade.

Pummelo

The taste is pleasant the edible flesh is pulpy, white, pink or red, depending on variety. It has several nutritional value; rich in vitamin C, minerals like magnesium, potassium, Vitamin B6, dietary fiber. Promotes good digestion, breaks down complex protein. It contains a "fatty burning enzyme" known as carnitine palmitoyl-transferase. Since it is rich in potassium prevents osteoporosis. The antioxidant property prevents premature aging process of sagging skin, wrinkles. It also contains spermidine, a chemical found in human sperm which delays aging process.

13.5.7 Grapefruit (*Citrus parodist*)

Unlike other citrus fruits which originated in Asia, grapefruit (*Citrus parodist*) is thought to have arisen in the West Indies. It is mostly cultivated in the USA, West Germany and South Africa. Grapefruit grows well, in the tropics also and has been introduced to our country and is cultivated in Punjab and some other parts. Grapefruit is probably a hybrid between pummelo and sweet orange. Next to orange, grapefruit is marketed in large quantities. The fruits are round

Grapefruit

or pear-shaped, generally smaller than pummelo with yellow skin and borne in clusters. Most kinds of grapefruits have a pale yellowish pulp, but there are also kinds with a pinkish pulp. The pulp is not as sweet as that of the orange. Grapefruits are much consumed as fresh fruits. The fruit is also canned, and this can be used in fruit salads and other dishes. Grapefruit juice and marmalade are also made from the fruit.

The world production is 9.76 million tonnes and India produced 257 thousand kilos, 2022.

13.5.8 Kumquat (*Citrus japonica*)

It belongs to *Rutaceae* family, *Citrus japonica*. Native to China, it has juicy and bitter flesh, its rind is fragrant and sweet. The tiny fruit resembles orange. The Vitamin C content, is high like orange but higher than grapes, banana and apple. Studies reveal consuming this fruit, maintains healthier blood pressure. It has many health promoting factors, it regulates digestion, healthy skin, eye, hair and boosts immunity. Lowers cholesterol, strengthens bone and improves nerve health.

Kumquat

It is used in garnishing cocktails, jams, jellies, candies and desserts. It has essential amino acids such as lime onene, alpha-pinene and monoterpenes. Rich in minerals such as potassium, calcium, rich in vitamin C and vitamin A and riboflavin.

Besides the above, it aids good digestion and regularizes bowel movement avoids gas formation, bloating and cramps. It prevents diabetes, boosts immunity by stimulating new cell growth, prevents infection and it is good for skin and eye care. Being rich source of vitamin A and beta carotene it acts as antioxidant, relieves stress, macular cells and reduces the development of cataract. It builds bone as it is good source of calcium. Since it is good a source of carbohydrates hence is good source of energy.

13.5.9 Mangosteen (*Gracinia magostan*)

It is a tropical fruit, having good fragrance. Its colour is burgundy-purple, having a leathery skin, containing most snow-white and sweet flesh. The mellow flavour is similar to mango. It is the national fruit of Thailand. It's edible flesh has snow-white triangular segment which can be with flat seed or seedless. The texture of the flesh is juicy and with a luscious mouthfeel. It has 16% sugar and has volatile compounds that give it the floral aromatic sweet tart; caramel and butter-like feel.

Mangosteen

It has several healing properties. Mangosteen rind has antioxidant xanthones, pulp or the juice has antifungal, antibacterial, anti-inflammatory properties and combat radicals and improves the immune system. It is rich in vitamin C, minerals like copper, manganese, and magnesium. Low in calories and has no saturated fat or cholesterol, but is rich in dietary fibre. It is good at promoting red blood cells, boosts immunity and reduces cholesterol. It is advised in tuberculosis, blood pressure, and Alzheimer's disease.

13.5.10 Buddha's Hand (*Citrus medica* var. *sarcodactylis*)

This fruit belongs to citrus family, also called as fingered citron. This is segmented into finger-like projection, like an 'open hand" or it can be "closed hand", also there are varieties that have half fingers. All these have a basal side like that of a palm of a hand with closed, open or half fingers. Due to its interesting formation, it is called as Buddha's Hand.

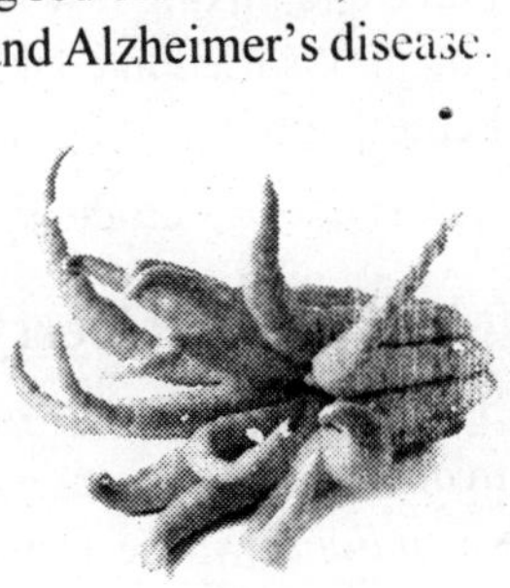

Buddha's hand

It grows in north eastern India, China, Japan and Malaysia. It is a shrub, with branches that are thorny, with oblong leaves four to six inches long. The shrub gives white flowers before fruiting. The fruit has a perfume like aroma, hence it adds zest to any preparations such as in cocktails, salads, desserts and can also be candied. The entire fruit is delicious and can be eaten whole. It has no juice or pulp. The closed hand symbolizes a prayerful gesture, hence offered at Temples. In traditional medicine, its dried and immature peels are used.

13.5.11 Other Citrus Fruits (*Citrus medica*)

Citron (*Citrus medica*) is a native of India. It grows wild, but it is cultivated to some extent. Many varieties are known. The fruits are of an unusual shape for citrus, it is elongated rather than globular with a thick, irregular and greenish-yellow to golden-yellow skin. The fruit is used mainly for pickling. Kumquat (*Fortunella spp*) is not a true citrus. In appearance, the fruits are like very small oranges, but they have an acidic taste. They are used for pickling or making into conserves.

The production of other citrus fruit in India 2021-22 was 463 kilo tonnes. Hence adding the total production of citrus fruit in 2021-22, 14.7 million tonnes.

13.6 Drupes

Drupes are edible fruits with thin skin, and juicy flesh enclosing a single seed (stone). Apricots, cherries, peaches and plums belong to this group. The fruits belong to the genus *Prunus* to which the almond also belongs. The stones of the fruit and the leaves of the plant, also have a flavour of almond essence.

13.6.1 Apricot (*Prunus armeniaca*)

Apricot (*Prunus armeniaca*) is a native of China, from where it has spread to India and other parts of the world. It grows well in warm temperate climates. In India, both wild and cultivated varieties are found in Kashmir, Himachal Pradesh and Uttar Pradesh. We export some apricot and other stone fruits, but we import much more than we export. The fruit is a drupe, similar to a small peach, 1.5–2.5 cm (0.6 – 1.0) in diameter, from yellow to orange, often tinged red on the side most exposed to the sun; its surface can be smooth or velvety with very short hairs. The flesh is usually firm and not very juicy. Its taste can range from sweet to tart.

Apricot

Apricots are eaten fresh in the regions where they are grown. They are highly perishable; so, they are preserved, canned or dried in larger quantities. They are also frozen, candied or made into a paste. Apricot nectar, is a popular beverage and is prepared by steaming and converting the ripe soft fruit into puree and mixing it with sugar syrup containing some citric acid. The kernels of apricots are pressed to obtain oils used in cooking. The kernels of some apricots are sweet and eaten like almond kernels. The kernel oil of sweet apricot is used as a substitute for almond oil.

The world production is 3.86 million tonnes and India produced 14.9 kilo tonnes in 2022.

13.6.2 Sweet Cherry (*Prunus avium*)

Sweet cherry (*Prunus avium*) is considered to be a hybrid of the wild form of the species *Prunus* var *avium* (commonly known as Mazzard or Gean) which gives small purple-black, sweet fruits, as with var *juliana*, whose fruits are heart-shaped, soft fleshed and var *duracina* with firm fleshed and often heart-shaped fruits. A cultivated cherry is thus a small spherical or heart-shaped fruit either dark-red, black or pale yellow, with more or less red flesh. It probably originated in Western Asia. In India, it is cultivated in Kashmir and Kulu Valley at an elevation of about 1,500 m.

Cherries

Sweet cherries are used as a dessert fruit. They are very perishable and are preserved by canning, brining, freezing or drying. Large quantities of cherry are bleached with sulphur dioxide "brine" (calcium carbonate or hydroxide solution) and made into marachino-type and creme-de-menthe cherries, which are used in fruit salads, fruit cocktails, ice cream and baking products. When brined cherries are treated with concentrated sugar syrup, the water in the fruit will be replaced with syrup and cherry candies are obtained. A liquor of high alcohol content (Kirschwasser) is obtained by distillation of fermented sweet cherries. An edible oil can be obtained from cherry kernels.

Sour cherry (*Prunus cerasus*) contains more acid and it is not used as a table fruit. It is used for canning and cooking. Cherry juice obtained from sour cherries that has a characteristic odour and sour taste and makes a good beverage when mixed with juice of sweet cherries.

The world cherry production is 4.36 million tonnes and India produced 10,934 tonnes, 2022.

Sour cherries the world production is 1.59 million tonnes.

13.6.3 Karonda (*Carissa carandas*)

It is a wild berry, grown in Nilgiri Hills, Western Ghats, West Bengal. It is astringent and is used for skin maladies, helps in digestive problems such as constipation and stomach pain. It is a great cure for anaemic conditions.

Karonda

13.6.4 Kundong Fruit (*Garcinia parvifolia*)

It is known by several names, Brunei cherry, Kedundong, Kumanjing, Kandis etc. It is a cherry-sized fruit with a red-yellow skin, that is juicy. Resembles mangosteen. They grow in hillside. The fruits are eaten and they are sour.

Kundong

13.6.5 Peach (*Prunus persica*)

Peach (*Prunus persica*) like apricot is a native of China. It was introduced to the West via Persia and was thought to be of Persian in origin, hence the name *Persica*. Peaches grow widely in temperate regions, particularly in the Mediterranean countries. The major producer of peach is USA. It is cultivated to some extent in India in Kashmir, Kulu Valley, Himachal Pradesh and the Kumaon Hills.

Peaches

The fruit is almost spherical with a groove on one side. The velvety skin varies from greenish-white to golden-yellow, with a crimson colouring, which may be almost non-existent or a complete covering. The colour of the flesh may be white or yellow, while the flesh around the stone is frequently red in colour. If the flesh adheres to the stone the peaches are classified as clingstone and, if it does not, as freestone.

Freestone peaches are soft and juicy and mostly used as table fruit or frozen. Clingstone peaches are large, hard fleshed and almost inedible in the raw state but become delicious when cooked in syrup and are most popular for canning. Significant quantities are used for the preparation of jams and confectioneries. Beverages, such as juice, nectar or peach brandy, are also prepared from peaches. The kernel after removing the cyanogen containing glucoside amygdalin (by hydrolysis) is reported to be useful as a substitute for almonds. The kernel oil is used for the same purpose as apricot oil.

Nectarine (*P. persia* var *nectarina*): This is a smooth-skinned peach. It has a much higher flavour and brighter colour than most peaches. It is generally smaller in size and of the clingstone variety.

The world production is 27.1 million tonnes and India's production is 2,78,000 tonnes, 2022-23.

13.6.6 Plums (*Prunus domestica*)

There are numerous species of plums (*Prunus domestica*) growing wild in the Northern Hemisphere. Best known among cultivated plums are the common plum or European plum (*P. domestica*) and Japanese plum (*P. salicina*).

Plums

The common plum resembles, apricot or peach in shape and size. Plums differ in colour; some are green, a few black and other red or purple. The Japanese plum is brightly coloured (orange-red or golden-yellow) but is usually inferior in flavour.

Certain types of plums, contain a sufficiently high proportion of sugar to dehydrate naturally without the removal of the pit and such dehydrated plums are prunes. For this purpose, types containing a large proportion of solids, particularly sugars, are preferred; the type "Splendour" grown successfully in South India is said to be very suitable. Prunes are canned and used in the preparation of prune pulp and prune beverage.

Fresh plums are used as dessert fruits and also cooked and eaten. They are also canned, dried, frozen and made into jam. Plum kernels yield a fatty oil resembling almond oil and can be used for the same general purpose.

The world production is 12.39 million tonnes and India's production 67,930 tonnes in 2021-22.

13.6.7 Annabelle Indian Hog Plum (*Spondias pinnata*)

It is highly acidic but also has a sweetish flavour of pineapple. It is used to make juice, pickle in cocktails. Rich in vitamin C, hence it is antioxidant, boosts immune system, helps in maintaining collagen, skin ligaments and cartilage in healthy condition. Since it is also rich in iron helps to produce haemoglobin and myoglobin. It is known as Ambasta, Aambrothaka, Madhuramlaka in Sanskrit and Ambado in Konkani.

Indian Hog Plum

13.7 Grapes (*Vitis vinifera*)

Grapes are one of the oldest cultivated plants. There are records of details of grape and wine production in Egypt dating to 2400 BC. Wines may have been made from wild grapes in the Caucasus region in even earlier times. The Greeks and Romans, developed grape cultivation (viticulture) and the use of grape wine by them was common. In India, grapes have been mentioned by Charaka and Sushruta in their early medical treatises in first century AD. There is no precise information about the commencement of grape cultivation in the country.

Grapes (Black)

Grapes (Green)

Grapes (Red)

There are more than 8,000 types of grapes that have been described in different parts of the world. Of these, a few may be growing in different vineyards. The principal source of all cultivated grapes throughout the world is *Vitis vinifera,* which probably originated in South-Eastern Europe. This is known as wine grape or European grape. Besides this, a number of species of grapes native to North America such as *Vitis labrusca* and *Vitis rotundifolia* are cultivated to a limited extent in eastern USA. However, even in the USA, *V. vinifera* is the most cultivated species. All the species of cultivated grapes are found in India.

The world production is 80.1 million tonnes and India's production is 3.40 million tonnes in 2022. In India Maharashtra 2.466 million tonnes; Karnataka 0.854 million tonnes; Tamil Nadu 0.050 tonnes in 2022-22.

With so many types of cultivated grapes, it is difficult to classify them. They are generally grouped as wine grapes and dessert grapes. The most important source of both these types are *V. vinifera*. In India, a large number of types of grapes have been cultivated experimentally at different places and times but the principal types commercially grown are Anab-e-shahi, Bangalore Blue, Bhokri, Cheema-7, Cheema-94, Kali-shahebi, Gulabi (Muscat Hamburg), Perlette and Thompson Seedless (Sultana).

The size and chemical composition of the berry, depends on the type of grape and method of cultivation. The wine grapes or grapes of European origin are elongated berries and the skin and flesh are tender. The grapes of American origin have tough skin and flesh. Among the grapes grown in India, Kishmish bears small berries and Anab-e-shahi the largest berries. The skin is made up of an epidermis and several layers of underlying cells, and the epidermis is covered by a layer of wax. The components of the skin are responsible for the colour, flavour and aroma of grapes. The pulp consists of several layers of cells and contains the major part of the juice. The berry contains four, two or no seeds. The seedless varieties are valued as table fruit and for the production of raisins.

Grapes are rich in reducing sugars. The mature fruit contains glucose and fructose in almost equal proportions and only small amounts of sucrose are found. The pectin content of grapes is usually small. Grapes are poor in protein. They, however, contain free amino acids. Nearly 60–90 per cent of the total nitrogen of grape juice is due to amino acids. This is of importance as a yeast develops in the fermentation of grape juice. The principal acids of grapes are the tartaric and malic acids which constitute well over 90 per cent of total acids. Citric acid is present in relatively small amounts. The various colours of grapes are due to the pigments of the skin. The green colour of the immature fruit is owing to chlorophyll which fades on ripening. The yellow colour is because of the flavone components. The red, blue, purple and black colours are due to anthocyanins. Grapes are poor sources of vitamins; even the vitamin C content is low (1.0 mg per 100 g of edible portion).

Over 80 per cent of the world production of grapes is utilized in making wine and brandy, 7 per cent is dried into raisins and the remaining is consumed as fresh fruit (table grapes) or processed juice. In India, grapes are mostly consumed as fresh fruit. Large size, thin skin and brilliant colour are appreciated. Thompson seedless is popular because of its seedless nature and pleasant flavour. Anab-e-shahi also enjoys good reputation. Grapes are also used as canned grapes and grape juice, both fresh and canned. Grape juice concentrates are also prepared and used. Certain types of grapes are dehydrated into raisins (see Sec. 13.11).

For methods of manufacture of wines and brandies see Chapter 12. By-products of wine manufacture are utilized for the preparation of grape-seed oil and tannins.

13.8 Melons

Melons belong to the same family as cucumbers, marrows and squashes (*Cucurbitaceae*). Melons are commonly eaten raw. Their flesh consists of about 94 per cent water and only about 5 per cent sugars. The seeds stripped of their hard coats may be eaten and also yield an edible oil.

13.8.1 Melon (*Cucumis melo*)

Melon or *Karbuj* (*Cucumis melo*) is a native of tropical Africa and is cultivated in the warmer regions of the world. It is cultivated throughout India. A large number of cultivated varieties have been developed to suit various climatic conditions. The varieties vary in size, colour and roughness of rind, taste, flavour and colour of the flesh. The skin may be soft or hard, yellow, green, cream or orange in colour, with plain or netted surface markings. The colour of the flesh varies from white to cream yellow, orange or green. Some of the commonly known varieties are musk melon, cantaloupe, honeydew, etc.

Muskmelon

Muskmelon, also called sweet melon, netted melon or nutmeg melon, is usually distinctly netted, with a raised network, generally lighter than the overall colour of the fruit, which may be yellowish or green. The surface may be segmented into broad ribs and grooves. The flesh is green to orange and has a musky odour. Cantaloupes have a scaly rind but are not netted. They are often deeply grooved and orange coloured. Honeydew is a smooth-skinned variety with pale green flesh which is not strongly scented.

13.8.2 Watermelon (*Citrullus vulgaris*)

Watermelon or *Turbuj* (*Citrullus vulgaris*) is also a native of tropical Africa and cultivated throughout India. The fruit is usually ellipsoidal and varies in size from small to about 50 cm across. The skin colour varies from white to yellow

Watermelon

and light green to dark green. The colour of the flesh is reddish or pink or yellowish-white. The seeds are numerous, small, black, brownish or white in colour. The edible portion of the fruit contains about 95 per cent water and 4 per cent carbohydrate. It is used as a dessert. The seeds may be used as food. They are oily and nutritious.

The world production is 104.93 million tonnes and India is 3.626 million tonnes, 2023 and India's production being 4.23 million tonnes in 2024–28.

13.9 Pomes

Pomes are fruits of apple and pear trees. The receptacle, which surrounds the ovaries in the flower, enlarges to become edible and juicy and encloses the cells containing the seeds. Though apples and pears are grouped under pomes, there are distinguishing features between the two kinds of fruits.

13.9.1 Apples (*Malus pumila*)

The Apple or *Seb* (*Malus pumila*) has been cultivated from time immemorial. Apples are the most important and widely cultivated fruits of temperate regions. They have been successfully cultivated in India since the middle of the Eighteenth Century both in the plains and hills of North India. It is now a commercial crop in the hilly areas of Kashmir, Kulu and Kumaon.

Apple

The world production of apples is 97.3 million tonnes and India's 2.59 million tonnes, 2023. Jammu & Kashmir, 2,064.3 million tonnes, Himachal Pradesh 506.7 million tonnes in 2023-24.

There are over 6,500 different types of apples, which can be recognized by a combination of many characteristics of the tree and fruits, found in various parts of the world. The fruits vary in quality, texture, size, shape, colour, flavour, scent, and seasonal and keeping qualities. All the cultivated apples, are derived from the common wild crab apple (*Malus pumila*) which grows in many regions of Europe, Asia and America. Some may be the offspring, of crossing with *Malus sylvestris*, a Wild North European variety with sour shiny green fruit, and *Malus mitis*, which is native only to Southern and Eastern Europe and gives sweet coloured fruits.

Apples are valued especially for their good as keeping qualities. Through proper selection, varieties of apples giving fruits which can be picked, in different seasons of the year have been developed. The cultivated types of apples in India are mostly those introduced from Europe and the USA. Some important types grown are Ambri Kashmiri (indigenous to the Kashmir Valley), Golden Delicious, Red Delicious, Baldwin, Jonathan, Cox's Orange Pippin, etc.

Apples are more or less spherical with a depression at each end. They vary in size and some varieties are slightly pointed at one end. The skin is smooth, tightly adhering to the flesh and varies in colour from green through yellow to red. The flesh is white or yellowish. The core running, through the centre of the fruit from depression to depression consists of units containing seeds.

The chemical composition of the apple fruit varies with fruit variety, climatic condition during growth and the stage of maturity. Of the total carbohydrates present about 80 per cent constitutes sugar. Fructose is the principal component (60 per cent), followed by glucose (25 per cent) and sucrose (15 per cent). Malic acid is the principal acid of apples constituting 90–95 per cent of the total acids. The astringent principles of apple include tannin and tannin derivatives. The relative proportion of sugars, acids and astringents make up the flavour of the fruit. The ratio of acid to sugar is a most noticeable feature. Fruits with high acid content are used for culinary purposes. Dessert apples, also have high acid content but they also have more sugars and this balance makes them a richly flavoured fruit. The vitamins, minerals and acids of apples are concentrated particularly in and just below the skin, and the fruit should be eaten unpeeled.

Apples are used extensively as a dessert and cooking fruit; sliced apples are canned, dehydrated or frozen. They are used in the preparation of jams, jellies, muraba, apple butter and apple sauce. Muraba is prepared from peeled, cut sections of the fruits. The pieces are bleached, in hot water containing sodium bi-sulphite; lime water or alum is added as a firming agent. The pieces are pickled all over and cooked in sugar syrup to which a small quantity of citric acid is added. Apple butter, is made by cooking the fruit with water until soft, followed by screening. The pulp is mixed with sugar or apple juice and the mixture is concentrated until the desired consistency is attained. Spices or other flavouring material may be added before the completion of cooking.

Apples are also used for making juice. The juice obtained from pressing the fruits is strained, pasteurized and bottled. For preparing a product with good flavour, juices from several apple varieties are blended. By inoculating apple juice, with wine yeasts alcoholic fermentation takes place giving cider, which contains up to 8 per cent alcohol. In the preparation of cider, fruits with low acid and high sugar and tannin content are used. Apple wines, are made by fermenting a mixture of apple juice and sugar so that the product does not contain more than 14 per cent alcohol. Apple brandy is obtained by distilling clarified cider in pot stills.

13.9.2 Pears (*Pyrus communis*)

Pear

Pears (*Pyrus communis*) are much like apples and there are many varieties of pears as in the case of apples. Amongst temperate fruits, the pear stands next to the apple in total world production. In India, the pear is cultivated on a much smaller scale than the apple. The fruits vary in size and are large at the calyx end (outer whorl of floral part) and taper off towards the other end. The skin is smooth, usually yellow and sometimes red. Pears are harvested when green and allowed to ripen in storage. The flesh ranges from soft and tender to hard and woody. The flavour varies from soft and bland to mild. Pears are used as a dessert fruit. They are canned in large quantities. They are used in cookery. The juice of pears is a beverage and fermented by the action of yeast to produce an alcoholic beverage (perry).

Pears are good source of dietary fibre and good source of vitamin C. Pears are less allergenic compared to other fruits and they are low in salicylates and benzoates, hence recommended in allergenic exclusion diets. Belongs to *Rosaceae* family. The pear is native to coastal and mildly sized tree, reaching 10-17 m tall, often with a tall, narrow crown; a few species are shrubby. The leaves are alternatively arranged, simple 2–12 cm long, glossy green on some species, densely silvery hairy in some others; leaf shape varies from broad oval to narrow lanceolate.

Pears and apples cannot always be distinguished by the form of the fruit; some parts look very much like some apples. One major difference is that the flesh of pear fruit contains stone cells (also called "grit").

The world production is 26.3 million tonnes and 3,09,000 tonnes in India, in 2022 and 3,41,460 tonnes in India 2023-24.

13.10 Tropical and Subtropical Fruits

Apart from the fruits belonging to different groups discussed above, there are several other fruits of tropical or subtropical origin. Many of them are native to tropical America and some to India and other tropical regions. Some of the fruits grown and consumed in India are the following:

13.10.1 Amla (*Emblica officinalis*)

Indian Gooseberry

Amla or Indian Gooseberry (*Emblica officinalis*) is a native of India, Malaya and China, and is met with, wild or cultivated, throughout the greater part of India. The fruits are depressed globose, 1–2.5 cm in diameter, fleshy and obscurely six lobed, containing six trigonous seeds. They are green when tender, light yellow or brick-red when mature. The fruits, are sour and astringent, and occasionally eaten raw. They are much esteemed for making pickles, preserves and jellies. The fruit is a rich source of pectin.

Amla fruit is probably the richest known natural source of vitamin C. The fruit juice contains nearly 20 times as much vitamin C as orange juice. Some antioxidants present in the fruit prevent or retard the oxidation of the vitamin and renders the fruit a valuable antiscorbutic in fresh as well as dry condition. *Amla* fruit finds several medicinal uses in indigenous medicine.

13.10.2 Avocado (*Persea americana*)

Avacado

Avocado pear or butter fruit (*Persea americana*) is native to Central America and traces back to 6000 BC, the original native name of aguacate orahuacatl still survives and a large number of types are grown in India. The fruits are somewhat the size and shape of a pear. They are yellow-green to maroon and purple in colour. The skin is thin and the pulp when ripe has the consistency of firm butter, creamy to bright yellow in colour with delicious nutty flavour.

To eat, the fruit is split open and the inedible stone in the centre is removed. The flesh is then scooped out and eaten raw or flavoured with pepper, salt or sugar. The pulp is also used in vegetable or fruit salads. Avocado contains more proteins (1.7 per cent) than any other fruit and contains up to 14 per cent fat.

75% of avocado energy comes from fat and it is monounsaturated fat present as oleic acid. Besides this, it has palmitic and linoleic acid. The saturated fat content is 14%.

It is source of Vitamin B, K, C, E and Vitamin A. It has phytosterols and carotenoids such as lutein and zeaxanthin.

Some people have allergic reactions of ulceration of mouth and throat, the other symptomatic urticarial, abdominal pain and vomiting in severe cases it is life-threatening.

Avocado lowers cholesterol, diabetes and blood pressure. The oleic monounsaturated fats acts as antioxidant and prevents artery blockage.

There are three basic families of Avocados, Mexican (*Persea americana* var, *drymifolia*), Guatemalan (*Persea americana* var. *guatemalensis*) and West Indian (*Persea americana* var. *americana*). Any of the hundreds of varieties available today will have descended from these families.

Some dieters avoid avocados, as they are high in fat. But two-thirds of the fat is monounsaturated, which benefits body and heart in particular. Avocados are cholesterol-free. They contain good amounts of folic acid, fibre, potassium, and vitamins C and E.

Once avocado has ripened, it can be stored in the fridge for five to seven days. Hard avocado should not be refrigerated. But avocado can be frozen as purees which are used for salad dressing, sandwich spread or as a base for a dip such as guacamole. The world production is 5567044 tonnes in 2016.

13.10.3 Banana (*Musa paradisiaca*)

Bananas (*Musa paradisiaca*) were derived by man in prehistoric times from wild bananas which grew in the regions stretching from India to New Guinea. They are now in all parts of the tropics. The cultivated kinds are sterile hybrid forms; they cannot be pinned down to an exact species. They belong to the genus *Musa.* The edible banana (plantain) is given the name *Musa paradisiaca.* Many of the cultivated varieties of bananas are grown in India and they show variation in habit, fruiting behaviour, colour and quality of fruits.

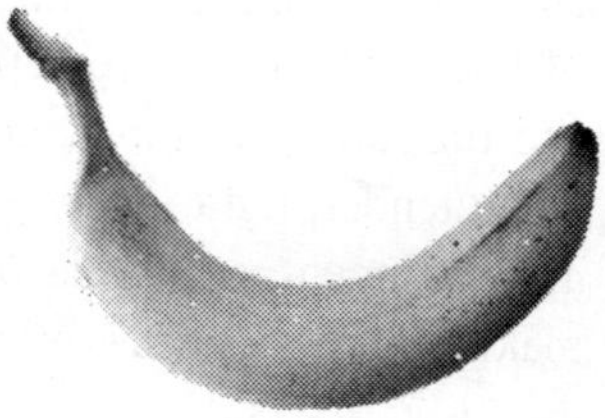
Banana

The fruits appear in a bunch consisting of a number (about 9–12) of half-spirals of fruit which are clearly separated from each other and is called "hands." Each hand contains 12–16 individual fruits, sometimes called "fingers." A bunch may consist of 120–200 individual fruits or bananas. The skin of the fruit is green when unripe and turns yellow when ripe. The skin is easily peeled off to reveal the edible flesh which, in most varieties, is white with a tinge of yellow and seedless. Bananas from dwarf banana plants are somewhat smaller and thinner-skinned than those of the usual variety.

Bananas are not allowed to ripen on the plant, but ripened after harvesting. In India, ripening is effected usually by smoking. In organized trade, ripening is carried out in specially controlled chambers where heating and ventilation are controlled. Bananas ripened by smoking or heating in closed chambers are not as sweet as those ripened slowly over the period of a week or two at a temperature of about 18–20°C. Bananas cannot be refrigerated. Chilled bananas do not soften normally and develop darkened areas and unpleasant odours.

Banana fruits are used in several different ways. The most widely known are dessert bananas, which, because of their high sugar content of 17–19 per cent, have a sweet taste and are eaten raw. Fruits are used in the Indian confections "*rasayanam*" and "*panchamrutham*" sugar coated chips, toffee, jams and jellies. The fruit pulp is dried and processed into flour or preserved in many forms for subsequent use. Bananas are also used for cooking. Bananas used for cooking have a higher starch and lower sugar content than dessert bananas. Many different varieties of cooking bananas are known, some are especially for steaming and some for roasting. Cooked bananas are the staple food in certain parts of Kerala, in many Pacific Islands and in East Africa. Bananas are used for making beer in East Africa where special varieties are grown for the purpose.

The world production of banana is 179 million tonnes and India is 34.5 million tonnes in 2022 and 40 million tonnes in 2030. In India, Maharashtra is 6,534.35 million tonnes, Andhra Pradesh is 5,830.93 million tonnes, Tamil Nadu is 4,719.95 million tonnes in 2023-24. India ranked first in world production in the year 2022.

13.10.4 Carambola (*Averrhoa carambola*)

Carambola (*Averrhoa carambola*) is a native of Indonesia, and it is grown throughout our country. The fruits which are 7 to 12 cm long, ribbed, and of a very attractive yellow colour, are borne in great profusion on the plant. They are also known as "star" fruit.

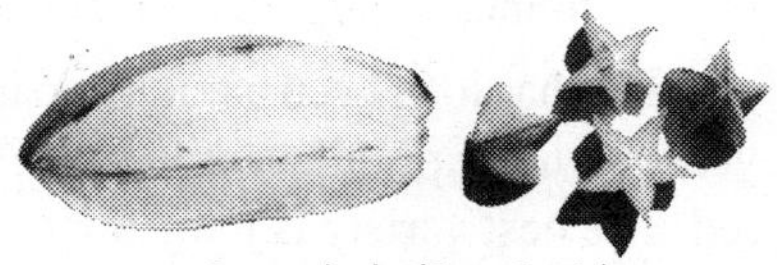

Carambola (Star Fruit)

The fruits, are very juicy but variable in taste; some are sweet and some are rather sour. The sweet variety is used in fruit salads, jellies, tarts and preserves, and in making a refreshing drink.

13.10.5 Dates (*Phoenix dactylifera*)

Date or *Khajur* (*Phoenix dactylifera*) is an important palm crop of ancient origin that grew in the Middle East, especially in desert oasis. The date is of Persian origin and Iraq is the most important date producing country, followed by Saudi Arabia, Algeria, Iran and Egypt. They are now cultivated in dry subtropical areas. There are no commercial plantations of good dates in India. Quite several trees are, however, found growing wild or cultivated in dry districts. The fruit is an oblong berry, reddish or yellowish-brown when ripe. It contains a seed that is cylindrical, hard, with a longitudinal furrow.

Dates (Dry)

Dates (Fresh)

Dates are generally classified into three types, soft, semi-dry and dry. Soft dates are often sold in pressed masses and are eaten raw or used in confectionery. Considerable quantities of these dates are consumed in India which are imported from West Asia. Among the semi-dry, one variety *Deglet Noor* is the world's most popular date. The dry dates are quite hard and can be kept for a long time. One variety of *churra* from Algeria is very popular in India and imported in large quantities.

Dates, fresh or dried, are an important article of diet in Arab countries. Their chief nutritional value is in their high sugar content which varies from about 60 per cent in soft dates to some 70 per cent in the dry types. They also have some content of vitamins A, B_1 and B_2, and nicotinic acid. Dates are widely used in bakery and confectionery. Dates can be canned as a paste after pitting, grinding and mixing with invert sugar syrup. Brandy of good quality is made from dates in Arabian countries.

In addition to the date palm, another variety of wild date palm (*Phoenix sylvestris*) is common throughout India and found in large numbers (about 29 million palm trees). It is mostly tapped for its sap which, fresh and unfermented, is *nira*, a refreshing sweet drink. The sap is utilized for the preparation of palm jaggery (*gur*) and sugar. *Nira* is fermented to make toddy (see Sub-section 18.3.2).

The world production is 9.7 million tonnes in 2016.

13.10.6 Guava (*Psidium guajava*)

Guava is native to Peru in South America, dates back to 880BC *Psidium guajava* is the botanical name, derives from the original native and Spanish name guajana *P. guinernse,* the guinea guava and *P. cattleyanum,* the strawberry guava, both grow in India and it is small edible fruits. Pink guavas contain lycopene.

Guava

In India Uttar Pradesh 1,007.4 million tonnes, Madhya Pradesh is 1,021.0 million tonnes, Bihar 431.6 million tonnes in 2023-24. India ranked first in world production in the year 2022.

This has long been naturalized in India and many varieties are cultivated. The fruits are green, turning yellow when ripe and vary in shape and size. The flesh is creamy white to yellow and, in some varieties, red. The best variety is juicy but the pulp is full of small seeds and has a somewhat sharp flavour.

Guavas are mostly eaten as fresh fruits. They are also canned to some extent, preserved spiced, or made into jam and marmalades. "Guava juice" is an excellent beverage. Guavas are notable for their high content of vitamin C which, in many varieties, is 4 to 10 times greater than in citrus fruits. They also contain a considerable amount of pectin.

13.10.7 Jackfruit (*Artocarpus heterophyllus*)

A large tropical fruit tree, the jackfruit tree (*Artocarpus heterophyllus*) is indigenous to India and grows plentifully throughout the warmer parts of the country, especially in Bengal, Bihar and the Deccan. The fruits are borne on the trunk and on the main branches. They are oval and oblong and sometimes weigh as much as 25 kg. The skin which is studded with short spikes, is pale green, becoming greenish-yellow and brownish, when ripe. The fruit contains a large number of seeds, each enclosed in a yellowish juicy sheath, with strong flavour. There are two common varieties: *Kapa* and *Barka.* The former has a sweet flesh and crisp pericarp, and the latter, which is considered inferior, has a thin mucilaginous and sour pericarp.

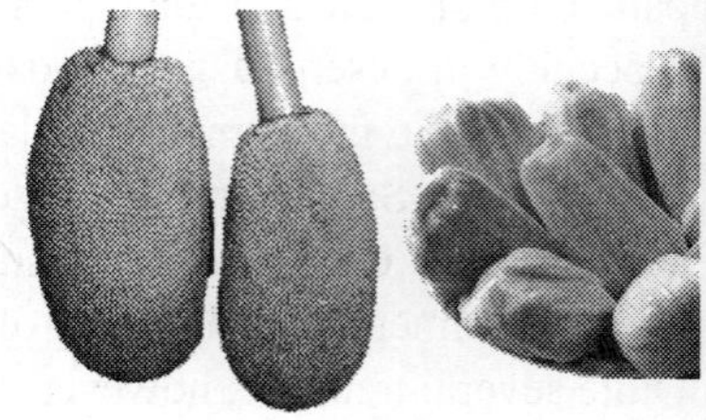

Jackfruit

Unripe jackfruit is used as a vegetable or made into pickles, while the ripe one is eaten fresh or preserved in syrup. The seeds are rich in starch and are eaten after roasting or boiling.

Breadfruit (*Artocarpus communis*) is a related species and its main nutritional constituent is starch and is usually eaten after baking or boiling. It forms a staple part of the diet where it is grown.

India's production is 1.4 million tonnes in 2018-19.

13.10.8 Durian (*Durio zibethinus*)

Comes from the mallow family, its botanical name is *Durio zibethinus.* Durian's stinking smell, can occupy a whole building. Hence it is not appreciated by many. The Maladorous aroma is compared with rotting onions or Limburger cheese. It resembles Jack fruit in exterior, but is small 15–30 centimetres long and having about the same size in diameter. The exterior yellow-yellow green in colour. It is filled with soft, meaty pulp that is cream-yellow or red. Within the pulp there are few seeds. The seeds can be eaten upon cooking. The export variety-Monthong is also known as "golden pillow" popular in Thailand and Malaysia.

Durian

It increases immunity, advised against heart attack, prevention of cancer. Has good dietary fibre. Rich in vitamin C, protein, folic acid, vitamin A and B, potassium, iron, calcium, magnesium, sodium, zinc and phosphorus are the minerals. An interesting fact is the stinking odour is due to the volatile sulphur compounds and it has 50 different odour-inducing factors.

PLATE 1: BERRIES

Blackberry

Blueberry

Longanberry

Boysenberry

Salmon Berry

Raspberry

Silvan Blackberry

Mulberry

Strawberry

CITRUS FRUITS

Orange

Lemon

Lime

PLATE 2: CITRUS FRUITS

Sweet Lime

Pummelo

Grapefruit

Mangosteen

Kumquat

Buddha's Hand

DRUPES

Cherries

Peach

Karonda

Apricot

Kundong

Plums

Indian Hog Plum

PLATE 3: GOOSEBERRIES AND CURRANTS

Gooseberries (Green)

Gooseberries (Red)

Currants (White)

Currants (Black)

Currants (Red)

GRAPES

Grapes (Black)

Grapes (Green)

Grapes (Red)

PLATE 4

MELONS

Watermelon

Muskmelon

POMES

Apple

Pear

TROPICAL FRUITS

Indian Gooseberry

Avocado

Banana

Carambola (Star Fruit)

Dates (Fresh)

Dates (Dry)

Guava

Jackfruit

Durian

PLATE 5: TROPICAL FRUITS

Jamun Fruit

Mango

Papaya

Passion Fruit

Pineapple

Sapota

Pomegranate

Ramphal

Sitaphal

Lakshman Phal

Hanuman Phal

PLATE 6: OTHER FRUITS

Figs

Woodapple

Rose Apple

Ice Apple

Longan

Langsat

Tamarillos

Kiwi

Sorrel Fruit

Paw Paw

Persimmon

Nectarians

PLATE 7: OTHER FRUITS

Pithaya (Dragon Fruit)

Ximenia

COLE CROPS

White Cabbage

Red Cabbage

Chinese Cabbage

Bokchoy

Knol-Khol

Brussels-Sprouts

PLATE 8: COLE CROPS

Watercress

Kale

Collard-Greens

Cauliflower (Orange)

Cauliflower (Purple)

Cauliflower (White)

Broccoli

Romanesco

ROOTS

Parsnip

Carrot

PLATE 9: ROOTS

Radish (White)

Radish (Red)

Beetroot

Rutabaga

Turnip

Celeriac

Arrachacha

Black Salsify

FRUIT VEGETABLES

Tomato

Bell-Pepper

Eggplant

PLATE 10: COLE CROPS

FRUIT VEGETABLES

Okra

Chow

CUCURBITS

Cucumber

CUCURBITS

Dosakai

Pumpkin

SQUASHES & GOURDS

Summer Squash

Summer Squash (Green)

GOURDS

Ridge Gourd

Sponge Gourd

Bitter Gourd

Kantola

Chinese Bitter Gourd

Chinese Melon

PLATE 11: GOURDS

Gac

Monk Fruit

Luffa Gourd

Oysternut

Parval

Tinda

Porknut

Tindora

Snake Gourd

Ash Gourd

Bottle Gourd

PLATE 12: LEAFY VEGETABLES

Agathi

Amaranth (Red)

Amaranth (Green)

Beet Green

Celery

Curry Leaves

Fenugreek

Spinach

Lettuce

Parsley

Purslane

Sowa

PLATE 13: LEAFY VEGETABLES

Basale alba

Chard

Green Mustard

Spring Onion

Raddish Leaves

Chekkurmanis

TUBER VEGETABLES

Potato

Sweet Potatoes

Tapioca

Yam

Colocasia

PLATE 14: TUBER VEGETABLES

Arrow Root

Artichoke

BULBS

Onions

Garlic

Leek

Asparagus

Bamboo Shoots

Rhubarb

Baby Corn

Sweet Corn

PLATE 15: MILLETS

Proso Millet

Little Millet

Kodo Millet

Barnyard Millet

Finger Millet

Foxtail

Pearl Millet

Sorghum

PLATE 16: ANNAM BRAHMA

ANNAM BRAHMA

Rainbrow Diet : From the seven kinds of food

CEREALS, PULSES, FRUITS, VEGETABLES

COLOURS

WHITE

VIOLET

INDIGO

BLUE

GREEN

YELLOW

ORANGE

RED

Courtesy : **Ms. Kamlakshi,** Chitrakala Parshit

ANNAM BRAHMA

From the seven kinds of food
Which the Father produced by intellect and ardor,
One of his foods was common to all beings,
Two he assigned to the Gods,
Three he made for his own use,
One he bestowed upon the animals.

On this, everything is based:
Both that which breathes and that which does not.
How is it then that these foods do not dwindle
When they are constantly eaten up
He who knows this permanence
Eats food with his mouth;
He goes to the Gods,
He lives on power.

(BU I,5,1-3)

13.10.9 Jambu Fruit (*Syzygium cuminni*)

Jambu or *Jamun* fruit (*Syzygium cuminni*) is found throughout India. There are several types of fruits that differ in colour and size. Two types are commonly met within India, the *Ra Jamun,* bearing big oblong, deep-purple or bluish fruit with pink, greyish, juicy sweet pulp and small stone; and the inferior *Kaatha,* bearing small fruits with acid pulp. The ripe fruit is widely eaten in India. It is generally subacidic and astringent to taste, but is palatable in tart and puddings or when taken with salt. Wine is prepared from ripe fruits in Goa. Fruits are also used for making preserves, squash and jellies.

Jamun Fruit

Extracts from the bark and seeds are used in the treatment of diabetes. Oral administration of alcoholic extract of the seeds to diabetic patients, reduces the level of blood sugar and glycosuria. Fresh seeds are superior to dried ones in this respect. The fruits have also been used in the treatment of diabetes. The blossoms of the tree are an important source of honey and the trees in the Western Ghats are reported to contribute 30–40 per cent of the annual harvest of honey in the surrounding areas.

13.10.10 Mango (*Mangifera indica*)

Mango (*Mangifera indica*) is the best loved and choicest fruit of India and occupies a prominent place among the fruits of the world. It has been cultivated in India for over 4,000 years and is believed to have originated from the foothills of the Himalayas. Mango occurs wild or semi-wild nearly throughout India. It is also grown in plantations and orchards. The total area under mango is estimated to be 1.6 million hectares, constituting about 60 per cent of the total area under fruits. In 2023 mango production was around 43 million tonnes, being 45% of the global output. A small fraction of country's production of mangoes is exported. The introduction of mangoes to other tropical areas of the world is comparatively recent.

Mango

The mango fruit, is a large drupe in varied shape, size, colour and flavour. The shapes are normally round, oval or oblong and the size ranges from plum-sized ones to giants (more than 22 cm long). The fruit skin may be thick or thin, leathery, green, yellow or red or a fanciful combination of these colours. The flesh may be whitish, yellow or orange. The pulp of some is fibrous throughout while the fibre may be absent or very little in others. The flesh may also be firm, soft or juicy, subacid or sweet and richly sweet-smelling. The fruit contains a solitary seed (stone) ovoid oblique, encased in a hard compressed endocarp.

About 1,000 types of mangoes are grown in various parts of India, each having its own peculiar taste, flavour and consistency of pulp. Only a few among them are commercial varieties. The famous and popular varieties are Alphonso (Badami), Bombay Green (Malda), Chowsa, Dusehri, Pairi (Raspuri), Neelam, Malgova, Safeda, Banganpalle and Bangalore (Totapuri).

Mango fruits contain 10–20 per cent sugar and are an important source of vitamin A. They also contain some vitamins B and C. They have a rich, luscious aromatic flavour and a delicious taste in which sweetness and acidity are delicately blended. This makes the mango fruit one of the most highly prized dessert fruits of the tropics. Ripe fruits are preserved by canning or used in the manufacture of juice and squash, jams, jellies and preserves. Young and unripe fruits are acidic and are used in making pickles, chutney and culinary preparations. The seed kernel contains an edible fat.

26.3 million tonnes is mango production 2022-23. In India, Uttar Pradesh 4,807.8 million tonnes, Andhra Pradesh 4,676.1 million tonnes, Karnataka 1,745.6 million tonnes in 2021-22. India ranked first in world production in the year 2022-23.

13.10.11 Papaya (*Carica papaya*)

Papaya (*Carica papaya*) is a native of tropical Central America but is now cultivated in many tropical areas.

Papaya

Modern papayas grow either on female plants or on hermaphrodite plants with flowers of both sexes.

Numerous varieties of papaya including the seedless varieties are successfully cultivated in different parts of India. The fruits are large and elongated. The colour of the skin of the ripe fruit is yellow or orange, but some varieties remain green. The fruit is a rich source of vitamins, particularly vitamin A. Ripe fruits contain 7–9 per cent sugars and are valued as breakfast fruit, usually with added sugar and lime juice. Preserves of various kinds such as marmalades are made from ripe fruits. The fruit is also used for making soft drinks. Unripe fruits are consumed as a vegetable.

Papaya is the commercial source of the enzyme papain, which is distributed throughout the plant but more concentrated in the latex of the fruit. The latex is obtained by making a longitudinal incision on the surface of the nearly mature fruit. The coagulated latex gives the protein hydrolyzing enzyme which is used in tenderizing meat. It is also used in the manufacture of chewing gum and in the brewing industry to digest protein fragments of chilled beer so that it remains clear.

The world production is 13.82 million tonnes and India's 5.34 million tonnes in 2022 and 6.3 million tonnes in 2024-25. In India production was Gujarat 1,061.23 million tonnes, Andhra Pradesh 934.70 million tonnes, Maharashtra 608.72 million tonnes in 2023-24. India ranked first in world production in the year 2022.

13.10.12 Passion Fruit (*Passiflora edulis*)

Passion Fruit (*Passiflora edulis*), originally native to Brazil, is found wild in India. Two forms of the fruit, the common purple-fruited form and a yellow-fruited form, are common in the country, but the latter is somewhat inferior in flavour.

Passion Fruit

The yellow, variety of fruit is from a different species, *P. laurifolia*. Its pulp is jelly-like, makes a good pleasant drink. It is not known, when the vine was brought into India but it now grows abundantly in the southern hills.

The ripe fruit may be eaten fresh as a dessert, but the fruit juice, which is free of seeds, is a popular drink. The juice is preserved by canning or freezing and is largely used, in blends with less acidic fruit juices and in the preparation of squashes, cordials, syrups, carbonated beverages and jellies.

Passion fruits get sweeter as they shrivel. 100 g (of pulp and seeds) yields 90 calories, 21.2 g carbohydrates, 13 mg calcium, 64 mg phosphorus, 348 mg potassium, 28 mg sodium 30 mg Vitamin C. The production in India, 2016–17 is 72 million tonnes.

13.10.13 Pineapple (*Ananas comosus*)

Pineapple

Pineapple or Ananas (*Ananas comosus*) is native to tropical America. The word pineapple derives from its remarkable resemblance to the cone of the large stone pine of southern Europe, and in fact, the word pineapple was in use in English for this pine cone long before the discovery of America. While called *ananas* in most Indian languages, it is called *poruthi-chakka* or Portuguese jackfruit in Malayalam, because of a resemblance in size and perhaps flavour between the two fruits.

The world production of pineapple is 29.36 million tonnes and India's 1.851 million tonnes. In India, West Bengal 347.08 million tonnes, Assam 282.42 million tonnes, Tripura 174.02 million tonnes in 2023-24.

It is now widely cultivated in tropical countries for its succulent fruit. Hawaii and Malaysia are the principal pineapple producing areas. It was introduced to India in the 16th century and is cultivated in Assam, West Bengal and the West Coast. The fruit has a rough surface and a crown of small leaves. The juicy flesh has a yellow to light orange colour.

The popularity of the pineapple, as a dessert fruit is mainly due to its sugar content and flavour; there is also a useful content of vitamins A and C. Large quantities of the fruit are canned as chunks or slices. Pineapple juice is a popular beverage. Fresh juice contains the proteolytic enzyme bromelin which aids in digestion but this is destroyed during canning.

13.10.14 Pomegranate (*Punica granatum*)

Pomegranate

Pomegranate or *Anar* (*Punica granatum*) is considered to be a native of Western Asia. It is now widely cultivated in the tropics and subtropics. It is found growing wild in the Himalayas and cultivated throughout India. The fruit is globular and a hard thick-skinned berry crowned with a persistent calyx. The interior is divided by walls of pith into several cells, each containing numerous seeds. Seeds are angular with fleshy testa, which is red, pink or whitish.

Everything from the pomegranate tree—from the fruit, flowers, leaves, bark and roots—is used. Its medicinal purposes range from bettering stomach problems to improving blood circulation with daily intake.

Several types of pomegranate are cultivated in India. The seed pulp in superior types is thick, fleshy and very juicy while in inferior types it is thin. The seed coat varies in hardness, some of the softer seeded types are known as seedless. The fruit is eaten raw. The seeds along with the fleshy portion are dried and commercially marketed as "Anardana" which is widely used as a condiment. A delicious juice is prepared from the fruits. Its quality depends to a great extent on its acid and sugar contents. The juice is largely used in the country as a cool drink.

Pomegranate juice contains the highest antioxidant capacity compared to other juices, red wine and green tea. Antioxidants are the naturally occurring substances in plants that protect the body from free radicals – "bad" chemicals in the blood. Free radicals alter cholesterol in a process known as oxidation, which is thought to speed up the hardening of the arteries.

India produced 3.06 million tonnes in 2023-24. In India, Maharashtra produces 1,763.99 million tonnes and Gujarat produces 684.32 million tonnes. Karnataka produces 305.72 million tonnes in 2021-22.

13.10.15 Sapota (*Achras sapota*)

Sapota

Sapodilla or *sapota* (*Achras sapota*) grows widely in its natural habitat of Central America and Mexico. It is now grown in other tropical countries. In India, the plant is grown largely in the states of Maharashtra, West Bengal and Tamil Nadu. The fruit is round or oval about the size of an egg, with a thin rusty brown skin. The unripe fruit contains an acid milky juice and some tannins. The fruit is only palatable when fully ripe when it has an attractive flavour. The flesh in the ripe fruit is yellowish-brown, and in its middle are embedded the black shining seeds which are not eaten. The fruit pulp is rich in sugar (14 per cent) and is mostly consumed as fresh fruit.

The bark of the sapota tree contains a latex which, after processing, is used as an edible product. The latex obtained after making an incision in the bark is collected and heat coagulated. The hardened material, chick-gum, which is white, contains about 45 per cent resins. Chick-gum provides, with the addition of various flavouring substances, the basis for chewing-gum manufacture.

India produced 878 thousand tonnes in 2023-24. In India, Andhra Pradesh produces 262.07 tonnes, Gujarat produces 255.01 tonnes, Maharashtra produces 129.14 tonnes.

13.10.16 Seetaphal (*Annona squamosa*)

Custard Apple

The *Annona* family comes from Peru and Ecuador. The seethaphal tree (*Annona squamosa*) also called sugar apple, occurs wild all over India. Seetaphal (*A. squamosa*, the custard apple); ram phal (*A. reticulata*) hanuman phal or lakshman phal (*A. cherimola*) are a large. Prickly custard apple (*A. muricata*), the pulp is very white, tender, delicate and so delicious that and its agreeable sweetness has a most delightful fragrance like rosewater.

The Seetaphal tree (*Annona squamosa*) occurs wild all over India. The fruits are yellowish-green. The flesh of the fruit is juicy, cream-yellow or white, delicately flavoured and tastes sweet. The seeds are many and brownish-black, smooth and oblong. It can be made into a drink and fermented liquor. India produced 8,28,250 tonnes of custard apple in 2023-24.

13.10.16.1 Lakshman Phal (*Annona muricata*)

Lakshman Phal

Lakshman Phal, *Annona muricata* is a species of the genus *Annona* of the custard apple tree family, *Annonaceae* Lakshman Phal as known in India is a native of Brazil. It is a rich antioxidant, and has a very high nutritional value. Clinically, it is known to have helped patients with TB, Cancer, AIDS, etc. It grows on a bushy tree about 6 meters in height, it has broad, oblong leaves and its heart-shaped green fruit is thorny on its outer skin. It is often, said to resemble a custard apple as it has creamy pulp fruit inside with blackish-brown seeds. Lakshman Phal is rich in potassium, calcium, magnesium, and sodium in small amounts which helps to overcome weak muscles and prevents cramps. The high amounts of magnesium in the fruit keep symptoms of bloating of stomach, its high amounts of copper aid healthy bones, and is an excellent source of natural carbohydrate. It also contains high vitamin C helps prevents, UTI or Urinary Tract Infection. The leaves of this fruit can be used in aromatherapy.

13.10.16.2 Hanuman Phal Soursop (*Annona cherimola*)

Hanuman Phal

Annona cherimola is species of the genus Annona from the family *Annonaceae*. It is a prickly green fruit growing on a tropical evergreen plant, with an edible white pulp and multiple seeds.

Soursop is a moderate to high-calorie fruit, giving about 66 Kcal per 100 gm of fruit, there is no fat content. It contains a large amount of Vitamin C, along with Vitamins B6, B12, and A. It contains essential minerals such as potassium, sodium, iron, magnesium, and calcium. It also contains about 3 to 4 gm of dietary fibres per 100 gm of fruit.

Vitamin A, and other antioxidants in the fruit contributes to the increased formation of visual cells, and helps to avoid the onset of macular degenerative diseases that damages the visual cells with aging and reduces the risk of developing cataracts. Soursop has anti-inflammatory and anti-microbial properties. Vitamins present in the fruit boost the immune system, it is extremely beneficial against several gastrointestinal problems and improves bowel movement, and prevents inflammation of the digestive tract and has potent antihelminthic properties.

Soursop is not recommended for consumption in pregnant or lactating women. The seeds contain irritant alkaloids which can cause irritation in the eyes and digestive tract.

13.10.16.3 Ramphal (*Annona reticulata*)

Ramphal

Annona reticulata is a small deciduous or semi-evergreen tree belonging to family Annonaceae. It is best known for its fruit, called custard apple, a common name it shares with fruits of several other species in the same genus, also called wild-sweetsop, bull's heart, bullock's-heart, or ox-heart. In Sanskrit, it is known as Lavani, Krishnabija. The flavour of the fruit is sweet and pleasant. The fruits vary in shape, heart-shaped, spherical, oblong or irregular. The size ranges from 7 centimetres (2.8 in) to 12 centimetres (4.7 in). When ripe, the fruit is brown or yellowish, with red highlights and a varying degree of reticulation. The flesh varies from juicy and very aromatic to hard with a repulsive taste.

Ramphal is known to enhance the immunity system of our body and neutralise free radicals due to vitamin C content. It may help to reduce the risk of developing cardiovascular problems. The vitamin B6 in the fruit helps to control fat deposited near the heart, further preventing heart-related issues, and this vitamin also inhibits the development of kidney stones iron content in Ramphal assists the production of haemoglobin and help transport oxygen to the various cells of the body.

13.10.17 Other Fruits

13.10.17.1 Figs (*Ficus carica*)

Figs

It is almost universally known simply as fig, common fig, edible fig. While the ancient history of the fig centres around the Mediterranean region, and it is most commonly cultivated in mild-temperate climates, it nevertheless has its place in tropical and subtropical horticulture.

The fruit is a syconium, that is, a fleshy, hollow receptacle with a small opening at the apex partly closed by small scales. It may be obovoid, turbinate, or pear-shaped, 1 to 4 in (2.5–10 cm) long, and varies in colour from yellowish-green to coppery, bronze, or dark purple.

In warm, humid climates, figs are generally eaten fresh and raw without peeling, and they are often served with cream and sugar. Peeled or unpeeled, the fruits may be merely stewed or cooked in various ways, as in pies, puddings, cakes, bread or other bakery products, or added to ice cream mix. Home owners preserve the whole fruits in sugar syrup or prepare them as jam, marmalade, or paste. The fruits are sometimes candied whole commercially. In Europe; Western Asia, Northern Africa and California, commercial canning and drying of figs are industries of great importance.

Some drying is done in Poona, India, and there is currently interest in solardrying in Guatemala. Dried cull figs have been roasted and ground as a coffee substitute. In Mediterranean countries, low-grade figs are converted into alcohol. An alcoholic extract of dried figs has been used as a flavouring for liqueurs and tobacco. The world production is 1.26 million tonnes and India's is 14,900 tonnes in 2019.

13.10.17.2 Wood-apple (*Limonia acidissima*)

It is the only species of its genus, in the family *Rutaceae.* Besides wood-apple, it may be called elephant apple, monkey fruit, curd fruit, *kath bel* and other dialectal names in India. The woodapple is native and common in the wild in dry plains of India and Sri Lanka and cultivated along roads and edges of fields and occasionally in orchards. It is also frequently grown throughout Southeast Asia, in Northern Malaya and on Penang Island. In India, the fruit was traditionally a "poor man's food" until processing techniques were developed in the mid-1950. There are two forms, one with large, sweetish fruits; one with small, acid fruits.

Wood apple

The fruit is round to oval, 2 to 5 in (5–12.5 cm) wide, with a hard, woody, greyish-white, scurfy rind about 1/4 in (6 mm) thick. The pulp is brown, mealy, odorous, resinous, astringent, acid or sweetish, with numerous small, white seeds scattered throughout the fruit.

The rind must be cracked with a hammer. The scooped-out pulp, though sticky, is eaten raw with or without sugar, or is blended with coconut milk and palmsugar syrup and drunk as a beverage, or frozen as an ice cream. It is also used, in chutneys and for making jelly and jam. The jelly is purple and much like that made from black currants.

According to analyses made in India, the pulp represents 36% of the whole fruit. The pectin content of the pulp is 3 to 5% (16% yields on a dry-weight basis). The seeds contain bland, non-bitter, oil high in unsaturated fatty acids.

The fruit is much used in India, as a liver and cardiac tonic, and, when unripe, as an astringent means of halting diarrhoea and dysentery and effective treatment for cough sore throat and diseases of the gums. The pulp is poulticed onto bites and stings of venomous insects, as is the powdered rind.

13.10.17.3 Targola/Taal (Ice Apple or Sugar Palm Fruit) (*Borassus flabellifer*)

It is a hard brown exterior like coconut, the pulp is a translucent jelly-like, cooling and similar in taste to fresh coconut and has a litchi texture.

It is rich in vitamin A, B and C also a good source of minerals like iron, calcium, zinc, phosphorus and potassium. This drink is good in dehydrated conditions,

Ice Apple

given in nausea, fatigue and heatstroke and liver problems. As it is rich in iron is prescribed to pregnant women.

13.10.17.4 Water Apple (*Syzygium aqueum*)

Its botanical name is *Syzygium aqueum*, it is also known as Janu Apple, Thai wax apple, bell fruit, rose apple, water apple. It has a pear shape but is a berry, Resembles watermelon, has high water content, is crisp and is refreshing fruit. The immature fruit skin is green and glossy, on ripening it turns to red. The flesh is white or pink and juicy, flavour is mildly sweet. Some have few or no seeds. See sec. 13.10.17.17 for Paneer fruit.

Water Apple

It quenches thirst, unripe fruit is used to make pickles, jelly or squash. Ripe fruit are used in salads. Its leaves have medicinal properties, used in fever, headaches, digestive and skin problems.

13.10.17.5 Bael Fruit (*Aegle marmelos*)

It is also called Bengal quince, Indian quince, golden apple, holy fruit, stone apple, *bel, bela, sirphal, maredu* and other dialectal names in India. The tree grows wild in dry forests on hills and plains of Central and Southern India and Burma, Pakistan and Bangladesh, also in mixed deciduous and dry dipterocarp forests of former French Indochina.

The fruit is round, pyriform, oval, or oblong, 2 to 8 in (5–20 cm) in diameter, may have a thin hard, woody shell or a more or less soft rind, grey-green until the fruit is fully ripe when it turns yellowish. It is dotted with aromatic, minute oil glands. Inside, there is a hard central core and 8 to 20 faintly defined triangular segments, with thin, dark-orange walls, filled with aromatic, pale-orange, pasty, sweet, resinous, more or less astringent, pulp. Embedded in the pulp are 10 to 15 seeds, flattened-oblong, about 3/8 in (1 cm) long, bearing woolly hairs and each enclosed in a sac of adhesive, transparent mucilage that solidifies on drying.

Bael fruits, may be cut in half, or the soft types are broken open, and the pulp, dressed with palm sugar, eaten for breakfast, as is a common practice in Indonesia. The pulp is often processed as nectar or "squash" (diluted nectar). A popular drink (called "sherbet" in India) is made by beating the seeded pulp together with milk and sugar. A beverage is also made by combining bael fruit pulp with that of tamarind. These drinks are consumed perhaps less as food or refreshment than for their medicinal effects.

Mature but still unripe fruits are made into jam, with the addition of citric acid. The pulp is also converted into marmalade or syrup, likewise for both food and therapeutic use, the marmalade being eaten at breakfast by those convalescing from diarrhoea and dysentery. A firm jelly is made from the pulp alone, or, better still, combined with guava to modify the astringent flavour. The pulp is also pickled.

The young leaves and shoots are eaten as a vegetable in Thailand and used to season food in Indonesia. They are said to reduce the appetite. An infusion of the flowers is a cooling drink.

The world production is 6,77,949 tonnes.

13.10.17.6 Lychee (*Nephelium litchai*)

A monograph written in China in 1059 AD on the litchi may be one of the earliest as a specific fruit. It was introduced into Bengal by the Portuguese at the end of the 18th century, but has rather exacting climatic requirements, and does well almost only in Ramnagar in north Bihar, and in Dehradun. It was earlier termed *litchi chinensis*.

It is widely known as litchi and regionally as *lichi, lichee, laichi, leeche* or *lychee*. The lychee is native to low elevations of the provinces of, Kwangtung and Fukien in southern China, where it flourishes especially along rivers and near the seacoast. Cultivation spread over the years through neighbouring areas of South-eastern Asia and offshore islands. Late in the 17th Century, it was carried to Burma and, 100 years later, to India.

Fruits are present in loose, pendent clusters of 2 to 30 and are usually strawberry-red, sometimes rose, pinkish or amber, and some types tinged with green. Most are aromatic, oval, heart-shaped or nearly round, about 1 in (2.5 cm) wide and 1 1/2 in (4 cm) long; have a thin, leathery, rough or minutely warty skin, flexible and easily peeled when fresh. Immediately beneath the skin of some varieties is a small amount of clear, delicious juice. The glossy, succulent, thick, translucent-white to greyish or pinkish fleshy aril which usually separates readily from the seed, suggests a large luscious grape. The flavour of the flesh is subacid and distinctive.

Lychees are most relished fresh, out-of-hand. Peeled and pitted, they are commonly added to fruit cups and fruit salads. Lychees stuffed with cottage cheese are served as salad topped with dressing and pecans. Or the fruit may be stuffed with a blend of cream cheese and mayonnaise, or stuffed with pecan meats, and garnished with whipped cream. Sliced lychees, congealed in lime gelatin, are served on lettuce with whipped cream or mayonnaise. The fruits may be layered with pistachio ice cream and whipped cream in parfait glasses as dessert. Halved lychees have been placed on top of ham during the last hour of baking, or grilled on top of a steak. Pureed lychees are added to the ice cream mix. Sherbet is made by extracting the juice from fresh, seeded lychees and adding it to a mixture of prepared plain gelatin, hot milk, light cream, sugar and, a little lemon juice, and freezing.

India's production in 2023-24 is 560.9 million tonnes.

13.10.17.7 Longan (*Dimocarpus longan*)

It is called as "little brother" of the larger red-skinned lychee. The flesh is translucent with black seed. They taste like the mixture of grape and pear. The skin is flexible that is soft, the rind below the stem should be loomed and popped into the mouth and spit the seed. The pulp is greyish-white translucent. It is rich in potassium, Vitamin C and low in sodium. It is used in a similar way as lychees in deserts, soups, smoothies, fruit salads, cocktails.

Longan

13.10.17.8 Langsah/Lotka (*Langsat*) (*Lansium domesticum*)

The fruit is translucent, small orb-shaped, unripe fruit is sour, when ripe it has a bitter-sweet taste of grapefruit. It is rich in proteins, carbohydrates, minerals, vitamins and dietary fibre because of this, it is good for digestive tract problems. The vitamin present is vitamin A, riboflavin and thiamine. Its seeds are being used as anti-malarial treatment.

Langsat

13.10.17.9 Tamarillos (*Cyphomandra betaceae*)

The tamarillo is native to the Andes of Peru, Chile, Ecuador and Bolivia. It is cultivated in Argentina, Australia, Brazil, Colombia, Kenya, the U.S. and Venezuela. The fruit, also called Tamarillos, will be two to four inches (5 to 10 cm) long, have an oval shape like an egg, and have skins that are red, purple, yellow, green or orangish. The red and purple ones have a darkish fruit inside and are more tart-tasting; the yellow or orangish ones are orange coloured inside and taste sweeter. The tarter tamarillos, such as the green ones, are generally used as a vegetable. The fruit is eaten by scooping the flesh from a halved fruit. They give a unique flavour when added to stews and curries. The tart tamarillos can be used as tomatoes: in sandwiches, salads, or in dishes. The sweeter ones can be used in fruit salads, desserts, etc.

Tamarillos

13.10.17.10 Kiwis (*Actinidia deliciosa*)

Native to the Yangtze Valley in China, where it is called "VanTao," it was never actually cultivated until a British botanist brought some samples to the West in 1900. By 1906, New Zealand began growing them as a commercial crop. It first became popular in North America starting in the early 1960s in California. It was called Chinese Gooseberry at the time but was then renamed Kiwi after the bird because of the fruit's brown skin. New Zealand has developed a new variety ZESPRI™ Gold which has yellow-coloured flesh inside and hairless brown skin. Kiwi grows on a woody vine and has hairy, brown skin. But inside, when sliced, it has a striking green flesh surrounding a ring of small black seeds. Kiwis are very rich in vitamin C.

Kiwi

The world production is 4.54 million tonnes in 2022 and 16.6 million tonnes produced in India, 2021-22.

13.10.17.11 Red Sorrel (*Rumex acetosella*)

Red Sorrel is grown around the world. Red Sorrel, an annual plant, is a member of the mallow family. It is very sensitive to frost and not cold hardy at all. It has reddish stems and green leaves. It flowers for a day with red flowers, then the petals drop off, leaving behind seed pods about 1 to 1 1/2 inches long (5 to 75 cm) The seed pods are referred to as the fruit. Red Sorrel is native to South-East Asia. It was introduced into North America in the late 1800s. The fruit needs to be harvested about 3 weeks after the plant flowered, while the fruit pods are still crisp, tender, plump and juicy. They will turn woody if left on the plant too long. The fruit is bright red and slightly tart. Some varieties are less tart than others. It is popular in the Caribbean, especially in desserts and to make wines and other beverages. It can be used to colour and flavour some rums. Fresh leaves of the plant are eaten in salads and as a potherb. Dried Red Sorrel fruit is used as the base for many commercial herbal teas. The dried variety from Sudan is preferred over that from Asia, as it is less tart and gives a reddish hue in teas rather than purple.

Sorrel Fruit

100 g seed pods yield 49 calories, 1.9 g protein, .1 g fat, 12.3 g carbohydrate, 14 mg ascorbic acid. 100 g leaves yield 43 calories, 3.3 g protein, .3 g, fat, 9.2 g carbohydrate and 54 mg ascorbic acid.

13.10.17.12 Pawpaw (*Asimina triloba*)

Pawpaw has two common names, both of which are already used. Pawpaw and Custard Apple in the English speaking-world, outside of North America, a Pawpaw is a papaya fruit. In North America, a Custard Apple is another fruit entirely. Pawpaws belong to the same family as Custard Apples.

Pawpaw

The fruit can weigh up to a pound (450 g), though 8 to 12 oz is usual (225 to 350 g), and 3 to 7 inches long (7.5 to 18 cm). The fruit grows in clusters. The skin ripens in the fall from a greenish-yellow to a purple-brown. Sometimes the skin may develop black spots, which do not affect the flesh inside. Some people compare its appearance to a fat, overripe banana; others to a big brown pickle. Inside the flesh is a pale yellow, with two rows of seeds. Each row will have 5 to 7 flat, dark brown seeds 1/2 inch to 1½ inches long (1 to 3 cm). The flesh will be soft when ripe, with the consistency of custard. When the fruit on the tree is ripe and ready to harvest, amongst the first visitors to the trees are wasps, who are very attracted to it. The fruit tastes a bit like a combination between pineapple, banana, pear and mango. Pawpaw can be eaten raw or in cooked items, though the flavour diminishes when cooked.

13.10.17.13 Persimmon (*Genus diospyros*)

A Persimmon is a fruit that looks like a bright orange tomato. Some people attempt to describe its flavour by comparing it to juicy pumpkin mixed with allspice and cinnamon. Kaki Persimmon is the most widely cultivated species, grown for its delicious fruit. It has a very sweet taste and fibrous texture. This species, native to China, is deciduous with broad, stiff leaves. Cultivation for the fruit extended first to other parts of East Asia and was later introduced to California and Southern Europe in the 1800s. American Persimmon (*D. virginiana*) is native to eastern North America. Colloquially known as a "pawdad." Black Persimmon or Black sapote (*D. digyna*) is native to Mexico. Its fruit has green skin and white flesh which turns black when ripe.

Persimmon

Fuyu Persimmon (*Diospyros kaki*) has squarish sides. It can be eaten firm or soft; Hychia Persimmon (*Diospyros kakihachiya*) is more cone-shaped. It is at its best when it is very ripe and soft; in fact, over-ripe before eating them as before that will be very tart and have; real pucker power.

Dried Persimmon (Dried Kaki) are persimmons that have been peeled and dried whole; they have a sweetness and texture like dates. To make them, in Japan at least where they are very popular, the fruit is harvested leaving a small portion of the twig on each. They are then peeled, attached to ropes via their twiggy bits, dipped in boiling water, then hung to dry for at least 1½ months. An edible white mould that looks like icing sugar will form on them when they are ready.

13.10.17.14 Nectarines (*Prunus leprechaun*)

Nectarines probably originated in China, reaching Europe via the Middle East. They were grown in the Roman Empire, but the Romans just viewed them as a variety of peach. There were six varieties in England by the 1620s. They were first recorded in America in Virginia in 1720.

Nectarines

Nectarines are related to peaches, part of the rose family. They are very much like hairless peach. They are not a cross between a peach and a plum. Some botanists now suspect that peaches may have been a cross between nectarines and almonds.

Nectarines are firmer, sweeter and juicier than peaches. They are round, with yellow skin that has a red flush to it. Inside, they have yellow flesh surrounding a large pit or stone in the middle.

Nectarines are usually just eaten out of hand, though they can be poached or used in relishes and chutneys. 1 medium nectarine (140 g/5oz) yields 70 calories, 16 g carbohydrate, 3 g fibre, 1 g fat, 1 g protein.

13.10.17.15 Pitahaya (*Selenicereus megalanthus*)

Pitahaya is a fruit that grows on a cactus vine. The cactus vine can grow in the ground or off trees. It is propagated by cuttings. The vine produces large flowers, then the Pitahaya fruit. The fruit is about 4 inches long (10 cm) with rubbery skin that is either yellowy-orange and rough, bumpy, and prickly-looking, or pink and smooth with triangle-shaped appendages growing from it. There is no apparent smell, the flesh inside will be creamy and either white or pink with a delicate sweet flavour and edible seeds throughout it, as the Kiwi fruit does. It has a delicate, sweet flavour.

Popularly known as Dragon fruit.

Pithaya (Dragon Fruit)

A pitahaya refers to dragon fruit, that belongs to the genus *Hylocereus* and it is grown in Mexico. whereas, Pitaya belongs to the genus *Stenocereus* indigenous to America. Both are cactus species.

Stenocereus or Pitaya: This sour fruit is eaten in arid regions of America. Its black seeds are crunchy but taste, rich in lipids. Its skin is pink and white flesh and mildly sweet and low in calories. It is used in punches, alcoholic beverages known as 'dragon blood punch' and the 'Dragotini'. Flowers are eaten out its decoction makes flavoured tea.

Hylocereus fruit is somewhat like watermelon, also used in medicine.

Hylocereus undatus (Pitaya blanca or white-fleshed pitahaya). This is the most commonly seen "dragon fruit".

Hylocereus costaricensis (Pitaya roja or red-fleshed pitahaya, also known as *Hylocereus polyrhizus*) red-skinned fruit with red flesh.

Hylocereus megalanthus (Pitaya amarilla or yellow Pitahaga, also known as *Selenicereus megalanthus*) yellow-skinned fruit with white flesh.

The red and purple colours in dragon fruit are due to betacyanins, a family of pigments that includes betanin (red colour of beetroot, red amaranth). This fruit is rich in vitamin C; contain very low cholesterol and is rich in antioxidants and is high in fibre. Recommended to prevent cardiac diseases. 100 grams of pitahaya contains 268 Kcal (1.20 kJ), carbohydrates 82.14 g, sugar 82.14, fibre 1.8, protein 3.57, vitamin 9.2 mg, calcium 107 mg, sodium 39% mg.

(*Source:* USDA database).

13.10.17.16 Ximenia (*Ximenia americana*)

Ximenia is a tree that grows wild in Africa and produces an edible fruit, also called Ximenia. The tree grows up to 20 feet (6 metres) tall and has rough, dark-grey bark. It has long, green shiny leaves and thorny branches. The tree can reproduce itself by seed. It flowers from August to October. The fruit is not very big, only about $1\frac{1}{4}$ inches (3 cm) long. It will ripen to orange, or red with white spots, or yellow, depending on the variety. An Ethiopian variety goes yellow. There will be 1 seed in each fruit. The pulp is bitter and tart. The seed is edible. Birds love this fruit

Ximenia

In addition to the above there are several other tropical and subtropical fruits grown and consumed in India. Some of the more important such fruits are figs (*Ficus carica*), lichi (*Nephelium litchi*), wood apple (*Limonia acidissima*), bael (*Aegle marmelos*), etc.

13.10.17.17 Paneer Fruit (*Syzygium jambos*)

Paneer fruit (*Syzygium jambos*) are likely to have originated in south-east Asia in and around Malaysia and Thailand. They are now widespread across the tropical world, via human settlers that took the plants where they migrated. Kerala has the largest concentration of Panneer trees in India. They are known as Malakkachampa in the hilly districts of Wayanad and Malappuram, in other parts of India, they are referred to as rose apples, golapi jamuk, jambuneredu, panneer pazham, and even gulab jamuni. All of them refer to the unique rose-scented flavour of the fruit. Commercial cultivation of the fruit has seen limited success, mostly because of the brief fruiting season, and because the fruit is very difficult to package–even slight mishandling can cause the fruit to bruise badly. This also causes the fruit to be priced very high in the market.

13.11 Dry Fruits

Preservation of foods by drying is one of the oldest methods of processing them. Large quantities of fruits are dried in different parts of the world. Dehydration extends the keeping qualities of the fruits well beyond their normal storage life, saves storage space and makes transportation convenient and easy. The process of drying, apart from removing water, causes some destruction of ascorbic acid and loss of the volatile substances responsible for flavour of fresh fruits. However, dried fruits are valued for their sweet flavour and dry fruits, such as prunes, figs, raisins, dates, apricots, bananas, apples, etc., are important articles of commerce. Most of the fruits grown for marketing as fresh fruits may be dried. However, most dried fruits are produced from crops grown solely for this purpose.

Sun drying: Sun drying is practiced in tropical and subtropical regions. It does not require any special equipment. Fruits are washed, peeled, prepared and placed on flat-bottomed trays. Fruits like thick-skinned grapes, peaches, etc., are dipped in a hot alkaline solution for a short time to crack or "cherk" the skin or to remove the peel to facilitate drying. In the case of apricots, the fruit is cut into halves, the pits removed and the halves placed in trays with the cups upward. The fruits are then treated with sulphur fumes to maintain their colour and also to avoid spoilage by micro-organisms. After sulphuring, the trays are kept in the sun with the occasional turning of the fruit till it is dried. The dried fruit is then stacked in boxes or bins to equalize moisture ("Sweating") before storage.

Mechanical dehydration: Using mechanical equipment dehydration is carried out. This consists of placing the prepared fruit inside a chamber (dehydrator) and drying the fruit under controlled conditions of temperature, humidity and rate of airflow. Different types of dehydration are used for this purpose. A usual method of dehydrating fruit mechanically is to subject it to dry in a tunnel drier. In this process, moist fruit on trays enters at one end and passes out at the opposite end as dried fruit. Hot air is circulated through the tunnel. The temperature and humidity used depends on the kind of fruit being dried.

A modern method of drying is by dehydration in vacuum, which can bring down the moisture content of fruits to 1–3 per cent. In this method, there is no damage to the structure of the fruit and its shelf life is quite high. Fruits dehydrated this way must be stored in vacuum or with nitrogen gas. Puff drying is another method used in drying fruits like apples and blueberries. In this method, the fruits are heated under pressure and suddenly the pressure is released. The water leaves the fruit and puff-dried fruit remains which is then further dried. For fruit juices and beverages, see subsection 12.4.1.

13.12 Jams, Jellies and Marmalades

Jams, jellies and marmalades are an important class of preserved fruits and their preparation has been in use for a long time. This method still finds wide application in fruit preservation in spite of modern methods like canning and freezing because it is simple and economical. The method is based on the formation of gel by the pectin present in fruit, in presence of a proper proportion of acids and sugar, when heated.

In a jam, the fruit tissues are held in position by the gel. In jelly, the clear fruit juice is set to a gel. Marmalade is a fruit jelly in which the slices or peels of the fruit are suspended. A jam made of a mixture of fruits to which nuts and raisins have been added is known as conserve, while fruit butter are those from the pulp of fruits. A preserve is whole fruit, or its large pieces, and is cooked in a heavy syrup till it becomes tender but still retains shape.

The pectic substances present in fruit are protopectin, pectin and pectic acid. The protopectin present in underripe fruits inhibits gel formation. The pectin present in the properly matured fruits forms a solution with water. To extract the pectin, the fruit is to be heated with a small amount of water because some of the pectic substances of the fruit remain in the solid portion. In the presence of sugars and acids present in fruit, the pectin sets into a jelly.

The formation of a firm jelly takes place only when pectin, acid, sugar and water are in definite proportions. When sugar is added to the pectin solution, it acts as a dehydrating agent and destabilizes the pectin-water equilibrium, and the pectin conglomerates form a network of insoluble fibres. Large amounts of sugar solution can be held in this mesh-like structure. The strength of the jelly depends on the structure of the fibres, their continuity and rigidity. The continuity of the network depends upon the amount of pectin present in the system, and the firmness depends on sugar concentration and acidity. An increase in sugar concentration increases the firmness of the jelly. A soft jelly can be obtained by decreasing the amount of sugar. However, the rate of setting is modified by acidity. The fibrils of pectin become tough in the presence of an acid and are thus able to hold the sugar solution in the interfibrillar spaces. If the amount of acid is large, the fibrils lose their elasticity, and as a result, the jelly becomes syrupy.

13.12.1 Jam

In the preparation of jams, ripe fruits are selected and thoroughly washed to remove dust and dirt. The fruits are chopped, mashed or diced depending upon the nature of fruit and the type of jam required.

If the fruit has little or no juice of its own a small quantity of water is added. Then the proper quantity of sugar (sucrose) is added. The finished product should contain 30–50 per cent invert sugar to avoid the crystallization of cane sugar in the jam during storage. If the fruit is deficient in acid and pectin, commercial pectin acid is added before the addition of sugar. Then the mixture is immediately heated with constant stirring. When done, it is packed in jars or cans. When packed in cans, the sealed cans are pasteurized for about 30 min.

13.12.2 Jelly

In jelly making, generally, a mixture of slightly underripe and ripe fruits is used. Since jellies are made from aqueous fruit extracts ordinarily it is not necessary to peel the fruit. The fruits are washed with water. Only a small quantity of water should be added to the fruit for the simple extraction of pectin. The amount of water added, of course, depends on the kind of fruit used. No water is added to highly juicy fruits. The pectin extract is clarified by passing it through folded cheesecloth, or a bag made of linen, flannel or felt. In jelly preparation, pectin is the most essential constituent. If the pectin content of the fruit is poor, commercial pectin is to be added. Similarly, if the acid content of the fruit is low, it is necessary to add fruits rich in acids or an acid, such as citric, tartaric or malic acid. The mixture is then heated to boiling point and cooked to the jelly stage. It is then put into glass containers or cans in the same manner as jam.

A good jelly should be transparent, well set, but not too stiff, and should have the original flavour of the fruit. It should be of attractive colour and keep its shape, when removed from the mould. When cut, it should retain its shape and show a clear-cut surface. It should be tender enough to quiver but not flow.

13.12.3 Marmalade

The term marmalade is generally associated with the product made from citrus fruits, such as orange, grapefruit and lemon, in which the shredded peel is included as the suspended material. Marmalade is made under the same conditions as used in the preparation of jelly. The pectin and acid content of the marmalade should be slightly higher than what is required for making jellies. The outer skin of the citrus fruits is peeled off from the fruits. The peeled fruit, cut into slices or crushed, is boiled with 2–3 times its weight of water for 45–60 min. to extract pectin. The aqueous solution from the boiled fruit is strained in some cases (for preparing jelly marmalade) or passed through a coarse sieve to remove coarse material (for preparing jam marmalade). To the fruit extract, shredded peels boiled in water for 10–15 min. are added. An appropriate amount of sugar is then added and the mixture heated to the jellying point. When the marmalade is ready, it is packed as in the case of jellies and jams.

CHAPTER

14 Vegetables

Vegetables are plants or parts of plants served with the main course of a meal. Apart from their nutritive value, vegetables probably do more than any other group of foods to add appetizing colour, texture and flavour to our daily food. With the wide choice of colour of vegetables, it is possible to select a vegetable with the desired colour to heighten the appearance of a meal. The texture of a vegetable varies depending upon whether it is served raw or cooked. The texture and appearance of meals can then be varied by the way the vegetable is served. There is a wide range in the characteristic flavours of vegetables. By a proper choice of vegetables, the desired flavour of a meal can be obtained.

The Indian population is mostly vegetarian. Vegetables form an essential item of food both for the rich and the poor. However, the intake of vegetables has been too low in our daily diet. There are two reasons for this: We have not been able to appreciate the vast potential of vegetables in our diet and, therefore, continue to depend too much on cereals. As per National Database published by National Horticulture Board India produced 204.6 million tonnes of vegetables during 2021-22. The area under cultivation of vegetables is 11.28 million hectares.

14.1 Classification

Vegetables are classified on the basis of the parts consumed of plants, such as roots, stems, leaves, flowers, etc. This is not satisfactory as some parts of plants may be grouped under more than one heading. Vegetables can be divided into two main groups: Winter or rabi vegetables and summer or Kharif vegetables according to their growing seasons. They are further subdivided into groups based on their cultural requirements. On this basis, some commonly used vegetables can be classified as follows:

1. Cole crops : Cabbage, cauliflower, knol-khol, Brussel sprouts, Chinese cabbage, broccoli, kale
2. Root vegetables : Carrot, parsnip, radish, turnip, beetroot, celeriac, arracacha, black salsify
3. Fruit vegetables : Tomato, bell pepper, eggplant, *okra*
4. Curcubits : Cucumber, pumpkin, squash, gourds
5. Leafy vegetables : Spinach, lettuce, purslane, amaranth, celery, fenugreek, non-traditional leafy vegetables, etc.

Table 14.1 Composition of Vegetables (per 100 gms of edible portion)

Name	Moisture	Protein	Total Fat	Total Fiber	Carbohydrate	Energy		Calcium	Phosphorous	Iron	β-Carotene	Thiamine	Riboflavin	Niacin	Vitamin B6 (Total)	Vitamin C
	g	g	g	g	g	KJ	Kcal	mg	mg	mg	µg	mg	mg	mg	mg	mg
Cabbage, violet (*Brassica oleracea var. capitata f. rubra*)	91.94	1.39	0.21	2.21	3.54	97	23	48	22.4	0.24	31.17	0.04	0.05	0.27	0.17	43.49
Cabbage, green (*Brassica oleracea var. capitata f. alba*)	91.85 ± 0.97	1.36 ± 0.07	0.12 ± 0.01	2.76 ± 0.20	3.25 ± 0.91	90	22	51.76	30.15	0.35	20.48	0.03 ± 0.005	0.05 ± 0.001	0.24 ± 0.02	0.13 ± 0.016	33.25 ± 4.21
Cabbage, Chinese (*Brassica rupa*)	93.19	1.58	0.13	2.01	2.36	75	18	58.46	33.05	0.39	5.5	0.01	0.05	0.38	0.19	19.32
Gogu leaves, red (*Hibiscus cannabinus*)	87.98	1.85	1.07	3.89	4.24	153	37	129	36.38	9.56	5143	0.12	0.05	0.56	0.31	35.43
Basella leaves (*Basella alba*)	92.68	1.57	0.45	2.21	2.01	82	20	211	37.26	2.66	2473	0.06	0.15	0.46	0.18	63.35
Bathua leaves (*Chenopodium album*)	88.77	2.5	0.44	4.01	2.56	116	28	151 ± 46.9	37.55		1075	0.06	0.51	0.54	0.17	41.03
Gogu leaves, green (*Hibiscus cannabinus*)	87.42 ± 0.41	1.86 ± 0.16	1.09 ± 0.03	4.59 ± 0.39	4.06 ± 0.18	152	36	145	41.99	7.65	5285 ± 856	0.13 ± 0.006	0.06 ± 0.009	0.58 ± 0.04	0.33 ± 0.012	29.65 ± 9.71
Garden cress (*Lepidium sativum*)	84.02	5.62	0.8	2.6	4.48	208 208	50	217	45.55	6.19	88.72	0.03	0.06	1.2	0.2	42.75
Agathi leaves (*Sesbania grandiflora*)	74.43	8.01	1.35	8.6	5.21	295	71	901	52.52	4.36	12582	0.26	0.33	1.18	0.22	121
Fenugreek leaves (*Trigonella foenum graecum*)	86.73 ± 0.66	3.68 ± 0.36	0.83 ± 0.02	4.90 ± 0.21	2.17 ± 0.32	144 144	34	274	53.05	5.69	9245	0.11 ± 0.015	0.22 ± 0.023	0.70 ± 0.05	0.38 ± 0.106	58.25 ± 17.08
Cabbage, collard greens (*Brassica oleracea var. viridis*)	89.53	3.63	0.27	2.98	2.79	126 126	30	170	54.67	2.67	104	0.03	0.05	0.26	0.24	40.76
Colocasia leaves, green (*Colocasia anti-quorum*)	83.61 ± 0.59	3.42 ± 0.29	1.38 ± 0.09	5.60 ± 0.18	3.69 ± 0.49	182	44	216	57.88	3.41	5758	0.08 ± 0.013	0.07 ± 0.015	0.80 ± 0.07	0.29 ± 0.031	40.71 ± 7.47

Cauliflower leaves (*Brassica oleracea var. botrytis*)	87.64 ± 1.33	3.90 ± 0.87	0.42 ± 0.02	3.43 ± 0.26	3.39 ± 0.70	148	35	96.7	62.82	2.42	146	0.05 ± 0.010	0.05 ± 0.011	0.21 ± 0.01	0.23 ± 0.016	52.84 ± 0.94 52.84 ± 0.94
Amaranth leaves, red and green mix (*Amaranthus gangeticus*)	86.37 ± 0.38	3.09 ± 0.14	0.53 ± 0.03	4.60 ± 0.36	2.87 ± 0.35	132	32	359	68.23	6.37	8464	0.01 ± 0.000	0.22 ± 0.030	0.69 ± 0.04	0.19 ± 0.015	77.24 ± 7.57
Amaranth spinosus, leaves, green (*Amaranthus spinosus*)	86.46 ± 0.48	3.54 ± 0.31	0.36 ± 0.02	5.10 ± 0.32	1.61 ± 0.40	110	26	372	72.46	4.36	1594	0.01 ± 0.000	0.13 ± 0.011	0.63 ± 0.02	0.22 ± 0.051	82.56 ± 8.24
Amaranth leaves, green (*Amaranthus gangeticus*)	86.85 ± 1.21	3.29 ± 0.57	0.65 ± 0.07	4.41 ± 0.10	2.28 ± 0.62	128	31	330 ± 74.2	73.22	4.64 ± 0.85	8553	0.01 ± 0.000	0.19 ± 0.028	0.71 ± 0.06	0.21 ± 0.010	83.54 ± 10.54
Amaranth leaves, red (*Amaranthus gangeticus*)	85.56	3.93	0.63	4.91	2.37	140	33	245	75.98	7.25	8457	0.01	0.269	0.62	0.22	86.2
Amaranth spinosus, leaves, red and green mix (*Amaranthus spinosus*)	86.64	2.8	0.34	5.57	1.45	99	24	93.89	85.02	4.2	1487	0.01	0.15	0.72	0.2	77.3
Brussels sprouts (*Brassica oleracea var. gemmifera*)	84.39	4.26	0.5	4.29	5.09	185	44	53.99	98.56	1.54	360	0.06	0.16	0.5	0.19	89.45
Drumstick leaves (*Moringa oleifera*)	75.65 ± 1.49	6.41 ± 0.35	1.64 ± 0.12	8.21 ± 0.19	5.62 ± 1.44	282	67	314	109 ± 20.7	4.56 ± 1.09	17542 ± 1425	0.06 ± 0.006	0.45 ± 0.042	0.82 ± 0.09	0.87 ± 0.074	108 ± 16.7
Beet greens (*Beta vulgaris*)	86.68 ± 1.35	2.38 ± 0.35	0.75 ± 0.02	3.64 ± 0.13	3.86 ± 1.63	145	35	207 ± 14.9	36.02 ± 4.80	5.80 ± 0.57	1703 ± 146	0.02 ± 0.01	0.17 ± 0.05	0.43 ± 0.08	0.13 ± 0.03	35.83 ± 5.51
Betel leaves, big (kolkata) (*Piper betle*)	84.93 ± 0.85	2.51 ± 0.29	0.75 ± 0.02	2.12 ± 0.20	7.37 ± 0.66	202	48	196 ± 13.7	51.73 ± 4.83	3.00 ± 0.77	4186 ± 524	0.03 ± 0.012	0.08 ± 0.012	0.45 ± 0.05	0.04 ± 0.007	18.40 ± 2.49
Betel leaves, small (*Piper betle*)	85.92 ± 0.16	2.62 ± 0.28	0.75 ± 0.04	1.97 ± 0.13	6.16 ± 0.33	183	44	207	55.72 ± 3.36	2.87 ± 0.29	4676 ± 622	0.02 ± 0.010	0.07 ± 0.009	0.47 ± 0.07	0.04 ± 0.005	24.51 ± 8.66
Knol-Khol, leaves (*Brassica oleracea var. gongylodes*)	86.2	3.12	0.35	2.76	6.16	178	43	368	55.02	2.51	12.04	0.06	0.15	0.86	0.28	71.11
Lettuce (*Lactuca sativa*)	92.27 ± 0.99	1.54 ± 0.48	0.27 ± 0.03	1.79 ± 0.24	3.01 ± 0.56	91	22	56.17	44.10 ± 11.69	2.73 ± 0.59	1285 ± 167	0.05 ± 0.013	0.09 ± 0.008	0.17 ± 0.02	0.08 ± 0.016	11.91 ± 3.07
Mustard leaves (*Brassica juncea*)	88.17 ± 0.56	1.11 ± 0.10	1.79 ± 0.24	1.32 ± 0.04	2.41 ± 0.46	127	30	191	71.62 ± 16.63	2.84 ± 0.12	2619 ± 372	0.08 ± 0.011	0.18 ± 0.015	0.58 ± 0.07	0.16 ± 0.007	60.32 ± 1.32

Pak Choi leaves (*Brassica rapa var. Chinensis*)	93.56	1.41	0.25	1.91	1.78	67	16	150	25.95	3.78	2450	0.02	0.22	0.66	0.96	55.6
Parsley (*Petroselinum crispum*)	77.76 ± 1.13	5.55 ± 0.34	1.14 ± 0.12	3.87 ± 0.05	9.43 ± 1.05	305	73	288	78.56 ± 15.86	5.51 ± 2.25	2710 ± 349	0.19 ± 0.022	0.10 ± 0.005	0.36 ± 0.01	0.19 ± 0.011	133 ± 16.3
Ponnaganni (*Alternanthera sessilis*)	79.43	5.29	0.71	6.74	5.17	213	51	388	58.26	3.88	5288	0.02	0.1	0.32	0.19	103
Pumpkin leaves, tender (*Cucurbita maxima*)	85.82 ± 1.04	4.21 ± 0.41	0.74 ± 0.03	2.25 ± 0.09	4.75 ± 1.01	185	44	271 ± 73.6	64.54 ± 10.74	5.58 ± 0.39	1455 ± 146	0.07 ± 0.010	0.13 ± 0.025	1.49 ± 0.09	0.17 ± 0.022	12.33 ± 0.17
Radish leaves (*Raphanus sativus*)	91.19 ± 0.53	2.22 ± 0.23	0.51 ± 0.05	1.82 ± 0.10	2.77 ± 0.34	109	26	234 ± 53.1	50.08 ± 15.00	3.82 ± 0.52	2591 ± 572	0.06 ± 0.005	0.13 ± 0.024	0.47 ± 0.06	0.16 ± 0.032	65.76 ± 18.69
Rumex leaves (*Rumex patientia*)	93.18	2.22 ± 0.23	0.51 ± 0.05	1.82 ± 0.10	2.33	82	20	131	32.4	3.67	2754	0.03	0.14	0.33	0.09	53.76
Spinach (*Spinacia oleracea*)	90.31 ± 0.46	2.14 ± 0.14	1.27	0.33	2.05 ± 0.31	102	24	82.29 ± 6.51	32.59 ± 8.08	2.95 ± 0.68	2605 ± 521	0.16 ± 0.016	0.10 ± 0.009	0.33 ± 0.03	0.15 ± 0.011	30.28 ± 4.71
Tamarind leaves, tender (*Tamarindus indica*)	71.69 ± 0.06	5.84 ± 0.01	0.49 ± 0.01	10.70 ± 0.02	10.04 ± 0.02	299	71	66.93	86.86	2.84	168 ± 21.2	0.12 ± 0.020	0.03 ± 0.007	0.79 ± 0.02	0.14 ± 0.010	28.22 ± 8.82
Other Vegetables							0									
Ash gourd (*Benincasa hispida*)	92.17 ± 0.42	0.79 ± 0.06	0.14 ± 0.02	3.37 ± 0.23	2.84 ± 0.22	73	17	19.39 ± 1.46	29.07 ± 8.45	0.47 ± 0.20		0.03 ± 0.003	0.01 ± 0.001	0.12 ± 0.02	0.18 ± 0.058	11.41 ± 1.31
Bamboo shoot, tender (*Bambusa vulgaris*)	94.56	1.33	0.35	1.55	1.67	68	16	10	39.63	0.33		0.06	0.06	0.25	0.13	15.74
Bean scarlet, tender (*Phaseolus coccineus*)	85.51 ± 1.22	2.86 ± 0.27	0.99 ± 0.06	4.50 ± 0.25	5.16 ± 1.45	179	43	43.48	62.13	0.73	35.52 ± 3.88	0.13 ± 0.016	0.12 ± 0.016	0.52 ± 0.08	0.31 ± 0.021	6.61 ± 1.00
Bitter gourd, jagged, teeth ridges, elongate (*Momordica charantia*)	90.87 ± 0.56	1.44 ± 0.17	0.24 ± 0.01	3.78 ± 0.16	2.82 ± 0.32	87	21	21.36	44.9	1.15	122	0.05 ± 0.005	0.04 ± 0.009	0.27 ± 0.03	0.05 ± 0.009	46.53 ± 2.81
Bitter gourd, jagged, teeth ridges, short (*Momordica charantia*)	91.60 ± 0.28	1.34 ± 0.12	0.24 ± 0.01	3.49 ± 0.18	2.53 ± 0.26	79	19	16.27	40.21	1.08	126	0.06 ± 0.008	0.04 ± 0.005	0.29 ± 0.03	0.04 ± 0.004	"50.87 ± 3.03 "
Bitter gourd, jagged, smooth ridges, elongate (*Momordica charantia*)	91.24	1.61	0.26	3.72	2.29	81	19	17.62	44.75	1.28	130	0.06	0.04	0.3	0.05	"54.30 "
Bottle gourd, elongate, pale green (*Lagenaria vulgaris*)	95.17 ± 0.33	0.53 ± 0.05	0.13 ± 0.02	2.12 ± 0.07	1.68 ± 0.33	46	11	15.42	16.01	0.26	44.05	0.03 ± 0.003	0.01 ± 0.001	0.14 ± 0.01	0.02 ± 0.005	4.33 ± 1.55
Bottle gourd, round, pale green (*Lagenaria vulgaris*)	94.50 ± 0.32	0.42 ± 0.02	0.12 ± 0.03	2.10 ± 0.15	2.53 ± 0.21	57	14	15.05	16.99	0.28	47.13	0.03 ± 0.004	0.01 ± 0.001	0.14 ± 0.01	0.02 ± 0.006	4.54 ± 1.78

Bottle gourd, elongate, dark green (*Lagenaria vulgaris*)	94.63	0.49	0.13	2.11	2.25	54	13	16.64	26.86	0.34	44.82	0.03	0.01	0.14	0.01	3.80
Brinjal-all varieties (*Solanum melongena*)	90.00 ± 0.90	1.48 ± 0.22	0.32 ± 0.04	3.98 ± 0.49	3.52 ± 0.80	106	25	16.59	32.56	0.37	146 ± 24.0	0.06 ± 0.016	0.11 ± 0.011	0.53 ± 0.08	0.07 ± 0.016	2.09 ± 0.85
Broad beans (*Vicia faba*)	84.20 ± 0.17	3.85 ± 0.13	0.15 ± 0.01	8.63 ± 0.15	2.11 ± 0.11	123	29	64.37	67.97 ± 8.14	0.94	6.38 ± 0.62	0.12 ± 0.01	0.10 ± 0.03	0.76 ± 0.00	0.23 ± 0.01	10.98 ± 0.97
Capsicum, green (*Capsicum annuum*)	93.89 ± 0.32	1.11 ± 0.11	0.34 ± 0.03	2.06 ± 0.22	1.84 ± 0.32	68	16	14.75	23 ± 5.42	0.48	328 ± 61.7	0.05 ± 0.007	0.03 ± 0.011	0.56 ± 0.05	0.15 ± 0.011	123 ± 7.8
Capsicum, red (*Capsicum annuum*)	92.99 ± 1.47	1.47 ± 0.36	0.47 ± 0.05	2.19 ± 0.17	2.14 ± 1.06	83	20	15.76	30.81 ± 5.81	0.38	246 ± 47.2	0.10 ± 0.042	0.03 ± 0.014	0.66 ± 0.21	0.24 ± 0.007	112 ± 5.5
Capsicum, yellow (*Capsicum annuum*)	93.38 ± 0.37	1.35 ± 0.35	0.41 ± 0.02	2.19 ± 0.13	1.95 ± 0.16	78	19	19.13 ± 4.17	43.33 ± 10.64	0.69 ± 0.12	166 ± 15.0	0.14 ± 0.012	0.02 ± 0.009	0.59 ± 0.20	0.25 ± 0.040	127 ± 12.5
Cauliflower (*Brassica oleracea*)	90.76 ± 0.22	2.15 ± 0.15	0.44 ± 0.03	3.71 ± 0.27	2.03 ± 0.22	96	23	25.16 ± 3.47	47.33 ± 10.61	0.96 ± 0.34	1.59 ± 0.66	0.04 ± 0.003	0.07 ± 0.007	0.31 ± 0.02	0.13 ± 0.020	47.14 ± 7.47
Celery stalk (*Apium graveolens*)	92.87 ± 0.22	0.98 ± 0.13	0.24 ± 0.04	2.09 ± 0.13	2.33 ± 0.23	69	16	38.73 ± 3.38	44.84 ± 9.18	1.36 ± 0.41	465 ± 57.3	0.03 ± 0.007	0.04 ± 0.008	0.48 ± 0.05	0.06 ± 0.010	12.30 ± 2.89
Cho-cho-marrow (*Sechium edule*)	93.78 ± 0.12	0.66 ± 0.07	0.15 ± 0.03	1.55 ± 0.08	3.47 ± 0.18	79	19	18.64 ± 2.31	21.61 ± 4.89	0.48 ± 0.11	1.57 ± 0.31	0.01 ± 0.000	0.03 ± 0.003	0.23 ± 0.02	0.07 ± 0.015	20.21 ± 5.48
Cluster beans (*Cyamopsis tetragonobola*)	84.65 ± 0.83	3.55 ± 0.38	0.37 ± 0.04	4.83 ± 0.54	4.91 ± 0.58	168	40	121	45.28	3.9	241 ± 32.8	0.05 ± 0.006	0.03 ± 0.005	0.71 ± 0.05	0.12 ± 0.008	17.96 ± 5.83
Colocasia, stem, black (*Colocasia antiquorum*)	91.15	0.76	0.34	3.01	3.83	100	24	29.46	20.31	0.77	4.97	0.02	0.04	0.16	0.06	5.15
Colocasia, stem, green (*Colocasia antiquorum*)	92.67 ± 0.44	0.91 ± 0.16	0.22 ± 0.02	2.33 ± 0.06	2.86 ± 0.34	81	19	40.21 ± 6.92	30.73	0.55	2.3	0.02 ± 0.004	0.03 ± 0.013	0.22 ± 0.03	0.07 ± 0.007	5.83 ± 1.28
Corn, Baby (*Zea mays*)	75.44 ± 0.98	2.69 ± 0.23	1.33 ± 0.23	6.09 ± 0.50	11.66 ± 1.4	306	73	76.51 ± 13.84	8.69 ± 1.35	1.45 ± 0.23	1.52 ± 0.33	0.15	0.07 ± 0.032	0.53 ± 0.07	0.16 ± 0.046	8.59 ± 1.48
Cucumber, green, elongate (*Cucumis sativus*)	92.96 ± 0.48"	0.71 ± 0.11	0.16 ± 0.04	2.14 ± 0.42	3.48 ± 0.47	82	20	16.39	28.34	0.46	5.33	0.02 ± 0.003	0.01 ± 0.000	0.35 ± 0.04	0.06 ± 0.013	6.11 ± 1.49
Cucumber, green, short (*Cucumis sativus*)	93.52 ± 0.44	0.83 ± 0.14	0.18 ± 0.05	2.13 ± 0.26	2.82 ± 0.49	73	17	19.25	29.74	0.59	4.8	0.02 ± 0.005	0.01 ± 0.000	0.35 ± 0.04	0.07 ± 0.008	6.21 ± 2.14
Cucumber, orange, round (*Cucumis sativus*)	92.8	0.98	0.24	2.46	3.01	82	20	21.98	23.17	0.45	5.55	0.02	0.01	0.36	0.04	"6.24 "
Drumstick (*Moringa oleifera*)	85.39 ± 0.64	2.62 ± 0.22	0.12 ± 0.01	6.83 ± 0.22	3.76 ± 0.70	123	29	33.3	52.87 ± 8.72	0.73 ± 0.18	17.28 ± 1.85	0.04 ± 0.002	0.07 ± 0.007	0.62 ± 0.03	0.12 ± 0.011	71.86 ± 19.13
Field beans, tender, broad (*Vicia faba*)	86.98	3.06	0.64	5.64	2.75	129	31	70.57	73.3	1.95	555	0.07	0.07	0.32	0.42	5.99

Field beans, tender, lean (*Vicia faba*)	85.57 ± 1.32	3.71 ± 0.62	0.60 ± 0.02	6.19 ± 0.47	2.85 ± 0.32	140	33	58.59 ± 5.21	76.54 ± 12.27	1.48 ± 0.39	556 ± 6.0	0.08 ± 0.006	0.07 ± 0.007	0.33 ± 0.02	0.38 ± 0.069	3.84 ± 1.24
French beans, country (*Phaseolus vulgaris*)	89.14 ± 0.52	2.49 ± 0.21	0.26 ± 0.02	4.38 ± 0.41	2.68 ± 0.48	102	24	55.99	59.86	1.25	413 ± 10.4	0.04 ± 0.005	0.06 ± 0.004	0.83 ± 0.03	0.37 ± 0.053	15.81 ± 4.23
French beans, hybrid (*Phaseolus vulgaris*)	90.11	2.12	0.19	4.18	2.63	93	22	49.9	45.9	0.98	388	0.05	0.05	0.77	0.44	1.38 1.38
Jack fruit, raw (*Artocarpus heterophyllus*)	85.52 ± 0.86	1.98 ± 0.16	0.35 ± 0.05	7.69 ± 0.20	3.48 ± 0.70	110	26	45.7	27.78	0.31		0.05 ± 0.014	0.05 ± 0.010	0.19 ± 0.02	0.04 ± 0.005	17.51 ± 6.00
Jack fruit, seed, mature (*Artocarpus heterophyllus*)	72.32 ± 0.53	5.79 ± 0.14	0.44 ± 0.03	8.63 ± 0.09	11.81 ± 0.74	322	77	37.56	29.33	0.37		0.06 ± 0.010	0.03 ± 0.008	0.19 ± 0.02	0.08 ± 0.005	9.68 ± 6.44
Knol - Khol (*Brassica oleracea*)	93.14 ± 0.27	1.58 ± 0.24	0.35 ± 0.02	2.75 ± 0.07	1.39 ± 0.21	67	16	35.26 ± 3.81	40.77 ± 4.47	0.24		0.04 ± 0.012	0.06 ± 0.014	0.37 ± 0.02	0.19 ± 0.033	64.70 ± 10.78
Kovai, big (*Coccinia cordifolia*)	92.78 ± 0.61	1.39 ± 0.23	0.24 ± 0.08	3.00 ± 0.26	2.01 ± 0.54	73	17	34.39 ± 5.90	36.90 ± 4.81	0.38	134 ± 9.8	0.04 ± 0.004	0.02 ± 0.002	0.55 ± 0.03	0.08 ± 0.012	17.62 ± 7.24
Kovai, small (*Coccinia cordifolia*)	92.4	1.22	0.24	3.25	2.41	80	19	37.12	26.29	0.29	147	0.04	0.02	0.51	0.05	21.08
Ladies finger (*Abelmoschus esculentus*)	89.06 ± 0.30	2.08 ± 0.37	0.22 ± 0.03	4.08 ± 0.20	3.62 ± 0.26	115	27	86.12 ± 6.93	57.48 ± 6.93		69.10 ± 10.41	0.04 ± 0.005	0.07 ± 0.009	0.61 ± 0.01	0.27 ± 0.027	22.51 ± 1.60
Mango, green, raw (*Mangifera indica*)	85.14 ± 0.59	0.69 ± 0.09	0.08 ± 0.02	3.01 ± 0.19	10.59 ± 0.37	205	49	27.00 ± 4.93	14.92 ± 2.22		72.37 ± 6.60	0.02 ± 0.003	0.02 ± 0.001	0.26 ± 0.02	0.13 ± 0.013	90.24 ± 10.47
Onion, stalk (*Allium cepa*)	88.35 ± 0.79	2.07 ± 0.21	0.26 ± 0.02	5.21 ± 0.10	2.99 ± 0.50	107	26	31.12 ± 7.53	28.53 ± 3.74		700 ± 2.6	0.03 ± 0.020	0.05 ± 0.014	0.14 ± 0.02	0.17 ± 0.052	27.23 ± 4.22
Papaya, raw (*Carica papaya*)	92.04 ± 0.44	0.50 ± 0.06	0.23 ± 0.03	2.28 ± 0.05	4.40 ± 0.37	100	24	22.72 ± 1.71	24.11 ± 6.35	0.84 ± 0.15	164 ± 60.8	0.02 ± 0.004	0.03 ± 0.007	0.12 ± 0.01	0.03 ± 0.008	20.73 ± 2.35
Parwar (*Trichosanthes dioica*)	91.57 ± 0.27	1.40 ± 0.10	0.30 ± 0.04	2.61 ± 0.07	3.54 ± 0.32	101	24	30.76 ± 3.08	33.81 ± 3.72	0.40 ± 0.08	13.10 ± 1.50	0.05 ± 0.007	0.05 ± 0.011	0.67 ± 0.04	0.20 ± 0.019	19.24 ± 6.61
Peas, fresh (*Pisum sativum*)	73.37 ± 1.13	7.25 ± 1.03	0.13 ± 0.02	6.32 ± 0.26	11.88 ± 0.67	340	81	28.24 ± 3.62	55.95 ± 2.74	3.09 ± 0.54	121 ± 12.5	0.27 ± 0.027	0.03 ± 0.004	1.28 ± 0.03	0.19 ± 0.020	38.40 ± 6.42
Plantain, flower (*Musa x paradisiaca*)	89.14 ± 0.59	1.47 ± 0.12	0.63 ± 0.02	5.25 ± 0.39	2.15 ± 0.43	89	21	34.06 ± 1.85	47.31 ± 5.74	0.20 ± 0.03	35.36 ± 7.72	0.02 ± 0.005	0.02 ± 0.005	0.28 ± 0.03	0.13 ± 0.009	6.49 ± 1.15
Plantain, green (*Musa x paradisiaca*)	76.15 ± 0.42	1.18 ± 0.20	0.23 ± 0.02	3.60 ± 0.27	17.58 ± 0.35	334	80	13.80 ± 2.56	31.69 ± 5.76	0.50 ± 0.11	3.01 ± 1.65	0.01 ± 0.001	0.05 ± 0.005	0.33 ± 0.04	0.10 ± 0.006	23.28 ± 2.40
Plantain, stem (*Musa x paradisiaca*)	87.53 ± 1.01	0.35 ± 0.05	0.16 ± 0.07	2.12 ± 0.04	8.64 ± 0.93	165	39	11.24 ± 2.30	16.31 ± 1.61	1.58 ± 0.15	2.39 ± 1.25	0.02 ± 0.003	0.02 ± 0.004	0.18 ± 0.02	0.14 ± 0.01	3.77 ± 2.74
Pumpkin, green, cylindrical (*Cucurbita maxima*)	91.73	0.87	0.18	2.53	4.22	"103 "	25	24.1	24.51	0.40 ± 0.05	363	0.03	0.02	0.44	0.05	7.29

Pumpkin, orange, round (*Cucurbita maxima*)	91.85 ± 0.45	0.84 ± 0.21	0.16 ± 0.02	2.56 ± 0.11	4.00 ± 0.64	97	23	23.06	22.18	0.34 ± 0.09	149 ± 16.8	0.03 ± 0.005	0.03 ± 0.003	0.41 ± 0.01	0.08 ± 0.015	8.04 ± 0.87
Red gram, tender, fresh (*Cajanus cajan*)	64	8.09	0.92	5.9	19.46	520	124	58.58	141	0.26 ± 0.10	165	0.23	0.09	2.14	0.3	15.13
Ridge gourd (*Luffa acutangula*)	94.99 ± 0.35	0.91 ± 0.08	0.14 ± 0.01	1.81 ± 0.13	1.72 ± 0.46	55	13	13.70 ± 1.38	33.06 ± 5.97	0.29	348 ± 31.4	0.02 ± 0.003	0.01 ± 0.002	0.20 ± 0.01	0.07 ± 0.005	5.42 ± 1.06
Ridge gourd, smooth skin (*Luffa acutangula*)	94.27 ± 0.62	0.98 ± 0.13	0.13 ± 0.01	1.85 ± 0.28	2.24 ± 0.41	64	15	14.96	39.25	0.36	349 ± 23.4	0.02 ± 0.004	0.01 ± 0.001	0.21 ± 0.01	0.09 ± 0.007	8.10 ± 2.67
Snake gourd, long, pale green (*Trichosanthes anguina*)	94.81 ± 0.28	0.98 ± 0.33	0.25 ± 0.01	2.27 ± 0.11	1.27 ± 0.15	52	12	24.6	23.27	0.16	61.29	0.03 ± 0.003	0.03 ± 0.002	0.34 ± 0.02	0.10 ± 0.017	2.72 ± 1.15
Snake gourd, long, dark green (*Trichosanthes anguina*)	94.92	0.89	0.25	2.27	1.23	50	12	27.11	31.03	0.42 ± 0.05	61.64	0.03	0.03	0.33	0.07	2.85
Snake gourd, short (*Trichosanthes anguina*)	94.35	0.54	0.26	2.29	2.15	61	15	17.9	21.33	0.5	62.84	0.03	0.02	0.33	0.06	2.3
Tinda, tender (*Praecitrullus fistulosus*)	94.41 ± 0.32	1.02 ± 0.04	0.17 ± 0.01	2.00 ± 0.04	1.90 ± 0.37	58	14	19.68 ± 3.27	30.37 ± 2.47	0.32	7.96 ± 1.10	0.02 ± 0.000	0.03 ± 0.005	0.56 ± 0.02	0.06 ± 0.008	14.20 ± 0.88
Tomato, green (*Lycopersicon esculentum*)	93.21 ± 0.46	1.12 ± 0.08	0.27 ± 0.07	1.62 ± 0.08	3.18 ± 0.40	87	21	8.49	22.5	0.47	32.33 ± 3.91	0.08 ± 0.043	0.05 ± 0.043	0.46 ± 0.16	0.07 ± 0.024	16.41 ± 2.52
Tomato, ripe, hybrid (*Lycopersicon esculentum*)	93.79 ± 0.42	0.76 ± 0.03	0.25 ± 0.02	1.58 ± 0.16	3.20 ± 0.30	79	19	8.9	15.45	0.2	1513	0.04 ± 0.004	0.02 ± 0.007	0.51 ± 0.02	0.08 ± 0.006	25.27 ± 3.52
Tomato, ripe, local (*Lycopersicon esculentum*)	93.62 ± 0.16	0.90 ± 0.07	0.47 ± 0.06	1.77 ± 0.04	2.71 ± 0.08	82	20	10.71	18.77	0.41 ± 0.03	905	0.03 ± 0.004	0.03 ± 0.004	0.52 ± 0.01	0.09 ± 0.005	27.47 ± 1.77
Zucchini, green (*Cucurbita pepo*)	92.83	1.1	0.51	2.3	2.33	84	20	17.26	21.38	0.52	85.79	0.05	0.09	1.03	0.25	15.78
Zucchini, yellow (*Cucurbita pepo*)	93.15	1.31	0.44	1.84	2.2	79	19	20.98	32.03	0.34	69.9	0.03	0.02	0.42	0.2	16.71
Root vegetables																
Beet root (*Beta vulgaris*)	86.95 ± 0.50	1.95 ± 0.14	0.14 ± 0.01	3.31 ± 0.32	6.18 ± 0.61	149	36	17.28 ± 2.25	36.33 ± 4.84	0.76 ± 0.12	10.14 ± 2.52	0.01 ± 0.001	0.01 ± 0.002	0.21 ± 0.01	0.07 ± 0.011	5.26 ± 0.85
Carrot, orange (*Dacus carota*)	87.69 ± 0.56	0.95 ± 0.15	0.47 ± 0.02	4.18 ± 0.30	5.55 ± 0.48	139	33	35.09 ± 5.89	43.06 ± 6.46	0.60 ± 0.24	5423 ± 450	0.04 ± 0.003	0.03 ± 0.003	0.22 ± 0.02	0.11 ± 0.016	6.22 ± 1.99
Carrot, red (*Dacus carota*)	86.07 ± 1.34	1.04 ± 0.09	0.47 ± 0.04	4.49 ± 0.19	6.71 ± 1.11	160	38	41.06 ± 8.47	25.81 ± 11.63	0.71 ± 0.37	2706 ± 298	0.04 ± 0.017	0.03 ± 0.016	0.25 ± 0.05	0.07 ± 0.012	6.76 ± 1.56

Colocasia (*Colocasia antiquorum*)	73.49 ± 0.32	3.31 ± 0.59	0.17 ± 0.03	3.22 ± 0.34	17.85 ± 0.94	372	89	30.18 ± 3.86	81.16 ± 11.90	0.66 ± 0.09	6.50 ± 1.16	0.06 ± 0.007	0.03 ± 0.002	0.51 ± 0.09	0.17 ± 0.038	1.83 ± 0.64
Lotus root (*Nelumbium nelumbo*)	76.26 ± 0.87	1.94 ± 0.32	0.93 ± 0.06	4.70 ± 0.04	14.67 ± 0.45	332	79	37.71 ± 2.79	74.30 ± 7.54	3.34 ± 1.31		0.07 ± 0.008	0.05 ± 0.023	0.43 ± 0.05	0.19 ± 0.017	26.63 ± 7.02
Potato, brown skin, big (*Solanum tuberosum*)	80.72 ± 0.40	1.54 ± 0.17	0.23 ± 0.02	1.71 ± 0.03	14.89 ± 0.40	292	70	9.52	43.42	0.57		0.06 ± 0.004	0.01 ± 0.001	1.04 ± 0.14	0.10 ± 0.008	23.15 ± 3.98
Potato, brown skin, small (*Solanum tuberosum*)	82.97	1.35	0.22	1.69	12.9	255	61	8.53	37.9	0.53		0.05	0.01	1.36	0.12	26.41
Potato, red skin (*Solanum tuberosum*)	79.72	1.83	0.22	1.68	15.43	306	73	8.62	30.39	0.66		0.06	0.01	1.13	0.1	25.04
Radish, elongate, red skin (*Raphanus sativus*)	89.32 ± 0.29	0.67 ± 0.03	0.13 ± 0.02	2.46 ± 0.16	6.71 ± 0.12	134	32	28.44	27.51	0.37	1.62	0.03 ± 0.007	0.02 ± 0.004	0.31 ± 0.02	0.07 ± 0.002	17.63 ± 3.89
Radish, elongate, white skin (*Raphanus sativus*)	89.05 ± 0.72	0.77 ± 0.08	0.15 ± 0.02	2.65 ± 0.15	6.56 ± 0.70	1135	271	30.2	30.1	0.36		0.02 ± 0.004	0.02 ± 0.003	0.30 ± 0.03	0.07 ± 0.008	19.91 ± 5.69
Radish, round, red skin (*Raphanus sativus*)	89.68	0.89	0.16	2.29	6.07	130	31	35.76	28.27	0.42	1.2	0.03	0.02	0.3	0.07	15.69
Radish, round, white skin (*Raphanus sativus*)	89.76	0.8	0.14	2.37	6.13	129	31	34.23	29.47	0.41		0.03	0.02	0.24	0.07	14
Sweet potato, brown skin (*Ipomoes batatas*)	69.21 ± 0.83	1.33 ± 0.12	0.26 ± 0.06	3.99 ± 0.05	24.25 ± 0.77	456	109	27.5	42.96	0.35	5376 ± 816	0.07 ± 0.085	0.04 ± 0.012	0.67 ± 0.09	0.12 ± 0.006	17.94 ± 1.40
Sweet potato, pink skin (*Ipomoes batatas*)	69.58 ± 0.22	1.27 ± 0.09	0.33 ± 0.06	3.94 ± 0.10	23.93 ± 0.15	452	108	28.93	37.6	0.51		0.06 ± 0.012	0.04 ± 0.001	0.69 ± 0.12	0.09 ± 0.007	22.20 ± 2.32
Tapioca (*Manihot esculenta*)	75.23 ± 0.55	1.03 ± 0.10	0.20 ± 0.01	4.61 ± 0.12	17.81 ± 0.57	334	80	25.89 ± 6.52	42.55 ± 11.04	0.81 ± 0.18		0.07 ± 0.003	0.02 ± 0.001	0.45 ± 0.01	0.09 ± 0.006	15.51 ± 3.19
Water Chestnut (*Eleocharis dulcis*)	73.34	0.86	0.37	3.02	21.46	400	96	37.15	62.83	0.77		0.02	0.02	0.74	0.13	5.26
Yam, elephant (*Amorphophallus campanulatus*)	74.39 ± 0.31	2.56 ± 0.28	0.14 ± 0.02	4.17 ± 0.05	17.46 ± 0.55	353	84	46.91	43.06	1.22	176	0.04 ± 0.004	0.05 ± 0.017	0.61 ± 0.10	0.22 ± 0.044	15.22 ± 1.84
Yam, ordinary (*Amorphophallus campanulatus*)	74.28 ± 0.63	2.18 ± 0.26	0.17 ± 0.02	4.08 ± 0.07	17.65 ± 0.57	349	83	16.19	49.46	0.77	158	0.04 ± 0.003	0.02 ± 0.006	0.56 ± 0.06	0.17 ± 0.06	13.88 ± 3.43
Yam, wild (*Dioscorea versicolor*)	69.35	3.07	0.3	4.57	20.95	430	103	44.13	55.94	1.04	230	0.121	0.015	0.7	0.2	14.06

Source : IFCT, NIN, ICMR, Hyderabad, 2017

6. Tuber crops : Potato, sweet potato, tapioca, Jerusalem artichoke
7. Bulbs : Onion, garlic, leek
8. Perennial vegetables : Asparagus, rhubarb, globe artichoke
9. Leguminous vegetables : Peas, beans

14.2 Composition

Vegetables differ widely in their chemical composition (Table 14.1). Vegetables, as a group, have a high water content, particularly in the greens. The crispness of greens depends on the water in the cells. Partial dehydration of cells results in a change from crisp to a limp leaf. The protein value of a vegetable is very low except with legumes. The carbohydrates present in vegetables are cellulose, starch and sugars. Cellulose, with hemicellulose and pentosans, forms the structural material of vegetables. Pectic substances, the cementing material, are between the cell walls of vegetables. Some vegetables like potato and tapioca, contain a high percentage of carbohydrates as starch. In immature vegetables, this carbohydrate is mostly in the form of sugar and gradually changes to starch as the vegetable matures. Vegetables, contain non-volatile acids, such as citric, malic, oxalic and succinic acids. These contribute to the flavour of vegetables. The very strong flavour characteristic of some vegetables like onion, garlic, cauliflower, etc., is due to certain sulphur-containing volatile compounds.

Vegetables contain various chemical compounds responsible for the wide range of colours in their raw and cooked condition. The pigment of the green vegetables is due to chlorophyll. The yellow and orange colour of vegetables, such as carrots and tomatoes, are on account of carotenoids. Flavonoids are responsible for the colour of red radishes and red cabbage.

14.3 Nutritive Value

The nutritive value of different vegetables, vary sufficiently and it is wise to serve a variety of vegetables to ensure that all the necessary nutrients from the vegetable category are included in the diet. Vegetables, as a group, contribute indigestible fibre, minerals and vitamins to the diet. Most vegetables, except those containing starch which provides a useful source of energy, are low in calories. Leguminous vegetables, provide proteins that, though, are incomplete owing to the limited quantities of essential amino acids in them. Vegetables are very low in fat content, and this is also responsible for their low calorific content.

Vegetable protein has the following acids; Arginine 7, Histidine 2.1, Lysine 2.1, tryptophan 1.9, cystine 2.0, methionine 3.2 and threonine 3.2, to build protein in the body. Hence vegetarian diet supplemented with milk and milk products does have to depend upon animal proteins. Fat is not present in vegetables.

Calcium and iron are two minerals found in significant amounts in vegetables. Green leafy vegetables and legumes contain these minerals in good quantity. However, in some vegetables, e.g., spinach, the calcium combines with oxalic acid present in the vegetable forming the insoluble calcium oxalate, which cannot be absorbed by the body. Vegetables also supply the other essential minerals required by the body.

Vegetables are good sources of vitamins A and C. Orange, and dark-green, leafy vegetables are rich in carotenes which are the precursors of vitamin A. The leafy vegetables are also rich sources of vitamin

C. Green peppers, Brussel sprouts, tomatoes, etc., are good sources of ascorbic acid. The indigestible fibre content of vegetables contributes to the roughage promoting the mobility of the food through the intestine.

Storage: All vegetables are best when fresh. Vegetables of high water content become wilted and tough when allowed to stand long after gathering, owing to loss of moisture. Flavour is also impaired because of enzyme action and the conversion of starch into sugar. Fresh vegetables of many kinds are now available throughout the year due to improved methods of agriculture, harvesting, transport and storage.

Succulent vegetables are chilled, washed, packed and refrigerated. Root vegetables are harvested when mature and stored under controlled temperature and humidity. The method of chilling and refrigeration is important. Tomatoes, for example, deteriorate because of excessive chilling and refrigeration. They stay best when cooled to temperatures not lower than 13°C. Nowadays, leafy vegetables are vacuum cooled before refrigeration. The short storage life of many vegetables is because they rapidly respire. This is controlled by refrigeration. This treatment is also useful in conserving the vitamin potency of the vegetables.

14.4 Cole Crops

Cole refers to any of various plants belonging to the genus *Brassica* and *Cruciferae* or mustard family. Brussels sprouts, cabbage, cauliflower, collards, kale, kohl, rabi, mustard, broccoli, turnips and watercress are cool season crops belonging to mustard. 15 to 21° C is the best means for cole crops to grow.

They are grown in winter. The many distinctive vegetables of this group, such as cabbage and cauliflower, are all derived from the wild cabbage (*Brassica oleracea*). Their common ancestry is apparent in the similarity of their inflorescence, flowers and fruits.

14.4.1 Cabbage (*Brassica oleracea* L. var *capitata*)

Cabbage or *Band Gobhi* (*Brassica oleracea* L. var *capitata*) is native to the Mediterranean coast and several varieties have been cultivated since ancient times. Its introduction into India is comparatively recent and five varieties are grown in the country. The cabbage is made of many rather thick and overlapping leaves attached to a short, thick stem, to form a head. The heads may be large or small, spherical, pointed or flattened with tightly folded leaves. The cabbage is an important vegetable and is used in curries, pickles, etc. It is used raw as an ingredient of salads and in the preparation of "cole slaw" (shredded cabbage). It is employed in the manufacture of sauerkraut, which is made by fermenting chopped, ground, or sliced cabbage in its juice, with a little salt added to it.

White Cabbage

Red Cabbage

The *red cabbage* differs from other cabbages in colour, mainly due to the content of anthocyanin pigments. Red cabbage is used chiefly for pickling.

Cabbage contains an antibiotic. It contains gefarnate and carbenoxolone-compound used as an anti-ulcer drug. Cabbage is also antibiotic. Hence the cabbage juice has this anti-ulcer health benefit.

Chinese cabbage

Chinese Cabbage

The *Chinese cabbage* also known as Pak choi (*Brassica chinensis*) has an elongated head and a very prominent central rib in the leaves can refer to two groups of Chinese leaf vegetables known as the Pekinensis Group (napa cabbage) and the Chinensis Group (bok choy). These vegetables are both subspecies of the turnip and belong to the same genus as cabbage, broccoli, and cauliflower. Both have many variations in name, spelling, and scientific classification, especially bok choy. Chinese cabbage, either of two widely cultivated members of the mustard family (*brassicaceae*) that are varieties of *Brassica rapa.*

It is grown to a limited extent in India. It is used as a salad.

Bok choy

Bok choy (Pak choi), also called spoon cabbage (*B. rapa*, variety *chinensis*), has glossy dark green leaves and thick crisp white or green stalks in a loose head. Young tender plants are often sold as "baby bochoy" and have a milder flavour. The plant is commonly used in stir-fries and is especially popular in Asian cuisine.

Napa or **nappa cabbage** belongs to the family of *Brassicaceae* (*Cruciferae*, cabbage family), the Genus of Brassica and the subspecies pekinensis, is a type of Chinese cabbage originating near the Beijing region of China, and is widely used in East Asian cuisine. It is referred to as "Chinese cabbage", 'wombok'. A cruciferous plant (*Brassicaceae*) it is closely related to species like broccoli, pakchoi or cauliflower, forms a tight head of crinkled light green leaves, is a cool-season annual vegetable. It grows to an oblong-shaped head, tightly arranged crinkly, thick, light-green leaves with white prominent veins with a yellow innermost layer. The vegetable is rich in Vitamin C (26 mg/100 g) and has a fair amount of calcium (40 mg/100 g). It tastes mild aromatic.

The world production is 72.6 million tonnes and India's production is 10.5 million tonnes in 2023 West Bengal 2.55 million tonnes, Odisha 1.18 million tonnes; Assam 0.78 million tonnes; Madhya Pradesh 0.76 million tonnes in 2021-22. India ranked second in world production next to China in the year 2023.

Knol-Khol

Knol-khol or *khol-rabi* is sometimes called "turnip-rooted cabbage". It looks like a turnip but is closely related to the cabbage. The word *khol-rabi* is German in which "khol" means cabbage and "rabi" turnip. It is used as a boiled vegetable.

It can be eaten raw or cooked, both the stem and the leaves are edible. Despite its common names, it is not the same species as turnip. The young stem, in particular, can be as crisp and juicy as an apple, although much less sweet.

There are several varieties, commonly available, including 'White Vienna', Purple Vienna', 'Grand Duke', 'Gigante', 'Purple Danube', and 'White Danube'. Coloration of the purple types is superficial: the edible parts are all pale yellow. The leafy greens can also be eaten. One commonly used variety grows without a swollen stem, having just leaves and a very thin stem, and is called *Haakh. Haakh* and *Monj* are popular Kashmiri dishes made using this vegetable. Kohlrabi also comes in three different *colours*: white, purple, and pale green. The bulbous kohlrabi stem is frequently used raw in salads or slaws. It has a texture similar to that of a broccoli stem, but with a flavour that is sweeter and less vegetal. Kohlrabi leaves are edible and can be used interchangeably with collard greens and kale.

14.4.2 Brussel Sprouts (*Brassica oleracea,* var. *gemmifera*)

Brussel sprouts (*Brassica oleracea,* var. *gemmifera*) are miniature cabbages that are borne close together all along the stem, instead of a single head. The sprouts are tender, delicious and have a distinctive and popular flavour. They are cooked and served as hot vegetables. They are suitable for quick freezing and large quantities are frozen. They are also canned.

Brussels Sprouts

Brussels sprouts look-like miniature cabbages, they are 2.5–4.0 cm (1.0–1.6 in) in diameter.

Raw Brussels sprouts (for 100 grams) are 86% water, 9% carbohydrates, 3% protein, and contain negligible fat, high levels of vitamin C and vitamin K, moderate B vitamins, such as folate and vitamin B_6; essential minerals and dietary fibre are medium. Excess consumption is not recommended for patients on anticoagulants due to high vitamin K content.

The buds can be prepared by boiling, steaming, stir frying, grilling, slow cooking, or roasting. Overcooking must be avoided as they develop a strong flavour and odour not liked by all. It can be eaten with Parmesan cheese and butter, balsamic vinegar, apple cider vinegar, bacon, pistachios, pine nuts, mustard, brown sugar, chestnuts, or pepper. Brussels sprouts can be sauteed and pickled.

14.4.3 Watercress (*Nasturtium officinale*)

It is an aquatic plant species with the botanical name *Nasturtium officinale.* This should not be confused with the profoundly different and unrelated group of plants with the common name of nasturtium, within the genus *Tropaeolum.*

Watercress is a rapidly growing, aquatic or semi-aquatic, perennial plant native to Europe and Asia, and one of the oldest known leaf vegetables consumed by humans. It is a member of the family *Brassicaceae*, botanically related to garden cress, mustard, radish, and wasabi—all noteworthy for their piquant flavour.

Watercress

The hollow stems of the watercress will float; the leaf structure is pinnately compound small, white and green flowers are produced in clusters and are frequently visited by insects, especially hoverflies such as *Eristalis* flies.

Watercress is 95% water and has low contents of carbohydrates, protein, fat, and dietary fiber. A 100 gram serving of the watercress provides 11 calories, is particularly rich in vitamin K, and contains significant amounts of vitamin A, vitamin C, riboflavin, vitamin 86, calcium, and manganese.

14.4.4 Kale (*Brassica oleracea*—Acephala Group)

Brassica oleracea—Acephala Group, also called *Borecole,* is a form of cabbage in which the central leaves do not form a head. It is considered to be closer to wild cabbage than most domesticated forms. The most important growing areas lie in Central and Northern Europe and North America. *Kale* grows more rarely in tropical areas as it prefers cooler climates. *Kale* is the most robust cabbage type—indeed the hardiness of *Kale* is unmatched by any other vegetable.

Kale

Kale freezes well and tastes sweeter and tastier after being exposed to a frost. Tender *Kale* greens can provide an intense addition to salads, particularly, when combined with other strongly-flavored ingredients such as dry-roasted peanuts, tamari-roasted almonds, or red pepper flakes.

Vitamin K is present in large amounts as in collard. It is a rich source of vitamin A, vitamin C, vitamin B_6, folate, and manganese. Kale is a good source of thiamin, riboflavin, pantothenic acid, vitamin E and several dietary minerals, including iron, calcium, potassium, and phosphorous. Kale contains high levels of polyphenols, such as ferulic acid, with levels varying due to environmental and genetic factors.

Kale is a source of the carotenoids lutein and zeaxanthin. As with broccoli and other cruciferous vegetables, kale, contains glucosinolate compounds such as glucoraphanin, which contributes to the formation of sulforaphane, a compound under preliminary research for its potential to affect human health. Boiling kale decreases the level of glucosinate compounds, steaming microwaving or stir frying has no significant loss.

Boiling, also diminishes most of the nutrients, while vitamins A, C, and K, and manganese remain substantial.

14.4.5 Cauliflower (*Brassica oleracea,* var *botrytis*)

Cauliflower or *Phul Gobhi* (*Brassica oleracea,* var *botrytis*) consists normally of a single stem bearing a large, swollen, rounded flower head consisting of a tightly packed mass of underdeveloped white or creamy-white flower buds, known as the "curd." This flower head nestles in the surrounding leaves. In the Winter Cauliflower, the inner leaves are wrapped over the curd and help to protect it from weather damage. Cauliflower is cultivated in most parts of India, especially the North-west, where it is grown on a large scale. Cauliflower is used as a cooked vegetable in curries, soups, etc. It is frequently employed as an ingredient in mixed pickles.

Cauliflower (Orange)

Cauliflower (Purple)

Cauliflower (White)

The *Sprouting Broccoli* is similar to the cauliflower in the structure of its flower heads, but instead of producing a single head, several smaller ones are formed in the axils of the leaves down the branches. This is reported to be unsuitable for cultivation in the tropics. Purple and white varieties are available; purple variety which turns green when boiled is more popular.

The anti-carcinogenic properties of *Brassica* vegetables such as *Broccoli*, *Brussel sprouts*, Cauliflower and Green Cabbage are fairly well-known, but now researchers think that overcooking them in boiling water destroys their anti-cancer properties.

The anti-carcinogenic effects of these vegetables come from the high content of substances known as glucosinolates which are metabolized to cancer-preventive substances known as isothiocyanates.

The after-effects of cooking on the glucosinolate content of vegetables by boiling, steaming, microwave cooking and stir-fry was examined the researchers who found that boiling reduced the chemical the most. In fact, after boiling for 30 minutes,77% of the glucosinolate content in *Broccoli* was lost. The other methods such as frying, steaming or microwaving gave no significant loss of total glucosinolate content.

There are four major colour variants of cauliflower–white, orange, green and purple.

White cauliflower is the most common colour of cauliflower having a contrasting white head (also called "curd") surrounded by green leaves. *Orange cauliflower* (*B. oleracea L.* var. *botrytis*) contains beta-carotene as the orange pigment, a provitamin A compound. This orange trait originated from a natural mutant found in a cauliflower field in Canada. *Green cauliflower,* of the *B. oleracea* botrytis group, is sometimes called broccoflower. The *purple cauliflower* contains anthocyanins, water-soluble pigments.

Cauliflower heads can be roasted, boiled, fried, steamed, pickled or eaten raw. The leaves are also edible but are most often discarded.

Boiling reduces the levels of cauliflower compounds, with losses of 20–30% after five minutes, 40–50% after ten minutes, and 75% after thirty minutes. However, other preparation methods, such as steaming, microwaving, and stir-frying, have no significant effect on the compounds.

The world production is 26.6 million tonnes and India's production is 8.57 million tonnes. West Bengal 1,997.17 tonnes; Madhya Pradesh 1,478.81 tonnes; Bihar 1,118.90 tonnes, in 2023-24. India ranked second in world production next to China in the year 2023-24.

Romanesco: It is an exotic variant of cauliflower. The spirals on the head follow Fibonacci pattern, it is an excellent source of Vitamin C, K, fibre and carotenoids. Romanesco varies in colour–brown, green, purple and yellow.

Romanesco

14.4.6 Broccoli (*Brassica oleracea*)

Broccoli, is native to Italy and was introduced to the USA in 1920. There are three types of broccoli. Calabrese broccoli or broccoli is the most common one. It has large 10–20 cms green heads with many stalks and grows well in cold-season. It is cooked, steamed or eaten raw. Broccoli is a versatile, unique package containing antioxidants including quercetin, glutathione, beta carotene, indoles, vitamin C, lutein, glucarate, suplforaphane. It has all the anti-cancer properties. It removes estrogen from the body and prevents breast cancer. Reduces cholesterol, has anti-viral and anti-ulcer properties. Helps in regulating insulin and blood sugar. Cooking destroys antioxidants and anti-estrogen activity. So ideal to eat raw in salads.

Broccoli

A 100 gram Broccoli gives 35 Kcal, a good source of vitamin C and vitamin K. Raw broccoli is moderate in vitamin B complex and manganese. It is low in carbohydrates, protein and fat, dietary fibre. Has some amount of carotenoid compounds lutein and zeaxanthin.

In 2022, global production of broccoli (combined for production reports with cauliflowers) was 26.06 million tonnes, with China (largest producer) and India (second largest producer) together accounting for 72.4% of the total world production.

14.4.7 Collard Greens (*Brassica oleracea* var, *viridis*)

Collard Greens

Collard greens are part of the *Acephala* Group of the species, which includes kale and spring greens. Based on their genetic similarity, they are grouped under same category. The word "colewort" (the wild cabbage plant), gives rise to name "collard".

Collard green contains different types of anti-cancer, anti-oxidant compounds such as lutein, vitamin C and beta-carotene. This helps in fighting breast cancer and are not recommended for kidney stone patients.

14.5 Root Vegetables

The root vegetables belong to different families but their cultural requirements are similar. They thrive best in the cold-season but some types, especially the Radish, are tolerant to high temperatures.

Root vegetables are storage organs, they store energy in the form of carbohydrates. The concentration of starches, sugars, and other types of carbohydrates vary in root vegetables. The high concentration of starch is of economic importance, such starchy root vegetables are an important staple food in tropical regions.

14.5.1 Carrot (*Daucus carota*)

The wild carrot *(Daucus carota)* is a native of Asia and Europe and occurs as a troublesome weed. The cultivated carrot (*var sativus)* or *Gajar* is derived from the wild carrot and grown all over the world. The colour of the root in the cultivated types varies from white to yellow, orange-yellow, light purple, deep red or deep violet. The shape varies from short stumps to tapering cones. Several types of carrots are grown in India. The indigenous types are marked by their larger size, darker colour and sweet taste. The European carrots, have a smooth surface, thin core, better shape and less fibrous structure than native carrots.

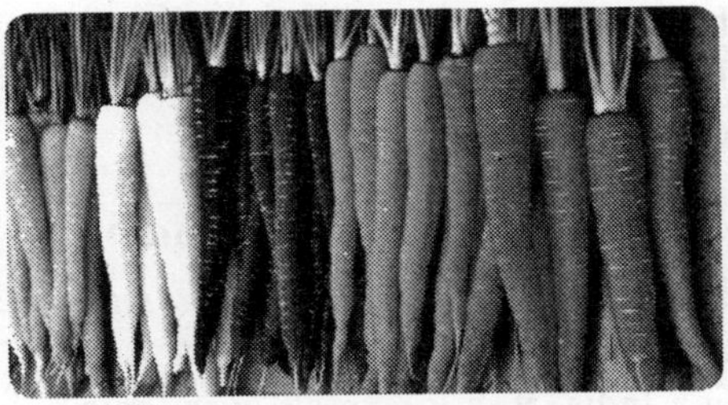

Carrot

Carrots are a rich source of carotene (which is maximum in orange carrots) and thus of vitamin A. Their high sugar content is indicated by their sweetness. Besides being one of the most valuable root crops grown for human consumption, they are used for feeding livestock. Carrots are used both raw and cooked, besides in preserves, pickles, etc.

Carrots are available in different colours and shapes, purple, black, white, yellow-orange, red. Orange carrots-highest in beta-carotene, contain smaller amounts of alpha-carotene, gamma-carotene lutein, zeaxanthin. Purple carrots, highest in anthocyanins, also contain beta-carotene and alpha-carotene and small amounts of lutein and zeaxanthin. Purple carrots that are orange inside: high in anthocyanins, beta and alpha-carotene. Purple carrots that are red inside: richest in anthocyanins and lycopene. Purple carrots that are white inside: anthocyanins little beta-carotene, Red carrots: highest in lycopene, also contain smaller amounts of lutein, beta-carotene, alpha-carotene. Yellow carrots-highest in lutein may also contain zeaxanthin. White carrots no pigment-giving antioxidants. The colour of yellow, orange and red carrots is the result of certain carotenoid pigments present in the root. These carotenoids can be divided into hydrocarbon pigments of carotenes and oxygenated pigments or xanthophylls.

The world production is 42.2 million tonnes and India's production is 3.9 million tonnes in India 2022-23.

14.5.2 Parsnip (*Pastinaca sativa*)

Parsnip

The parsnip (*Pastinaca sativa*) is a vegetable crop of minor importance in India. The wild parsnip is abundant in Europe. The fleshy roots contain a good quantity of sugar and starch and have been used from early times as food for man and livestock and also for making parsnip wine. The parsnip is recognized by its characteristic smell, hollow, furrowed stems, and large simply pinnate leaves with ovate, lobed and toothed leaflets.

Parsnips resemble carrots and can be used in similar ways, but they have a sweeter taste, especially when cooked. It can be baked, boiled, pureed, roasted, fried, grilled, or steamed and eaten raw. They give a rich flavour when used in stews, soups, and casseroles. Parsnips can also be fried or thinly sliced and made into crispies.

The parsnip is rich in vitamins and minerals, especially potassium with 375 mg per 100 g. Several of the B-group vitamins are present, vitamin C is reduced in cooking. Since most of the vitamins and minerals are found close to the skin, many will be lost unless the root is finely peeled or cooked whole. It also contains antioxidants and both soluble and insoluble dietary fibre. Parsnip has an excellent anti-cancer properties.

14.5.3 Radish (*Raphanus sativus*)

Radish (White)

Radish (Red)

Radish or *Mooli* (*Raphanus sativus*) is thought to be a native of China and India. It is grown all over India. The radish varies in size, shape and colour. The shape varies from nearly spherical to cylindrical and elongated. The colour may be white, pink, red, purple or red with white tips. The usually cultivated variety in India is white with a conical shape that is very pungent. Radish is eaten raw and used as a salad vegetable. Some varieties are cooked and spiced before serving. The leaves are also boiled and eaten.

Different varieties are varying in size, flavour, colour, and duration/time taken to mature. Roots can be globular, tapering, or cylindrical. The colour ranges from white to pink, red, purple, yellow, and green to black, but the flesh is usually white. They get colour from anthocyanins. Red varieties use anthocyanin, pelargonidin as a pigment, and purple cyanidin. The chemical compounds including glucosinolate, myrosinase, and isothiocyanate give the sharp flavour to radish.

Radishes are annual or biennial brassicaceous crops. The flesh of radishes harvested timely is crisp and sweet but becomes bitter and tough if the vegetable is left in the ground too long. The leaves are used as a leaf vegetable. The seed can also be sprouted and eaten raw; root can be raw as a crunchy salad vegetable.

Eating raw radish is practised from ancient times as a carminative medicine. Few slices of radish daily are good for piles, constipation and indigestion.

India produced 3.19 million tonnes in the year 2023-24.

14.5.4 Turnip (*Brassica rapa*)

Turnip

Turnip or *Salgam* (*Brassica rapa*) was known in Europe from prehistoric times and it is now cultivated in other parts of the world. It is grown as a cold season crop in the plains of India. It is cultivated primarily for its swollen and fleshy tap-root which is used either raw or cooked. The green leaf tops are also used as boiled greens. The structure of raw turnip makes it a pleasing addition to salads.

Small, tender varieties are grown for human consumption, while larger varieties are grown as feed for livestock. In the north of England, Scotland, Ireland, Cornwall and eastern Canada (Newfoundland), turnip (or *neep*) often refers to rutabaga, a larger, yellow root vegetable in the same genus (Brassica) also known as swede (from "Swedish turnip").

The boiled greens are a rich source of vitamin K, with vitamin A, vitamin C, and folate also in significant content. Boiled turnip greens also contain substantial lutein. Boiled turnip is 94% water, 5% carbohydrates, and 1% protein, with negligible fat.

Eating cooked turnip regularly checks the formation of phlegm, increases vitamin A content in the body protects the eyes, prevents constipation and uric acid in urine.

The world production of carrot and turnips is 42.2 million tonnes and India produced 3.9 million tonnes in 2022.

Rutabaga

Rutabaga

Rutabaga (*Brassica napobrassica*) is a root vegetable that originated as a cross between the cabbage and the turnip. The roots are eaten in a variety of ways, and the leaves can be eaten as a leaf vegetable. It is roasted, baked, boiled, used in soups, uncooked and thinly sliced in a salad. The roots and tops are also used as animal feed in winter.

14.5.5 Beetroot (*Beta vulgaris*)

Beetroot

The beetroot or garden beet (*Beta vulgaris*), used as a vegetable, is closely related to the sugarbeet and naturally has high sugar content. It is grown in certain parts of the country throughout the year. There are several varieties of garden beet differing in form, colour and time of maturing. They are generally spherical with a small taproot and are medium sized and deep red. The beetroot is commonly used as a salad root or boiled in water, peeled and eaten cold, or pickled in vinegar. It is also used as hot vegetable. The beet greens are also useful, either boiled or even as salad greens.

Beets are used as food colouring, in 19th century, wine often was coloured with beetroot juice and as a medicinal plant. Many beet products are made from other *Beta vulgaris* varieties, particularly sugar beet. From middle-age beetroot is used in the treatment of conditions, especially illnesses relating to digestion and the blood. Raw beetroot is a rich source of folate and a moderate source of manganese.

14.5.6 Celeriac (*Apium graveolens*—Papaceum Group)

It (also known as "turnip-rooted celery" or 'knob celery') is a specially selected Cultivar Group of celery, grown as a root vegetable for its large and well-developed taproot rather than for its stem and leaves. The root is used when it is about 10–12 cm in diameter or the size of a large potato. Celeriac may be used raw or fresh. It is best to peel celeriac before use since the outer skin is tough and stringy. It has the celery flavour, so it is often used as a flavouring in soups and stews; it can also be mashed or used in casseroles and baked dishes. The hollow stalk of the upper plant can be cut into drinking straw lengths, rinsed out, and used for tomato drinks such as "Bloody Mary." The tomato juice moving through the stalk is lightly permeated with the celery flavour. Nutritionally, celeriac is low in carbohydrates.

Celeriac

There are numerous cultivars available, especially in Europe, where root vegetables are popular. Celeriac has good keeping properties and should last 3 to 4 months if stored between 0° and 5 °C and not allowed to dry out.

14.5.7 Arracacha (*Arracacia xanthorrhiza*)

Arracacha is a garden root vegetable originally from the Andes, somewhat intermediate between the carrot and celery. Its starchy taproot is a popular food item in South America, especially in Brazil where it is a major commercial crop. The leaves are similar to parsley and vary from dark green to purple. The roots resemble fat short carrots, with lustrous off-white skin. The interior may be white, yellow, or purple.

Arrachacha

The boiled root has about the same uses as boiled potatoes, including side dishes, purée, dumplings and *gnocchi,* pastries, etc., with the advantage of its flavour and (depending on the variety) its intense colour. Because it is highly digestible (due to the small size of its starch grains), purée and soups made from it are considered excellent for babies and children.

The yellow cultivar contains substantial amounts of carotenoid pigments, precursors to vitamin A, to the point that excessive consumption of arracachas may cause yellowing of the skin (a condition that is not considered to be harmful). The young stems can be eaten cooked or in salads, and the leaves can be fed to livestock.

14.5.8 Black Salsify (*Scorzonera hispanica*)

The black salsify or Spanish salsify, also known as black oyster plant, serpent root, and viper's grass, is a perennial member of the sunflower family (*Asteraceae*), cultivated as a root vegetable in the same way as some of the members of the salsify genus *Tragopogon,* to which it is closely related. The black salsify is native to Southern Europe and the Near East. It has heads of yellow ray flowers. The thin black taproot grows up to one metre long and up to 2 cm in diameter. It has black skin with a white internal substance.

Black Salsify

The black salsify is considered nutritious: it contains proteins, fats, the glycosides asparagine, choline and laevulin, as well as minerals such as potassium, calcium, phosphorus, iron, sodium, and vitamins A, B_1, E and C. Since it also contains the glycoside, inulin, which consists of fructose, it is particularly suitable for diabetics.

14.6 Fruit Vegetables

Apart from *cucurbits,* several other fruits find extensive use as vegetables. Some of them are the following:

14.6.1 Tomato (*Lycopersicon esculentum*)

The tomato (*Lycopersicon esculentum*) is of South American origin and the improved varieties of the wild fruit are grown widely throughout the world. Its high vitamin content and multiple uses in culinary preparations have made the tomato an important vegetable outranking all other vegetables, except the potato, in popularity and value. In India, the tomato is a very important vegetable available throughout the year.

Tomato

Many varieties of tomatoes exist all over the world, differing in size from that of a gooseberry to bigger than a cricket ball. The shapes also vary with varieties from perfect round to elliptical or oval. Tomatoes vary in shades of attractive yellow, orange and scarlet, when fully ripe. The fruits are juicy, the fleshy cone embedding liberal amounts of soft tiny seeds. The fruits are highly perishable, cannot be stored at low temperature, and require special care in handling, transport and marketing.

Unripe green tomatoes are used as vegetables as they lend themselves to making a wide range of dishes. However, only a negligible fraction of tomatoes are used as green vegetables.

Tomato is a major source of lycopene an antioxidant and anti-cancer agent. Lycopene intervenes, in the chain reactions of oxygen free radical molecules and promotes health.

The rich, ripe, succulent fruits are relished raw. Their soft and crisp consistency together with their attractive colour, flavour and tenderness make them ideal for salads. Tomatoes are also eaten fried, baked or stuffed and are used for the preparation in soups, sauces and ketchups. Large quantities of fruits are canned, either whole or as tomato juice or purée.

The *cherry tomato* (*var cerasiforme*) is characterized by its smaller and more numerous fruits. The fruits are palatable and make an interesting addition to salads. The same is true of the "pear tomato" (*var pyriforme)* which is pear-shaped. Both cherry and pear tomatoes may be either red or yellow in colour.

The *tree tomato* (*Cyphomandra betacea*) belongs to the same family as tomato and is native to Peru. The tree tomato is a tropical fruit of minor importance and grows best at medium to high altitudes. The fruits are of the size of an egg, reddish-yellow or purple when ripe. They are eaten raw but are usually stewed.

The world production is 186.1 million tonnes and India's production is 20.7 million tonnes in 2022. India ranked second in world production of tomatoes next to China in the year 2022.

14.6.2 Bell Pepper (*Capsicum annuum*)

Bell pepper, also known as sweet pepper (*Capsicum annuum*) is of tropical American origin and is cultivated in India. The fruits are large-sized. The pericarp is thick and mildly pungent. Unripe fruits are generally green and when ripe the fruits are red, yellow or brown. Immature fruits, while still green, are used in salads and as vegetables. The pungent types of capsicum (*Capsicum nigrum*) are used as a spice. India produced 0.59 million tonnes Capsicum in 2023-24.

Bell Pepper

But now different colours red, yellow, orange, white & purple bell peppers are available. Less pungent ones are known as sweet pepper. China is the largest producer of bell pepper.

14.6.3 Eggplant (*Solanum melongena*)

The name eggplant, the white varieties known as garden eggs and easter egg.

The eggplant or brinjal (*Solanum melongena*) is a native of India and is widely grown throughout the country and in the tropical, subtropical and warm temperate regions of the world. It is known as eggplant (aubergine) because the fruit of many varieties looks something like a large egg. The fruit is a glossy firm-fleshed berry containing numerous seeds. It may be egg-shaped, pear-shaped or cylindrical, and 10 to 25 cm long. The colour is either white or deep purple in different varieties. It is used as a cooked vegetable, sliced and fried or boiled, or eaten in curries and other dishes. Brinjal roasted, mashed and spiced with salt, onion, chillies, etc. (*bharta*), is a popular dish in India.

Eggplant

Due to its texture, it is used to substitute meat. It belongs to genus *Solanum* related to tomato and potato. Its skin and seeds are edible but cannot be eaten raw as a potato.

Raw eggplant can have bitter taste with astringency but becomes tender with complex flavour when cooked. It can be allergic to people who are hypersensitive, eggplant is high in histamine.

The world production is 59.3 million tonnes and India produced 12.8 million tonnes in 2022. In India, West Bengal 3,029.02 tonnes: Odisha 2,127.48 tonnes; Gujarat 1,533.67 tonnes, 2021-22. India ranked second in world production next to China in the year 2022.

14.6.4 Okra (*Hibiscus esculentus*)

Okra, also known as "lady's finger" or *bhindi* (*Hibiscus esculentus*) is a native of tropical Africa and is now widely grown in the tropics and subtropics. The fruits may be long (up to 20 cm) and, when ripe, are too fibrous to be digested. They are picked in the immature stage, cooked and eaten as a vegetable in various forms. Okra contains mùcilaginous material that imparts a characteristic texture and taste to the vegetable and this accounts for its use in soups and stews.

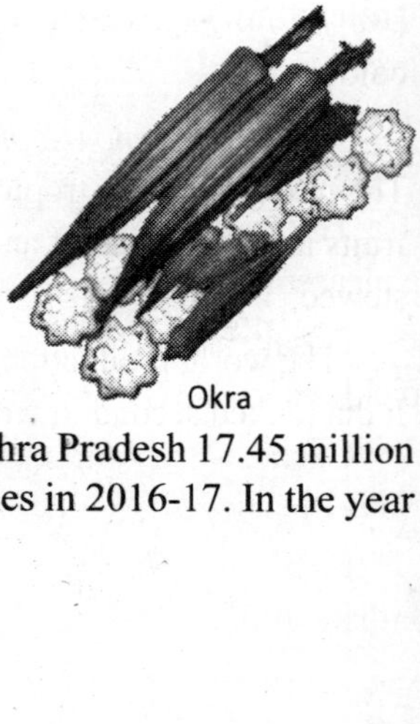

Okra

The world production is 89,00,434 tonnes and of India's is 55,07,000 tonnes in 2016 and 60,003 million tonnes in India 2016–17. In India, Andhra Pradesh 17.45 million tonnes Jammu & Kashmir 7.08 million tonnes; Assam 15.82 million tonnes in 2016-17. In the year 2014, India ranked first.

14.6.5 Chow-Chow (*Sechium edule*)

Chayote or chow-chow (*Sechium edule*) is the fruit of a hairy herb. The fruits vary in shape, size and colour, varying from whitish to dark green. They are more or less pear-shaped or roundish with a single large seed. Those shaped like pears have deep fissures at the blossom end. The surface may be deeply wrinkled or corrugated, smooth or very prickly.

Chow-Chow

Spiny Chayote has prickles on its skin. The skin is not edible, not only because of the prickles but because it will be tough. These need to be peeled, either before cooking, or it can be baked, cut into half.

The fruits, young shoots, leaves and large fleshy roots are all used as culinary vegetables. The fruits, in particular have many uses—creamed, baked, fried. The large tuberous root looks and tastes like yam. It is used as food in many tropical areas and starch, said to be a substitute for arrowroot, starch can be obtained from it.

14.7 Cucurbits (*Cucurbitaceae*)

Vegetables, such as cucumbers, pumpkins, squashes and gourds, belong to the family *Cucurbitaceae*. These are tender crops and grown during summer months. They have more or less similar cultural requirements. They can be grown on sandy soils and require plenty of water. Differences in flavour, consistency and appearance of *cucurbits* are related to their composition which determines their suitability for different purposes. Some varieties are excellent for culinary use during the early stages of maturity but very poor for the same use at later stages, while the converse may be true of other varieties.

14.7.1 Cucumber (*Cucumis sativus*)

The cucumber or *Kheera* (*Cucumis sativus*) is native to India and has been cultivated for a very long time. It is now cultivated in the tropics and subtropics of the world and is a popular vegetable crop. Numerous varieties of cucumber are cultivated. The cultivated forms are broadly divided into two groups, the hot-weather forms and the rainy-season forms. The former yields small, egg-shaped, dark green fruits known as gherkins (*Cucumis anguria*). The rainy-season varieties have much longer fruits and are more commonly grown in India. Some fruits are long, with fairly thick rinds, while others are small with thin and smooth rinds. The colour of the fruit varies from pale whitish-green to dark green turning brownish-yellow or rusty-brown when mature, with white inner meat. The cucumber is commonly eaten raw, in salads and sandwiches, or pickled. The seed kernels of cucumber are edible and used in confectionery.

Cucumber

The burpless variety of cucumber has thinner skin, easy to digest and has a pleasent taste. They can grow up to 2 feet and are seedless.

Dosakai is yellow cucumber, spherical, cooked and used in sambar, soup, pickles and chutney.

Cucumber have mild melon flavour, is due to unsaturated aldehydes. Some rinds of cucumber have a bitter taste due to cucurbitacins.

Cucumbers and gherkins: the world production is 94.7 million tonnes and India's production is 1,99,018 tonnes in 2022.

Dosakai

14.7.2 Pumpkin (*Cucurbita moschata*)

The pumpkin or *Kaddu* (*Cucurbita moschata*) is native to tropical America and grown throughout India. A large number of varieties are grown. The fruits are large, oblong, oval or round, usually flattened at both ends and grooved. The colour of the flesh may vary from yellow to orange, and it has a hollow cavity. The seeds are numerous, white to tan in colour, with dark marginal bands. Pumpkins are used as cooked vegetables. They are also used to make pumpkin pie. Pumpkin seeds are rich in both fats and proteins. They are fried in deep oil, salted and eaten. An edible oil can be derived from pumpkin seeds.

Pumpkin

Pumpkin contains high beta-carotene, hence helps in preventing numerous health problems including heart attack, cancer and cataract.

Pumpkins, squash and gourds: the world production is 22.8 million tonnes and India's production is 5.57 million tonnes in 2022.

14.7.3 Squashes (*Cucurbita pepo*)

Squashes are similar to pumpkins, though they show botanical differences. Like pumpkins, the squashes are of American origin and are varieties of a single species *Cucurbita pepo.*

Summer squash: The summer squash or *Chappan Kaddu*, also known as vegetable marrow (*Cucurbita pepo*) is a popular vegetable in the UK. The short fruit-stock is hard, deeply furrowed, with 5 to 8 ridges and is only slightly swollen where it joins the fruit. The fruits may be green, whitish, or irregularly striped green and white. The flesh is white with no cavity and the seeds are embedded in the flesh. The immature fruit is used and as a boiled vegetable.

Summer Squash

Summer Squash (Green)

Winter squash: The winter squash or *Vilayati Kaddu* (*Cucurbita maxima*) is popular in the hills. The fruit-stock is soft and spongy. The fruit is round, medium-sized, yellow to bright orange in colour with light specks. It has long-keeping qualities. The flesh is thick and has a fine texture. The fruits are eaten when mature and take about twice as much time as vegetable marrow to reach this stage.

Winter squashes contain less water, more proteins, fats, carbohydrates and considerably more vitamin A than summer squashes.

14.7.4 Gourds

Gourds include a number of popular vegetables cultivated in India.

Ridged Gourd (*Ribbed Gourd*)*:* The ridged gourd is the edible fruit of *Luffa acutangula,* which is cultivated throughout India. The gourd is a popular vegetable when tender; on ripening, it becomes fibrous and unpalatable. *Luffa acutangula* var *amara,* a wild form of the cultivated variety resembles the ridged gourd in every respect, except that the leaves, flowers, fruits and seeds are smaller. All parts of the plant are exceedingly bitter.

Ridge Gourd

Sponge Gourd (*L. cylindrica*) fruits differ from ridge gourd. They are smooth, cylindrical, and unusually 25–30 cm long. This gourd is said to be indigenous to India. Both edible and bitter forms are known. Tender fruits of sponge gourd are used as a vegetable. On maturing, the fibrous bundles harden and the pulp becomes bitter and inedible.

Sponge Gourd

Bitter Gourd: The bitter gourd or *karela*, also known as balsam pear (*Momordica charantia*), is grown all over the country and is an elongated fruit (5 to 25 cm long) tapering at the ends. The fruit is green when unripe turning to yellow-orange when ripe. There is also a white variety. The fruit though bitter is wholesome and esteemed as a vegetable. When young, it may be sliced and preserved after drying for use in the off-season. The fruit is also pickled. The young fruits are cooked and eaten; they are often steeped in saltwater after peeling and before cooking to remove the bitter taste.

Bitter Gourd

The bitterness is due to quinine or an anti-material component and has medicinal properties particularly in treating diabetes. India produced 1.13 million tonnes in 2021-22.

Kantola (*Momordica diocia*): This gourd is used all over India. Its usage is similar to Karela. It is faintly bitter. It has some medicinal properties. It is small and spherical.

Kantola

Chinese bitter melon (Momordica charantia) and Taiwan bitter melon (*momordica charantia*): are less bitter than Indian Karela. Chinese is variety when they ripen are pulpy seed and becomes brilliant red and giant sweet. Taiwans bitter melon is paler in colour, hardly bitter but bland, they are sliced and eaten raw.

Concombre sauvage (*Momoridica foctida*) is native to Africa. Fruits are three to four inch long covered with soft spines which becomes pricky when fruit dries. The fruit is cooked and eaten. All parts of the plants have medicinal use.

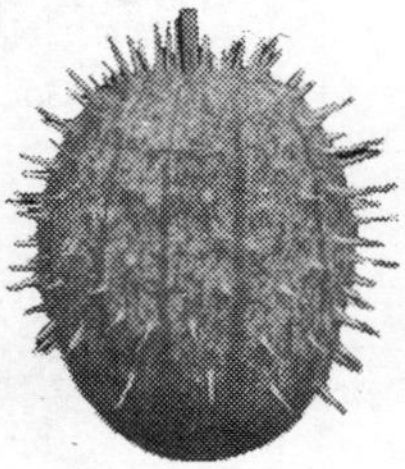

Chinese

Gac (*Momordica cohinchinensis*) is unrelated to Jack fruit, resembles jack fruit. It grows on Wine like any other gourd or cucumber, has red axils around the seeds. It is popular in Vietnam. It has a higher concentration of bioavailable beta-carotene than any other vegetable, 10 times that of carrots and 70 times lycopene provided by tomatoes. It has a number of important phytonutrients and vitamin E.

Monk fruit: (*Fructus momordica*) native to China and Thailand. Though related to bitter gourd (*genus Siraitianot momordica*), it is 300 times sweeter than cane sugar with nil calories. Hence it is used as a natural sweetener having no side effects of artificial sweeteners.

Chinese Bitter Gourd

Luffa gourds are of two kinds angled or smooth luffa. Anguled luffa (*Lufa acutangula*), smooth *Luffa cylindrica alt* L. *aegyptiaca* when dry they are used as bath a sponge.

Oystersnut (*Telfairia pedata*) is native to Tanzania and Mozambique. The flesh of the gourd is edible, has a number of seeds that provide protein, also the seeds give sweet cooking oil. The seeds are eaten raw, boiled roasted or pickled. The extracts pulp is rich in fats and protein and used as fodder.

Parval Gourd (*C. trichsanthes diocia*): they grow to 6 inches long but are harvested when they are 2–3 inches. The seeds are larger among the edible gourd and are crunchy. The skin is very thin, a little hard and hence they are scraped. It has a pleasant flavour when cooked.

Porknut (*Hodgsania macrocorpa*): It is grown in Himalayas, Assam, China. Each fruit has eight large seeds, which are 50% fat contents, when raw they are toxic, but when heated or cooked before use they taste like fatty pieces of pork. The nuts are used in curries, the flesh is inedible. The plant has medicinal value.

Tinda (*Proceitrullus fistuolosus* alt *citrullus vulgaris*): It is native to India. This gourd is seen in an immature stage when it is 3 inches in diameter and its leaves and skin need to be peeled. The mature seeds are edible.

Tindora (*Coccinia grandis*): Native to India. It is green 2.5 to 3 inches in length and is like a tiny cucumber. When mature it becomes scarlet red. It is raw and is more crunchy than cucumber. It can be cooked or pickled.

Gac

Monk Fruit

Luffa Gourd

Oysternut

Parval

Tinda

Porknut

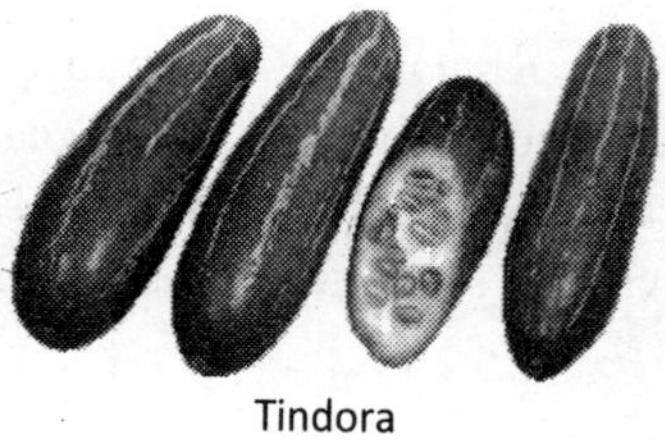
Tindora

Snake Gourd: The snake gourd or *chichinda* (*Trichosanthes anguina*) is of Indian origin and is a popular crop throughout India. The fruits are narrow and cylindrical and can reach up to 50 cm in length and 8 cm in thickness. They are greenish when young or pale green-white, sometimes striped, changing to bright orange when ripe. They are pickled when immature and sliced before boiling.

Snake

Ash or White Gourd: The ash gourd or *petha* (*Benincasa hispida*) is a native of Java and Japan and is grown throughout India and other tropical countries. The fruits are like pumpkins with white flesh containing numerous seeds. The young fruit is used as a vegetable and made into curries, while ripe fruits are cut into pieces and candied. The seeds are fried and eaten.

Ash Gourd

One of the medicinal properties of ash gourd is its raw juice is used as a remedy for severe dysentery.

Bottle Gourd: The bottle gourd or *lauki* (*Lagenaria vulgaris*) grows wild in India. The fruits are large, long (up to 1.8 m) with numerous long, white seeds. The young fruits are used as boiled vegetables. When the fruits dry, the hard shells are used as containers. India produced 2,860 thousand tonnes in 2021-22. Bottle gourd is also known as "Indian opo" or "plain opo". They can be the shape of long or spherical.

Bottle

14.8 Leafy Vegetables

In India, leafy vegetables or greens from many plants have been used in the diet from ancient times. They are nutritionally very important and are rich in vitamins and minerals.

14.8.1 Agathi (*Sesbania grandiflora*)

This plant is grown as a shade, and support tree for pepper and betel vines. Tender leaves, pods and flowers of this tree are eaten as vegetables. Leaves are considered to be an excellent source of vitamin C and calcium. The leaf protein is considered to be of good quality with good digestibility and biological value. Agathi flowers are sweetish in taste and succulent. They are a good source of thiamine, nicotinic acid and vitamin C.

Agathi

14.8.2 Amaranth (*Amaranthus*)

The genus *Amaranthus* includes about 60 species of the herb of which some 25 occur in India. Their tender leaves and shoots are used as vegetables. Some are grown in the hill tracks as grain crops.

Amaranth (Red)

Amaranth (Green)

A. gangeticus (*Lal sag*) is a greenish or dark red tender herb with purple tinted or dark green leaves. The tender shoots are used as vegetables.

A. spinosus (*Kautewali chaulai*) is an erect spinous herb varying in colour from green and red or purple. The plant has considerable food value.

14.8.3 Beet Green (*Beta vulgaris* var *benghalensis*)

The beet green or spinach beet (*Beta vulgaris* var *benghalensis*) is native to India and closely related to the garden beetroot and sugarbeet but is solely grown for its leaves, which are used as green vegetables like spinach as it has the same flavour. In addition to the succulent leaves, the long and green stalk also is used as a vegetable.

Beet Green

14.8.4 Celery (*Apium graveolens,* var *dulce*)

Wild celery (*Apium graveolens, L.* var. *duluce*) is a native of the Mediterranean region and grows wild in the Himalayas. Celery is a particularly useful vegetable, as it can be eaten raw, in salads or as a cooked vegetable, or in soup. The seeds are also used for flavouring purposes.

Celery

14.8.5 Chekkurmanis (*Sauropus androgynans*)

Thavasai murungai or *Chekkurmani* (*Sauropus androgynans*) is a leafy vegetable very rich in vitamins (*multivitamin green*) and minerals. The leaves and tender shoots are eaten either raw or steamed.

Chekkurmanis

14.8.6 Curry Leaves (*Murraya koenigii*)

The curry leaves tree (*Murraya koenigii*) is cultivated throughout India for its aromatic leaves. The leaves of the plant are extensively employed as flavouring in curries and chutneys. They are a rich source of vitamin A. The leaves on steam distillation give an oil that may find use as a perfume. The leaves are also considered as tonic and carminative.

Curry Leaves

14.8.7 Fenugreek (*Trigonella foenum-graecum*)

Fenugreek or *Methi* (*Trigonella foenum-graecum*) is a native of Eastern Europe. It grows wild in parts of North India and is also cultivated all over the subcontinent for its green leaves and seeds. The fresh plant is eaten as a vegetable. Its seeds have been used as medicine since ancient times. The ground seeds are used as a spice (see Chap. 20). The dried leaves and flowers are also used for flavouring.

Fenugreek

14.8.8 Indian Spinach (*Besella rubra*)

Spinach

Beng or *Mayalu* (*Besella rubra*) is grown almost in every part of India. Red-leaved and green-leaved varieties are grown. The young stems and leaves are markedly fleshy. They make very wholesome spinach.

14.8.9 Lettuce (*Lactuca sativa*)

Lettuce

The garden lettuce (*Lactuca sativa*) is considered to have originated in Western Asia. There are three or four common types of garden lettuce: Cabbage or head lettuce, which has a cabbage-like round and compact head, with outer leaves green and inner leaves light green; *cos* or *romaine* lettuce forming conical heads with narrow pointed leaves, which are crisp and dark green; and leaf lettuce, with loose curled, soft and tender leaves. As with other green vegetables, lettuce is rich in vitamin A and minerals and is the best known of all green salad crops. Sometimes it is also cooked. However, it is not as extensively used in India as in Western countries.

14.8.10 Parsley (*Petroselinum crispum*)

Parsley

Parsley or Ajmood (*Petroselinum crispum*) is an aromatic herb. There are two types of cultivated parsley: those cultivated for leaves and those cultivated for their turnip-like roots. Only the former type is cultivated in India. The fresh leaves mask even strong culinary odours and are commonly used for garnishing and seasoning. They are also eaten fresh, incorporated in salads, and used as an ingredient in soups, stews and sauces. The leaves are also used to make a sort of tea that is considered to possess antiscorbutic properties.

Parsley is an anti-cancer agent as it contains a high concentration of antioxidants like monoterpenes, phthalides and polyacetylenes. It helps detoxify carcinogens and neutralize certain carcinogens in tobacco smoke and has diuretic activity.

14.8.11 Purslane (*Portulaca oleracea*)

The common purslane or *Kulfa* (*Portulaca oleracea*) is found throughout India as a seed and is also a cultivated vegetable. Its leaves are small, succulent and fleshy; its stems are tender. It is used as salad and also cooked.

It is a succulent annual, trailing plant, grows well in poor soil. It is cooked as a vegetable, good in salad, soups and stews. It is antibacterial, antiscorbutic, depurative, diuretic and febrifuge. Rich in omega-3 fatty acid (α-linolenic acid), low in calories, an excellent source of vitamin-A, vitamin-C, B-complex vitamins. They are two varieties of betalain alkaloid pigment reddish, β-cyanine and yellow, B-xanthine. Both pigments are antioxidants.

Purslane

14.8.12 Sowa (*Anethum sowa*)

Sowa

Sowa (*Anethum sowa*) is a herb found throughout India. It is used as a flavouring agent. The seeds (dill) are well known for their medicinal properties and they enter into the composition of various indigenous medicinal preparations.

14.8.13 Spinach (*Spinacia oleracea*)

The spinach or *Vilayati Palak* (*Spinacia oleracea*) is a native of South-West Asia and extensively cultivated in India. There are two types of spinach: One has triangular leaves and prickly seeds (winter spinach) and the other with round leaves and smooth seeds (summer spinach). The leaves are smooth, soft and succulent. Spinach leaves are eaten as a boiled vegetable and in soups. Spinach is much richer in protein than other leaf vegetables and it also has a high vitamin A content. It is a good source of minerals but the high content of oxalate in the leaves makes the calcium unavailable in diets.

Spinach is a very good source of antioxidants and cancer and cancer antagonist contains four times more beta carotene and three times more lutein than broccoli. Due to its high oxalate content, it's not recommended for patients with kidney stones. Cooking destroys some of its antioxidants hence can be cooked lightly or eaten raw.

14.8.14 Malabar Spinach (*Basella alba*)

Basella alba

It is commonly known as Malabar spinach, red vine spinach, climbing spinach, creeping spinach, buffalo spinach and Ceylon spinach. They are red or green in colour. It is a vine, grows fast to a length of 33 feet, it is succulent, its leaves are heart shaped, a mild flavour with a mucilaginous texture. It is good source of vitamin A and C, iron and calcium and it has certain phenolic phytochemicals that have antioxidant properties. This green is used in soups and curries.

14.8.15 Chard (*Beta vulgaris*)

Chard

This leafy vegetable is highly nutritious as it is rich in dietary value of vitamin A, K, C and E and also provides 19% calories (79 kilojoules).

14.8.16 Green Mustard (*Brassica juncea*)

Green Mustard

Mustard is basically grown to remove heavy metals in the soil like lead & cadmium. It is used as phytoremediation. Leaf mustard is popular in North India as *sarso ka saag* which is eaten with *makki ki roti*, maize flour roti.

There are several varieties of garlic mustard, snow mustard, curried mustard, large peliope mustard and head mustard.

14.8.17 Spring Onion (*Allium fistulosum*)

Spring Onion

Scallions or green onion is used as salad vegetable belonging to *allium* or onion species. Spring onion includes green, shallot, leek, chive, spring onion and Chinese onion. The greens of onion are garlic lacking the bulb scallions or tubular green leaves. They are used both raw in salads or in soups cooked as curries or stir fry vegetables.

14.8.18 Radish Leaves (*Raphanus sativus*)

Radish Leaves

It is rich in vitamins and minerals, iron, phosphorous, folic acid, calcium and vitamin C. Health benefits are used in treating diabetes and rheumatism, also as a detoxifying agent, increases immunity, reduces fatigue and good in fibre, used as a diuretic, used to treat piles and jaundice.

14.8.19 Non-traditional Leafy Vegetables

Non-traditional leafy vegetables are seldom used by our population. Generally, the poor and the tribals prefer to include them in their diets, while the people from urban and well-to-do families do not. Consumption of indigenous green leafy vegetables has its effects on increasing dietary intakes of iron and pro-vitamins, as well as other minerals and vitamins.

The non-traditional leaves, viz., *chenchalaku* (*Digera arvensis*), *elukajemudaku* (*Merremia-emarginata*), *avisaku* (*Sesbania gradiflora*), *gurugaku* (*Celosia argentia*), *duradagundaku* (*Ischnemone indica*), thummikura (*Lucas aspera*), payilaku (*Trianthema portulacastrum*), *atikamamidi* (*Boerhavia diffusa*), *boddaku* (*Tinospora cordifolia*) and *pippintaku* (*Acalypha indica*) are grown in and around the fields, near canals and waste-lands and edible portions collected from Nellore and Prakasam districts of Andhra Pradesh. Proximate composition of Non-traditional leafy vegetables on fresh weight basis per 100 g edible portion is given in Table 14.2.

14.9 Tuber Vegetables

Tubers are an important source of subsidiary foods. They are rich in carbohydrates and usually store well. They form a group of one of the most important vegetables. Of the numerous tubers, potato, sweet potato and tapioca (cassava) are of importance.

The area under these crops in the world in 2022 was 17.8 million hectares with production of 374.8 million tonnes and an average yield of 21.06 thousand kg per hectare. In the same year, the corresponding figures for India were 2.33 million hectares, 60.1 million tonnes and 25.8 thousand kg per hectare. The Indian production of the tubers can be boosted.

14.9.1 Potato (*Solanum tuberosum*)

Potato

The potato or *Alu* (*Solanum tuberosum*) is native to South America, where it has been used as a food for over 2,000 years. From there it was introduced to Europe in the 16th Century. It appears to have been introduced to India in the 17th Century by the Portuguese. The potato is cultivated almost throughout India up to an altitude of 3,300 m.

The potato plant is a perennial herb. It has fibrous roots and many rhizomes (underground stems) which become swollen at the tip to form the edible tuber which is the potato we eat. Potato tubers vary in size, shape, colour, depth of eyes, etc., which are important varietal characteristics. The tuber skin is generally smooth, but may sometimes become rough and scaly. The skin colour varies from pale yellow to brown; sometimes the tubers are coloured light red or purple to shades of violet or blue and often the colour is restricted to the eye only. Spaced on the surface of the tuber are the eyes, which bear the buds; there are several buds in each eye. In most of the commercial varieties, the flesh of the tuber is whitish, pale yellow or yellow.

Potatoes fall into categories like starchy, waxy and a category that lies somewhere in between these two, that impact the outcome of your dish. They vary in texture and behave differently when cooked.

Starchy: Like the classic Idaho or Russet, these potatoes are (obviously) high in starch and low in moisture. They are fluffy, making them great for boiling, baking and frying, but they do not hold their shape well, so they should be avoided in dishes like casseroles, gratins and potato salads.

Waxy: Like Red Bliss or New Potatoes, these have low starch content and are often characterized by a creamy, firm and moist flesh that holds its shape well after cooking. They're typically great for roasting, boiling, casseroles and potato salads.

All-Purpose: These potatoes have a medium starch content that falls somewhere in between the starchy and waxy potatoes. They are a true multi-purpose potato, and therefore can be used for just about any cooking application. A classic example is the Yukon Gold.

The common varieties in use today are *kufri sundhuri, k. Jyoti, k. Pukhraj, bhahaar, k. chip sona, k. Lavkar* and more. In eastern Uttarakhand and Bihar we have rajendral which is very local. In Gujarat they are badshah. Then, there is French fries variety santana. Lately, Rosetta has become popular for chips.

The world production is 375 million tonnes and India's production is 60.14 million tonnes in 2023. In India, Uttar Pradesh 19,173 tonnes; West Bengal 13,000 tonnes; Bihar 8, 200 tonnes, 2022-23. India ranked second in the world production of potatoes next to China in the year 2023.

Potatoes are a valuable article of diet. Under suitable conditions, potatoes yield a higher food value per hectare than any cereal. Their principal disadvantages, in comparison with cereals, are their high water content (about 78 per cent) which adds to their cost to transport and their shorter storage life. As cooked vegetables, potatoes are served in a large variety of ways—boiled, steamed, fried, baked, roasted, or as an ingredient in soups, stews and fries. They are processed into products, such as potato chips, dehydrated mashed potatoes, frozen potato products (frozen French fries), potato flour, etc. Potatoes are also used for the production of potato starch and dextrose. Industrial alcohol is produced by the fermentation of cooked potatoes. Considerable quantities of potatoes are used for feeding livestock.

Potato contains protease inhibitor which is anti-cancer; it has high potassium content prevents blood pressure and strokes.

14.9.2 Sweet Potato (*Ipomoea batatus*)

The sweet potato or *Sakarand* (*Ipomoea batatus*) is not botanically related to the potato; the chief resemblance between the two crops is that both have edible tubers of about the same size. This is also a native of South America and is now commonly grown all over the tropics.

Sweet Potatoes

The tubers are formed below the ground and are usually of an elongated shape, but sometimes more nearly spherical. The outer skin is either white or a shade of red or purple. The inner flesh is usually white, or in some varieties yellow, and it is rich in vitamin A. The nutritive value of the sweet potato is mostly in its starch content. It also contains some free sugar which gives the tuber its sweet taste in several and a small amount of protein. Sweet potato is cooked by boiling, mashed and used ways.

Besides simple starches, raw sweet potatoes are rich in complex carbohydrates, dietary fibre and beta-carotene (a provitamin A carotenoid) and have moderate vitamin B_5, vitamin B_6 and manganese. Baking brings small changes in micronutrient density with higher content of vitamin C. The dark orange flesh has more beta-carotene than those with light-coloured flesh.

Sweet potato is a blockbuster source of beta-carotene and antioxidant which helps prevent heart disease, cataracts, strokes and numerous cancers.

The world production is 86.4 million tonnes and India produces 1.184 million tonnes in 2022.

14.9.3 Tapioca (*Manihot esculenta*)

Tapioca

In other countries, tapioca (*Manihot esculenta*) plant is generally called "cassava" or "manioc" and the starch prepared from cassava tapioca. In our country, both the plant and the starch extracted from it are called tapioca. The plant is native to the warmer parts of America. Three species have been introduced to India. *M. esculenta* is widely cultivated in the country for its starchy tuber. The main tapioca growing area in the country is Kerala; Tamil Nadu ranks next to Kerala.

India produced 4.74 million tonnes in 2021-22. Tamil Nadu produced 3,971.2 tonnes: Kerala 414.5 tonnes; Andhra Pradesh 168.4 tonnes, 2021-22.

There are many types of tapioca and they are conveniently divided into two groups: "Sweet" and "bitter." The bitter types contain substances from which hydrogen cyanide can arise and are poisonous if eaten raw. However, under different soil and climatic conditions, one variety may change to the other. The swollen tuberous roots are the edible parts and they vary in number, size, shape, length and colour.

Tapioca is the staple food of the poorer section of the population of our country and other developing countries. Its nutrient content consists extensively of starch with particularly low protein content. Its prolonged use can lead to malnutrition. Tapioca is cooked and eaten and can also be consumed in the form of chips and flour. The most important commercial use of tapioca is in the production of starch and sago (granulated globules of starch).

In Africa, tapioca, particularly the bitter variety, is consumed after subjecting it to fermentation. Fermentation detoxifies the bitter principle. Three main articles of food prepared from tapioca are *gari, lafun* and *fufu*.

14.9.4 Yams (*Dioscorea*)

Yam

These are the cultivated species of the genus *Dioscorea.* About 50 varieties are found in India. A large number occur in the wild state, a few are cultivated for their edible tubers, the true yams.

This tuber has a rough skin difficult to peel, softens after heating. The skins vary in colour from dark brown to light pink. The vegetable is majorly composed of a softer substance known as the "meat" and its colour may be white or yellow to purple or pink in mature yams. Yam tubers can grow up to 15 m (49 ft) in length and 7.6 to 15.2 cm (3.0 to 6.0 in) high. The tuber may grow into the soil up to 1.5 metres (4.9 ft) deep. When compared to potato, yam has a lower glycemic index. The protein content and quality of roots and tubers are lower than other food staples. As a relatively low-protein food, yam is not a good source of essential amino acids. Eating cooked yam with colocasia reduces rheumatic pains and eases difficult breathing in asthma patients.

The world production is 88.26 million tonnes and India's production is 8,16,750 tonnes in 2021.

Yams form a cheap source of carbohydrate food and are extensively used by the hill tribes. The cultivated types of yams are comparable to potatoes in taste and quality. The tubers of some species are employed for the extraction of starch on a commercial scale. Some are used for alcohol production.

Khamalu or Asiatic Yam is *D. alata.* The tubers contain 21 per cent starch. The starch grains are transparent. The tuber is also considered to be of medicinal value. *D. esculenta* var spinosa (*Muram sanga*), once extensively cultivated in India, has lost its importance since the introduction of potatoes. The tubers have a sweetish taste; in flavours and mealiness, they closely resemble potatoes.

Zamin-khand or Elephant Foot *(Amorphophallus campanulatus)* is cultivated in the plains of India and gives large tubers weighing 4 to 8 kg. The tubers keep well for long periods. They are used for edible purposes.

14.9.5 Colocasia (*Colocasia antiquorum*)

Colocasia

Arvi (*Colocasia antiquorum*) is a perennial tuberous plant, native of South-Eastern Asia. It grows wild in moist and shady places in India. Numerous varieties are known varying in colour of leaf blades and in the size, shape, palatability and nutritive value of tubers. The tubers vary in size considerably in different varieties from small roundish ones, nearly1–2 cm in diameter, to big and elongated tubers 15 cm in diameter and 60 cm in length.

The tubers are rich in starch and used in the same way as potatoes. They are somewhat sweeter and more easily cooked than potatoes. The flesh is mealy and possesses a delicate nutty flavour when cooked.

Young leaves and stalks are edible and can be cooked and used like spinach. Leaves which are unopened or just about to open are more satisfactory than older leaves.

14.9.6 Other Tubers (*Maranta arundinacea*)

Arrowroot or *Jikhos* (*Maranta arundinacea*) is a tropical plant with swollen starchy rhizomes. It is cultivated chiefly in the West Indies. There is very limited cultivation of the crop in Kerala. The rhizome contains 25 to 30 per cent starch which is in very fine grains and very easily digested. It is thus particularly suited for invalid diets.

Arrowroot

Jerusalem Artichoke or *Aatichoka* (*Helianthus tuberosus*) is cultivated for its edible tubers throughout the temperate regions. The tubers may be eaten raw or boiled, they are also pickled, made into chips or ground into flour. The carbohydrate content of the tubers varies from 8 to 18 per cent. Inulin is the principal carbohydrate of the tuber. Jerusalem Artichoke is a commercial source of levulose used as a sweetening agent by diabetics.

14.10 Bulbs

About twenty-seven species of bulbous herbs are found in India of which onion. (*Allium cepa*), garlic (*Allium sativum*) and leek (*Allium ampelorasum* var. *porrum*) are important vegetables.

Onions

Onion: Onions are extensively cultivated in India. The underground bulbs, which constitute the crop, vary in size, colour, firmness and strength of flavour. Onion is a valuable vegetable and is used either as a salad or spice or for cooking with other vegetables. Its characteristic pungency is due to volatile sulphur compounds (See Chap. 9).

The world production is 110.6 million tonnes and India's production is 31.7 million tonnes in 2022. In India Maharashtra produces 13,301.7 tonnes; Madhya Pradesh 4,740.6 tonnes; Karnataka 2,779.5 tonnes, 2021-22. India ranked first in the world production and China stood in second position.

Garlic

Garlic: Garlic has long been cultivated in India. Because of its pungency, it is generally regarded as a flavouring agent rather than as a vegetable, (See Chap. 9). Garlic and onion are believed to have been native to Afghanistan region.

Garlic is used to treat an array of illnesses. It is broad-spectrum antibiotic that combats bacteria, intestinal parasites and viruses. Helps lower blood pressure, blood cholesterol and discourages blood clotting. Acts as a decongestant, expectorant, antispasmodic, anti-inflammatory agent. Boosts immune response. Helps relieve gas, has antidiarrheal, estrogenic and diuretic activity. Cooking does not diminish garlics blood thinning and cardioprotective capabilities.

The world production is 29.15 million tonnes and of India is 3.21 million tonnes in 2022. In India, Madhya Pradesh 2,016.13 tonnes, Rajasthan 539.18 million tonnes; Uttar Pradesh 210.90 million tonnes in 2021-22.

Leek

Leek: Leek or *kirath* is of Mediterranean origin, where it has been cultivated for about three to four thousand years. In India, it is a garden crop and is grown during the cold-season. The elongated bulb is the part of the plant that is used as a vegetable. It is white, narrowly ovoid and resembles the green onion but is much larger. Leek is mild flavoured and is eaten raw when tender. It is cooked as a separate vegetable or in soups.

The world production is 2.11 million tonnes in 2022.

14.11 Perennial Vegetables

Several vegetables, botanically unrelated, which are similar in that they are perennials are of some importance. Some of them are the following:

Asparagus (*Asparagus officinalis*): This is a native of Europe. This has been cultivated since ancient times. The part eaten is the young shoot or spear which arises from the root stock. The shoots are green-tipped or purple-tipped and white towards the base, where the soil has kept light away from them. They are cylindrical, with scale-like leaves. Asparagus is used in soups or usually poached in water and served with butter.

Asparagus

Asparagus is a good source of glutothionine, an antioxidant and has anti-cancer activity.

The world production is 8.82 million tonnes in 2022.

Bamboo Shoots: These are the thick pointed shoots emerging from the ground under a bamboo plant. Many species of bamboo are grown in India. The shoots at the emerging stage are soft and used as an article of food. The tender shoots are soaked in water, boiled, and used in curries and for making pickles.

Rhubarb (*Rheum rhapontiun*): This is of European origin and extensively cultivated in Europe and America for its long, fleshy stalks, which are usually red. In India, rhubarb grows well on the hills in cool climate. The type of rhubarb grown in India is mainly *Rheum emodi*. Rhubarb is a vegetable, not a fruit. Its bright stalk is used as a fruit, because of its high acidity, but some cultures do use it as a vegetable in savoury dishes. The bright-red stalk Rhubarb is the tartest stalk. Rhubarb can also be pink, light-red, green or white stalks. The redder the stalk, the sourer it will be. The leaves are extremely poisonous. They contain in abundance a toxic amount of oxalic acid, which causes cramps, nausea, and often, death. Rhubarb is mostly used for desserts, in pies, puddings and stewed sweet sauces. Rhubarb jam makes a good filling for layered cakes and cookies.

Bamboo shoots

Rhubarb

Rhubarb always needs to be sweetened with a fair amount of sugar. Strawberries are the usual favourite fruit to mix with rhubarb. Rhubarb also goes great with raspberries, currants, blackberries, apricots and peaches. But just as with sugar, it's easy to overwhelm the flavour of rhubarb with other fruit. Rhubarb is high in vitamin C and dietary fibre.

Rhubarb contains high auxiliaries, hence avoided in kidney stone patients.

Artichoke or Globe Artichoke: The artichoke or *hathichak* (*Cynara scolyrnus*) originated in the Mediterranean region and is cultivated to a limited extent in India. The young flower heads or chokes with numerous large scales or bracts are used as a vegetable. The flower head may be eaten raw, baked, fried, boiled, stuffed or served with various sauces or dressings. The world production is 1.58 million tonnes in 2022.

Artichoke

14.12 Other Vegetables

14.12.1 Leguminous Vegetables

Legumes are among the earliest food crops to be cultivated by man. Their importance in human diet is considered in Chapter 17. The seeds are separated from the pods of many pulses like peas, red gram, etc., while tender, and are used as vegetables. Others like beans, which produce fleshy pods, are consumed as green vegetables.

Green beans (*Phaseolus vulgaris*)-in it's dry form is known as kidney bean (refer under pulses). There are 130 varieties of green bean. Their succulence and flavour pods are grown in home gardens. The colour of the pod can vary from green, purple, red, or streaked or yellow podded known as wax beans.

Green bean pods contain a string, a hard fibrous strand running the length of one side of the pod. This is removed before cooking, cut in small segments and used. There are beans that are now available which do not have strings. The world production is 23.34 million tonnes in 2022.

14.12.2 Drumstick (*Moringa oleifera*)

The drumstick (*Moringa oleifera*) is indigenous to India and is cultivated all over the country. The tree is valued mainly for the tender pods which are esteemed as a vegetable. They are cut into slices and used in culinary preparation; they are also pickled. Seeds are consumed after frying.

Tender leaves and flowers are used as vegetables. The leaves are rich in vitamins A and C, and are considered useful in scurvy and catarrhal affliction.

14.12.3 Mushroom (*Agaricus campestris*)

Edible mushrooms are non-poisonous fungi. The wild fungus which is commonly eaten is *Agaricus campestris.* Found in pastures, it has a white cap, when young, connected to the stem by a membrane, which tears as the cap expands. The colour of the cap gradually turns pink and finally dark purplish-brown. Other edible fungi popular in different countries are the truffle, oyster mushroom, etc. Commercial production of mushroom requires control of humidity, temperature, ventilation and dark growing conditions. Mushrooms are used as ingredients in many cooked dishes. Large quantities are canned and used in the manufacture of cream of mushroom soup.

Mushroom is a longevity tonic, heart medicine and cancer remedy. The shiitake compound, lentinan is a broad spectrum anti-viral agent improves immune functioning.

The world production is 48.34 million tonnes and of India is 2,80,000 tonnes in 2022.

14.12.4 Baby Corn

It is a vegetable taken from standard maize (corn) plants harvested early, while the ears are very small and immature. Baby corn is typically eaten whole, cob and all, in contrast, to mature maize, whose cob is typically too hard for human consumption. It is consumed both raw and cooked. When cooked, its culinary and physical properties (from the point of the human palate) do not change significantly; texture remains relatively the same, as does taste, which is relatively bland either raw or cooked.

Baby Corn

Baby corn is used in a wide variety of dishes in many cuisines throughout the world. Such usage includes soups, salads, stir fry's and vegetable dishes. In the West, it is often sold canned in water or brine.

Baby corn is low in calories, high in fibre and, like all vegetables, cholesterol free. It contains zinc and vitamin B3.

Corn has anti-cancer and anti-viral activity as it contains protease inhibitor. It boosts estrogen.

14.13 Salads

Salads are generally green vegetables that are eaten uncooked. The term includes vegetables with or without other foods, and seasoned with a salad dressing. Salads are made by a mixture of greens, or they may be composed of raw, cooked, or canned fruits, vegetables, meats, poultry, or fish. Nuts, cheese or eggs also may be used as ingredients.

A number of greens are used in salads. They include lettuce, spinach, parsley, endive and celery. Other vegetables commonly used are tomatoes, cucumbers, onions, cabbages and cauliflowers. These help contribute to the colour, flavour and palatability of the diet.

Salads are served in different ways with the meal. Frequently they are used as an appetizer or first course. Some fish salads and fruit salads serve this purpose. Salads are also used as a separate course, between the main course and dessert. They also serve as the main course. Meat, poultry, fish, egg and potato salads mixed with crisp vegetables are suitable for use as a main course. Fruit salad can also be used as dessert.

14.14 Food Groups: Fruits and Vegetables

Food groups history as food guides came as early as 1916–30; indicating guidelines to select food for young children. In 1940, Basic Seven became an improved version but lacked serving sizes of food. Basic Four followed in 1970. After a decade fifth group was included of fats, sweets and alcohol. In 1984 Food Wheel emphasized on three calorie level. In 1992 Food Pyramid visualization gave a variety of proportion of added fats and sugar and in 2005 steps to be followed to reach the Pyramid was given. Lastly 2011 "My Plate" was a simple version of all the above. Here interestingly a major food occupied on the plate was 2 to 4 servings of fruit and 3 to 5 servings of vegetables followed by equal proportion of cereals and protein foods.

All the above are from USDA (United State of Dietary Allowances). Other countries have added their cultural practices for the food group, like Greece and Spain included Olive Oil, whereas France brought in wine. Hence, food groups are greatly influenced by country's culture. Fruits and vegetables form major part of the food groups.

Among foods, fruits and vegetables meet man's aesthetic, organoleptic, olfactory aspects, besides being gastronomic, appeasing hunger, appetite, and satiety. This requires a practical experience and experiential wisdom for working with natural aspects of fruits and vegetables, to retain all their flavours, aromas, and textures. An epicurean can judge the quality of prepared food, particularly fruits and vegetables. Hence, the difference between fruits and vegetable is essential in preparation.

Vegetables contain 90–96% water when compared to fruits, which have 80 to 90% water. In the vegetable cells, water is found as bound water to form true solution with mineral and organic molecules. Bound water, found in the cell membrane, cytoplasm, and nucleus, as a swelling agent, to form colloidal structure, which is difficult to remove by drying or by dehydration. (See Sec. 11.4 & 11.1.6).

Carbohydrate forms 90% of dry matter in fruits and vegetables. Besides being best source of energy, they play major role in biological systems and they are produced by photosynthesis in green plants. As energy; glucose, fructose, maltose and sucrose, besides giving energy are fermented by microorganism, in high concentrations they act as preservative, on heating browning reaction takes place. *Cellulos* and hemicelluloses are not soluble in cold water nor digestible, hence useful as roughage. Pectin presents gum like substance to hold plants cell together their colloidal solution provides viscosity with sugar and acid to make jams and jelly.

Proteins are present to a very small degree, 1.0–5.5%. They form colloidal solution and are insoluble above 50°C. Plant protein's biological value is low compared to animal protein. Percentage of Fats in fruits and vegetables is very low (0.5%) only nuts have 55% fat with an exception of Avocado, which has 14% fat.

Vegetables contain more minerals than fruits, calcium, and phosphorous are essential for calcium fixation in human body. Vegetables through photosynthesis yield chlorophyll, which is a good source of Iron (Refer Chapter 8). Vitamins are water and fat-soluble, facilitate in enzyme systems and in metabolism of major nutrients, carbohydrate protein must be modified. Fat-soluble vitamins are found in animal products and are found precursor such as beta carotene in Vitamin A. These are found in yellow, orange, and green vegetables. Vitamin C is rich in citrus fruits, guava, lemon, oranges, amla and kiwi fruit (Refer Chapter 6).

Natural enzymes bring about ripening and take part in biochemical reactions in fruits and vegetables. They bring about flavour; colour and textural changes. Natural enzymes are deactivated in the fruits and vegetables and make them edible. Deactivation occurs around 50°C to improve the fruit and vegetables and make them edible. Natural enzymes include classes of Hydrolases (lipase, invertase, tannase, chlorophyllase, amylase and cellulase) and oxidoreductases (peroxides, tyrosinase, catalase, ascorbinase, polyphenoloxidase). When low viscosity is needed then heat is not applied and enzyme activities are allowed to proceed. This process is known as Cold Brake Process used in canning to preserve fruits and vegetables. Temperature, water, pH, and chemicals control the enzyme activity.

Natural enzymes such as methylesterase hydrolyses pectin, dissolve its action, which is observed in tomato juice. Heating deactivates the enzymes, adding lime juice (vit C) to cut portions of apples inhibits enzymatic action. Pineapple has bromelain and papaya has papain. They are used to tenderize meat. (Refer Chapter 10).

Colour and colour changes are due to the natural pigments. They are pigments such as chlorophyll, Carotenoids, anthocyanins and anthoxanthin, flavonoids and tannin (refer Chapter 8).

The experimental wisdom is an aesthetic intuition, creative culinary skill that creates signature dishes. The inclusion of fruits and vegetables in a diet refines, bridges, the gulf between art and science into experimental enjoyable wholesome Food culture (refer Chapter 32).

CHAPTER

15 Cereals

Cereals supply the bulk of the food consumed by the human race. They are the cheapest source of food energy and constitute a high percentage of the calorie and protein intake of man, particularly in developing countries. Cereals have been grown since primitive times. During the long period of the cultivation of cereal crops, new species and varieties have evolved, to suit the cultural conditions of different parts of the world. Cereals are also used as animal feed and for industrial purposes.

Cereal grains belong to the monocotyledonous family, Gramineae or Grass family. The principal cereal crops are rice, wheat, maize (corn), sorghum (jowar), millets, barley, oats and rye. Of these rice and wheat are the chief cereals of the human diet. However, as a source of carbohydrates related to land use, maize ranks first among the cereal grains, followed by rice, sorghum and wheat.

15.1 Cereal Production

India is the world's second-largest producer of Rice, Wheat and other cereals. The huge demand for cereals in the global market is creating an excellent environment for the export of Indian cereal products. The important cereals are-wheat, paddy, sorghum, millet (Bajra), barley and maize etc. According to the, 2021-22, the production of major cereals like rice, maize and bajra stood 255 million tonnes, 35.7 million tonnes and 8.48 million tonnes respectively. India is not only the largest producer of cereal as well as the largest exporter, of cereal products in the world. India's export of cereals stood at ₹ 91,134 crores 10.98 billion dollars during 2023-24. Rice (including Basmati and Non-Basmati) occupy the major share in India's total cereals export with 95% during the same period. Major Export Destinations (2023-24) are Saudi Arabia, Iran, Iraq, UAE, Vietnam and Benin.

15.2 Structure of Cereal Grains

Cereal grains are the fruits of the grass family of plants. The grain develops from flowers or florets which are enclosed in a pair of bracts or leaves, called lemma and palea. The ovary and the ovule within it, after fertilization by pollen, develop into the grain. In wheat, rye, common varieties of maize, some varieties of sorghum and barley, the lemma and palea become free from the grain at threshing and form chaff. Thus, wheat, oats, maize and sorghum are said to be naked grains called caryopsis. In the case of rice, oats, some varieties of barley, and sorghum, the lemma and palea adhere to the grain and do not come away during threshing. Thus, these grains are covered or coated caryopsis. The bracts adhering to the grain constitute the hull or husk. The threshed rice with husk is known as paddy.

The cereals vary in their grain size and weight. Their size and the average grain weight for 1,000 grains are used in grading the cereals.

The overall structure of all cereal grains is similar, differing from one cereal to another in detail only. Grains of wheat, rye, maize and grain sorghum (naked caryopsis) consist of fruit coat (pericarp) and seed. The seed comprises the seed coat, germ and endosperm. Grains of rice, barley and oats (covered caryopsis) have, in addition, fused palea and lemma which constitute the husk outside the fruit coat. Each of the main parts of the grain-pericarp, seed coat, germ and endosperm are further divided into various layers, tissues and regions. This is shown in Fig. 15.1 for wheat grain.

Pericarp: The outer layer (epidermis) of the cereals consist of thin-walled, long, rectangular cells. Next to the epidermis is the hypoderm of varying thickness. The innermost layer of the pericarp tears during the ripening of the seed and in the mature grain they are represented by a layer of branching hypha-like cells known as "tube cells." The pericarp of wheat is thin and papery while the sorghum pericarp consists of several tissue layers, is pigmented, and the outer surface is covered with a waxy cuticle.

Seed coat: The seed coat or testa is a thin single or double layer, with the cellular structure almost obliterated. The inner layer of the testa of wheat is often deeply pigmented which gives the grain its characteristic colour. Next to the testa is the hyaline layer (nucellar layer), which is colourless and devoid of any obvious cellular structure.

Aleurone: The endosperm is surrounded by one or more layers of cells known as aleurone. In wheat, the aleurone is a single layer of thick-walled cubical cells and constitutes 7 per cent of the grain by weight. The cells contain about 20 per cent each of protein, oil and mineral matter, and 10 per cent of sugar, principally sucrose, neo-ketose and raffinose. The cells are also rich in nicotinic acid. The aleurone cells also contain tiny grains of phytic acid with some protein (aleurone grains).

The aleurone is two to four cell layers thick in barley, two or three layers thick in rice of the species *indica,* and five to six layers thick in the species *japonica*. The cells are rectangular with thin cell walls. In rye, oats and sorghum the aleurone is a single layer of cells and in maize, it is generally a single layer, although a type of maize has two to six layers.

The aleurone layers generally surround only the starchy endosperm and cease where the latter abuts on the scutellum. In rice, however, the aleurone layer extends from the upper end of the embryo to its base. The aleurone layer and all the covering external to it comprise the "bran."

Endosperm: The endosperm itself consists of cells of various sizes, shapes and different compositions. The endosperm cells consist mainly of starch and protein, the starch being in the form of spherical granules which are single granules or tightly packed together, and embedded in a matrix of protein. The size and shape of the starch granules in the endosperm cells vary from one cereal to another. The granules in wheat, rye, barley, maize and sorghum are simple, whereas those in rice are compound, i.e., up to about 60 granules are compounded together. Oats contain both simple and compound grains, the former predominating.

Embryo: The germ or embryo consists of many parts. It is separated from the endosperm by the scutellum, which has the function of mobilizing the stored food reserves in the endosperm and transmitting them to the embryo when the grain germinates. The germ and scutellum are rich in protein and fat, while most of the B vitamins in the grain are present in the scutellum.

15.3 Composition of Cereal Grains

The chemical constituents of cereals are carbohydrates, proteins, lipids, minerals and water, together with small quantities of vitamins, enzymes and other substances. The percentage composition of cereal grains is given in Table 15.1.

Carbohydrates: Carbohydrates are the major constituents comprising about 80 per cent of the dry matter of the cereals. The carbohydrates are customarily considered in two parts: the "crude fibre," which is the portion of carbohydrate insoluble in dilute acids and alkalis under prescribed conditions and the "soluble carbohydrates" which are the remainder left after accounting for crude fibre, proteins, fat and mineral matter. The fibre constituents are cellulose, hemicellulose and pentosans. Of the soluble carbohydrates, starch is the most important carbohydrate in all cereals. Small quantities of dextrin and sugars are also present. Free sugars present include simple sugars, such as glucose and galactose, and oligosaccharides like sucrose, maltose and raffinose. Knowledge of the proportion of fibre and soluble carbohydrates is of importance concerning nutritional and digestibility studies.

The husked caryopses of rice, barley and oats have a crude fibre content 2–5 times that of naked caryopsis. Removal of the husk of rice and oats during processing increases the protein content of the product; dehusked rice is still comparatively low in protein content, but dehusked oats equal or exceed wheat in protein content.

Table 15.1 Percent composition of cereals (on dry basis) per 100 g of edible portion

Name of Cereal	Moisture (g)	Protein (g)	Fat (g)	Minerals (g)	Fibre (g)	Carbohydrates (g)
Barley *Hordeum vulgare*	12.5	11.5	1.3	1.2	3.9	69.6
Maize (dry) *Zea mays*	14.9	11.1	3.6	1.5	2.7	66.2
Oatmeal *Avena sativa*	10.7	13.6	7.6	1.8	3.5	62.8
Rice (raw, hand pounded) *Oryza sativa*	13.3	7.5	1.0	0.9	0.6	76.7
Rice (raw, milled)	13.7	6.8	0.5	0.6	0.2	78.2
Rye* *Secale cereale*	11.0	12.1	1.7	1.8	2.0	73.4
Wheat (Whole) *Triticum aestivum*	12.8	11.8	1.5	1.5	1.2	71.2
Wheat flour	12.2	12.1	1.7	2.7	1.9	69.4
Triticale**	—	16.3	—	2.18	3.9	—

Source: Nutritive Value of Indian Foods, NIN, ICMR, Hyderabad, India, 1984.

*The Wealth of India, Vol. IX, CSIR, New Delhi, India, 2005.

**Wheat Research in India, Indian Council of Agricultural Research, New Delhi,1996.

Protein: The protein content of the different cereals varies and that of rice is lower than that of all other cereals. The protein content of different varieties of the same cereal also varies. Proteins are found in all the tissues of cereal grains, the higher concentration occurring in the embryo, scutellum and aleurone layers than in the starchy endosperm, pericarp and testa. Within the endosperm, the concentration of protein increases from the centre to the periphery. The types of proteins present in cereal are albumins, globulins, prolamines (gliadins) and glutelins.

The proportions of these proteins differ in different cereals. The gliadins and glutelins are known as "gluten" proteins; they form, with water and salt, the substance "gluten" when a flour-water dough is kneaded. The gluten has elasticity and flow properties of a unique value for the baking of bread and other products.

The amino acid compositions of the proteins in the cereal grains vary. They are generally low in the content of lysine. The biological value of the proteins in germ and aleurone is higher than that of the endosperm proteins; the lysine content of the former proteins is some 2–2.5 times greater than in the proteins of the latter tissue.

Lipids: Lipids are present to the extent of 1–2 per cent in wheat, rice, rye and barley, 3 per cent in maize and 4–6 per cent in oats. More lipids are present in germ and bran than in other parts of the grain. For example, wheat germ contains 6–11 per cent lipids, bran 3–5 per cent and endosperm 0.8–1.5 per cent. Similarly, the lipid content of maize germ is 35 per cent and the bran contains 1 per cent lipid. The lipids are mostly the triglycerides of palmitic, oleic and linoleic acids. Cereals also contain the phospholipids, lecithin.

The lipids in milled cereal products undergo two types of deterioration: hydrolysis due to the action of the enzyme lipase present in the grain and oxidation by the action of the enzyme lipoxygenase or non-enzymatically in the presence of oxygen. These changes give rise to unpleasant flavours. When the germ is separated from the endosperm as in the milling of cereals, the keeping quality of the milled products is improved.

Minerals: The husks of the cereal caryopsis of rice, barley and rye are rich in minerals, the ash content of rice husk being 22.5 per cent, the ash containing mostly silica (96 per cent). The kernels of these cereals and those of naked caryopsis also contain minerals, about 95 per cent of them being the phosphates and sulphates of potassium, magnesium and calcium. A considerable part of phosphorus in cereals is present in the form of phytin, the calcium, magnesium salt of phytic acid (inositol hexaphosphoric acid). Phosphorus and calcium present in phytin are not available for absorption. Some mineral elements like copper, zinc, manganese and iron are also present in very small quantities in cereals, oats being particularly rich in iron. Rye and oats have the highest calcium content of all cereals.

Vitamins: B-group vitamins are present in all cereals, more or less to the same extent, except niacin, which is more in wheat, rice, barley and sorghum. The distribution of the vitamins in different grains and different parts of the same grain is not uniform. Oils from cereal grains are rich in vitamin E.

Enzymes: Cereal grains contain many enzymes and of these, the amylases, proteases, lipases and oxidoreductases are of importance from the point of view of cereal technology. Ungerminated wheat, barley and rye have β-amylase activity but exhibit no α-amylase activity. Upon germination, β-amylase activity increases and α-amylase activity slowly appears. The proteases are relatively more in the germ. The lipases of cereals are responsible for the fatty acids appearing during the storage of cereals and their products.

Nutritive value: The nutritive value of cereals depends on their chemical composition. The composition of processed cereals is different from that of the whole grain. As the nutrients of cereals are not uniformly distributed in the grain, milled products like bran, germ, flour and grits vary considerably in the composition according to the type and extent of milling to which they are subjected. The nutritive value also depends on the nature of the processed product.

15.4 Storage of Cereals

Cereals, if not properly stored, deteriorate. The moisture content chiefly determines the extent of deterioration. Temperature, the supply of oxygen, characteristics of the grain and infestation with moulds and insects also contribute to deterioration.

Cereal grains, although stored in the dormant state, continue to respire producing heat, water and carbon dioxide. This facilitates the growth of moulds which are invariably present in the grain. The growth of moulds produces many enzymes that cause chemical deterioration of grains.

A moisture content of less than 14 per cent is considered safe for the storage of cereals. The grains should, therefore, be dried by appropriate methods so that the moisture content is less than 14 per cent and stored in such a way as to prevent damage due to insects and rodents.

15.5 Wheat (*Triticum*)

Wheat is used principally for human consumption. It is converted into flour for the production of bread and other bakery products. It is used as "chapatti" (unleavened pan baked bread) in India. Owing to its high price, the use of wheat for industrial purposes and animal feed is very limited.

Wheat is being cultivated from prehistoric times (5000 BC). The wild wheat types, emmer *(Triticum dicoccum)* and einkorn *(Triticum monococcum),* were developed from a type of wild grass. These are husked wheats, i.e, the lemma and palea form the husk, which remains attached to the kernel after threshing. Emmer is generally regarded as one of the ancestors of the wheat grown today.

Wheat is grown throughout the world. It is adaptable to different soils, climates and elevations. Seeds sown in late autumn germinate slowly until the spring. Snow in winter covers the young plants and protects them from frost. This is winter wheat. Wheat sown in spring and the crop harvested in early autumn is known as spring wheat.

Wheat belongs to the genus *Triticum* and there are over 30,000 species and varieties. The principal wheats of commerce are the common or bread wheat (*T. aestivum*); macaroni wheat (*T. durum*) and club wheat (*T. compactum*). Wheat was cultivated in India as early as 4000–5000 years ago. Most of the wheat grown in India is the bread and macaroni varieties.

15.5.1 Wheat Production

The world production is 784 million tonnes and India's production is 113.3 million tonnes in 2023-24. India ranked second in world production of wheat next to China in the year 2023-24.

The world wheat production has been increasing from year to year. Over fifteen years period from 1957 to 1971, the world wheat production increased from 199 million tonnes to 354 million tonnes. The 1980 world wheat production was 444.9 million tonnes which increased to 549 million tonnes in 2005. This has been achieved without a corresponding increase in the cultivation area, which remained fairly constant at about 200–220 million hectares. The increase in production, without an appreciable increase in the area of cultivation is due to an increase in yield from 11.0 to 27.5 quintals per hectare.

In terms of area, India ranked fourth and in production fifth, among the wheat growing countries of the world in 1980, but in 2005, it emerged as the second-largest wheat producing nation in the world. Unlike the rest of the world, there has been an increase in the area of wheat cultivation. Between 1966 to 1976, the area under wheat cultivation increased from 12.5 to 20 million hectares while in 2005, it further increased to 24.8 million hectares. In terms of wheat production, the figures are 10.4 to 28.3 million tonnes (between 1966 to 1976), 36.5 million tonnes (1980–81) and 65.1 million tonnes (2005).

The increase in wheat production in India is not the result of just an increase in the area of production, but also due to higher yield per hectare. During the period 1966 to 1976, the yield per hectare increased from 8.3 to 14.1 quintals. This further increased to 26.2 quintals per hectare during 2005–06. This is the result of the "Green Revolution," i.e., the rapid development of high-yielding varieties. The usual cultivated wheat was replaced by dwarf wheat. New strains of dwarf wheat obtained from Mexico were developed through mutation breeding, then hybrids between the Indian and foreign wheat were developed. Every year between 600 to 700 new strains are developed to locate superior and disease-resistant varieties suitable for growth in different parts of the country. This resulted in a wheat revolution increasing production by more than 300 per cent, yield by 80–90 per cent, and per capita availability of wheat increased from 23.4 to 66 kg.

Most of the wheat produced in India is used up in the country. In a predominantly rice-eating country, wheat consumption has caught up well. Approximately 90 per cent of wheat consumption in India is in the form of chapati. Bread consumption also is showing signs of a significant annual increase. More than 1.5 million tonnes of wheat are used in the production of bakery products. The two processed wheat products, breads and biscuits, have reached the rural poor in India, unlike other processed foods.

15.5.2 Structure and Composition

Wheat grains are ovoid in shape, rounded at both ends. The germ is at one end and a tuft of fine hair at the other (Fig. 15.1). Along one side of the grain, there is a furrow or crease, an infolding of the aleurone and all covering layers. The presence of the crease complicates the milling process of wheat.

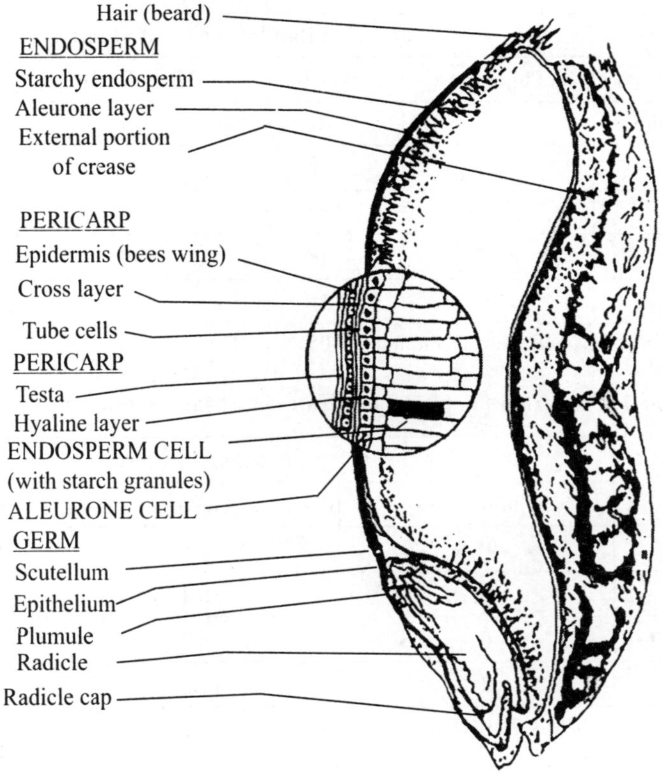

Fig. 15.1 Diagrammatic longitudinal structure of wheat grain

Composition: The chemical composition of the wheat kernel varies widely, being influenced by the environment, soil and variety. The values reported for Indian wheat are: Moisture, 8.0–17.0; starch, 63.0–71.0; sugars, 2.0–3.0; protein, 8.0–15.0; crude fibre, 2.0–2.5; fat, 1.5–2.0; and ash, 1.5–2.0 per cent. The protein content of improved Indian wheat varieties has been reported to vary from 9.1 to 14.2 per cent.

Minerals: Wheat is a good source of mineral nutrients. It contains a significant amount of iron, phosphorus, magnesium, manganese, copper and zinc. The mineral constituents present in Indian wheats are (mg/100 g): calcium, 41.0; magnesium, 138.0; phosphorus, 306.0 (phytin 238.0); iron, 4.9. The mineral constituents are distributed mainly in the outer layers and embryo of the kernel, and when wheat is milled for white flour the minerals for the most part pass on to the by-products of milling.

Vitamins: Whole wheat is a good source of thiamine and nicotinic acid, but is relatively poor in riboflavin. Other members of B-vitamins are present in small quantities. The level of B-vitamins appears to be directly related to the protein content of wheat. The vitamins are not uniformly distributed in the grain. The distribution of some of the B-vitamins in the structural parts of the kernel of Indian wheat is given in Table 15.2. When wheat is milled for white flour, a large part of aleurone layer is lost as bran and the resulting white flour is devoid of a major part of the B-vitamins.

Carbohydrates: Amongst carbohydrates of wheat, practically all of the starch is in the endosperm, while the soluble sugars are mostly found in the germ. The carbohydrates of bran are largely cellulose and hemicellulose. The distribution of carbohydrates in wheat fractions is presented in Table 15.3.

Table 15.2 Distribution of B-vitamins in the structural parts of wheat

Structural part	Vitamins (per cent of total)			
	Thiamine	Niacin	Riboflavin	Pantothenic acid
Pericarp, testa and hyaline	1	4	5	8
Aleurone	31	84	37	39
Endosperm	3	11.5	32	41
Scutellum	62.5	1	14	4
Embryo	2	1	12	3.5

Source: *Wealth of India,* Vol. X, CSIR, New Delhi, India 2005.

Table 15.3 Distribution of carbohydrates in wheat fractions (per cent)

	Fraction of wheat		
	Endosperm	Germ	Brain
Starch	95.8	31.5	14.1
Sugar	1.5	36.4	7.6
Cellulose	0.3	16.8	35.2
Hemicellulose	2.4	15.3	43.1

Source: *Wealth of India*, Vol, X, CSIR, New Delhi, India, 2005.

Protein: The proteins of wheat may be divided into two major groups—the non-gluten protein albumins and globulins, and gluten proteins (mainly gliadins, glutenins and insoluble residual proteins). The two groups of proteins differ in their solubility, chemical composition and role in dough formation and baking.

The gluten proteins are rich in glutamic acid, mainly as glutamine and proline but have a lower content of basic amino acids and tryptophan. The high content of glutamine as also asparagine is important in determining the characteristic of gluten. In contrast, the non-gluten proteins (albumins and globulins) contain higher amounts of lysine, arginine and tryptophan and low levels of glutamine and proline. The bran and germ proteins have a higher content of essential amino acids and a more balanced amino acid composition than the inner endosperm proteins. Thus the biological value of endosperm proteins is much lower than that of the whole wheat protein.

Lipids: The total lipid content of Indian wheat varies from about 0.97 to. 2.28 per cent. The lipid content of endosperm (1–2 per cent) is less than that of bran (5–6 per cent) or germ (8–15 per cent) but the proportion of compound lipids in the endosperm is much higher. Wheat germ oil is produced commercially and it is rich in vitamin E. The oil is also rich in essential fatty acids.

15.5.3 Wheat Types

Wheats are classified according to the texture of the endosperm and the protein content. The way the grain breaks down in milling depends on the texture of the endosperm. The property of the flour and its suitability for various uses depend upon the protein content.

The endosperm texture may be vitreous (steely, flinty, glassy, horny) or mealy (starchy, chalky). The vitreous or mealy character is hereditary but is also affected by the environment. Thus, macaroni wheat, emmer wheat and einkorn wheat are wheat with vitreous kernels, whereas bread wheat and club wheat are mealy. Vitreous kernels are translucent and appear bright against a strong light, whereas mealy kernels are opaque and appear dark under similar circumstances.

Wheat types may also be classified as hard or soft, and as strong or weak. Vitreous grains tend to be hard and strong, mealy grain to be soft and weak but the association is not invariable. Hardness is related to the degree of adhesion between starch and protein. "Hardness" and "softness" refer to the way in which the endosperm breaks down on milling. In hard wheats, fragmentation of the endosperm tends to occur along the lines of the cell boundaries, whereas the endosperm of soft wheat fractures in a random way. Hard wheats yield coarse, gritty flour and soft wheats give very fine flour. World wheat are arranged according to their degree of hardness as extra hard, hard, medium and soft.

The strength of wheat relates to its baking quality. "Strong" wheats produce large loaf volume, good crumb structure and good keeping qualities. Such wheats have high protein content. Hard wheats are thus employed for the production of flour for making bread. "Weak" wheats have a low protein content and form only a small loaf with a coarse crumb structure. The flours of weak wheats are good for biscuits and cakes, although unsuitable for bread-making. Hard and semi-hard white wheat and amber durum are popular for the preparation of chapati. The main types of wheats are classified according to their baking strength as strong, medium and weak.

15.5.4 Milling of Wheat

Wheat is consumed mostly in the form of flour obtained by milling the grain while a small quantity is converted into breakfast foods, such as wheat flakes, puffed wheat and shredded wheat. Indian wheats have good milling properties. Barring some softer wheats, Indian wheats are hard, flinty and of amber colour. The moisture content at harvest is low, usually 8–10 per cent.

The traditional procedure for milling wheat in India has been stone grinding (*chakki*) to obtain whole meal flour (*atta*). This method results in a 90–95 per cent extraction rate of flour which retains almost all the nutrients of the grain while simultaneously eliminating that part of the grain that is most indigestible like cellulose, and phytic acid which binds and carries away minerals. Therefore, Indian style flour is not technically "whole wheat" but it is superior to the usual whole grain flour that is produced by simply grinding everything to a fine powder. Stone grinding is gradually giving place to power driven small and big *chakkis* and to modern flour mills.

In modern milling, wheat is first subjected to cleaning to remove various types of impurities together with damaged, shrunken and broken kernels which are collectively known as "screenings". Impurities that adhere to the grain are removed by washing or by dry scouring which loosens the impurities which are then blown away by an air current. Other impurities in the form of particles unattached to the grain are separated by making use of characteristics in which the impurities differ from wheat. These include separation based on differences in size, shape, terminal velocity in air currents, specific gravity, magnetic and electrostatic properties, colour, surface roughness, etc. The total quantity of screenings removed generally amounts to 1–1½ per cent of the grain fed to the machine.

Next, the cleaned wheat is subjected to conditioning. This improves the physical state of the grain for milling and sometimes improves the baking quality of the milled flour. The process involves the adjustment of the average moisture content of the wheat. When the moisture content is optimum (i.e., 15–17 per cent), the bran is toughened and separation of the endosperm from the bran becomes easy.

Finally, the cleaned and conditioned wheat is subjected to milling to separate the endosperm from the bran and germ and to reduce the endosperm to flour fineness to obtain the maximum extraction of white flour from the wheat. The reduced endosperm is known as flour (white flour) and the germ, bran and residual endosperm obtained as by-products are used primarily in animal feeding.

Flour milling is achieved by grinding in roller mills. Grinding is carried out in four or five stages, i.e., in a gradual reduction process. Each grinding stage gives a "grind" consisting of a mixture of coarse, medium and fine particles, including a proportion of flour. The different-sized particles are sorted by sifting and the coarse particles are conveyed to a subsequent grinding stage.

In each grinding stage, the endosperm is separated from the bran coats. The coarse fraction from the last grind can yield no more endosperm and forms the by-product "bran." The percentage of wheat converted into flour from the first grind to the fourth grind will be approximately 30, 66,78 and 81.

In India, several modern roller mills are working in different parts of the country. In 1981, there were 306 roller flour mills in the country and they produced 3.1 million tonnes of wheat products a year. Wheat is generally ground into *atta* (wholemeal), *suji* or *rava* (semolina) and *maida* (flour). Within these broad grades, there are finer divisions like high gluten and low gluten *atta*, and low gluten, medium gluten and high gluten *maida*. Specifications for ground products are prescribed by the Indian Standards Institution (ISI) which are given in Table 15.5. In other countries, specifications have been worked for flours suited for particular applications like bread, biscuits, cakes, etc.

Recent developments in milling consist of fine grinding and air classification of flour particles to yield fractions with different protein contents. This is known as "protein displacement milling." This technique provides a means of obtaining from the flour of a given wheat various fractions markedly different in protein content and, therefore, suitable for different uses. It is possible to get from soft wheat (protein 10 per cent) a fraction containing 20 per cent protein. Similarly, a fraction containing 30 per cent protein can be obtained from hard wheat. By combining various fractions obtained by air separation, it is possible to obtain flours of any desired specification from one parent flour.

Table 15.4 Indian Standards Institution specification for atta, suji and maida

Requirements	Values on dry basis					
	Atta		Suji	Maida		
	Low gluten	High gluten		Low gluten	Medium gluten	High gluten
Moisture % (max)	13	13	13.5	13.0	13.0	13.0
Total ash % (max)	2.5	2.5	1.0	0.7	0.7	1.0
Acid insol. ash % (min)	0.1	0.1	0.05	0.05	0.05	0.05
Gluten (dry) % (max)	7.0	9.0	6.0	7.00	8.00	10.00
Crude fibre % (max)	2.5	2.5	—	—	—	—
Alcoholic acidity in H_2SO_4 % (max)	0.1	0.1	0.1	0.1	0.1	0.1

Source: *Wealth of India,* Vol. X. CSIR, New Delhi, India, 2005.

15.5.5 Wheat Flour

Wheat flours obtained at different stages of the gradual reduction process differ in terms of the proportion of the endosperm, germ and bran contained in it. Flour quality also depends upon the region of the wheat from which the endosperm is obtained. Thus, wheat flours differ widely in baking quality, colour, size, fibre and ash content and nutritive value. In other words, the quality of each machine flour is distinctive and flour streams from different machines can be blended to obtain flours of desired quality.

Bleaching: Flour contains a yellow pigment (xanthophyll) which is not desired in the making of white bread. When the flour is exposed to air the colour of the flour is bleached by oxidation. When the flour is stored in bulk this change is slow. The bleaching process is accelerated by treating the flour with chemicals. The chemical additives are used for bleaching flours used only for bread, biscuits or cakes and not for wholemeal *atta* used for making *chapati*. The chemicals used for bleaching include chlorine, chlorine dioxide, benzoyl peroxide and acetone peroxide.

Maturing: The bread making quality of freshly milled flour improves with storage for 1–2 months. The change occurs more rapidly if the flour is exposed to the action of air. During such aerated storage enzymatic changes occur. Fats are first hydrolyzed by lipases to fatty acids which are then oxidized by lipoxygenase. Due to the action of reductases, disulphide bonds decrease in number and sulphydryl groups increase. These changes are known as maturation or "ageing." Maturation brings about changes in the physical properties of gluten during fermentation in such a way that results in better bread being obtained. Like bleaching, chemical substances or "improvers" accelerate maturation. Bleaching agents, like chlorine dioxide and chlorine both bleach and act as improvers. Other improvers used are potassium bromate, potassium persulphate, ascorbic acid, azodicarbonamide (ADA) and L-cysteine hydrochloride.

Nutritive value: Wheat provides in addition to energy (calories), considerable quantities (20 per cent) of the human requirements of proteins, B-vitamins, calcium and iron. The nutritive value of 100 per cent wholemeal (*atta*) is the same as that of wheat. Because of preference for white bread, white flour (*maida*) having decreased protein, B-vitamins and mineral contents is being produced by roller mills. In the case of commercial Indian flours, the percentage decrease in protein content is about 4; lysine, 36.3; thiamine 49.5; riboflavin, 71.7 and nicotinic acid, 67.0. There is also a decrease of more than 50 per cent in the calcium, total phosphorus, phytin phosphorus and iron contents.

The nutritional deficiency of milled wheat flour is made good by supplementation, fortification and enrichment. Wheat germ contains a high proportion of proteins of balanced amino acid composition. Supplementation of wheat flour with 10–15 per cent defatted germ flour brings about a striking improvement in the nutritive value. Addition of lysine, minerals and vitamins increases the nutritional value of the wheat flour. The enrichment used in different countries differs. White flour thus enriched is known as "enriched flour."

15.5.6 Wheat Products

Wheat flour: The maximum amount of today's consumption is of wheat flour. Wheat flour is either white (if the bran and germ have been removed, leaving only the endosperm) or brown (which is either wholemeal flour containing bran, germ, and endosperm, or wholemeal flour mixed with white flour in various proportions). The flour is known as "strong" if it has a high gluten content, and "soft" if the gluten content is low. Strong flour (also known as "hard flour" or "bread flour"), which is high in gluten, forms a certain toughness that holds its shape well once baked. Soft flour is comparatively low in gluten and so results in a finer texture. Soft flour is usually divided into cake flour, which is the lowest in gluten, and pastry flour, which has slightly more gluten than cake flour. All-purpose flour is a blended wheat flour with an intermediate gluten level which is marketed as an acceptable compromise for most household baking needs,

Pasta: is a type of food made from the flour of various grains, water, and sometimes eggs, which is mixed, kneaded and formed into various shapes, and boiled prior to consumption. While the name comes from Italy, pasta is very popular all over the world. The English word *pasta* generally refers to noodles and other food products made from flour and water paste, often including egg and salt. Less frequently, the term *maccheroni* is used for the same products, especially when in combination with cheese. Dried Italian-style pasta is made from durum wheat semolina, which gives it a light yellow colour and a slightly chewy texture when properly prepared. Certain American pastas are produced from a mixture of Farina and Semolina. Such pastas often have an inferior texture and flavor and are only usable in a casserole or other dish where texture is less important. Pasta is made either by extrusion, where the ingredients are forced through holes in a plate known as a die or by lamination, in which dough is kneaded, folded, rolled to thickness, then cut by slitters. Fresh pasta cooks quickly and has a delicate taste, but spoils quickly due to its high water content. Dry pasta generally contains about 10% moisture, which makes it shelf stable for about three years.

Macaroni: is typically machine-made dry commercial pasta, used in contrast to fresh pasta made at home or in small local businesses. Macaroni technically must not contain eggs. Although usually commercially made, some more advanced home machines do allow for the fresh creation of macaroni pasta. *Macaroni* is a corruption of the Italian word *maccherone* and its plural *maccheroni*. Thomas Jefferson is credited with introducing the first macaroni machine in the United States, in 1789, when he returned home after serving as ambassador to France.

Wheat bread: Bread is a popular food in Western and most other societies except for the Asian societies that typically prefer rice. It is often made from a wheat-flour dough that is cultured with yeast, allowed to rise, and finally baked in an oven. Owing to its high levels of gluten (which give the dough sponginess and elasticity), common wheat (also known as bread wheat) is the most common grain used for the preparation of bread, but bread is also made from the flour of other wheat species (including durum, spelt and emmer), rye, barley, maize (or corn), and oats, usually, but not always, in combination with wheat flour. Although common wheat is best suited for making highly-risen white bread, other wheat species are capable of giving a good crumb.

Semolina: Semolina is coarsely ground grain, usually wheat, with particles mostly between 0.25 and 0.75 mm in diameter. The same milling grade is sometimes called Farina, or grits if made from maize. It refers to two very different products: semolina for porridge is usually steel-cut soft common wheat whereas "durum semolina" used for pasta or *gnocchi* is coarsely ground from either durum wheat or other hard wheat, usually the latter because it costs less to grow. Non-durum semolina porridge or farina has come to be known in the United States by the trade name *Cream of Wheat*. Semolina pudding is made by boiling or baking the grain with milk and sweeteners. The pudding can be flavoured with vanilla, served with jam, and eaten hot or cold. In Italy (Tuscany) spaghetti made with semolina is called *pici*. In most of India, it is known as *sooji*; in Southern India, *rava*. In much of North Africa and the Middle-East, it is made into the staple couscous. In Turkey "irmik helvasi" (*halva* of semolina), made with semolina scorched with sugar, butter, milk and pine nut, is a very popular traditional dessert which is made especially after funeral ceremonies. It can be used as an alternative to corn meal to "flour" the underside of fresh pizza dough to prevent it from sticking to the peel.

Wheat beer: is a beer that is brewed with a significant proportion of malted wheat. It is common for wheat beers to also contain malted barley. The addition of wheat lends to wheat beers a light flavour and pale colour. Wheat beers are brewed using both ale and lager brewing techniques. The two most common varieties of wheat beer are Belgian *Witbier* and German *Weizenbier.*

Wheat gluten: also called seitan (pronounced *SAY-tahn),* wheat meat, gluten meat, or simply gluten, is a foodstuff made from the gluten of wheat. It is made by washing dough made from wheat flour in water until the starch is rinsed away, leaving only the gluten, which can then be cooked and processed in various ways. Wheat gluten, although not as well known, is an alternative to soy-based meat substitutes such as tofu; some types may taste even more like meat than tofu due to their chewy and/or stringy texture.

Wheat Bran Flakes: is a breakfast cereal containing 100% of the United States' Recommended Dietary Allowance of eleven vitamins and minerals, including vitamins Bl, B3, B5, B6, B12, C, E, and Iron, Riboflavin, Folic Acid, and Zinc. One 3/4 cup serving contains 3 grams of protein, 5 grams of dietary fibre and 90 calories, 5 of which come from fat.

Shredded Wheat: is a breakfast cereal made from whole wheat. It comes in two sizes, bite-sized (3/4 in × 1 in), and normal size, that may be crumbled up with hands before adding milk. Both sizes are available in a *frosted* variety, which has one side coated with sugar. Some manufacturers have produced "filled" versions of the bite-size cereal containing a raisin at the centre, or apricot or cranberry filling. The wheat is first cooked in water until its moisture content reaches about 50%. It is then *tempered,* allowing moisture to diffuse evenly into the grain. The grain then passes through a set of rollers with grooves on one side, yielding a *web* of shredded wheat strands. Many webs are stacked together, and this moist stack of strands is crimped at regular intervals to produce individual pieces of cereal with the strands attached at each end. These then go into an oven, where they are baked until their moisture content is reduced to 5%.

15.6 Rice (*Oryza sativa*)

Rice is the staple diet for more than half of the world's population and is consumed principally in Asia. Rice forms up to 80 per cent of the food intake in some countries. It is cooked in boiling water and eaten mostly with cooked pulses, vegetables, fish or meat. In India, several types of dishes are prepared from rice flavoured with spices and other ingredients. Other rice preparations include parched rice, puffed rice, and fermented preparations like "*idli*" and "*dosa*." Because of the shortage of rice and its high price, it finds limited industrial applications. By products of rice, such as bran, rice polishings and paddy straw are used for feeding livestock.

15.6.1 Production

Rice (*Oryza sativa*) probably originated in South-East Asia, where it has been grown for many centuries. The production of rice in China dates back to 3000 BC. Rice is grown in the tropics where rain and sunshine are abundant; 90 per cent of the world area under rice cultivation is in Asia. It grows under diverse conditions. It grows in swamps, underwater and on drylands. It grows below sea level, in plains and at high altitudes. There are different varieties of rice suited for growth under different environmental conditions. It is estimated that there are over 1,00,000 different varieties of rice in the world. The total number of types of rice in India runs to many thousands, varying in colour, length, breadth, smell and nature of starch.

The world production is 800 million tonnes and India produced 177.6 million tonnes in 2023. India ranked second in world production of rice next to China in the year 2023.

15.6.2 Structure

Paddy is a covered caryopsis. The husk which generally forms about 21 per cent varies in thickness and the ease with which it can be separated from the kernel of different types of rice. Rice grain resembles wheat but is smaller than wheat, is flattened laterally and has no ventral furrow. The pericarp with the underlying aleurone layer, the starchy endosperm and the germ of the grain, on an average, amount respectively to 6.0, 91.75 and 2.25 per cent of the grain. The aleurone layer is generally thicker in the *japonica* variety of rice than in the *indica* rices. In the *indica* rices, maximum development of aleurone layer is observed in rices with purple or coloured pericarp and in larger, bolder grains, than in fine and slender ones. The endosperm is of two kinds, the glutinous and the non-glutinous, the former being more sticky when cooked than the latter.

Varieties of rice are classified according to kernel weight, length and breadth. Based on the ratio of the length to the breadth, the grains are described as slender, medium or bold. In India, rice is classified as shown in Table 15.5.

Table 15.5 Classification of rice (Indian)

Kernel size	Length (mm)	Ratio of length to breadth
Long slender	6 and more	3 and > 3
Round bold	< 6	< 3
Medium slender	< 6 or 4.5	2.5 to 3
Short slender	< 6	3 and > 3
Short bold	< 6	< 2.5

Source: Richharia and Govindaswamy, *Rice of India*, Central Rice Research Institute, Cuttack, 1966.

15.6.3 Composition

The chemical composition of rice is influenced to some extent by genetic and environmental factors. The composition of Indian rice is: moisture, 10.9–13.8; proteins, 5.5–9.3; carbohydrates, 73.4–80.8; fibre, 0.2–1.0; and mineral matter, 0.8–2.0 per cent. The germ, the pericarp and the aleurone layers, which are richer than endosperm, in nutrients like protein, minerals and vitamins are separated from the grain during milling along with the husk. The chemical composition of rice obtained by dehusking by different methods is given in Table 15.7

Table 15.7 Chemical composition of rice obtained by different dehusking methods

		Raw rice		Parboiled	
	Husked	Home pounded	Milled	Home pounded	Milled
Moisture (%)	9.7	9.6	9.7	12.6	13.3
Protein (%)	7.7	7.3	6.9	8.5	6.4
Fat (%)	1.8	1.2	0.54	0.6	0.4
Carbohydrates (%)	78.1	80.1	82.06	77.4	79.1
Crude fibre (%)	1.1	0.7	0.2	—	—
Mineral matter (%)	1.6	1.1	0.6	0.9	0.8
Calcium (mg/100 g)	15.9	13.0	10	10	10
Phosphorus (mg/100 g)	368	182	87	280	150
Iron (mg/100 g)	4.0	28	2.2	2.8	2.2
Thiamine (mg/100 g)	360	210	105	270	210
Nicotinic acid (mg /100 g)	3.5	2.5	1.0	4.0	3.8

Source: *Wealth of India,* Vol. Vll, CSIR, New Delhi, India, 2001.

The major carbohydrate of rice is starch (72–75 per cent). The amylase content of the starch varies according to grain type, the longer grained and superior types containing up to 17.5 per cent amylose while some coarse types are completely devoid of it. Glutinous rice consists almost entirely of amylopectin. Rice also contains some free sugars like glucose, sucrose and dextrin. In some samples fructose, galactose and raffinose are also found. The fibre of rice is the hemicelluloses made up of the pentoses, arabinose and xylose.

The protein content of rice is lower than that of wheat. One-fourth of protein in the whole rice is present in the germ, the aleurone layer and a few layers of cells beneath it. A glutelin (oryzenin) is the principal protein of rice. Rice also contains small quantities of albumin, globulin and prolamins. The proteins of the husked and polished rice have a lower biological value but a higher digestibility than those of rice bran and rice polishings. Parboiling has no effect on the biological value or digestibility of the proteins of the polished rice. The nutritive value of rice proteins is of a high order, being superior to that of wheat and other cereal products. The rice proteins are richer in arginine compared to other cereal proteins. They are deficient in lysine and threonine.

In its mineral content, rice resembles other cereals. Most of the minerals present in rice are located in the pericarp and germ. Polished rice is poor in calcium and iron. Coloured types of rice contain more iron than white rice. The phosphorus content is high, about 4 per cent of it is present as phytic acid. Rice also contains some trace elements.

Several enzymes, present in rice, include amylases, proteases, lipases, oxidases, peroxidases and phenolases. On storage, the oxidase activity of rice remains constant, but the amylase, lipase and peroxidase activities decrease. The activity of α-amylase in fresh rice is probably responsible for its sticky consistency after cooking.

The pigments of coloured rice are anthocyanins and carotenoids. Some types of rice possess a characteristic sweet aroma which is recognized when the grain is boiled. In India, the "basmati" rice is highly esteemed for its peculiar aroma.

15.6.4 Parboiling

The parboiling of rice originated in India and has been widely practised in this country since ancient times. It is estimated that more than half of India's rice crop is parboiled. Parboiling is particularly good in the case of coarse and medium rices of soft structure because such rices suffer excessive breakage when milled raw. Parboiling involves soaking paddy in water for a short time followed by heating once or twice in steam and drying before milling.

Several commercial methods are used for parboiling rice. In one method (HR conversion process), wet paddy is held in a vessel under reduced pressure for some time, then steeped in water at 75°–85°C for 2–3 hours under pressure, the steeping water is drained off and the paddy heated under reduced pressure for a short time with live steam in a steam-jacketed vessel. The product is then dried. In another method (Malek process), paddy is soaked in water at 30°C for 4–6 hours, steamed under pressure for 15 min. and dried. The product is called Malekized rice.

Parboiling of paddy has several advantages. Dehusking of parboiled rice is easy, and the grain becomes tougher resulting in reduced losses during milling. Milled parboiled rice has greater resistance to insects and fungus infection. The nutritive value of rice increases after parboiling because the water dissolves the vitamins and minerals present in the hulls and bran coats and carries them into the endosperm. Thus, valuable nutrients which would otherwise be lost with the husks and bran in rice milling are retained by the endosperm. The milling and polishing of raw rice result in losses of 75 per cent of vitamin B_1, 56 per cent of riboflavin and 63 per cent of niacin, whereas after parboiling, these losses are reduced by 58, 35 and 11 per cent, respectively. Finally, the parboiled rice will not turn into a glutinous mass when cooked.

Parboiling has some disadvantages. The colour change and, sometimes, the unpleasant smell of parboiled rice is not preferred. These changes are due to defective steeping during parboiling. During steeping, fermentative changes take place resulting in the yellowish colour and off-flavour of rice. These defects are overcome in the modern methods of parboiling.

15.6.5 Milling

Milling of rice (paddy) consists of cleaning to remove small and large heavy impurities, dehulling and "milling"—a process that removes the coarse outer layers of bran and germ. Paddy, on milling, yields approximately 20 per cent hulls, 8 per cent bran, 2 per cent polishings and 70 per cent rice.

Paddy is milled in India either by home pounding or in mechanized rice mills. Home pounding is most commonly done using a pestle-and-mortar made of wood and worked by hand or foot. Pounding is continued till the charge has been sufficiently husked, after which it is winnowed and polished by light hand pounding. The average recovery of rice, including broken rice, in home pounding is higher than in rice milling. Home pounded rice has a short storage life owing to the high content of fat in the bran which develops rancidity.

In modern milling, rice is cleaned by using various types of machinery, as used in the case of other cereal grains. The cleaned rice is then dehulled in a huller. This is a shelling device and there are different devices to carry it out. Rice is passed through two stone or rubber discs rotating at different speeds and, by the shearing action on the grain, the hull is pulled away. The whole kernel from which the hulls have been removed is known as "brown rice." This is then milled in a machine called a pearler to remove coarse outer layers of bran and germ by a process of rubbing, resulting in unpolished milled rice. There is always a certain amount of breakage of rice in this milling. Unpolished rice is liable to develop rancidity and so it is next polished in a brush machine, which removes the aleurone layer and yields "polished rice." Sometimes the polished rice is further treated in a device known as *trumbol,* to give a coating of sugar and talc to produce a brighter shine on the grains.

The milled rice consists of unbroken kernels (the heads) and broken kernels. The latter are then separated, based on their size, into large fragments (second heads), medium ones (screenings) and the smallest ones (brewer's rice).

Polishing of brown rice is also carried out by solvent extraction milling (SEM). In this case, the brown rice is soaked in an oil so that the bran layer is softened and then wet-milled in presence of rice oil and hexane. The debrowned rice is rinsed with hexane and the solvent is removed by suitable methods. From the bran-and-oil mixture, the solvent and bran are recovered. This method has many advantages over the conventional method. The yield of heads is up by 10 per cent; the decrease in fat content of rice increases its storage life. The bran contains 17–20 per cent protein but less than 1.5 per cent fat and is thus good for use in dietetic food, snacks, etc. The rice oil (about 2 per cent yield on rice weight) has edible and industrial applications.

15.6.6 Cooking and Nutritive Value

Freshly harvested rice have poor cooking qualities when compared to rice from paddy stored for a few months after harvest. The rice from freshly harvested paddy cooks to a glutinous mass has a low swelling capacity and causes digestive disorders. Well-stored rice grains swell on cooking to about four times their original volume, while freshly harvested rice scarcely swells to double its size when cooked. This is due to the high α-amylase content of fresh rice, that acts on starch in the kernel but is inactivated during storage.

There is considerable loss of vitamins, minerals and proteins during the milling of rice. Washing of rice before cooking results in the loss of B-vitamins. Over 60 per cent of thiamine of milled rice is lost during washing. Depletion of nutrients during cooking is generally less serious than due to washing. The common method of cooking, which uses the excess water that is subsequently discarded, causes the maximum loss.

In countries where rice is the staple diet, continuous and exclusive use of polished rice causes beriberi, due to the deficiency of thiamine. To remedy the deficiencies of polished rice, white rice is enriched with the required nutrients (fortified rice). This consists of treating the white rice with a solution of vitamins in an acid solution and then coating the grain with a film of zein and abietic acid in an alcoholic solution. After the film has dried the grains are dusted with talc. The film prevents the loss of vitamins owing to washing in the traditional method of cooking.

The cooking time of rice, particularly brown rice, is of the order of 35–45 min. This is reduced to 2–15 min. in the case of "quick-cooking rice." This is the rice that is partially pre-cooked in water and dried under special controlled conditions or cooked by dry-heat. This is also prepared by passing rice soaked in water through a microwave oven. Quick-cooking rice is as good in texture and nutritional value as the original rice. Instant rice is fully precooked and dried rice.

15.6.7 Rice Products

Rice flour: This is made from second heads in pulverizing machines. Rice flour of 9–13 per cent moisture content, contains 5–9 per cent of protein, 0.4–1.0 per cent of fat and yields 0.4 to 0.7 per cent ash. It is used in refrigerated biscuit manufacture to prevent sticking, in baby foods as a thickener, and in waffle and pancake mixes as a water absorbent. In India, rice flour is also used in the preparation of vermicelli, papad, sandige (curls), and in a number of other preparations.

As already stated, in order to improve the nutritional status of persons who subsist almost entirely on rice, it is necessary to have varieties that contain a well-balanced complement of vitamins, minerals and amino acids. It is not easy to supplement the whole rice grain with adequate quantities of proteins. However, the protein content of rice flour can be increased and flour preparations containing as much as 26 per cent protein have been obtained. Such protein-rich flours can be used as substitute for milk in feeding children over one year old.

Parched rice: About 4–5 per cent of the total supplies of rice in India is converted into rice products—parched rice, parched paddy and rice flakes. Parched rice is prepared by throwing rice into sand heated to a high temperature in an iron or earthen pan. On stirring, rice begins to crackle and swell. Then the contents of the pan are removed and sieved to separate the parched rice from sand. Parboiled rice is preferred in making parched rice. Parched rice is a crisp product with a greyish to brilliant white colour and is sold either salted or unsalted. It is eaten as such or used mixed with buttermilk or milk.

Parched paddy (Puffed rice): Sun-dried paddy is filled in earthen jars and is moistened with hot water. After 2–3 min., the water is decanted and the jars are then kept in an inverted position for 8–10 hours. Next, the paddy is exposed to the sun for a short time and then parched in hot sand as in the preparation of parched rice. During parching, the grains swell and burst into a soft white product. The parched grains are sieved to remove sand and winnowed to separate the husk.

Flaked rice: Flaked rice is made from parboiled rice. Paddy is soaked in water for 2–3 days to soften the kernel, followed by boiling in water for a few minutes. After cooking, the water is drained off, and the paddy is heated in a shallow earthen vessel or iron pan, till the husks break open, after which it is pounded by a wooden pestle, which flattens the rice kernel and removes the husk. The husk is separated by winnowing. Flaked rice is thin and papery and of white colour. It can be stored without deterioration for several months. The vitamin content is equal to that of parboiled rice and many preparations are made out of it by adding suitable flavouring and sweetening agents.

Rice starch: Rice starch granules are quite small and are embedded in a protein matrix. To separate them from protein, broken rice is steeped for 24 hours in 5 times its weight of 0.3 per cent caustic soda. The caustic soda treated granules are washed, dried and grounded into flour. The flour is then mixed with about ten times its weight of caustic soda solution. This removes the gluten. After 24 hours, the starch that settles down is removed, washed and dried.

Rice starch is used as food, especially in puddings, ice creams, pies and custard powder. Its principal use is in the laundry as a stiffening agent. Rice starch also finds use in cosmetics, in face and dusting powders, as a thickener, in calico printing, in finishing textiles and for making dextrins, glucose and adhesives.

In Japan, China and other Eastern countries, rice is employed for the manufacture of alcoholic beverages. *Saki*, the Japanese national drink, is prepared by fermenting rice with a fungus (*Aspergillus oryzae*). Rice based beverages are not popular in India.

15.6.8 Byproducts of Rice

Rice bran: The bran is the most nutritious byproduct of rice milling and is used almost exclusively as a feedstuff. It is generally contaminated with husk, which lowers its nutritive value. Rice bran contains about 12 per cent protein and 15 per cent fat. Once separated from the grain, the fat of rice undergoes hydrolysis by lipases to form free fatty acids, which then undergo oxidation by peroxidase, that reduces the nutritive value of bran and causes digestive disturbances.

Rice bran oil: Bran oil is obtained by extraction from rice bran with solvents. Bran oil is also obtained in the solvent extraction milling of rice. The oil contains a high percentage of unsaturated fatty acids, yet it is quite stable because of the presence of natural antioxidants. When refined, bleached and deodourized, it is used for salad dressing and as cooking oil.

Bran after solvent extraction has a higher percentage of protein than the original material. With its low-fat content it keeps well. It is a more palatable feed than the undefatted bran.

Rice polishings: Rice polishings are also rich in nutrients. They are not recovered in sizeable quantities in India. They are mostly used as animal feed.

Husk: Paddy husk contains about 22 per cent ash of which 95 per cent is silica. Because of its high silica content, it is used as an abrasive. Large quantities of husk are used in India as fuel for boilers, kilns and household purposes. Its fuel value is not good, being only about half that of bituminous coal. Other uses of rice husk include roughage for animal feed, insulating material, paper making, etc. The husk contains about 12 per cent pentosans and is thus used for the production of furfural, though it is not as good as oat husk and corn cobs for this purpose.

15.6.9 Wild Rice (*Zazania aquatica*)

Zazinia aquatica: Wild rice, also known as "Indian rice" or water rice, is an American species which grows in lakes and rivers. American Indians use wild rice as a staple food. Neither the wild rice plant nor the grain resembles rice. Because of its aquatic habit, it is called rice.

Wild rice is self-sown and a self-perpetuating annual plant. The ripe rice seeds drop from their stalk in late autumn and lie dormant on the lake bottom till spring. As the water becomes warmer, the seeds germinate and the stalk rises above the water. The stalk continues to grow until the grains are almost mature. Wild rice is harvested, dried in the open air and then it is parched and the hulls removed by pounding. The primitive method of growing and processing wild rice by American Indians has now been replaced. It is now grown under controlled conditions and processed by modern methods.

The composition of wild rice is similar to that of other cereals. Its vitamin content is of the same order as that of whole wheat. Wild rice is now used in American cooking as a principal food in combination with poultry and game birds or as a side dish.

15.6.10 Brown Rice (*Oryza aquatica*)

Brown rice is unmilled or partly milled rice, a kind of whole grain. It has a mild nutty flavour, is chewier than white rice, becomes rancid more quickly, but is far more nutritious. Any rice, including sticky rice, long-grain rice, or short-grain rice, may be eaten as brown rice. In much of Asia, brown rice is associated with poverty and wartime shortages, and in the past was rarely eaten except by the sick, the elderly, and as a cure for constipation. This traditionally looked-down-upon kind of rice is now more expensive than common white rice, partly due to its low consumption, the difficulty of storage and transport, and higher nutritional value.

Brown rice and white rice have similar amounts of calories, carbohydrates, fat and protein. The difference between the two lies in processing and nutritional content. If the outermost layer of a grain of rice (the husk) is removed, the result is brown rice. If the husk and the bran layer underneath are removed, the result is white rice. Several vitamins and dietary minerals are lost in this removal and the subsequent polishing process. A part of these missing nutrients, such as Bl, B3, and iron are sometimes added back into the white rice making it "enriched," as food suppliers in the US are required to do by the Food and Drug Administration (FDA). One mineral that is not added back into white rice is magnesium; one cup of cooked long-grain brown rice contains 84 mg of magnesium while one cup of white rice contains 19 mg.

15.6.11 Black Rice

Black rice is one of several black-coloured heirloom plants producing rice variants such as Indonesian black rice, forbidden rice, or wild rice. High in nutritional and medicinal value, forbidden rice is rich in iron and considered a blood tonifier. Unlike other black rice from Asia, it is not glutinous or rough. This grain is high in fibre and has a deep, nutty taste. The deep colour of black forbidden rice, and the deep purple colour when cooked, suggest the presence of phytonutrients. It has a relatively high mineral content (including iron) and, like most rice, supplies several important amino acids.

15.6.12 New Rice for Africa ("*NERICA*")

It is an interspecific cultivar of rice developed by the West Africa Rice Development Association (WARDA) to improve the yield of African rice varieties. The new rice for Africa was created by crossing *O. glaberrima* and *O. sativa.* Because the different species do not naturally interbreed, a plant tissue culture technique called embryo-rescue was used to assure that crosses between the two varieties survive and grow to maturity. The new rices display heterosis, the phenomenon in which the progeny of two genetically different parents grow faster, yield more, or resist stresses better than either parent.

15.6.13 Bhutanese Red Rice

It is a medium-grain rice grown in the Kingdom of Bhutan in the Eastern Himalayas. It is the staple rice of the Bhutanese people. Bhutanese red rice is red *japonica* rice. It is semi-milled some of the reddish bran is left on the rice. Because of this, it cooks somewhat faster than unmilled brown rice. When cooked, the rice is pale pink, soft and slightly sticky. This rice became available in the United States in the mid 1990s.

15.6.14 Glutinous Rice

This (also called sticky rice, sweet rice, waxy rice, *botan* rice, *mochi* rice, and pearl rice) is the main type of rice grown and consumed by the Lao of Laos and Northeast Thailand, areas which are considered to be the primary centre of origin and domestication of Asian rice (*Oryza sativa* L). It has been cultivated in this area for 4,000 years. An estimated 85% of Lao rice production is of this type. Despite the misleading name, glutinous rice does not contain dietary gluten (i.e., does not contain glutenin and gliadin), and thus should be safe for gluten-free diets. The word *glutinous*, meaning glue-like or sticky, comes from the Latin *glūtinōsus*. The term glutinous rice refers to rice having no (or negligible amounts of) amylase, and high amounts of amylopectin, the two components of starch. Amylopectin is responsible for the sticky quality of glutinous rice. Most varieties of rice become sticky to one degree or another when cooked, but these should not be confused with "sticky rice" made from glutinous rice.

The improved rice varieties that swept through Asia during the Green Revolution were non-glutinous types and Lao farmers rejected them in favour of their traditional sticky varieties. Gradually though, improved higher-yield strains of sticky rice became available from the Laotian *National Rice Research Programme*. By 1999, more than 70% of the area along the Mekong River Valley was of the newer strains.

15.6.15 Basmati Rice

A high-quality, high-priced aromatic rice produced exclusively in India and Pakistan is Basmati rice. In India, this variety of rice is mainly grown in the States of Punjab, Haryana and Uttar Pradesh. Basmati rice is very distinct from other rices. The grains are long and slender with dimensions of 6 mm and above in length and 2 mm or less in breadth possessing a typical aroma. On cooking the kernels increase to about twice in length and remain soft, and fluffy even after cooking. Nearly all traditional varieties of Basmati rice have intermediate amylase gelatinization temperature and gel consistency.

The area under Basmati rice cultivation tends to fluctuate from year to year depending upon market price and incidence of disease and pests. According to a rough estimate, the area in India under Basmati is 10 lakh hectares and the total production is 2.1 tonnes per hectare and requires improvement through the use of appropriate agronomic management techniques. Around 1.3 million tonnes of Basmati rice are exported annually to West Asian countries and to the USA.

15.6.16 Patna Rice (*Oryza sativa)*

A variety of the species and one of the varieties of long-grain white rice, is extensively cultivated in the Indo-Gangetic plains, in and around Patna, capital of Bihar State, India. Patna rice is known for its elongated kernel with grain length greater than 6 mm and has been used as a staple food by the local people for thousands of years. Sometimes, Patna rice is also called *Parimal* rice locally.

This mildly flavoured rice comes from the Bihar region of the Ganges plains. It has a robust, long and narrow, opaque grain that keeps its shape well for curries. Basmati rice is closely related to Patna rice but has a stronger aroma. Patna rice is the most esteemed in UK and USA and is the highest-priced rice in the grocery stores.

15.6.17 Sona Masuri

It is a medium-grain rice grown largely in the Indian states of Andhra Pradesh and Karnataka. It is lightweight and aromatic and considered to be premium quality.

15.7 Maize (*Zea mays*)

Maize (*Zea mays*), known as "corn" in the USA, is utilized in more diversified ways than any other cereal. With its high percentage of carbohydrates, lipids and protein, it is nutritious for human consumption. A high percentage of maize grown in developing countries is used for food; in India it is 80–90 per cent. The ready-to-eat breakfast cereal "cornflakes" is a maize product. In developed countries, maize is used as an animal feed.

Maize is also used for the manufacture of starch, sugar (corn sugar, dextrin), syrup (corn syrup), industrial alcohol and alcoholic beverages. Corn also finds several other uses.

15.7.1 Production

The origin of maize is considered to be America, particularly in southern Mexico. The USA is one of the major corn producing countries in the world with a production of more than 50 per cent of the world's crop. But the United States' share of world area under maize crop has decreased from about 40 per cent to less than 25 per cent because of the development of high yielding strains of hybrid maize. The yield of maize in USA increased from 13.9 quintals per hectare in 1935 to 89.2 quintals per hectare in 2003–04. The world area under maize cultivation and production in 2004 was 142.3 million hectares and 637 million tones, respectively.

Maize is extensively cultivated in India both in the plains and in the hill regions. Both in acreage and production, it is next to rice, wheat, sorghum and pearl millet. During 2023-24, it was planted in an area of 9.96 million hectares with a production of 35.67 million tonnes. The yield of improved hybrid varieties of maize in India is 35.8 quintals per hectare compared to 58 quintals per hectare world average.

15.7.2 Varieties of Maize

The principal maize varieties are flint corn, dent corn, sweet corn, popcorn, flour corn and waxy corn. The classification is based on the nature and distribution of starch in the endosperm.

Flint Corn: Flint corn has very hard kernels. The texture is due to a rather thick layer of hard starch and protein just under the bran layer. Flints mature early. In India, mostly flint and semi-flint varieties are grown.

Dent Corn: This has hard starch at the sides, while the major part of the endosperm contains soft starch. At maturity, a typical dent-like depression appears at the crown. Dent corn comprises the largest maize crop in the United States.

Sweet Corn: The corn has a large proportion of carbohydrates in the kernel as dextrin and sugar in the unripe kernels which are tender. When matured and dried, the kernels are hard and have a wrinkled surface. Practically all canned corn is sweet. A small amount of sweet corn is dehydrated or frozen.

Pop Corn: A major part of the endosperm of this type of corn comprises hard starch on all sides, with a very small core of soft starch. When the corn is popped the endosperm expands with the formation of a fluffy white irregular mass. The thick outer layers of the corn remain attached to the puffed endosperm in an unexpanded form.

Flour Corn: The grains of this type of corn is large and soft and the endosperm is very friable. These characteristics permit easy grinding of the grain into flour.

Waxy Corn: This contains a high proportion of amylopectin. It is of industrial importance.

15.7.3 Structure and Composition

The grain of maize is much larger than those of other cereals. The basal part is narrow and the apex broad. The scutellum of maize is large and forms 10–13 per cent of the grain. The embryo, scutellum and the endosperm are within the pericarp and testa, which are fused to form a "hull" that corresponds to the bran of other cereals. The hulls of maize are lost in threshing.

Maize grains may be white, yellow or reddish in colour. Its kernel, like the kernel of other cereals, consists of three main parts, namely, the hull or bran coat with high fibre content, embryo rich in oil, and the starchy endosperm. The average composition of Indian maize is as follows: moisture, 14.9; protein, 11.1; fat, 3.6; fibre, 2.7; other carbohydrates, 66.2 and minerals, 1.5 per cent. Using hybrids, maize of different compositions can be obtained. Those with high protein and lysine content are not good for milling.

Starch is the predominant carbohydrate of maize (66–74 per cent on a dry basis). The amylose content is about 27 per cent. High amylose corn contains 55–80 per cent amylose. High amylose corn is only partially gelatinized when a water suspension is boiled. In waxy varieties of maize, almost 100 per cent of the starch is amylopectin. Lower saccharides present in the grain in small quantities are glucose, fructose, sucrose and raffinose. Cellulose and hemicellulose are the principal constituents of maize hulls.

In maize (whole grain) the proportion of the various types of proteins are as follows: albumin, 16.3; globulin, 6.5; prolamine, 3.5; glutelin, 23.5; insolubles, 21.3 per cent. The predominant protein in the endosperm of the common varieties of maize is the prolamine known as zein. Maize germ is rich in glutelin accounting for 49–54 per cent of the total protein of germ. The content of essential amino acids like lysine, tryptophan and methionine in maize protein is low and the nutritive value of maize is lower than that of wheat and rice.

The major lipids of maize oil are triglycerides. Phospholipids and glycolipids are present in small quantities. About 84 per cent of the total fat of the kernel is found in the germ and 15 per cent in the endosperm. The triglycerides have a high proportion of oleic and linoleic acids.

Maize is deficient in the vitamin niacin. The grain contains niacin, but 50–80 per cent of it occurs in a bound form as niacytin which is biologically unavailable and renders maize deficient in niacin. The disease pellagra, which is prevalent among some people who rely upon maize for a large proportion of their daily food, is caused by a deficiency of niacin. Maize is a fairly good source of phosphorus, contains an appreciable amount of iron, but is low in calcium. The phosphorus occurs mostly as phytin.

15.7.4 Milling

Maize is milled by a dry or wet process. In both processes, the germ is separated from the grain in order to extract and recover germ oil. The germ oil is a valuable product, but if allowed to remain a constituent of maize meal would lead to the development of rancidity. After degermination, the dry milling employs roller mills and the process is somewhat similar to wheat milling. Wet milling involves a steeping stage and complete disintegration of the endosperm to recover starch and protein.

In dry milling, the object is to recover the maximum amount of grits with the minimum amount of flour, with the least possible contamination of the germ. The grains are cleaned and conditioned by addition of cold or hot water or steam, which results in the loosening and toughening of the germ and bran. The endosperm is moistened to an ideal moisture content such that the yield of grits is maximum. The conditioned grain is passed through a suitable machine to separate the bran and germ. The stock after degermination is dried to 15–15.5 per cent moisture content and then sifted, to produce several fractions. The large, medium and fine fractions (hominy) are then milled in roller mills. This consists of several stages. All the finished grits, meal (cornmeal is a product somewhat smaller than grits, but still much coarser than corn flour) and flour are sifted. The yield of products in dry maize milling is as follows: grits, 40; coarse meal, 20; fine meal, 10; flour, 5; germ 14 and hominy feed 11 per cent.

In India, maize is ground for wholemeal atta in power-driven or hand-operated *chakkis*. The meal is sifted to remove fibre. In large-scale milling, *maida* and *suji* are produced. Grits are used in the preparation of porridge, to make corn flakes, as a brewing adjunct and to manufacture glucose by hydrolysis. Oil is extracted from germ, while bran and germ meal are utilized as animal feed.

Maize is wet-milled to obtain starch, oil, cattle feed and the products of starch hydrolysis, viz., liquid and solid glucose and syrup. The first step in wet milling is steeping. The cleaned maize is steeped for 48 hours in warm water (50°C) containing some sulphur dioxide. Steeping in water softens the kernel and assists separation of the hull, germ and fibre from each other. After steeping, the steep water is drained off, and the maize is coarsely ground in degerminating mills to free the germ from the grain. Then the ground material flows down separating troughs in which hulls and grits settle, while the germ overflows.

The germ is then separated, dried and oil extracted by hydraulic pressing or by using a solvent. The degerminated material in the separating troughs is then finely ground in a *bhur* or attrition mill. The hulls and fibre, which are not reduced so much in size, can then be separated from the protein and starch by sieving. The suspension of starch and protein from wet screening is adjusted to a specific gravity of 1.04 by dewatering over string filters and the starch is separated from the protein by continuous centrifugation. Finally, the starch is filtered and dried. The protein in the steep water is recovered by vacuum evaporation and dried as "gluten feed" for animal feeding.

The byproducts of wet milling of maize find several uses. The steep water from wet milling contains free amino acids, proteins, carbohydrates, minerals and growth adjuncts. It is concentrated to about 50 per cent of solids and is used as a nutrient for the micro-organisms producing penicillin and other antibiotics. Maize oil, rich in essential fatty acids, finds use as a salad oil. Its high smoke point makes it suitable for use as a cooking oil. The protein concentrates, maize bran and oil cakes are used as animal feeds.

15.8 Millets

Millets are among some of the oldest dual cultivated crops used for humans and fodder for animals. It is a grass like crop, small seeded. Besides India, it is the staple food of China and Africa. Chinese believe that millet was brought from the heavens by Houji–"Lord Millet" and it was considered a sacred crop by them.

It is known by other names such as 'siridhanya'–rich and refreshing grains. Its fermented drink Kaffir or Bamba beer is a malted millet brew in Africa.

In India, millets have a special reference in the oldest Yajurveda scripts V_{12}. Foxtail (*priyangava*), barny and millet (*aanara*) and black finger millet (*shyaamaka*), this indicates that millet consumption was very common, pre-dating to the Indian Bronze Age (4,500 BC). It bridges the gap between agricultural and non-agricultural produce.

There are many favourable factors that millets override over other cereals. They grow very comfortably in an arid land, require less water and withstand high temperature above 46°C (115 F). Even saline soil is suitable for millets cultivation. Rice crop requires two and a half times more water when compared with millet crop. Millets are also known as "miracle grains". The other factor being it reduces carbon dioxide in the atmosphere; it contributes to mitigating climate change. It is harvested in just 65 days. They are Nutri-cereals, a term self-explaining as it is rich in protein, essential fatty acids, dietary fibre, B vitamins, minerals such as calcium, iron, potassium, magnesium and manganese. Millets have low a glycemic index. Millets contain antioxidants, flavonoids and certain important amino acids like tryptophan. Anti-oxidants present in millets neutralize free radicals and clear other toxins. Quercetin, curcumin, ellagic acid, phenolic acids, avenanthramides, flavonoids, lignans and phytosterols and catechins primarily neutralize enzymatic activity within our body. Millets protect against the onset of age related diseases like Parkinson's etc.

Millets are nutritionally comparable to major cereals and serve as a good source of protein, micronutrients and phytochemicals. Processing methods like soaking, malting, decortications, and cooking affect the anti-oxidant content and activity. While sorghum and most of the millets contain about 10% protein, 3.5% lipids, finger millet contains 12–16% protein and 2–5% lipids. Millets are very good sources of micronutrients such as vitamins and minerals. Millets have a better amino acid profile. On the other hand, millets contain fewer cross-linked prolamins, which may be an additional factor contributing to the higher digestibility of the millet proteins.

The use of millets as a whole grain makes the essential nutrients such as dietary fibre, minerals, phenolics and vitamins concentrated in the outer layer of the grain or the seed coat from the part of the food and offer their nutritional and health benefits. Millets are not only comparable to major cereals concerning their nutritional features but are very good sources of carbohydrates, micronutrients and phytochemicals with nutraceutical properties. The millets generally contain 7-12% protein, 2-5% fat, 65-75% carbohydrates and 15-20% dietary fibre. The essential amino acid profiles of the millet protein are better than maize. Similar to cereal proteins, the millet proteins are poor sources of lysine, but they complement well with lysine-rich vegetable (leguminous) and animal proteins from nutritionally balanced composites of high biological value.

As millets are gluten-free, they have considerable potential in foods and beverages and can meet the growing demand for gluten-free foods and will be suitable for individuals suffering from celiac disease.

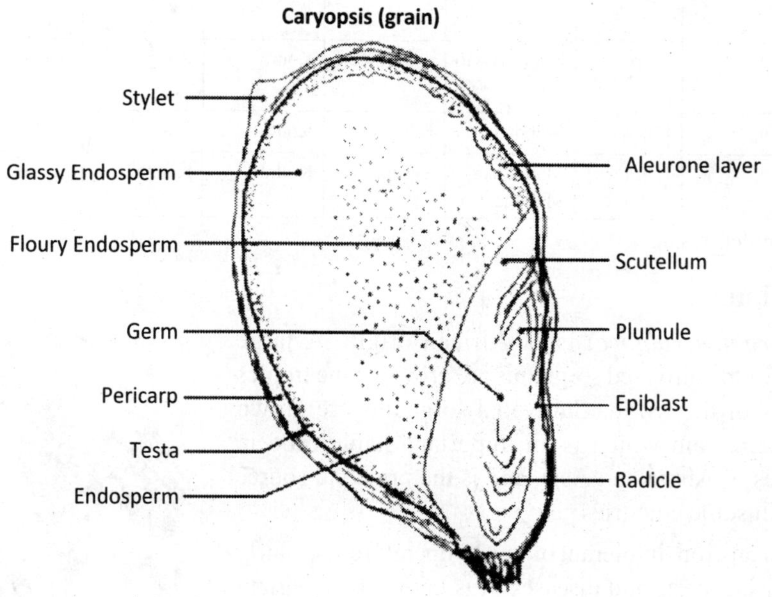

Fig. 15.2 General structure of millet grain

Source: https://www.researchgate.net

Global Distribution and Production of Millets

According to FAO statistics (2023), the world production of millets was 30.8 million tonnes from an area of 30.6 million hectares. Nearly a decade earlier (2013), the world production of millets was down to 29.8 million tonnes from an area 29.6 million hectares. Africa was the largest producer of millet in 2021 (38.4 million tonnes), followed by Asia (25.7 million tonnes) and India (10.91 million tonnes). Relative to wheat, rice, maize and barley, sorghum ranks fifth in importance, in terms of both production and area planted, accounting for 5% of the world cereal production.

Table 15.7 Vernacular Names of Millets

English	Sorghum	Pearl millet	Finger millet	Little millet	Kodo millet	Foxtail/ Italian millet	Barnyard millet	Proso millet
Hindi	Jowar	Bajra	Mandua	Kutki	Kodon	Kangni, Kakum	Sanwa, Jhangon	Barre
Sanskrit	—	—	Nandimukhi, Madhuli	—	Kodara	Kanguni	Shyama	China
Kannada	Jola	Sajjai	Ragi	Same	Harka	Navane	Oodalu	Baragu
Tamil	Cholam	Kamboo	Kelvaragu	Samai	Varagu	Tenai	Kuthiravaali	Panivaragu
Telugu	Jonna	Sajjalu	Ragulu	Samalu	Arikelu, Arika	Korra, Korralu	Udalu, Kodisama	Varigulu, Varagalu
Malayalam	Cholam	Kamboo	Moothari	Chama	Varagu	Thina	—	Panivaragu
Marathi	Jcwari	Bajri	Nachni	Sava	Kodra	Kang, Rala	Shamul	Vari
Gujarati	Juar	Bajri	Nagli, Bavto	Gajro, Kuri	Kodra	Kang	Sama	Cheno
Bengali	Juar	Bajra	Mandua	Kangani	Kodo	Kaon	Shamula	Cheena
Punjabi	—	Bajra	Mandhuka, Mandhal	Swank	Kodra	Kangni	Swank	Cheena

Source: http://millets.res.in

15.8.1 Sorghum

Sorghum (*Sorghum vulgare*) is of African origin. A large variety of wild and cultivated sorghums are grown in the tropics and subtropics of the world. Cultivated sorghums are grown chiefly for their grain which is an important staple food in many countries of Africa and Asia, and is the principal source of beverages in some countries.

Sorghum

It is a tropical crop, intolerant of low temperatures but fairly resistant to serious pests and diseases. It is known by a variety of names (such as great millet and guinea corn in West Africa, Asia and parts of Middle East).

The whole grain or broken grain may be cooked like rice or the whole grain ground to flour and used to make '*rottis*'. In other parts of Asia also, it is used this way. In Africa, sorghum is used as food in various forms as porridge, gruel, and parched, popped or malted grain. From a blend of wheat flour and sorghum flour, baked products like muffins, bread and cakes can be produced. In advanced countries, the grain is used chiefly as an animal feed. Sorghum plants are widely used as fodder, either green or as hay and silage. The sugar content of some sorghum stems is high (sweet sorghum) and these are used for making syrup. Sorghum grain is used as a source of starch in the fermentation industry for producing industrial alcohol and solvents.

A number of varieties of sorghums are cultivated in different agro-climatic and ecological conditions. In addition, considerable genetic diversity, combined with free inbreeding between themselves and human selection of sorghum for widely different purposes have contributed to great divergence and variation among sorghums. Thus, there is much confusion and divergence of opinion regarding the classification of *Sorghum.*

There is a huge range of physical diversity; however, sorghum is classified into four group:

(1) grain sorghum (2) forage sorghum glum (3) grass sorghum or (4) Sudan sorghums and broomcorn.

Sorghums are grouped using these characteristics

The colour of the pericarp (white, yellow or red). Presence or absence of pigmented testa, with/without tannins, the thickness of pericarp, endosperm colour-white, hetero yellow or yellow, endosperm type-normal, hetero waxy or waxy.

Production

Production of Sorghum in India has come down from 4.24 million tonnes during 2015-16 to 4.15 million tonnes during 2022-23; bajra production was 8.07 million tonnes in 2015-16 and 12.3 million tonnes in 2022-23, Ragi production was 1.19 million tonnes in 2015-16 and 2.26 million tonnes in 2022-23 and small millets production was 22,000 tonnes in 2015-16 and 4.28 lakhs tonnes in 2022-23. The world production is 61.4 million tonnes and India's is 4.15 million tonnes, in 2022.

According to FAO 2022, Sorgum is Eighth major cereal after Wheat, Rice, Maize, Barley, Rye, Oats and millets.

Structure and Composition

The structure of the grain of sorghum is similar to that of other cereals, consisting of an embryo, a relatively large scutellum and endosperm, enclosed in a seed coat (testa) and a fruit coat (pericarp). The testa and pericarp are fused together. In the outer layer of the pericarp, and in some cases beneath the pericarp; there is a layer of pigment.

The sorghum grain is small and rounded, varying in colour from off-white to varying shades of red, yellow or brown. The grain size varies, the weight ranging from 7.0 to 61 g per 1,000 grains, with most sorghums weighing between 20 to 30 g per 1,000 grains.

The chemical composition of sorghum grain is similar to that of maize. Generally, sorghum has more protein than maize, a lower fat content and about the same amount and proportion of carbohydrate components. The proximate analysis of Indian sorghum grain gave the following values: moisture, 11.9; protein, 10.4; fat, 1.9; fibre, 1.6; other carbohydrates, 72.6; and minerals, 1.6 per cent. Minerals present in the grain are calcium, magnesium, potassium and iron.

In comparison with maize, sorghum grain contains approximately the same quantities of riboflavin and pyridoxine but more pantothenic acid, nicotinic acid and biotin. Nicotinic acid occurs in the grain in an available form. In general, the vitamins occur in much higher concentrations in the germ than in the endosperm or the bran. The riboflavin contents of the germ and bran are the same.

Starch is the major carbohydrate of the grain. The other carbohydrates present are simple sugars, cellulose and hemicelluloses. The amylose content of starch varies from 21 to 28 per cent. Starch from waxy varieties contains little amylose. Both waxy and regular starches contain free sugars to the extent of 1.2 per cent, sucrose being the major constituent (0.85 per cent) followed by glucose (0.09 per cent), fructose (0.09 per cent), maltose and stachyose. Sorghum grain contains no detectable amount of glucoside, but on germination, a cyanogenetic glucoside, dhurrin, is formed and the concentration of the glucoside in a three-day-old seedling is 3.5 per cent. Dhurrin releases hydrogen cyanide on hydrolysis leading to the poisoning of animals consuming such sorghum.

The protein content of the grain varies according to varieties and growing conditions. The percentage of different protein fractions to the total protein of sorghum grown in India is: albumin, 5; globulin, 6.3; prolamine, 46.4; and glutelin, 30.4. Prolamin and glutelin are principally present in the endosperm. Amino acid analyses of various protein fractions show that there is better distribution of all essential amino acids in the globulins than in the prolamins. Sorghum protein is superior to wheat protein in biological value and digestibility. However, as an exclusive source of protein, B-vitamins and minerals in the diet, sorghum is inferior to wheat. A vegetarian diet based on some varieties of sorghum is somewhat better than a rice-based diet.

Sorghum lipid consists mostly of triglycerides. Phospholipids constitute about 5 per cent of the total lipids of sorghum. Nearly half of the phospholipids is lecithin. Sorghum also contains some wax. The triglycerides are rich in the unsaturated fatty acids, oleic and linoleic, their percentage is 33 and 47, respectively.

A few red-and-brown phenolic pigments occur in the pericarp and seed top of several varieties of grain sorghum. These pigments are tannins accounting for 0.2–2.0 per cent of the grain and are responsible for the low palatability and digestibility of sorghum food products and for the off-colour of starch obtained by the wet-milling of the grain. White or yellowish grain contains very little tannins. Some varieties of sorghum grains contain anthocyanins. Grains with yellow endosperm are rich in carotenoid pigments (up to 10 parts per million) but the white grains contain only traces (1.5 parts per million).

Milling

The coarse fibre has one disadvantage; phytates interfere with absorption of calcium and with other foods. But now with advanced milling process introduced it has been possible to overcome this limitation.

Sorghum grains are processed by dry milling, wet milling and by fermentation. The products of milling are chiefly starch and feed products. In India, however, very few processed products of sorghum are commercially produced. Dry milling is used to obtain products low in fibre, fat and ash, and wet milling to make starch and its derivatives. The residue from wet milling is used as a feed.

The dry milling process starts with the cleaning of grains. The cleaned grain is conditioned, by addition of water, to soften the endosperm, and milled by the conventional roller mills to separate the endosperm, germ and bran from each other. The endosperm is recovered in the form of grits, with minimum production of flour. Yields of various fractions from the dry milling process are: grit, 76.7; bran, 1.2; germ, 11; and fibre, 10 per cent. Bran and germ are further processed, as in the case of maize, by dry milling for the preparation of oils and feeds.

Another milling process for sorghum is "pearling" or decortication. In this case cleaned grains are wetted by spraying water for 2–3 min. and immediately milled in a rice huller, to remove a major part of the coarse fibre, pigment and phytin, with minimum degree of cracking of the grain. A maximum of 12 per cent polishing can be carried out. This type of milling can give products rich in protein (up to 27 per cent), and which are also high in fat and give a high yield of ash, but are low in fibre. These products are used in the preparation of food products of high protein content.

Wet milling of sorghum is carried out by methods similar to that of maize wet milling. However, the milling of sorghum is more difficult than that of maize because of the small size and spherical shape of the sorghum kernel and the dense high-protein peripheral endosperm layer. Manufacture of starch is the main purpose of wet milling. However, some of the pigments of the pericarp and sub coat of the grain leach out and stain the starch. Thus, grains with dark-coloured outer layers are not satisfactory for wet grinding.

Sorghum starch is indistinguishable from corn starch and can be used interchangeably with corn starch in most industrial applications. Sorghum oil obtained from germ fraction, after refining, is used for salads and general cooking. Kernel residues containing bran and gluten are processed as cattle feed.

Sorghum is as good as barley for malting purposes (see Subsection 15.10.4). The sorghum malt is used in the preparation of infant foods and malt extracts produced from sorghum are employed in the pharmaceutical industry. Sorghum malt has been widely used in Africa for brewing "kafir beer" which contains about 3 per cent alcohol.

Sorghum content of carbohydrate in the form of starch, soluble sugar, fibre, cellulose and hemicellulose. The non-structural carbohydrate (NSC) as starch has amylopectin and high amylose starch. The pigment in the pericarp determines the colour (pink, green, yellow) of the sorghun. The starch is linear of glucose joined by 21-4 glucosidic amylopectin.

Amylose present is 23 to 30% has a higher gelatinization temperature (71-80%) and is highly viscous.

Sorghum as health food is processed as Ready to eat/Ready to cook (RTE/RTC) such as Multigrain *atta*, flakes, *rawa*, pasta etc. under the name "eatrite". These have high nutritional value, having a low glycemic index. Like in all the cereals, sorghum also is deficient in lysine, which however, can be easily overcome with vegetables and pulses.

Health Benefits

It has slowly digestible starch (SDS) in good amounts, which has functional property, prolongs absorption and digestion of carbohydrates in the intestine. This SDS is favourable for dietary management and also for metabolic disorders such as diabetes and hyperlipidemia. Sorghum is rich in dietary fibre and has a low glycemic index, helps in prevention and control of type 2 diabetes. Besides, anti-carcinogenic properties of sorghum have been well documented. Sorghum is rich in dietary fibre and has unique chemical and physical characteristics adding bulk to the diet, viscosity, water holding and absorption capacity, increases satiety and thereby lowers chances of obesity.

15.8.2 Finger Millet

Finger millet (*Eleusine coracocna*) a cereal grass grown mostly for its grain.

Finger millet is so called because the ear (head of grain) consists of about five spikes that radiate, sometimes in a curving manner, from a central point, rather as the fingers attached to the palm of the hand. The Indian variety of finger millet has rather long spikes and the African one shorter curving spikes. They vary in colour from deep brown to shades ranging from red to almost black. There is also a race of ragi which gives white seeds.

Finger Millet

Finger millet is a robust, tufted, tillering annual grass, up to 170 cm high. The grain is readily digestible, highly nutritious and versatile, and can be cooked like rice, ground to make porridge or flour, or used to make cakes Malted grains are recommended for infants and elderly people. Finger millet is also used to make liquor (arake or areki in Ethiopia) and brewing beer. Its by-products used for livestock feeding.

Finger millet contains lower levels of protein (6-8%) and fat (1-5-2%), 65-75% carbohydrates, 15-20% dietary fiber and 2.5-3.5% minerals. Finger millet is the richest source of calcium (300-350 mg/100 g) and other smaller millets are a good source of phosphorus and iron.

The Naked caryopsis of finger millet with brick red coloured seed coat is generally used in the form of wholemeal in the traditional food preparations such as *roti*, *mudde* and *ambali* (thin porridge). Epidemiological studies have shown that regular consumption of whole grain cereals and their products can protect against the risk of diabetes mellitus, gastrointestinal diseases and cardiovascular risks. Finger millet proteins are unique because of the sulphur-rich amino acid contents.

15.8.3 White Ragi

White ragi has higher protein (12.3 g/100 g) and iron (12 g/100 g) than the brown ragi protein (8.7 g/100 g) and iron (4.4 mg/100 g). White ragi is devoid of tannin, while brown ragi has 2.4 g of tannin. Malting decreases the tannin by 54 per cent in brown ragi and phytin phosphorous by 58 and 65 per cent in brown and white ragi, respectively. Ionisable iron (27 and 55%) and soluble zinc (81 and 25%) contents increased significantly after malting brown and white ragi. There were no significant differences in the amino acid compositions of brown and white ragi proteins. The better nutritional quality of white ragi over that of brown ragi may be due to the absence of tannins in the white ragi variety. Although protein content has significant negative association with calcium content, white seeded types have moderate levels of calcium. The variability was moderate and high for protein and calcium, respectively. Finger millet is also a good source of essential amino acids like arginine, lysine, methionine, etc.

Health Benefits

Finger millet synthesizes nitric acid, improves immunity and releases growth hormone. It reduces healing time of wound or injury and repairs the damaged tissue and increases muscle mass, blood circulation and decreases blood pressure. Hence reduces depression, headache, migraine and insomnia. Improves insulin release and memory. Reduces infertility in sperm production.

Decreases adipose tissue, it brings down plasma triglycerides hence reduces cardiovascular diseases. Also it has a low glycemic index, polyphenol present act as anti-diabetic and antioxidant components.

Stomach digestibility is enhanced because it inhibits alpha amylase activity.

Ragi is rich in calcium and iron and hence good for growing children and it reduces the risk of anaemia in women. Green Ragi is recommended for hypertension, liver disorder, asthma and for lactating mothers.

15.8.4 Pearl Millet

Pearl millet (*Pennisetum glaucum*) originated in Central tropical Africa and is widely distributed in the drier tropics in India. It was introduced into the Western state in the 1850s and became established as minor forage in the Southeast and Gulf Coast states. The plant was probably domesticated as a food crop some 4000 to 5000 years ago along the southern margins of the Central highlands of the Sahara. As pearl millet cultivation expands into non-traditional areas in temperate and developed countries, production constraints from diseases are assuming greater

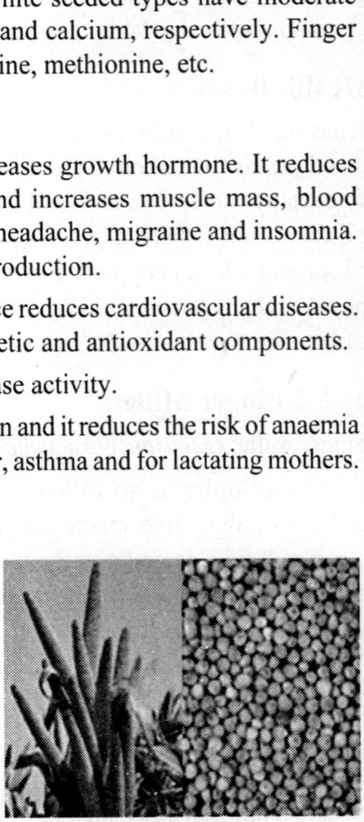

Pearl Millet

importance. Dissemination of accurate information on diseases of the crop has not kept pace with the increased interest in pearl millet as a viable crop in non-traditional areas. Pearl millet is well adapted to growing areas characterized by drought, low soil fertility, and high temperature. It performs well in soils with high salinity or low pH. Because of its tolerance to difficult growing conditions, it can be grown in areas where other cereal crops, such as maize or wheat, cannot survive.

Pearl millet contains a considerably high proportion of proteins (12-16%) as well as lipids (4-6%). The lipid content of pearl millet was considered to be higher than other cereals. The principal fatty acids of pearl millet are linoleic, oleic, palmitic and stearic. The total dietary fibre in pearl millet (20.4%) and finger millet (18.6%) was higher than that in sorghum (14.2%), wheat (17.2%) and rice (8.3%). The niacin content in pearl millet is higher than all other cereals.

Bajra

About 85 per cent of bajra produced in the country is used as food. It constitutes the staple diet of nearly 10 per cent of the Indian population. It is consumed after dehusking and cooked in the same way as rice. More commonly, it is ground into flour and made into chapaties. It is also made into thin porridge. The grain is sometimes eaten after it is parched, the product being similar to popcorn. The grain is suitable for the preparation of malt. An intoxicating drink is obtained from its malted seeds.

Bajra grains, ground or softened by soaking in water, find use to a limited extent as animal feed. The green plant serves as excellent fodder and is cultivated in developed countries only for animal feeding. Bajra straw is also used as fodder but is of inferior quality.

The processing of bajra and other millets for industrial purposes has not yet been developed. Pearling of bajra to about 8 per cent polish leaves most of the germs intact and the nutritive value is not seriously affected. Pearling improves appearance of the grain and traditional dishes prepared by using the flour from pearled grain will have a better look and taste. The dry milling of the grain has not yet been developed. Wet milling has been investigated, but because of the smallness of the grains, it is more difficult to determinate it than maize and sorghum, although the potential yield of oil from millet exceeds those from the other cereals. Separation of protein from starch is also more difficult with this millet than with sorghum or maize.

Health Benefits

The presence of lignin and phytonutrient act as a strong antioxidant which is beneficial for cardiovascular conditions. It's a special property of slow-releasing blood sugar, increase insulin sensitivity, high fibre content makes it one of the good millet for diabetic patients.

Pearl millet keeps stomach medium alkaline hence prescribed for prevention of ulcer condition. The presence of magnesium controls blood pressure. A respiratory problem such as asthma is observed. It is ascribed that magnesium also prevents cancerous cells.

Due to high fibre content, it not only gives satiety and but also helpful in reducing diet. The presence of phytic acid is useful in the maintenance of cholesterol level in the blood.

The other benefit of high fibre is, it reduces the formation of gall stones as it prevents increased production of bile juice, also recommended in allergic conditions.

Though it has a good amino acid profile, these get destroyed at the high cooking temperature but retained when cooking at low temperature is adopted.

15.8.5 Proso Millet

Proso Millet

Proso millet (*Panicum miliaceum*) is an annual grass, growing from seed. Its origin goes back in history to at least, as far as 2000 B.C. It is reported to have been grown in the Central regions of Europe. Proso millet is a relatively low demanding crop and diseases are not known. Because of this Proso millet is often used in organic farming systems in Europe. In the United States, it is often used as an intercrop.

It has a short growing season, and needs little water. The water requirement of Proso is probably the lowest of any major cereals. It is an excellent crop for dryland and no-till farming. The plants reach an average height of 100 cm. The seedheads grow in bunches. The seeds are small (2-3 mm) and can be cream, yellow, orange-red, or brown in colour.

Health Benefits

It is effective as it lowers serum triglycerides and hence advisable in cardiovascular diseases and in hyperlipidemic rats. Because it improves plasma levels of adiponectin (HDL) cholesterol, it is good for type-2 diabetic patients, also it is low in glycemic index. Generally, this millet is rich in copper, magnesium also vitamins particularly vitamin B6 and folic acid. It is sold as a health food due to its lack of gluten, hence used in diet who cannot tolerate wheat.

15.8.6 Barnyard Millet

Barnyard Millet

Barnyard millet (*Echinochloa crusgalli*) is multipurpose both as food and fodder. It has a good source of protein, easily digestible, has good fibre content both soluble and insoluble fraction. However it's carbohydrates are slow to digest, suits people who lead a sedentary lifestyle. Linoleic acid, palmitic and oleic acid contents good. Due to the fact it has a high degree of amylase, it is resistant starch. Hence a good millet diet for cardiovascular, diabetes patients. It is good for reducing blood glucose and lipids levels.

Health Benefits

Studies on rats using this millet showed that it lowers blood glucose, serum cholesterol, triglycerides when compared to rice and other millets. Also beneficial to type 2 diabetic patients as it has a low glycemic index. It is beneficial as it has essential linoleic fatty acid and tocopherol vitamin.

15.8.7 Kodo Millet

Kodo Millet

Kodo millet (*Paspalum scrobiculatum*) is a widely grown in damp habitat in subtropical and tropical. It is indigenous millet more grown in Uttar Pradesh. Its protein content is 11% and is low in fat 4.2% had high fibre (14.3%) content. Its digestibility is a good and high amount of lecithin hence good for the nervous system. It is a good source of niacin, pyridoxine, folic acid and minerals such as calcium, iron, potassium, magnesium and zinc. As it had no gluten, it is recommended in gluten-free diet. It had been found to be good for postmenopausal women who also have cardiovascular diseases and having high blood pressure.

15.8.8 Foxtail Millet

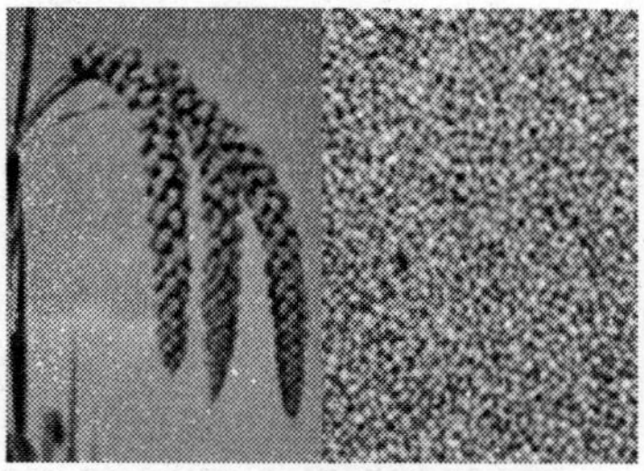

Foxtail

Foxtail millet (*Setaria italica*) is one of the oldest cultivated millet and native to China, ranks second in world production, provides six million tons of food for the poorer section of the population. It grows well in high altitude. It cannot tolerate soggy soil. It is a drought tolerant crop and also a short-term crop. It is used for both human and animal consumption.

Health Benefits

Aqueous extract of foxtail millets has excellent anti-hyperglycemic activity. It is useful in dyspepsia condition and its green fresh seeds are diuretic and strengthen virility. It is 12.3% crude protein and 3.3% minerals.

15.8.9 Little Millet (*Panicum sumatrense*)

Little Millet

It is grown all over India. As the name suggests, it is smallest of millets. Its plants are herbarium and grow straight for the height of 30 cms to 1 m. Its leaves are linear, having lamina and membranous having hairy ligules. It withstands both drought and soggy soil. It can grow in high altitude. It has a dual purpose as food as it is used as fodder for animals and good for the human being. Small millets are more nutritious compared to fine cereals.

Health Benefits

It helps control blood sugar, lower triglycerides, LDL/VLDL cholesterol and increases HDL cholesterol. Because of a low glycemic index, it is good for diabetic, gastric and cardiovascular patients. It helps in bodybuilding tissues and energy metabolism. It is rich in antioxidants.

15.8.10 General Nutritional Feature of Millets

Carbohydrate

Carbohydrates in millets are non-structural carbohydrates (NSC) and structural carbohydrates. Sugar, starch and fructose form the non structural carbohydrates and cellulose, hemicellulose and pectin substance are structural carbohydrates. Starch is the chief non structural carbohydrates. Thermal properties of pasting quantities indicate whether they are short and cohesive. The water binding capacity is very low and their swelling capacity at 90°C but not stable as in maize. Waxy millet cooks rapidly and has high viscosity, poor stability and paste clarity. The gel formation and retrogradation are not good.

The soluble sugar content is 1.3 (0.8-4.2%) the sucrose is 75%, the soluble sugar 0.9 to 2.5%, free reducing sugar and fructose ratio 0.6-1.8 and 0.3-7% respectively.

Starch can be rapidly digestible starch (RDS) or slow digestible starch (SDS) and resistant starch (RS) all these depend upon digestibility. Slow digestible starch (SD) content of millets makes it ideal for type 2 diabetes and cardiovascular patients. Millets flour of pepsin preheated before cooking or during cooking plays an important role in slow digestibility.

Overall structural carbohydrates form dietary fibre which is of prime importance for easy bowel movement.

Proteins

Protein depends upon the amino acid profile which is low compared to other cereals. Protein in millets is in endosperm 80% germ 16% and pericarp 3%. Lysine the important amino acid is a basic limiting factor. Albumin and globulin are found in germ, also germ contains globulin and gluletin fraction in lysine. The barn-green, matured has good amount of lysine. Arginine and glycine lower in isoleucine, leucine and phenylalanine. In general millets proteins are less digestible hence absorption of amino acids is not optimum.

Fatty Acids

Most of the fatty acids are polar or non polar and unsaponifiable. The non polar lipids 70-80% and they are triglycerides, 8.5%, sterols 4.1%, triglycerides 4.0%. The less polar lipids Glycolipids 2.5-6.2%, and phospholipids 17-25%. The unsaponifiable compounds are 3-5%, they include carotenoids, phytosterols and tacosterols.

Phytochemicals and Phenolic Acids

Tannins, phenolic acids, anthocyanins, phytosterols and pinacosanols are found. Phytochemicals are prohealth factors. Millets are also good source of phenolic compounds with phenolic acids, flavonoids and tannin. Sorghum is unique millet as it has anthocyanin, adds colour to the prepared food.

Condensed tannin, proanthocyanidins or procyanidins have high molecular weight. These resist moulds and deterioration in the grain which is present in black sorghum. Processing sorghum decreases tannins by 52% to 72%. Here tannins are not lost, in processing tannins bind to other molecules that are protein, carbohydrates and minerals.

Table 15.8. Proximate Composition and Dietary Fibre (per 100 g)

Millets and Cereals	Moisture (g)	Protein (g)	Ash (g)	Total Fat (g)	Dietary Fibre (g)			Carbo-hydrates (g)	Energy (KJ)
					Total	Insoluble	Soluble		
Bajra (*Pennisetum typhoideum*)	08.97±0.60	10.96±0.26	1.37±0.17	5.43±0.64	11.49±0.62	9.14±0.58	2.34±0.42	61.78±0.85	1456±18
Sorghum (*Sorghum vulgare*)	09.01±0.77	09.97±0.43	1.39±0.34	1.73±0.31	10.22±0.49	8.49±0.40	1.73±0.40	67.68±1.03	1398±13
Ragi (*Eleusine coracana*)	10.89±0.61	07.16±0.63	2.04±0.34	1.92±0.14	11.18±1.14	9.51±0.65	1.67±0.55	66.82±0.73	1342±10
Little Millet (*Panicum millare*)	14.23±0.45	08.92±1.09	1.72±0.27	2.55±0.13	06.39±0.60	5.45±0.48	2.27±0.52	65.55±1.29	1449±19
Kodo Millet (*Setaria italica*)	14.23±0.45	08.92±1.09	1.72±0.27	2.55±0.13	06.39±0.60	4.29±0.82	2.11±0.34	66.19±1.19	1388±10
Foxtail Millet*	–	12.30	–	4.30	–	–	–	60.09	331
Barnyard Millet*	–	06.20	–	2.20	–	–	–	65.55	307
Proso Millet*	–	1.10	–	1.10	–	–	–	70.04	341

Source: *Indian Food Composition Tables, NIN – 2017 and *Nutritive value of Indian Food, NIN – 2007*
http://millets.res.in

Table 15.9. Mineral and Trace Elements

Millets and Cereals	Aluminium (mg)	Arsenic (mg)	Cadmium (mg)	Calcium (mg)	Chromium (mg)	Cobalt (mg)	Copper (mg)	Iron (mg)	Lead (mg)	Lithium (mg)
Bajra (*Pennisetum typhoideum*)	2.21±0.78	0.97±0.24	0.003±0.001	27.35±2.16	0.025±0.006	0.030±0.015	0.54±0.11	6.42±1.04	0.006±0.002	0.003±0.001
Sorghum (*Sorghum vulgare*)	2.56±0.59	1.53±0.04	0.002±0.002	27.60±3.71	0.010±0.003	0.012±0.007	0.45±0.11	3.95±0.94	0.008±0.003	0.001±0.001
Ragi (*Eleusine coracana*)	3.64±0.69	–	0.004±0.004	364±58	0.032±0.019	0.022±0.009	0.67±0.22	4.62±0.36	0.005±0.002	0.003±0.003
Little Millet (*Panicum millare*)	–	0.49±0.15	0.001±0.000	16.06±154	0.016±0.006	0.001±0.00	0.34±0.08	1.26±0.44		
Kodo Millet (*Setaria italica*)	1.07±0.83	–	–	15.27±1.28	0.021±0.027	0.005±0.003	0.26±0.05	2.34±0.46	–	0.027±0.003
Foxtail Millet*	–	–	–	–	0 030	–	1.40	–	–	–
Barnyard Millet*	–	–	–	–	0.090	–	0.60	–	–	–
Proso Millet*	–	–	–	–	0.020	–	1.60	–	–	–

Source: *Indian Food Composition Tables, NIN – 2017and *Nutritive value of Indian foods, NIN – 2007*
http://millets.res.in

Table 15.10. Water-soluble Vitamins profile of millets

Millets and Cereals	Thiamine-B1 (mg)	Riboflavin-B2 (mg)	Niacin-B3 (mg)	Pantothenic Acid - B5 (mg)	Total B6 (mg)	Biotin-B7 (µg)	Total Folates - B9 (µg)	Total Ascorbic acid (mg)
Bajra (*Pennisetum typhoideum*)	0.25±0.044	0.20±0.038	0.86±0.10	0.50±0.05	0.27±0.09	0.64±0.05	36.11±5.05	–
Sorghum (*Sorghum vulgare*)	0.35±0.039	0.14±0.014	2.10±0.09	0.27±0.02	0.28±0.023	0.70±0.06	39.42±3.13	–
Ragi (*Eleusine coracana*)	0.37±00.041	0.17±0.008	1.34±0.02	0.29±0.19	0.05±0.007	0.88±0.05	34.66±4.97	–
Little Millet (*Panicum millare*)	0.26±0.042	0.05±0.008	1.29±0.02	0.60±0.07	0.04±0.005	6.03±0.57	36.20±7.04	–
Kodo Millet (*Setaria italica*)	0.29±0.054	0.20±0.018	1.49±0.08	0.63±0.07	0.07±0.017	1.49±0.18	39.49±4.52	-
Foxtail Millet*	0.59	0.11	3.20	0.82	–	–	–	–
Barnyard Millet*	0.33	0.10	4.20	–	–	–	–	–
Proso Millet*	0.41	0.28	4.50	1.20	–	–	–	–

Source: *Indian Food Composition Tables, NIN – 2017 and *Nutritive value of Indian foods, NIN – 2007*
http://millets.res.in

Table 15.11. Fat Soluble Vitamins profile of millets

Millets and Cereals	Ergocalcife (µg) Alpha	Tocopherols (mg)				Tocotrienols (mg)			α-Tocopherol (mg)	Phylloquinoes-K1 (µg)
		Beta	Gamma	Delta	Alpha	Gamma	Delta			
Bajra (*Pennisetum typhoideum*)	05.65±0.27	0.10±0.010	–	1.42±0.20	–		–	–	0.24±0.02	02.85±0.63
Sorghum (*Sorghum vulgare*)	03.96±0.03	0.04±0.010	–	0.27±0.03	–		–	–	0.06±0.01	43.32±4.34
Ragi (*Eleusine coracana*)	41.46±3.12	0.09±0.010	–	0.66±0.06	–		–	–	0.16±0.01	03.00±0.44
Little Millet (*Panicum millare*)	03.75±0.80	0.28±0.140	0.67±0.40	–	–		0.28±0.09	–	0.55±0.16	04.47±0.38
Kodo Millet (*Setaria italica*)	–	0.03±0.010	–	0.43±0.12	–		0.19±0.05	–	0.07±0.02	03.75±0.63
Foxtail Millet*	–	–	–	–	–	–	–	–	–	–
Barnyard Millet*	–	–	–	–	–	–	–	–	–	–
Proso Millet*	–	–	–	–	–	–	–	–	–	–

Source: *Indian Food Composition Tables, NIN – 2017 and *Nutritive value of Indian foods, NIN – 2007*
http://millets.res.in

Table 15.12. Carotenoids profile of millets

Millets and Cereals	Lutein (µg)	Zeaxanthin (µg)	Lycopene (µg)	β-Cryptoxanthin	γ-Carotene	β-Carotene	Total Carotenoids
Bajra (*Pennisetum typhoideum*)	29.69±08.72	9.30±1.23	–	–	–	28.23±9.42	293±55.7
Sorghum (*Sorghum vulgare*)	09.08±01.77	7.48±2.41	–	–	–	08.29±1.30	212±48.9
Ragi (*Eleusine coracana*)	25.53±05.82	1.45±0.23	–	–	–	01.53±0.25	154±25.6
Little Millet (*Panicum millare*)	07.82±01.76	5.24±1.66	–	–	–	01.91±0.89	120±09.0
Kodo Millet (*Setaria italica*)	59.40±07.01	3.91±1.08	–	–	–	01.41±0.29	272±25.1
Foxtail Millet*	–	–	–	–	–	–	–
Barnyard Millet*	–	–	–	–	–	–	–
Proso Millet*	–	–	–	–	–	–	–

Source: *Indian Food Composition Tables, NIN – 2017 and *Nutritive value of Indian foods, NIN – 2007*
http://millets.res.in

Table 15.13. Starch and Individual Sugars profile of Millets

Millets and Cereals	Total available CHO (g)	Total starch (g)	Fructose (g)	Glucose (g)	Sucrose (g)	Maltose (g)	Total Free Sugars (g)
Bajra (*Pennisetum typhoideum*)	56.02±2.57	55.21±2.57	0.21±0.01	0.60±0.02	–	–	0.81±0.01
Sorghum (*Sorghum vulgare*)	60.96±1.70	59.70±1.70	0.57±0.07	0.10±0.01	0.60±0.04	–	1.27±0.05
Ragi (*Eleusine coracana*)	62.47±1.24	62.13±1.13	–	0.25±0.06	0.12±0.02	–	0.34±0.06
Little Millet (*Panicum millare*)	56.43±4.09	56.07±4.12	–	0.24±0.10	0.13±0.01	–	0.37±0.09
Kodo Millet (*Setaria italica*)	66.25±2.90	64.96±2.93	–	0.89±0.11	0.40±0.02	–	1.29±0.10
Foxtail Millet*	–	–	–	–	–	–	–
Barnyard Millet*	–	–	–	–	–	–	–
Proso Millet*	–	–	–	–	–	–	–

Source: *Indian Food Composition Tables, NIN – 2017 and *Nutritive value of Indian foods, NIN – 2007*
http://millets.res.in

Table 15.14. Fatty Acid Profile of millets

Millets and Cereals	Palmitic (mg)	Stearic (mg)	Palmitoleic (mg)	Oleic (mg)	Linoleic (mg)	Total Saturated Fatty Acids (mg)	Total Mono Saturated Fatty Acids (mg)
Bajra (*Pennisetum typhoideum*)	729±21.3	128±19.6	6.97±0.45	1040±39.8	1844±56.7	875±34.5	1047±39.9
Sorghum (*Sorghum vulgare*)	149±5.6	14.22±0.79	–	3.14±13.7	508±18.3	163±6.2	314±13.7
Ragi (*Eleusine coracana*)	290±15.4	27.86±2.43	–	585±36.3	362±15.3	317±17.0	585±36.3
Little Millet (*Panicum millare*)	487±26.1	102±11.9	–	868±24.2	1230±42.9	589±31.9	868±24.2
Kodo Millet (*Setaria italica*)	211±0.9	28.40±1.22	3.21±0.11	291±7.2	576±17.8	246±2.3	297±6.8
Foxtail Millet*	6.40	6.30	–	13.0	66.50	–	–
Barnyard Millet*	10.80	–	–	53.80	34.90	–	–
Proso Millet*	–	–	–	–	–	–	–

Source: *Indian Food Composition Tables, NIN – 2017 and *Nutritive value of Indian foods, NIN – 2007*
http://millets.res.in

Table 15.15. Amino Acid Profile of millets

Millets and Cereals	Histidine	Isoleucine	Luecine	Lysine	Methionine	Cystine	Phenylalanine	Threonine	Tyrptophan	Valine
Bajra (*Pennisetum typhoideum*)	2.15±0.37	3.45±0.74	08.52±0.86	3.19±0.49	2.11±0.50	1.23±0.33	4.82±1.18	3.55±0.40	1.33±0.30	4.79±1.04
Sorghum (*Sorghum vulgare*)	2.07±0.20	3.45±0.63	12.03±1.51	2.31±0.40	1.52±0.50	1.06±0.30	5.10±0.50	2.96±0.17	1.03±0.21	4.51±0.71
Ragi (*Eleusine coracana*)	2.37±0.46	3.70±0.44	08.86±0.54	2.83±0.34	2.74±0.27	1.48±0.23	5.70±1.27	3.84±0.45	0.91±0.30	5.65±0.44
Little Millet (*Panicum millare*)	2.35±0.18	4.14±0.0.08	08.08±0.06	2.42±0.10	2.21±0.10	1.85±0.14	6.14±0.10	4.24±0.12	1.35±0.10	5.31±0.16
Kodo Millet (*Setaria italica*)	02.14±0.07	4.55±0.22	11.96±1.65	1.42±0.17	02.69±0.16	1.92±0.05	6.27±0.34	3.89±0.16	1.32±0.19	5.49±0.23
Foxtail Millet*						–	–			
Barnyard Millet*						–	–			
Proso Millet*						–	–			

Source: *Indian Food Composition Tables, NIN – 2017 and *Nutritive value of Indian foods, NIN – 2007*

http://millets.res.in

15.9 Barley (*Hordeum*)

Barley belongs to the genus *Hordeum* which includes both wild and cultivated forms of barley. Most cultivated barleys have been classified into two groups, *H. vulgare,* the six-rowed barley, and *H. distichon,* the two-rowed type. The six or two rows refer to the number of grain rows on the spike. In both types of barley, there are hulled and hull-less varieties. In the hulled varieties, the hull or husk is adherent to the kernels after threshing, whereas in the hull-less or naked varieties it is loose and easily removed during threshing. The type of barley grown in different parts of the world depends upon the climatic conditions. The most predominantly cultivated barley in India is the six-row type.

Barley is one of the world's oldest cultivated cereals. It was used as a bread grain in early times. Nowadays, barley is extensively used as food, cattle feed and for malting and brewing. Barley is by far the most important cereal grain for malting because of its specific physical and chemical properties. Hull-less types of barley are unsuited for malting, but they are useful as food, having higher digestibility than the hulled types.

15.9.1 Production

In 2022, world production of barley was 154.88 million tonnes, led by the European Union producing 34% of the world total. Russia, Germany, and France were major producers.

15.9.2 Composition

The hull content of hulled barley is about 13 per cent. The average composition of Indian barley is as follows: moisture, 12.5; protein, 11.5; lipids, 1.3; mineral matter, 1.5; fibre, 3.9; and carbohydrates, 69.3 per cent. Among minerals, iron is in high proportion. Along with the B vitamins, small amounts of vitamins A, D and E are present. Barley starch contains 19 per cent amylase and 81 per cent amylopectin. Among free sugars, sucrose and raffinose, with smaller amounts of glucose and fructose, are present. The percentage of the four classes of proteins present in barley is albumin, 2.9; globulin, 18.5; prolamin, 37.4 and glutelin, 41.2. The lysine content of the total protein is low. The biological value of barley protein is less than that of wheat.

15.9.3 Milling

Barley is milled to make blocked barley, pearl barley, barley groats (grits), barley flakes and barley flour. The sequence of operations is as follows.

Barley is cleaned and conditioned, i.e., its moisture content is adjusted by drying or damping. In some countries, blocked barley or occasionally the whole grain is subjected to bleaching by sulphur dioxide. The conditioned barley is next subjected to blocking (shelling) and pearling (rounding). Both blocking and pearling are abrasive processes differing in degree of removal of the superficial layers of the grain. Blocking removes part of the husk, and pearling the remainder of the husk and part of the endosperm. Aspiration of the blocked or pearled grain removes the abraded portions. The grain is then cut into portions known as grits. The grits are graded by size and then rounded in a pearling machine and polished. Barley flakes are made from pearl barley by steaming and flaking on a smooth large-diameter roller.

Pearl or blocked barley is converted into barley flour in roller mills. Barley flour can also be milled from whole barley. The flour is also a byproduct of the cutting, pearling and polishing processes. The average yield of barley flour from pearl barley is 82 per cent representing 58 per cent of the grain, i.e., an overall extraction rate of 48 per cent based on the original grain, while 59 per cent can be obtained by using blocked barley.

Barley is used in India mainly as human food. Barley flour is generally mixed with wheat or gram (legume) flour for preparing *chapatis*. Wheat flour mixed with barley or barley and rye or oats flour is used in making bread. In Western countries, one of the principal uses of barley is feed for animals (barley meal) either alone or mixed with other grains. It is a particularly good feed for pigs and horses. Barley husk contains about 34 per cent fibre and is relatively indigestible. For animal feed, barley with low husk and high-protein content is desirable.

Another important use of barley is in malting, for brewing in the manufacture of beer and distilling in the manufacture of whisky.

15.9.4 Malting

Malting is a controlled germination process that activates the enzymes of the resting grain resulting in the conversion of cereal starch to fermentable sugars, partial hydrolysis of cereal proteins and other macromolecules. Barley is the grain most generally used in the production of malt which finds industrial uses in breweries and distilleries. In commerce, the term malt is applied to barley malt. Small quantities of other cereals are used for malting and they are designated as wheat malt, ragi malt, jowar malt, etc.

Both two-row and six-row hulled barleys are used in malting. In India, mostly six-row barley is used to produce malt for brewing. Malts used in brewing must have a low nitrogen content and this limits the use of nitrogenous fertilizers in the cultivation of barley used for malting. The malt required for the distilling industry is somewhat different from that used for brewing; there should be a proper selection of barley used for malting purposes depending upon the use to which the malt is put.

The malting operation starts with the drying of the grain in a kiln so that the moisture content of the grain is between 10 per cent and 14 per cent. Control of moisture content accelerates maturing of grain and sometimes improves malting quality. After drying and cleaning the grain is stored for at least 3 weeks, before malting. This allows secondary ripening processes to occur, so that the grain can attain full germinative power. For malting, the stored grain is steeped in water. The time required for steeping depends on the temperature and extent of aeration of the steep water. Generally, steeping continues for some 50–70 hours, after which time the surplus water is drained off from the grain which is then spread on the floor for 7–8 days, while germination takes place. The grain malt is then kiln-dried to arrest enzymatic activity, without destroying the enzyme. The dried and cleaned product is malt.

A high proportion of the malt produced is used in most countries in brewing and manufacture of distilled liquors. A small portion is used for the manufacture of industrial alcohol. In India, most of the malt produced is used in brewing. Other uses of malt include textile desizing, pharmaceutical preparations, breakfast cereals, malted milk concentrates, infant foods, bakery products and candies.

Malt extract is prepared by mashing malt and concentrating the mash liquors into syrup. It contains about 40–55 per cent maltose, and small quantities of dextrin, glucose and proteins. It has high nutritive properties and is prescribed as food during periods of convalescence and used in many pharmaceutical preparations.

For brewing and distilling, see Subsections 12.6.2 and 12.6.3.

15.10 Oats and Rye

15.10.1 Oats (*Avena sativa*)

Oats (*Avena sativa*) form one of the most nutritious of all cereals for human use, but the chief disadvantage is the difficulty in removing large proportions of hulls (20–30 per cent) from the grain. Oatmeal obtained from the removal of husk is a common article of breakfast (porridge) in Europe. Oatmeal flour is not suited to bread making.

Production: Oats, which were probably first cultivated in Europe, are important feed grain and fodder crop.

The world production is 26.39 million tonnes, 2022.

Composition: Many varieties of oats are grown. The most cultivated varieties are *A. sativa* and *A. byzantine.* It is the latter variety that is most widely cultivated in India. The grain is cylindrical and comprises the caryopsis or kernel, often called the "groat" and enclosed in the hull or husk. The average kernel content is 75 per cent. The composition of the Indian oatmeal is as follows: moisture, 10; protein, 13.6; fat, 7.6; carbohydrate, 62.8; and ash, 1.8 per cent. The grain contains considerable quantities of B-vitamins.

Processing: The processing of oats in mills is different from that of wheat because of the difference in the structure and composition between the two cereals. The husk of the oat grain is tough and fibrous and quite inedible for human beings. The fat content of oats is high and the grain contains an active lipase. The protein of the oat kernel does not form gluten when mixed with water. Thus, oatmeal and oat flour cannot be used in making bread that compares with light and spongy wheat bread.

In milling, cleaned oats are subjected to kiln-drying to inactivate the lipase. This process is known as stabilization. Lipase serves no useful purpose in milled oat products, and if present, it would act on the fat to release undesirable free fatty acids. Stabilization also reduces moisture content and facilitates the subsequent shelling of the oats. The kiln-dried oats are then shelled resulting in the splitting off of the husk. The shelled groats are then polished and after removal of "oat dust," they are transversely cut so that each kernel gives about four to five pieces (pinhead meal). This is subjected to further grinding when "oatmeal" is obtained. The average yield of oatmeal is 57 per cent.

Oat flakes or rolled oats are manufactured from pinhead meal (or from whole uncut groats) by cooking the pinhead meal in a steamer, rolling the cooked product while hot, moist and plastic, between heavy rollers and drying the flakes so formed.

The main byproducts of oat are oat husk (10 per cent), oat dust (20 per cent) and meal seed (10 per cent). All these contain varying fractions of kernel material. Oat dust and meal seeds (husks and kernel fragments in approximately equal proportions) are used as animal feed. The husk (*bhusa*) mixed with other byproducts of oatmeal milling is also used as cattle feed. Oat husk is industrially used as a raw material for the manufacture of furfural.

15.10.2 Rye (*Secale cereale*)

Rye belongs to the genus *Secale* and the common by cultivated variety is *S. cereale.* This is an important food crop in Eastern Europe. This is the bread grain of the poor people and as the living standards rise, the consumption of rye bread falls, while that of wheat bread rises and thus there is a gradual decline of rye production. Small amounts of rye are used for the production of distilled liquors. Outside Europe, rye is used mainly for animal feed.

Production: Rye grows satisfactorily in poor lands and is more resistant to pests and diseases than wheat and can withstand the cold better and is thus cultivated in Northern and Eastern Europe.

The world production is 13.14 million tonnes, 2022.

Rye crop is grown for grain in this country over a very limited area in the north-western Himalayan area. Besides this, rye is grown in small areas for cultivating ergot. Ergot is a product of the ergot fungus (*Claviceps purpurea*) which infects many species of grasses and is particularly liable to infect rye. Wheat, barley and oats are also attacked but comparatively rarely. Ergot is toxic and, if consumed in large quantities, causes gangrenous diseases.

Composition: The chemical composition of rye grain is as follows: moisture, 11.0; protein, 12.1; fat, 1.7; fibre, 2.0; total carbohydrates, 71.2 and ash, 1.8 per cent. The mineral content of the grain is; calcium, 61; potassium, 45.3; magnesium 155; iron, 4.8 mg per 100 g and iodine 7.2 μg per 100g. Rye contains more B-vitamins than wheat.

Milling: The products of rye milling are flour for soft bread, coarse rye meal for hard breads and rye flakes for hot breakfast cereals.

The processes of rye milling are similar to wheat milling and comprises of cleaning, conditioning and the milling process proper.

Uses: Rye bread is a widely eaten food in Northern Europe. Some non-food uses of rye include rye whisky and use as an alternative medicine in a liquid form, known as rye extract. Often marketed as Oralmat, rye extract is a liquid obtained from rye and similar to that extracted from Wheatgrass. Its benefits are said to include a strengthened immune system, increased energy levels and relief from allergies, but there is no clinical evidence for its efficacy. Rye straw is used to make corn dollies.

15.10.3 Triticale (*Triticum secale*)

Triticale is a hybrid cereal from a cross between wheat (*Triticum*) and rye (*Secale*).

The world production is 14.16 million tonnes, 2022.

The primary producers of triticale are Germany, France, Poland, Australia, China, and Belarus. In 2005, according to the Food and Agriculture Organization, 13.5 million tonnes of triticale were harvested in 28 countries. However, triticale as a crop is still relatively unknown by the general population.

Work for the introduction of triticale as a cereal grain in India is being carried out since 1974. It has been found that better yields are obtained under the rainfed conditions of hills than in the plains. The grains have 14–18 per cent protein as against 12–15 per cent in wheat and the lysine content is 3 per cent compared with 2.5 per cent of wheat protein. *Chapatis* are acceptable up to a 50 per cent level of incorporation of triticale flour.

15.11 Breakfast Cereals

Breakfast cereals are divided into two major groups: those that require cooking before serving and those that require no cooking, called ready-to-eat cereals. The former class, the gruels and porridges made from cereal grains, are among the first cereal grain foods of mankind. Ready-to-eat cereals were developed about 100 years ago and, since then, breakfast cereals have become very popular and per capita consumption is increasing in recent years. These are economical, convenient, and flavourable foods, suitable for daily consumption by all age groups. They are produced in different forms, colours and flavours with a nutritional adequacy equalled by only a few other foods. Different cereals are used as raw materials, and the form of product or dish obtained will also be different.

15.11.1 Uncooked Breakfast Cereals

Uncooked breakfast cereals are processed in two general ways. One is the reduction in particle size and the other elimination from the product of some of the fibrous substances found in the whole grain. Their processing reduces the cooking time and improves the texture and digestibility of food. Recent technological advances have resulted in reducing the cooking time to the point where the addition of boiling water to packed food will give a fully prepared product

The important wheat product extensively used in India in the preparation of a variety of breakfast foods (e.g., *upama*) is semolina. This is also the largest consumed wheat product in other countries under the name "farina." The addition of disodium phosphate reduces the cooking-time of farina and an "instant" farina is in the market. This farina is ready to eat after a minimum boiling time. Farinas flavoured with malt and cocoa are also marketed.

Bulger is another wheat preparation which is excellent for breakfast. It is extensively used in West Asian countries. This is prepared by a multistage cooking process by spraying water. When starch is partially gelatinized (moisture content is 40 per cent) the material is cooled and dried. The pearled product is cracked. Bulger takes more time to cook than the refined cereal product. But it can be cooked to prepare several dishes usually made from rice. Hence it is used as a substitute for rice.

Oat cereal is most commonly consumed as oatmeal and rolled oats. These are used to make porridge. The starch in oatmeal is ungelatinized and the particles are relatively coarse in size. Consequently, the preparation of porridge from oatmeal requires prolonged heating. Rolled oats (oat flakes) are partially cooked (1/3 starch is gelatinized) during manufacture. Thus, porridge making from rolled oats requires only a brief cooking time.

Maize cereals, maize meal and hominy grits are used as hot breakfast cereals. In some countries corn meal mixed with whole soyabean meal is used as food.

Whole milled rice is occasionally cooked as breakfast cereal. An instant rice is in the market which is used as breakfast cereal. This consists of rice milled into particles of the size of semolina. Because of the size the product is an instant cooking. It does not require any heating apart from the addition of boiling water.

15.11.2 Ready-to-eat Cereals

These include flaked, puffed, shredded and granular products, generally made from wheat, maize or rice. Sometimes oats and barley are also used. The basic cereal may be enriched with sugar, syrup, honey or malt extract. All types are prepared by processing which tends to cause dextrinization rather than gelatinization of starch.

Flaked Cereals: Wheat, maize (corn) and rice are commonly used cereals. In the case of wheat or rice, the whole grain is cleaned, conditioned to suitable moisture content and lightly pressed between smooth rollers to fracture the outer layers. Whole wheat or rice so prepared or maize grits are cooked under pressure and the flavourings are added. The cooked cereal is then dried to 15–20 per cent moisture. The conditioned grain is flaked between heavy flaking rolls and the flakes are then toasted.

Puffed Cereals: Whole grain wheat, rice and oats are cleaned and conditioned. They are then fed into an externally heated, sealed pressure chamber. Steam is injected into raise the internal pressure in the chamber to about 14 kg/cm^2 and then suddenly released by opening the chamber when owing to the expansion of water vapour the grain is blown up to several times its original size. Alternatively, dough made from maize meal or oat flour blended with rye flour and flavourings, such as malt and cocoa, is cooked under pressure and pelleted. These pellets can be used for puffing in place of whole grains.

Shredded Products: Mostly, wheat is used to prepare this product. Wheat is cooked in water to gelatinize the starch. The cooked grain is cooled and rested for some hours for conditioning. The conditioned grain is fed into shredders and the material emerging as long parallel shreds are received on a slowly travelling band. A thick mat is built up by the superimposition of several layers. The mat is then cut into desired shapes and baked at 260°C for 20 min.

Granular Products: These are prepared from wheat. A dough is made of the yeasted wholemeal, wheat flour and malted barley flour. The dough is fermented for about 5 hours and the bread is baked. The bread is then broken up, dried and ground to the desired fineness.

Flaked and puffed cereal products can be sugar-coated. Sucrose syrup containing other sugars (e.g., honey) is used for the purpose. The cereal particles are placed in a bowl, and as it rotates, molten sugar syrup is slowly dripped upon the mass. By proper technique, a product with a hard transparent coating that does not become sticky even under humid conditions can be obtained.

The keeping qualities of breakfast cereals depend to a large extent on their fat content. Thus, products with low-fat cereals or cereal fractions keep well. The keeping quality also depends upon the degree of unsaturated fatty acids in the fat. If they are present, permitted antioxidants may be used in the preparation of the cereals. The nutritive value of the breakfast cereals can be enhanced by the addition of appropriate nutrients in the process of the preparation of the cereal.

CHAPTER

16 Cereal Products

Cereal grains have been used for centuries for food because of the ease of growing them and their storage stability. An account of the eight major cereals used as food and some of the products obtained from them has been given in Chapter 15. The cereals most important in human food are wheat and rice. Wheat is consumed mostly as baked products throughout the world. Rice, in addition to its use as detailed in Chapter 15, is also used as a fermented product. An account of the processing of these cereals to produce baked, fermented and other products is considered in this chapter.

16.1 Flours

Wheat flour, and to some extent barley flour, have been used from pre-historic times in all civilizations for the preparation of unleavened breads, probably much like the modern Indian *chapatis*. Whether baked in primitive or modern ways, wheat is to be first ground to flour. Wheat was ground by stone milling till the invention of roller mills. With the improved techniques of flour milling, the use of flours of more than one quality or fineness became possible. For each purpose, flour of a particular quality is needed; for bread making a hard wheat flour containing a high level of protein is required, while for biscuits wheat flour with a low protein content is desirable. According to modern specifications, the flours should also contain minimum levels of nutrients, such as vitamins and minerals or other ingredients.

Flour, or flour mixtures, when mixed with water, form doughs or batters. Doughs are thick; they cannot be beaten but have to be frequently kneaded. Batters, on the other hand, are usually beaten during their preparation and they are of a consistency that is capable of being dropped or poured. Doughs and batters are complex because of the variation in the composition of the various flour mixes, the type of reactions they undergo when mixed, and the method employed in preparing them.

Wheat flour when mixed with an appropriate amount of water forms a dough that is elastic. The elastic substance is called gluten. Other cereal flours, except to slight extent rye, do not form gluten. Because of its gluten forming property, wheat flour is used in the preparation of baked products, such as breads (yeast breads), quick breads, cakes, pastries, etc.

Gluten formation of wheat flour is due to the wheat proteins. It is the result of a complex formed between gliadin and glutenin when flour and water are worked together during dough formation. Neither glutenin nor gliadin have the ability to form gluten alone. Each of these proteins have their own tertiary structure due to various types of bonds, including the disulphide (S-S) bonds. During dough formation, the disulphide bonds are cleaved to sulphydryl bonds (-SH) by the reducing agents present in flour and new disulphide bonds are formed by the oxidizing agents, linking together separate molecules resulting in gluten formation. In addition to disulphide bonds, other types of bondings also make important contributions to dough development during the mixing of flour and water. Lipids present in wheat flour also play an important role in gluten development. Flours with low lipid content require more mixing to develop the gluten in a dough than those with normal lipid content.

Depending upon the nature of the baked product, different types of flour are milled. The milling of whole wheat flour, white flour and enriched flours has been already discussed in Chapter 15. Some of the other types of flours made for baking are the following:

16.1.1 Bread Flour

Bread flour should form good gluten when mixed with water and form bread with a good volume when baked. Thus, bread flours should have high protein content. They are milled from blends of hard winter and spring wheat, and their moisture content, protein content, ash content, starch quality, protein quality and particle size are all controlled. Bread flours are used mainly for making products leavened with yeast.

16.1.2 Self-Raising Flour

This flour is used domestically for making puddings, cakes, pastries, etc. This is made from milling weak wheats of low protein content. Hard wheat up to 20 per cent can also be used. The moisture content of the flour should not exceed 13.5 per cent to prevent premature reaction between the chemicals present in the flour. The flour contains leavening agents (Section 16.2), alkaline and acidic substances that react and evolve carbon dioxide during dough formation. Sodium bicarbonate and acid calcium phosphate or some other acid ingredients are the chemicals used in the ratio of 1.16 per cent bicarbonate and 1.61 per cent acid calcium phosphate on flour weight. A slight excess of bicarbonate gives rise to an unpleasant odour and a brownish-yellow colouration.

16.1.3 All-Purpose Flour

All-purpose flour (household or family flour) is made from hard wheat or a blend of hard and soft wheats and has a moderate protein content. It does not contain self-raising agents. It is suitable for use in yeast and quick breads, biscuits, pastries and cakes. A variation of this flour is "instantized flour." This is instant blending flour. This is made by a special agglomerating procedure whereby a number of individual flour particles are combined into readily pourable particles.

16.1.4 Biscuit Flour

Biscuit flour is made from weak wheats of low protein content. Depending on the type of biscuit, special types of flours are made. The flour should make a dough having more extensibility, but less spring (resistance) than bread dough. Dough pieces should retain their size and shape after being stamped out. The extensibility of biscuit flour dough may be increased by treatment with a proteolytic enzyme, or with the reducing agent sulphur dioxide, or by the addition of sodium metabisulphite to the doughs.

16.1.5 Cake Flour

Cake flour is a medium-strength flour ground from soft low-protein wheat of low-amylase activity and is very fine in structure. The purpose of flour in cakes is to allow an aerated structure to be retained after the cake has been built up. The stability of the final cake depends largely on the presence of uniformly swollen starch granules; hence, the starch granules should be undamaged during milling, be free from adherent protein, and be unattacked by amylolytic enzymes.

Pastry Flour: Pastry flours are similar to cake flour, are made of soft wheat, and are fairly low in protein. They are finely ground and they can be used for all baked products other than breads.

16.1.6 Enriched Flour

Enriched flour is flour with nutrients added to it. According to the FDA, a pound of enriched flour must have the following quantities of nutrients to qualify: 2.9 milligrams of thiamin, 1.8 milligrams of riboflavin, 24 milligrams of niacin, 0.7 milligrams of folic acid, and 20 milligrams of iron. Calcium may also be added at a minimum of 960 milligrams per pound.

16.2 Leavening Agents

In the preparation of baking products, the dough and batter are to be leavened. Leavening is increasing the area of a dough or batter by creating or occluding in them small bubbles of gas, mainly carbon dioxide (produced by yeast or chemical agents), air or water vapour. Vapour is formed from water during baking of all doughs and batters. Air is incorporated by beating the viscous batter.

16.2.1 Air

Air is a leavening agent present in all batters and doughs. To some extent all baked products—yeast breads, quick breads, cakes and biscuits—depend on air leavening. Air is responsible for only a small portion of the total increase in the volume of the finished product but is important because the effectiveness of water vapour as a leavening agent depends on the presence of air in the batter and dough. Even the effectiveness of carbon dioxide in leavening depends upon the distribution of air, as carbon dioxide does not form new gas cells in the batter or dough but diffuses into and expands the existing air cells. Air incorporated through the mixing of the dough ingredients expands when the mix is warmed in the oven and causes an increase in the volume of the baked product.

The amount of air contained in batters depends upon the extent of mixing of batters, the viscosity of the batter, the volume of ingredients, and the length of time elapsing before baking. Generally, increased mixing encases more air in a product. However, when egg white foams are folded into the batter, there should be minimum mixing as, on excessive mixing, egg foam becomes less elastic (sub sec 27.7.1) and causes loss of air with a reduction in volume. When extensive creaming of fat and sugar is employed as in the preparation of cakes, a fat-sugar-air foam is formed making tiny air pockets. The air in such a foam contributes a small but highly significant leavening action.

It is difficult to enclose air in the more viscous mixtures than in the less viscous mixtures. Since temperature affects viscosity, the mixes are to be worked at temperatures enabling the maximum trapping of air. The proportion of ingredients also influences the viscosity of a batter or dough. An extremely fluid mixture with a high proportion of liquid is incapable of holding a large amount of air. Some ingredients influence the amount of air held in batters and doughs. For example, mixes containing egg white have more air than those with egg yolk or whole egg. There is a loss of some air when batters are stored for some time prior to the preparation of the product. Hence, it is desirable to bake a product as soon as possible after preparing a batter.

16.2.2 Steam

Steam, like air, is an ever present leavening agent. Even a small amount of water in a batter or dough causes an appreciable leavening action as the water expands (1,600 times) when converted to steam during baking. Steam alone cannot leaven a mixture. Its action must be combined with that of air and/ or carbon dioxide.

16.2.3 Chemical Leavening Agents

The principal means of leavening flour mixes is by carbon dioxide, which is generated by the action of chemical leaveners or by the action of micro-organisms on sugars. The most important chemical agent used in leavening is baking powder. Baking soda and acid ingredients, and sometimes ammonium carbonate, are also used as leavening agents.

Baking powder consists of sodium bicarbonate (soda) and an acid component, which may be single or in combination with another acid. The baking powders are named after the acid ingredient used in the powder, as tartrate powder, phosphate powder and combination powder. The acid component reacts with soda when the powder is moistened; this happens when leavening agents are added to batters and doughs, releasing carbon dioxide according to the following reaction:

$$\underset{\text{Baking soda}}{NaHCO_3} + \underset{\text{Acid}}{HX} \longrightarrow NaX + H_2O + CO_2$$

Baking powder also contains an inert filler, which is commonly corn starch. The starch serves two purposes. It acts as a buffer between soda and the acid and prevents their going into action when exposed to air, by absorbing moisture. It also helps standardize the powder to release a standard amount of carbon dioxide. Baking powder yields 12–14 per cent of available carbon dioxide. In order to achieve this, the weight of soda is kept constant (28–30 per cent by weight), while the weight of the acid component is varied according to the amount needed to release the necessary amount of carbon dioxide. To standardize the powder, the difference in weight is corrected by the addition of the filler.

Sometimes powdered and dried egg albumen is added to the baking powders. It dissolves in cold water and increases the viscosity of the dough which helps to hold gas bubbles in the dough, thus increasing the effectiveness of the baking powder.

Tartrates are commonly used as the acid component of baking powder in the form of tartaric acid or potassium hydrogen tartrate (cream of tartar). The reaction is:

$$\underset{\text{Baking soda}}{2NaHCO_3} + \underset{\text{Tartaric acid}}{\begin{array}{c} COOH \\ | \\ CHOH \\ | \\ CHOH \\ | \\ COOH \end{array}} \longrightarrow \underset{\text{Sodium tartrate}}{\begin{array}{c} COONa \\ | \\ CHOH \\ | \\ CHOH \\ | \\ COONa \end{array}} + 2H_2O + 2CO_2$$

Tartrates leave virtually tasteless residues but they act as cathartics (purgative) and diuretics. However, these substances are safe in their normal application and usage levels. The disadvantage of use of a tartrate is that it is fast-acting and quickly releases all the gas at room temperature.

Phosphate powders react somewhat slower than tartrates at room temperature but they still lose a high percentage of their gas before baking. The acid ingredient is anhydrous monocalcium phosphate in the form of small crystals with a water-insoluble coating that protects against decomposition in the presence of moisture and retards reaction with soda. The reaction between the phosphate and soda is as follows:

$$8NaHCO_3 + 3CaH_4(PO_4)_2 \longrightarrow Ca_3(PO_4)_2 + 4Na_2HPO_4 + 8H_2O + 8CO_2$$

Because of the ready release of carbon dioxide with tartrates and phosphates, the flour mixes must be handled quickly to avoid loss of carbon dioxide and therefore volume. Even then, there will not be sufficient carbon dioxide to maintain the maximum volume until the structure sets.

To overcome the above defects, slow-acting powders are used. Such powders give very little gas at room temperature but release all the available gas only at the temperature of the oven. A slow-acting acid component is sodium aluminium sulphate.

$$6NaHCO_3 + \underset{\text{Sodium aluminium sulphate}}{2NaAl(SO_4)_2} \longrightarrow 2Al(OH)_3 + 4Na_2SO_4 + 6CO_2$$

The reaction between the components is that the keeping qualities of sulphate baking powders are good but the flavour of the residue of sodium sulphate is objectionable to many people. Also, the sulphate is unsuitable as a single leavening acid because the crust of a baked product will set before a sufficient quantity of gas has been generated to produce the desired volume.

Because of the limitations of the baking powders described above, double-acting powders are in use. These powders begin to react at low temperatures and give some smoothness and viscosity to the batter but their action is complete only when they are exposed to a high temperature. The double-acting powder contains two acid-reacting ingredients, the familiar ingredients being monocalcium phosphate and sodium aluminium sulphate.

Instead of baking powders, sodium bicarbonate and an acid can be used as leavening agents and this has been in use from early times in baking. Acids commonly used are provided by sour milk, buttermilk and fruit juices. In this case, an exact amount of soda is to be used, for an excess of soda will result in an unpalatable product and the colour of the product will be modified from white to yellow.

Sodium bicarbonate does not require an acid for the release of carbon dioxide. It decomposes when heated producing carbon dioxide and water.

$$2NaHCO_3 \longrightarrow Na_2CO_3 + H_2O + CO_2$$

However, the sodium carbonate produced has an unpleasant taste and an alkaline odour. Therefore, sodium bicarbonate is not used alone and when used a suitable quantity of acid is added so that a neutral residue is formed.

Carbon dioxide is produced when ammonium carbonate or bicarbonate is heated.

$$\underset{\text{Ammonium bicarbonate}}{NH_4HCO_3} \longrightarrow \underset{\text{Ammonia}}{NH_3} + H_2O + CO_2$$

No solid residue is left behind in this reaction and it is thus an advantage to use these compounds as leavening agents. However, the ammonia imparts a detectable odour unless it is completely removed. Ammonium bicarbonate is used as a leavening agent in baking biscuits and crackers as they have a large surface-to-mass ratio and ammonia escapes when baked at high temperature.

16.2.4 Yeast

A biological method of leavening is by yeast fermentation. Yeast is a unicellular micro-organism that reproduces rapidly in the presence of sugars under appropriate conditions of pH (4-6) and temperature (30°C). During the growth and multiplication of yeast, the sugar decomposes into alcohol and carbon dioxide. This change takes place anaerobically and is known as fermentation. There are many strains of yeast that bring about fermentation. The particular strain of yeast used in baked products is *Saccharomyces cerevisiae.*

A large number of reactions take place leading to the production of the final products and the overall reaction can be represented thus

$$\underset{\text{Sugar}}{C_6H_{12}O_6} \longrightarrow \underset{\text{Alcohol}}{2C_2H_5OH} + 2CO_2$$

The carbon dioxide liberated during fermentation in the flour mixture leavens batters and doughs, and the alcohol produced is driven off during the baking process. Secondary products of fermentation, e.g., acids, carbonyls and esters, may affect the gluten, or impart flavour to the baked product.

Flour contains about 1.5 per cent sugar on a dry weight basis. Sucrose is normally added to yeast doughs. Yeast contains several enzymes that act upon carbohydrates. Invertase of yeast hydrolyzes sucrose to glucose and fructose, which are fermented. Flour contains ample β-amylase and a small amount of α-amylase. Some maltose is formed in the dough through the action of flour amylases on starch. Maltose is also hydrolyzed by yeast maltase to glucose, which is then fermented. Fermentation of glucose is brought about by several enzymes collectively known as zymase.

Yeast used for leavening is marketed in two forms: compressed yeast and active dry yeast. Properly selected yeast strains are grown in a medium of molasses containing the necessary nutrients under controlled conditions. When growth ceases, yeast cells are separated by centrifugation, mixed with a small amount of starch, and compressed into cakes. Compressed yeast has a moisture content of 72 per cent and is the most active form of yeast for bread making, but is unstable at room temperature. It must be stored at 1° to 3°C and even at this temperature, it is active only for about five weeks.

The active dry yeast is propagated in the same way as compressed yeast using special strains of *S. cerevisiae.* It is then recovered, compressed, extruded and dehydrated at approximately 43°C to about 8 per cent moisture. The dried material is then ground into granular active dry yeast. The shelf life of dry yeast is over two years if stored at 5°C and six months when held at 32°C.

In some cases, leavening is brought about by the combined fermentation of yeast and bacteria. The yeast produces carbon dioxide for leavening and the bacteria produce the acids that impart a distinctive flavour. Bacteria can themselves also be used for leavening; under controlled conditions, bacteria grow and act on sugar-producing carbon dioxide and hydrogen, which, in batter and dough, act as leaveners.

16.3 Fermented Products Based on Rice

In a manner similar to the fermentation of wheat dough for the making of bread, rice batter is leavened by natural fermentation and several dishes, such as idli, dosa, appam and others, are prepared. Of these, idli is the most popular breakfast food in most parts of India, especially in South India.

16.3.1 Idli

There is no record in history as to how idli originated. It is, however, in use since a long time, particularly in Tamil Nadu. The product is a steamed pudding from a thick fermented batter of rice and a split dehusked pulse, black gram (*Phaseolus mungo*). The two ingredients are soaked and ground separately in a stone pestle and mortar; the black-gram dhal into a fine paste and rice coarsely. The ingredients are then mixed together, salted to taste, and allowed to ferment overnight for 12–18 hours. The mixture rises and is then steamed in flat plates or perforated cups when soft, spongy, tasty and easily digestible idlies are obtained.

To avoid the labour of wet grinding both the contents, the practice of dry grinding of rice into semolina has been developed. The use of rice semolina free from flour is found to improve the texture of idli. The presence of fine rice flour in semolina would induce more adhesiveness or pastiness than is desirable for the idli texture. For the same reason, parboiled rice, which is relatively hard in texture and would give less flour during grinding, is found to be more suitable than raw rice for making soft and spongy textured idlies. However, idlies prepared from parboiled semolina are less tasty than those prepared from raw rice. The starch in parboiled rice is precooked and it may be fermented to a greater extent than raw rice.

For the best acceptability, texture and quality of idli, the proportion of rice to black-gram dhal is 2 : 1. The proportion of water used is between 2: 1–2 : 2 parts of water per unit dry weight of the mix. If the proportion of black-gram dhal is less, the quality of the product made from such composition is poor and the idli will not be soft. Black-gram dhal cannot be substituted by other legume flours. Idlies prepared by substituting black-gram by Bengal gram, green gram, soya bean flour or other bean flour will be either less spongy or brittle and may have unacceptable flavours.

The speciality of black-gram in idli preparation is owing to the mucilaginous material present in it, which is generally absent in other edible legumes. The mucilaginous material is a complex carbohydrate containing galactose and arabinose (galactoarabinan) together with small amounts of rhamnose and galacturonic acid. The complex carbohydrate is combined with a protein in mucilage. It is believed that this mucilaginous principle helps in the retention of carbon dioxide during the fermentation of the thick batter and is thus responsible for the soft spongy honeycomb texture of the idli. It is also believed that the traditional wet grinding of black-gram dhal into a viscous batter entraps air bubbles inside the paste and makes for leavening action. Also, the entrapped air may assist the fermentation itself making for liberation of more gases for leavening.

The use of components containing mucilage-like material such as guar bean (*Cyamopsis tetragonoloba*), lady's finger or fenugreek seeds can partially stimulate the desired texture in idli but their use is not desirable because they all give a product with undesirable flavour or taste.

The fermentation of idli batter is a mixed auto fermentation. The micro-organisms present in the ingredients and those from the air bring about the fermentation. Several wild yeasts together with different types of bacteria are implicated in fermentation. The bacteria recognized in idli fermentation are *Lactobacillus delbrueckii, L. lactis, Streptococcus lactis, S. faecalis, Leuconostoc mesenteroides* and *Pedicococcus cerevisiae.* Fermentation is mediated and influenced by both the fermenting components, black-gram flour and rice semolina. Though its auto fermenting power is poor, rice semolina contributes micro-organisms and also acts as a substrate. Black-gram flour plays a major role in the fermentation both as a good source of micro-organisms and also as a vigorous fermenting substrate. Micro-organisms developed during the pre-soaking of black-gram have a high auto fermenting ability and also more potential to act on rice semolina. Acid and gas production during fermentation is mostly due to the bacteria. A temperature of 25°–30°C is favourable for fermentation. Temperature up to 40°C accelerates the rate but some undesirable smell occasionally develops at a higher temperature. The optimal condition of fermentation is 30°C for 16 hours.

Fermentation brings about physical and chemical changes in the idli batter. With the progress of fermentation, there is an increase in batter volume (owing to gas formation), acidity and non-protein nitrogen. The reducing sugars decrease initially and then tend to increase. The initial pH of 6.2 of the batter decreases to 4.5 to 5.0 at optimum fermentation and falls to 4 when incubated for 72 hours.

The process of fermentation increases the nutritive value of idlies. It also increases the digestibility by virtue of its spongy structure, which facilitates enzyme action during digestion. There are, however, conflicting reports about its digestibility. Idli is made from a mixture of cereal and pulse and is, therefore, better than bread made from cereal alone in its nutritive value. If the idli mix is fortified with nutrients, its growth promoting value is enhanced.

Instant idli mixes eliminate the traditional method of grinding of both ingredients. In this case, the leavening is produced by the action of chemical leavening agents. The texture of idli made by instant mixes may be as good as the one prepared by fermentation, but the flavour is bland as the characteristic fermentation smell is absent.

16.3.2 Dosa

Dosa is another common fermented product used in India. This is prepared from a fermented batter of rice and pulse in proportions ranging from 6 : 1 to 10 : 1. Both the ingredients are finely ground, unlike in the idli batter, which contains the rice component in a coarse consistency. The dosa batter is very thin and dosa is baked on a hot pan. The thickness of the dosa pancake depends upon the consistency of the batter. Thin batter gives a thin pancake, although it may stick to the pan.

Unlike in idli preparation, the ingredients needed for dosa need not be just rice and black-gram. Pure rice or a mixture of rice, wheat, sorghum, maize or millets could be used. Black-gram could be substituted by other pulses like green gram or Bengal gram. The micro-organisms involved in dosa batter fermentation are the same as those involved in idli batter fermentation.

Dosa prepared from fermented rice and black-gram batter as plain a pancake is soft, tasty and has a characteristic flavour. Sometimes, a crisp preparation is preferred. This is made by pan frying and by the application of an edible oil or butter, and served with spiced vegetables, particularly spiced potatoes when it is called masala dosa.

If the dosa batter contains very little or no pulse, the pancake is generally baked thick on the pan. This product is known as appam. Sometimes, fermenting toddy is added to the batter to assist the fermentation and this gives a tasty soft appam.

16.3.3 Appam

Appam is a fermented rice pancake, and is a speciality of the South Indian Coastal State of Kerala. It has a soft spongy middle, laced with crispy edges.

Rice powder is mixed with water and yeast, and the batter is left to ferment for 6 hours. The batter is poured into a vessel called *appachatti* and tossed with oil to make circular appam. It is usually eaten with a side dish made of coconut called chutney, or with sweetened coconut milk. It can also be served with stew, or typically with *kadala* — a spicy dish made with Bengal gram.

Appam also refers to another South Indian sweet dish, which owes its origins to Tamil Nadu. This is made with flour, jaggery, clarified butter — ghee — and bananas. A batter made out of flour, jaggery and banana is poured into a vessel called *appakarai,* which has ghee heated to a high temperature. The appams take the shape of small cup and are fried until deep brown.

16.3.4 Dhokla

Dhokla is a fermented food prepared from rice and Bengal gram. This is popular in Western India, particularly in Gujarat. This is prepared from a batter of coarsely ground rice and Bengal-gram dhal allowed to ferment at low temperature. The fermented batter is steamed in a pie dish, cut into diamond shapes and seasoned.

16.3.5 Other Fermented Products

Some other fermented foods based on rice used in the country are *ambali*, prepared from a thick fermented batter of finger millet flour and rice, *kanji* (ganji), fermented surplus water from cooked rice, and fermented rice or *kali,* which is leftover cooked rice to which water is added and the mixture allowed to ferment overnight.

16.4 Bread Making

Bread (yeast bread) is an important part of the diet of a majority of the world's inhabitants. Making bread by baking leavened cereal dough is a very ancient practice. Over the years great strides have been made in scientifically making bread.

There are three requirements in bread making. The first is the development of dough by mixing the ingredients in the correct proportion, the second is the aeration of the dough by leavening agents, the third is the baking of the leavened dough. Baking coagulates the dough material by heat so that the gas is retained and the structure of the material is stabilized. The aerated, finely vesicated crumb in the baked product is very helpful for the easy mastication of bread.

16.4.1 Ingredients

The main ingredients of bread are flour, water, yeast and salt. Other ingredients which may be added include malt flour, soya flour, yeast foods, milk and milk products, fat, fruit and gluten.

Flour: As already indicated, flour proteins are of prime importance in the development of bread dough. When the proteins in the flour combine with water, a complex between gliadin and glutenin is formed, resulting in the development of gluten. Gluten has peculiar extensible properties, i.e., it can be stretched like an elastic material and possesses a certain degree of recoil or spring. There are instruments (mixogram, farinograph) which can determine the quantities and quality of gluten which a flour can yield. Properly developed gluten makes the dough easy to handle, either by hand or by machine and permits a large amount of expansion during fermentation and the early stages of baking. Glutenin controls the elasticity of the gluten and the time required for dough development, while gliadin proteins are responsible for loaf volume.

Other flour components also have important roles in bread making. Starch granules become closely associated with gluten during dough mixing and this prevents an excessively cohesive structure. If the starch has been damaged during milling, it absorbs water thus competing with gluten proteins for available water. Flour amylase attacks only damaged starch. It is therefore essential that the flour should contain adequate damaged starch to supply sugar during fermentation. Excess starch damage, however, has an adverse effect on the quality of bread; loaf volume is decreased, and the bread is less attractive in colour.

Water: An important function of water is in gluten formation. The amount of water absorbed to make a dough of standard consistency depends upon the proportion of protein and damaged starch. Water also dissolves sugar and salt and serves as a dispersion medium for yeast cells. Water brings about the partial gelatinization of starch during baking. As previously mentioned, some leavening also occurs as a result of steam formation from water or other liquids used during baking.

Sometimes milk is used as a solvent for dry ingredients. Milk increases the food value of the bread.

If fluid milk is used it should be scalded to kill the bacteria that might interfere with dough consistency and loaf volume. Care must be taken to prevent the destruction of yeast when scalded milk is added. It is better to use non-fat dry milk and water in place of fluid milk.

Yeast: Functions of yeast are already described in Subsection 16.2.4.

Salt is mainly used as a flavouring agent. Salt has also a retarding effect on yeast fermentation. In its absence, fermentation takes place very rapidly and the dough is too sticky to knead properly. The result is the coarse texture of the baked bread.

Sugar: Added sugar is not essential for bread making. Small quantities of sugars are present in the flour, and are readily used up by the yeast. However, if no sugar is added, fermentation is slow because sugar for yeast activity must be formed by the action of amylases on starch. Therefore, small quantities of sugars are added. If the added sugar content exceeds 10 per cent of the weight of flour, it will retard fermentation by the osmotic effect of dissolved solute on the yeast cells. Excess sugar also interferes with gluten formation as it competes with gluten protein for water. The brown colour of the crust of bread is due to the Maillard reaction between the protein and sugars, which occurs during baking. The amount of sugar also influences the tenderness and volume of baked products.

Other ingredients: Fats and oils, when used in the flour mix, have a tenderizing effect. The nature of fat used is also important in determining the texture of the product. Fats, in addition, contribute to the flavour of the product.

In all the preparations of commercial bread, small amounts of other ingredients are added to modify the properties of bread. These include enzymes, yeast foods, and dough improvers. Enzymes used are proteases acting on the gluten to alter dough extensibility, amylases acting on starch and supplying fermentable sugars to the yeast, and consumed fresh which whiten the bread by destroying flour pigments and perhaps also affect the flavour. Ammonium sulphate and phosphate are used as yeast nutrients to encourage yeast growth and accelerate gas production. Oxidizing agents are used to improve the handling characteristics of the dough and the specific volume and texture of the finished product. The most common oxidizing agent used is potassium bromate. The oxidizing agents alter the mechanical properties of the dough by causing the formation of additional disulphide bonds between gluten molecules. Propionates are added to inhibit mould growth.

16.4.2 Dough Development

Dough development generally takes place by two methods: the straight dough and sponge systems. In addition, there is the continuous dough making process, the activated dough development process and no-time dough making process. The proportion of the ingredients used in dough making depends upon the method employed, the type of flour used, the time given for fermentation, and the nature of the final product.

Straight dough system: In this method, all the ingredients are mixed together at one time and allowed to rise. This is the method used by home-makers and some bakers. The proportion of ingredients used in this method is 1.25 parts of yeast, 1.8 parts of salt and 55.3–57.1 parts of water per 100 parts of flour. The yeast is dispersed in some of the water and the salt is dissolved in another portion. The yeast suspension, the salt solution, and the rest of the water are then blended with flour, water added being at such a temperature that will bring the mixture to 27°C. The dough is then kneaded by hand or machine. After the dough rests for some time (about 2 hours), it is "knocked back," i.e., it is manipulated to push out the gas that has been evolved. This process of knocking back will even out the temperature and give a more thorough mixing. It is then allowed to rise again until the bulk has almost doubled (after about

1 hour). This is known as "first proofing." The dough is then moulded into loaf shape and allowed to rest in the baking pan for 45 to 60 min. at 38°– 48°C for the final proof and is then baked for about 30 min. with steam injected into the oven to produce a glaze on the crust.

Sponge system: The sponge system consists of two steps: the sponge stage and the dough stage. The sponge is made by mixing yeast, water and about half the flour. The batter is set aside in a warm place for some hours. The fermented mixture has a sponge-like appearance from which, the method derives its name. This is called the first dough. The remainder of the flour, and salt, sugar and fat, if desired, are next added to make a dough of required consistency, which can then be kneaded. It is then allowed to ferment for a short time before proofing and baking.

The sponge system, being a longer process, requires less yeast than is used for the straight dough system, and gives bread maximum flavour. The speed and extent of fermentation can be controlled by the temperature and by regulating the salt and/or sugar added. The method, however, suffers from the disadvantage of being more complicated than the straight dough system.

Continuous process: Continuous dough making is a mechanical process that may be considered as a modification of the sponge process. In this process, the flour, discharged from a hopper, is continuously mixed a liquid pre-ferment or "brew" containing yeast, salt, flour, etc. (sponge), in regulated quantities. The dough is allowed no fermentation time, but instead is subjected to intense mechanical mixing whereby the correct conditions for baking are obtained. In the absence of fermentation, it is essential to incorporate a fair quantity of an oxidizing agent into the dough. In the mechanical dough development. the disulphide bonds holding the protein molecules in their original conformation are broken down by the physical force of the intense mixing energy. The dough is extruded through a pipe, cut into loaf-sized portions, proved and baked. This process gives bread with a characteristic and very even crumb texture and results in considerable time-saving in comparison with the normal process.

Activated dough development process: This is a chemical development process that achieves dough maturity without using either the usual fermentation method or mechanical method. A rapid reducing agent, L-cysteine and a slow-acting oxidizing agent, potassium bromate (or a mix of potassium bromate and ascorbic acid) are added to the dough at the mixing stage. The reducing agent cleaves the disulphide bonds and the oxidizing agent stimulates the formation of new crosslinks to stabilize the desired elastic three-dimensional gluten structure.

No-time dough: The dough is made using a larger amount of yeast (12.5 per cent on flour weight) and a temperature higher than that used for normal fermentation systems (30°–32°C), and after 15 min. it is moulded and the doughs are proved for 1 hour at 43°C. The bread made this way has a thick-walled crumb structure, but stales rapidly.

16.4.3 Baking

Loaf-sized breads and rolls are baked in an oven pre-heated to 204°C. After the first 15 min. of baking. the temperature is reduced if the crusts become too brown. Baking is continued until the bread is fully baked. Too high or too low a temperature for baking is avoided. High temperature causes crust formation before rising is complete. Low temperature permits the dough to rise excessively and possibly fall before coagulation takes place.

During the first 10–12 min. of baking, there is an increase in dough volume. This increase in volume is known as "ovenspring." This is caused by an expansion of the gases owing to the high temperature of the oven and due to increased enzyme activity in the centre of the dough. As the centre of the dough heats up slowly, the enzymes are inactivated at higher temperatures. As baking continues, gluten expands without breaking and finally forms a rigid structure due to coagulation. This helps the retention of the rapidly expanding gases. Excess of gases, carbon dioxide, alcohol and water vapour, leave the structure and starch gelatinizes. The crust colour becomes dark due to browning reaction.

Microwave baking; In conventional oven baking, the dough is heated by thermal heating. The heat is not uniform throughout the bread loaf; the outside of the loaf gets heated rapidly, while the centre is still in the form of a dough. The slow heating of the interior of the bread allows activity with undesirable effects. This could be overcome by the use of microwave baking (Sec. 28.2.4). Microwaves penetrate the dough very rapidly and cook the loaf uniformly from outside to inside. The rapid heating of the interior inactivates the α-amylase within a short period. Hence, microwave baking permits the use of flour with an abnormally high α-amylase activity. This method of baking also permits the use of flours with low protein content. In the conventional baking of dough with low protein content, the gases evolved during baking are lost rapidly as they are being produced, because the crumb cells are too weak to retain them. In microwave heating, however, gases are produced at a faster rate than they are lost, because the dough is heated rapidly throughout. Microwave baking by itself does not produce a crust on bread loaf. To develop a crust it is desirable to apply a certain amount of thermal heat. Both thermal and microwave heatings can be applied in the same oven. Microwave baking, however, is more expensive than conventional baking.

Bread cooling: The bread from the oven is to be cooled before slicing and packing. When the bread leaves the oven, the crumb has a temperature of about 100°C and a moisture content of 45 per cent at the centre. The crust is hotter and its moisture content is 1–2 per cent and it cools rapidly. During cooling, moisture moves from the interior towards the curst and then to the atmosphere. This results in the loss of the texture of the crust and the crispness of freshly baked bread. Therefore, bread is to be cooled without much loss of moisture. This is achieved by subjecting loaves to a counter current of air-conditioned to about 21°C and 80 per cent relative humidity.

16.4.4 Bread Staling

Once out of the oven, bread begins to stale. The manifestations of staling are the toughness or leathery nature of the crust along with the development of the dry, harsh texture of the crumb and a stale flavour. The basic cause of staling is the transformation of starch from one form to another at temperatures below 55°C. The starch becomes more crystalline below this temperature. The change in the form of starch results in the binding of less water leading to rapid hardening, and to the shrinkage of the starch granules away from the gluten skeleton with which they are associated, with the consequent development of crumbliness. These changes occur in bread even though it is sealed in a moisture/vapour-tight wrap. It is believed the changes in starch during staling are more due to the amylopectin portion of starch than the amylose portion. Amylose is insolubilized irreversibly by retrogradation during baking and hence cannot influence the staling that occurs subsequently. Amylopectin undergoes a heat reversible association resulting in staling. Some consider that both amylose and amylopectin are involved in staling. Staling can be reversed by heating. Storage of bread at refrigerator temperature causes staling at a maximum rate.

Microbiological spoilage: Bread undergo microbiological spoilage due to the growth of moulds and undesirable bacteria. At the high temperature of baking, mould spores are destroyed. However, the moulds that deposit on bread during the handling process develop during storage and affect the quality of bread. Mould infection can be prevented by the addition of sodium or calcium propionate.

Some bacteria which are members of the *Bacillus mesenthericus* group, if present in dough, are not destroyed in the interior of bread during baking and develop in bread later, bringing about a change in colour, texture and disintegration of the crust; which is known as "rope." Propionates also eliminate ropiness in bread.

16.5 Quick Breads

Quick breads are a variety of products made quickly and usually baked immediately after the mixing of the ingredients, and some are usually served warm. Less development of gluten is required in quick breads than in yeast breads. Leavening action is faster than in yeast breads and the leavening agent, when used, is baking powder or baking soda and sour milk. Examples of quick breads are biscuits, muffins, popovers, waffles, griddle cakes, etc. The ingredients of all quick breads are flour, milk, salt and shortenings. The additional ingredients are egg, baking powder and sugar. The flour for quick breads should have a medium to high protein content. Gluten formed from such flours should have sufficient strength to retain the leavening agents—air, steam and carbon dioxide. All-purpose flour and cake flour are most commonly used for baking quick breads.

The liquid most commonly used in flour mixture is milk. Fresh whole or skim milk or nonfat dry milk is used. The advantage of nonfat dry milk is that two to four times the usual milk solids can be used, thus increasing the nutritive value of the product. The amount of liquid used in a flour mixture depends upon the nature of the product. For example, the ratio by volume of flour to liquid is 1½ : 1 in waffles, 2 : 1 in muffins and 2 : ¾ in biscuits.

Fats have a tenderizing effect on dough. They coat the flour particles and keep them separated, thereby reducing the tendency for the mix to form heavy continuous bonds of gluten. Fats also contribute to flavour and colour. A number of fats and oils are used as shortening agents.

Quick breads generally contain eggs. They contribute to the leavening, colour, flavour and nutritive value of quick breads. They also act as a liquid in helping to moisturize dry ingredients and develop gluten. The coagulation of egg proteins during baking lends stability to the baked product. When eggs are in the flour mix they enclose a large volume of air, and this becomes an effective means of leavening during baking. Sugar is used in quick breads primarily as a sweetening agent. It reduces the gluten strength, develops colours and contributes to the tenderness of baked products.

Apart from the kind and proportion of ingredients used in the mix, the success of quick bread preparation depends on the technique used in mixing them. The method used for mixing are stirring, creaming (working sugar into fat to incorporate air which results in foam), beating, kneading, cutting in (incorporating fat into flour mix), and folding (incorporating one ingredient with another). These techniques require suitable equipment.

16.5.1 Biscuits

This is the one processed wheat product that has found acceptability even in the rural parts of the country. The production in 2004 was about 700,500 tonnes. The proportion of flour (5 parts) to liquid, which is milk (1 part), is important. The other ingredients are baking powder, fat and salt. The dry ingredients are mixed and sifted together and fat is cut into the flour mixture. Vegetable oil can satisfactorily replace solid fat. Milk in the optimum amount is then added and stirred until the mixture stiffens. The biscuit dough is then kneaded on a lightly floured suitable surface to obtain the desired amount of cohesiveness. The extent of kneading depends upon the amount of stirring used to mix the dough. Under-kneaded doughs give biscuits that are very tender, coarse in texture, small in volume, and have a rough crust. Optimum kneading (10–20 min.) produces biscuits with fine structure, smooth crust and better appearance; over-kneading produces a compact, toughened product. When the dough is sufficiently kneaded, it is rolled on baking sheets to the desired thickness cut to the required size, and baked in a hot oven (210 to 232°C) for about 15 min.

16.5.2 Muffins

Muffins usually combine flour, milk, salt, shortening, egg, sugar, and baking powder. The proportion of flour to milk is 2:1 by volume. The mixing of the ingredients consists of stirring a mixture of milk, egg and melted shortening or oil into the combined dry ingredients (muffin method). An alternative is to cut fat into the dry ingredients before milk and egg are added. The batter should not be smooth. Over-mixing decreases tenderness with peaked tunnels that go towards the peak. Muffins from poorly mixed batter are light, even textured and have a pebbly surface. Once the muffin batter has been mixed, it is transferred to baking cups at once and the muffins are baked in a hot oven (218°C) for 20–25 min.

16.5.3 Popovers

Popovers are made of thin batter (pan batter) which contains equal volumes of flour and milk and a high proportion of egg. Since the volume of liquid is great, cohesive gluten is not formed. Egg provides extensible proteins that supplement the gluten flour. The leavening agent is steam formed by the liquid used. Popover ingredients are mixed until the batter is smooth and poured into pans and baked at 232°C for 20–30 min.

16.5.4 Waffles and Pancakes

Waffle, pancake and griddle cake mixtures contain flour, liquid, baking powder, salt and egg. Griddle cake mixture contains less egg and fat than waffle and pancake mixtures. The batter is made by the muffin method, i.e., by beating the liquid and dry ingredients until there are no flour lumps in the batter. Waffles are made in thermostatically controlled waffle irons, while griddle cakes are made using a griddle. Pancakes are made by pouring the batter and spreading it into a circle, as in the preparation of dosa. Pancakes should be turned when the bubbles formed during the baking of the first side have popped and the batter is pleasing brown. The second side is then browned.

16.6 Cakes, Cookies and Pastries

Baked products are often used as desserts. These include cakes, cookies and pastries. There are different types of these products.

16.6.1 Cakes

There are two classes of cakes: shortened and unshortened. The shortened cakes contain fat as an essential ingredient and are leavened chiefly with baking powder. These include white, yellow and chocolate cakes, and pound cakes. Unshortened cakes do not contain fat as a basic ingredient. They are leavened by air or steam. These include angel food cake and others. Chiffon cakes have characteristics of both shortened and unshortened cakes but they contain fat in the form of oil.

Shortened cakes: Shortened cakes are of two types: the standard shortened cake or butter cake leavened by carbon dioxide from baking powder, and pound cake which has no added leavening agent, apart from air, incorporated in the cake. The textures of the two types of shortened cakes are different.

Pound cakes have a close grain and are compact in character. A good shortened cake has fine grain cells of uniform size, thin cell walls, and a crumb that is more elastic than crumbly.

The major ingredients of shortened cakes are similar to those of muffins, though the proportions are quite different. Eggs, sugar and shortening levels are greater in cakes than in muffins. Cakes also contain some flavouring ingredients. In the formation of cakes, there is a balance between the tenderizing ingredients—sugar and fat, and structural ingredients—flour and egg. In the case of high-sugar (high-ratio) cakes, in which the weight of sugar is more than that of the flour, the proportion of other tenderizing and structural ingredients should be adjusted such that the weight of the shortening does not exceed the weight of eggs. In white cakes, the weight of egg white might be higher than that of shortening because the protein content of egg white is less than that of whole egg or egg yolk. The weight of liquids—milk, water and egg—in the batter should not be less than the weight of sugar; otherwise, the high sugar level will interfere with the hydration of proteins and gelatinization of starch.

Shortened cakes are made from cake flour or all-purpose flour. The bleaching and maturing agents used in the preparation of cake flour have some tenderizing effect on the gluten. Chlorine, for example, increases the dispersibility of flour proteins. It also facilitates the stabilizing interactions between starch and proteins, and between starch and lipid. The liquid used in cakes is mainly milk in different forms. Sometimes fruit juices or pulps are used. The leavening agent used in cakes, as in the case of biscuits and muffins, is baking powder. Eggs have important functions in the baking of cakes. They contribute to the structure of the cake and egg yolk emulsifies the shortenings in the batter. Sugar affects the flavour and structure of the cake. Sucrose, the sugar normally used, is a nonreducing agent and thus it does not contribute much to the browning.

Butter is the most common shortening used. Margarine or any hydrogenated vegetable oil can be used in its place. Shortenings strive to tenderize gluten. The fat serves the important function of entrapping air during the creaming process, thereby leavening the batter and increasing the volume of the baked cake. Nowadays, shortenings with a surface active lipid are used. These help in the emulsification and are easy to handle since they are liquids.

Many flavouring materials like vanilla, spices and synthetic flavours are used in small quantities in cake preparation. These ingredients have no effect on the cakes other than imparting flavour. Other ingredients added for flavour are cocoa, chocolate, fruit juices and other forms of fruits. Some of these affect the volume of liquid to be added.

Mixing: Different methods are employed in mixing the cake ingredients.

The conventional method: This method consists in creaming the fat until it is plastic, i.e., the fat is neither liquid nor hard, but is of a malleable consistency. Sugar is gradually added to the fat with continued creaming. As sugar is mixed, the air is trapped in the plastic mixture. Egg or egg yolk is beaten into the creamed mixture till the maximum incorporation of air takes place. Flour sifted with baking powder and salt is then added alternatively with milk and flavouring to the fat-sugar-egg mixture. If white cake is being made, beaten egg white is folded into the batter after the other ingredients have been added.

When the amount of fat is small the above method is modified. About half of the sugar is beaten into the egg white or whole eggs until the mixture is foaming and stiff, then the mixture is folded into the batter after all the ingredients have been added.

The muffin method: In this method egg, milk and melted fat are combined and blended together. This method saves time as no creaming is necessary. However, the disadvantage is that the finished product has a coarse texture and distinctly less keeping qualities. This method is used when the cake is consumed fresh.

The single-stage method: This is a very quick way of making cakes from mixes. In this method, the dry ingredients are sifted together and then, when the shortening and half or most of the milk have been added, the mixture is blended for a set length of time. Then the egg and any remaining liquid are added and mixing is done again for a specified length of time and the batter is finished. There are different modifications to this method. The advantage of speed and ease of preparation of cakes by this method is offset by the coarse texture and the more rapid rate of staling of cakes.

Baking: A shortened cake batter can stand for some time, but it is better to bake it as quickly as possible after being mixed. Cake batters can, however, be frozen if they are to be baked at a later time. The quality of the cake depends upon the way in which it is baked. It is important that the batter used in the pan is such that the cake will fill the pan at the end of baking. The size of the baking pan is also important. Shallow pans are better than deeper pans for cake baking. The material of which the pan is made is also important as it affects the speed of baking. Faster baking pans produce cakes having larger volume and better overall crumb quality than the less efficient pans. However, the disadvantage of cakes from the faster baking pans is that they are peaked and brown on the sides than on top. Baking temperature varies with ingredients in the batter and the size, shape and material of the pan. The oven temperature commonly used for baking shortened cakes ranges from 177°C to 191°C. Cakes when fully baked should not be removed immediately from the oven. They should be allowed to stand for 15 to 20 min. before they are removed and this helps the interior of the cake to become firm.

Cakes may be baked in microwave ovens. The structure of the cake thus baked compares favourably with that of cakes baked in conventional ovens. The disadvantage of the use of a microwave oven is that the browning of the crust is not uniform.

We next take up unshortened cakes, which include angel cakes, sponge cakes and chiffon cakes.

Angel cake: The basic ingredients of angel food cake are flour, sugar and egg. The other ingredients are salt, flavourings and cream of tartar or an acid. The proportion of sugar in the cake mix is high because no other tenderizer is used. Sugar interferes with gluten development and thus tends to produce a more tender and fragile cake, when used in increasing amounts. Sugar also has a stabilizing effect on egg white foam and allows more beating without the over-coagulation of the white proteins. Cream of tartar is added to egg whites for angel food cake for it makes the cake whiter, finer in grain and more tender than it would be without it. The cream of tartar can be substituted by citric or tartaric acids. The acids bring down the pH, and this stabilizes the foam by coagulating some of the proteins that surround the air cells of the foam. Also, the flavonoid pigments of flour which are yellow in alkaline medium are white in neutral or acid pH. Thus an angel food cake made with cream of tartar is whiter than one made without it.

To prepare angel food cake, the egg whites are beaten so that a fine division of air cells takes place to produce a fine cake with a large volume. Under-beating incorporates less air and results in a small cake with thick cell walls. Over-heating results in a low volume owing to the rupture of over-extended cell walls during the baking process. To the properly beaten egg white at room temperature, cream of tartar and salt are added, and the beating is continued until the foam forms peaks. A portion of sugar is then added and beating at slow speed is continued when air cells surrounded by films of syrup containing egg protein are formed. Egg white foams, into which sugar has been incorporated is known as "meringue" (Subsection 22.8.4). Thus angel cakes are meringue cakes. Finally, flour is folded into the meringue so that flour particles are uniformly distributed in the syrupy film around the air cell. The mixture is transferred to the pans and baked at 177°C.

Sponge cakes: These do not differ much from angel cake except that both egg yolk and egg white are used. Lemon juice is generally an acid ingredient. The egg yolks are beaten until they are thick. Then sugar, salt, water and lemon juice are added and the whole mass is beaten until it is fluffy. The flour is folded lightly into the mixture, after which the egg whites, beaten stiff but not dry, are folded. In the alternative, egg yolk prepared as above is combined with beaten egg whites before the flour is folded into the mixture. Instead of using separated egg components, the whole egg itself could be used. The eggs and lemon juice are beaten until the mixture is stiff and the sugar is added to the egg mixture with gentle mixing. The cake prepared by any of the above methods is then baked as in the case of angel cake.

Chiffon cakes: Chiffon cakes usually contain a larger proportion of egg than shortened cakes and oil. The cake is prepared by sifting together the dry ingredients followed by the addition of the oil, egg yolk, liquids and flavourings and the whole mixture is well blended. The whites are then beaten with cream of tartar until the peaks just bend over; the batter is carefully but thoroughly folded into the beaten whites. The cakes are then baked in the usual way.

Black Forest gateau: (also commonly called Black Forest cake) Typically the Black Forest gateau consists of several layers of chocolate cake, with whipped cream and cherries between each layer. These layers are topped with additional whipped cream, maraschino cherries, and chocolate shavings. In some European traditions, sour cherries are used both between the layers and for decorating the top. Traditionally, Kirschwasser (a high grade cherry schnapps) is added to the cake, although other liquors are also used (rum is common in Austrian recipes).

Cheesecake: Cheesecake is a sweet, cheese-based dessert. Cheesecake is one of the most common desserts in the world and perhaps one of the oldest involving a dairy product other than milk. Cheesecakes can be made of ricotta cheese, havarti, quark, or, more usually, cream cheese. Other ingredients such as sugar, eggs, cream and fruit are often mixed in as well. Flavourings such as vanilla or chocolate may be added, and a fruit topping, like strawberry is frequently added. Typically, the cheese filling or topping covers a crust, which may be pastry, cookie, digestive biscuit or Graham cracker-crumb. Sometimes the base is a layer of cake. Contrary to what its name suggests, cheesecakes are more like custards and are required to be baked at lower temperatures. A common difficulty with baking cheesecakes is their tendency to "crack" when cooled. This is due to the coagulation of the beaten eggs in the batter. There are various methods to prevent this. One method is to bake the cake in a hot water bath to ensure even heating. Alternatively, a little corn starch blended into the batter prevents the coagulation of eggs.

Cupcake: (or fairy cake) is a small cake designed to serve one person, usually made in a small paper cup container. As with larger cakes, frosting and other decorations are usually applied. A simple cupcake uses the same ingredients as most other standard cakes - incorporating butter, white refined sugar, eggs, and flour. Cupcakes evolved from muffins during the nineteenth century and gained the name "cup" cakes or "measure" cakes because of the use of the practice of measuring the ingredients, using a standard-sized cup, instead of the previous practice of weighing the ingredients. The fact that these little cakes were baked in cup-shaped muffin baking containers gave double meaning to the term "cup cake," and was probably the main factor for "cupcake" becoming the U.S. standard term.

Fruitcake: Fruitcake is a heavy cake made of dried or candied fruits and nuts that are soaked in brandy or rum, often used in the celebration of weddings and Christmas. The earliest recipe lists pomegranate seeds, pine nuts, and raisins that were mixed into barley mash. In the Middle Ages, honey, spices, and preserved fruits were added and the name fruitcake was first used. The modern fruitcakes are fundamentally butter cakes, with just enough dough to bind the fruit. The cakes are saturated with liqueurs or brandy, and covered in powdered sugar, both of which prevent mould. Brandy or wine-soaked linens are used to store the fruitcakes.

16.6.2 Cookies

Cookies are made by the same general methods as are used in making conventional cakes. The ingredients are also similar to those of cakes. The main difference is the decreased amount of liquid in the cookie dough. The other differences are the increased amount of fat and egg and the smaller amount of leavening agents used. There are many varieties of cookie recipes and the different types of cookies are prepared as follows.

Drop cookies: These are made by dropping the mixture from a spoon onto a cooky sheet and baked in an oven at 190°C for 10 to 15 min. until nicely browned.

Bar cookies: They are also known as sheet cookies, and are baked by spreading the dough (similar to that of drop cookies) in a shallow pan. The individual bars are cut after baking.

Rolled cookies: Rolled cookies are made from refrigerated stiff dough. The dough is rolled and cut into the desired shapes and baked.

Meringue cookies: Such cookies are made with dough prepared by beating egg whites until stiff and adding sugar slowly. Other ingredients are folded in and the batter is dropped on a sheet and baked.

Sponge cookies: They are made like meringue cookies, using the whole egg rather than just the egg-white.

Refrigerator cookies: Refrigerator cookies are made from stiff dough that is refrigerated to become even stiffer. The dough is typically shaped into cylinders which are sliced into round cookies before baking.

Moulded cookies: Moulded cookies are also made from stiffer dough that is moulded into balls or cookie shapes by hand before baking.

Pressed cookies: Pressed cookies are made from soft dough that is extruded from a cookie press into various decorative shapes before baking. Spritzgebäck is an example of a pressed cookie.

16.6.3 Pastry

Pastries include several baked products made from doughs containing medium to large amounts of fat. These include pies, which are very popular in the United States, puffy pastries, Danish pastries, etc. The success of pie-making depends mainly on the quality of the crust.

Plain pastry is leavened primarily by the steam produced during baking. The ingredients in pastry are flour, salt, fat and water. Generally, the proportion of flour, fat and water is 6:2:1. This mixture gives a tender pie crust. If a less rich crust is required, a mixture with flour to fat ratio of 4:1 is used. Generally, all-purpose flour is used for plain pastry. Butter, margarine and hydrogenated vegetable oils are used as shortenings. Oil may also be used but the pastry will be crumbly and greasy.

In the preparation of the pastry, flour and salt are mixed after which the fat is cut into the flour. Water is then gradually added with stirring and worked into the dough. The dough is then shaped into a ball, flattened into a circular shape, and transferred to a pie pan and baked in a hot oven at 218°C until the surface is delicately browned. Then the filling is placed on the crust.

16.7 Macaroni Products

Macaroni products also termed *pasta products,* include macaroni, spaghetti, vermicelli, noodles and other similar products. Macaroni products originated in the Orient many years ago and were taken to Italy in the Middle Ages and have become the country's national food. From Italy, macaroni products spread to other parts of the world. The per-capita annual consumption of pasta products in Italy is over 31 kg.

Pasta products are made from semolina of durum wheat or other hard wheats. The macaroni industry is in an infant stage in India. A few small units produce the macaroni products by utilizing semolina available from local roller mills. There is considerable scope for the production of high quality pasta products in India since the raw material required, namely, durum wheat of good quality, is grown in the country. Vermicelli is produced from suji mainly on a cottage industry scale and used in the preparation of sweet dishes like milk vermicelli puddings. Rice-like macaroni products, such as "mock rice" and "rycena," are used as rice substitutes in times of rice scarcity. Fortified and nutritionally satisfactory macaroni products can be manufactured and made available in an acceptable form.

In the manufacture of macaroni, the semolina is made into a stiff dough using 25–30 per cent of water on semolina weight, at 32°–38°C. The dough is then extruded at high pressure through appropriate dyes to make tubes or strap-shaped products. Heavy pressure ensures that the product is translucent and free from air bubbles. Finally, the product is dried at controlled temperatures and humidity and cut into desired lengths.

Eggs are often added to the dough used in the manufacture of macaroni products. Other materials used are groundnut meal, soya flour, and cassava flour. The preparation can be enriched by the addition of vitamins and amino acids.

16.8 Origin of Flatbread

Nomads used cereals ground in stone and baked on stone. Man's first adventure to use cereals as flour is 6000 years old and bakers oven known to the world was in Babylon 4000 BC. The earliest *tandoor* is of Persians origin and bought to India by Arabs in 3000 BC via Afghanistan. The archaeological evidence of that are traced in excavation in Mesopotamia, Egypt and Indus valley civilisation. This evolutionary agricultural path was followed on east-west axis according to Diamond J. (2002).

The process of making flatbread still remains the same. The advantages of the flatbread over brick or loaf bread, is their volume being flat easier for transportation, does not need an oven, they can be prepared by millets and legumes. The versatility further is that it can become a plate to hold the accompanied dish and a pinched portion can serve as spoon. These factors are universal so their popularity continues.

16.8.1 Flatbread Classification

They are broadly classified as follows:

Pancake: Pancake are prepared using fermented semi-fluid batter. Across the region, pancake is made of teff flour and is called as *Injera* in Ethiopia, Anjeroin, Somali is made of sorghum or maize flour, the Yemeni *lahoh* and the Sudanese *kisra*. The Indian *Dosa* is prepared using a mixture of local rice flour and black gram (refer 17.7.3).

Unleavened Breads: Unleavened flatbreads are prepared using consistent dough without leavening. This bread is of thin layer and is easier to chew. Turkish *yufka*, *taftoon*, *tuftun* from Iran, lavash in Armenia. The Indian and Pakistani *chapathi* and *roti* are few examples of unleavened breads. *Rumali roti* is another example of unleavened breads. *Rumali* meaning handkerchief, as this bread is so thin that it can be folded like a handkerchief.

Leavened Thick Breads: Single layered flat bread with consistent dough, leavened eventually punched. The traditional way to leaven bread was to use sourdough – using a portion of the previously processed

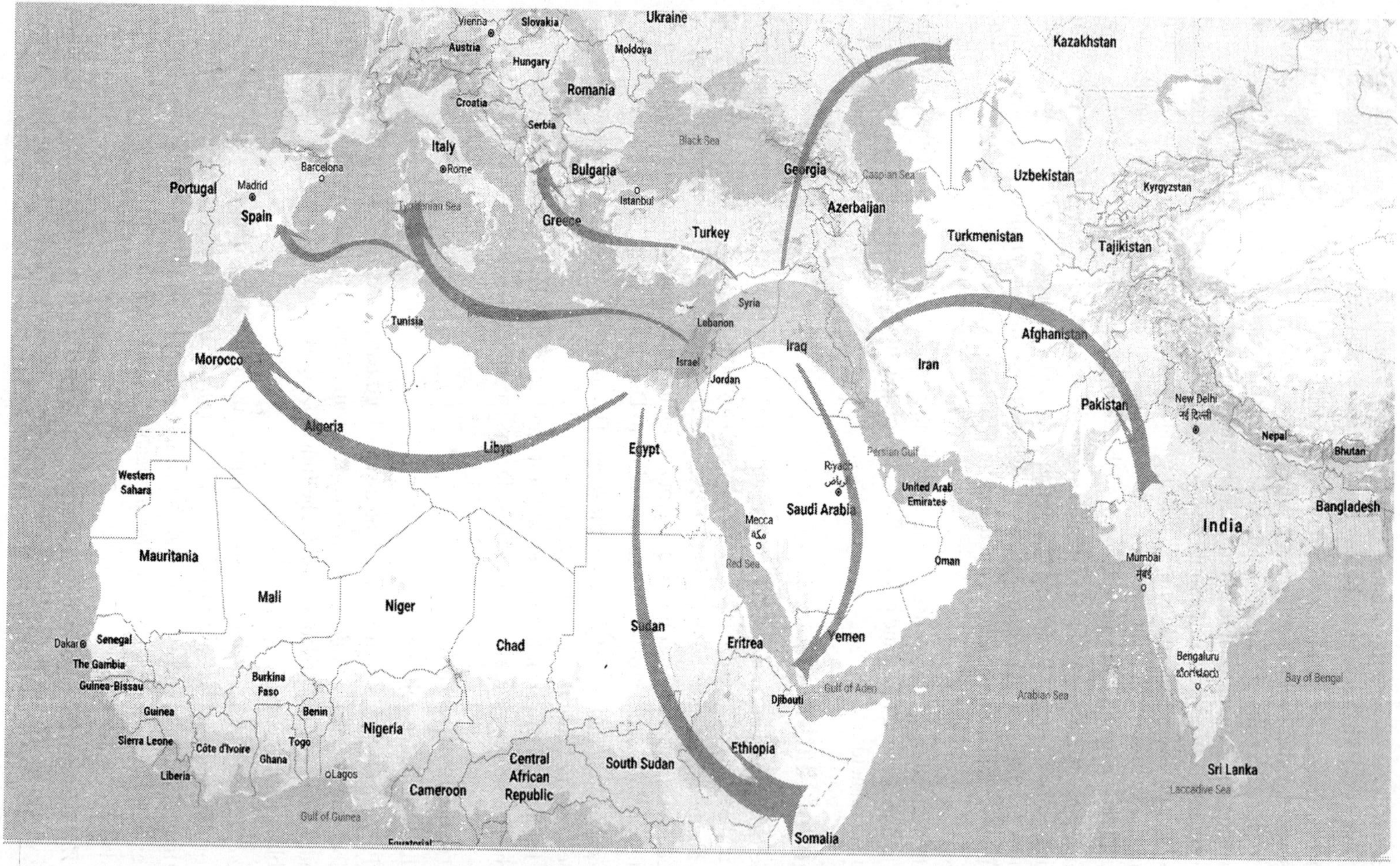

Diffusive pathway of flatbreads. Flatbreads substantially followed the same path as cereals (wheat and barley), starting from the Fertile Crescent. From there, flatbreadsspread westward around the Mediterranean, across North Africa and southern Europe, northward across the Anatolian peninsula to the Balkans and to Central Asia, and eastward to India. Interlinks with another agricultural center of origin in Ethiopia, contributing some indigenous crops including sorghum, teff, and pigmented tetraploid wheat, are found across the Arabian Peninsula.

(**Source:** Journal of ethnic food)

dough, but now baker's yeast is commonly used. Leavening makes bread softer and bread thickness can be up to 3-4 cms. Algerian, Tunisian, and Moroccan *matlouh* or *kesar matoulah*, *malka* or agroum, Moroccan *tanchnift*, Turkish *pide*, *batlana*, the Indian and Pakistani *naan*, *kulcha*, *khameeri*, Italian *pitta*, *scacciuni*, the Iranian *barbadi*, *jow*, named after Persian word for barley, because it is prepared from barley flour, Uzbek and *Kazakh lepeshka*.

Leaveaned Thin Bread: double layered flatbread with consistent dough leavened and thin. The dough puffs up or inflates during baking in the oven and on cooking the bread deflated giving a soft and flexible bread with a characteristic 'pocket' that can be stuffed. These are: the Lebanese and Syrian khobz, the Greek pita, the Albanian pite, the Turkish pide, the Bulgarian pitka, and the Italian pizza, the Egyptian *baladi* bread or *aeesh baladi* or *atah baladi* meaning national bread, the Maroccon *batbout*, the Iraqi *samoon*.

16.8.2 *Chapati* Making

Dough fermentation is similar two bread making (refer to 16.1 and 16.4.1). For making *Chapati*, flat Indian bread semi-hard white wheat with amber colour is best (refer 15.5.3 *Triticum aestivum*). The ideal stone-ground or *chakki* ground wholemeal flour or *atta* gives 90-95% extraction of flour is used. Milled flour has recently improved, in getting the fraction containing 20% protein obtained from soft wheat, and 30% protein from hard wheat.

Proteins in the flour are of prime importance. The mixograph and farinograph are used to measure the consistency of the dough. The texture are measured by shortometer which measures break of the products. The force required to retain shear-value of baked products, Warner-Bratzler shear are useful. Rheology determines viscosity-elasticity of products. The texture of dough determines the quality of finished product.

Doughs are thick mixture of wheat flour with water, needs kneading to develop gluten. Gluten is a protein formed between glaidin and gluten, when flour is mixed with water Refer (16.1).

Lipids content of the dough if it is high, then less kneading is required, low lipids content needs more kneading. Any addition of bran decreases the volume but adds nutritive value that is of fibre.

Damaged branch implies, increase in higher *farinograph* or increase in water absorption. The enzyme alpha-amylase and beta-amylase are exposed. Hence, damaged starch increases enzyme activity, and improves the dough quality.

16.8.3 Water

Water is the second most important compound besides the flour in the dough formation. Next intermolecular development occurs in the gluten which depends upon not only on water but the effect of the mixer or kneading procedure. The gluten, the skeleton protein absorbs the largest amount of water compared to starch, which relatively absorbs less amount of water 30-35% of its dry weight.

The mixing itself is a procedure in three stages; First simply mixing, second hydration and the third is tension of bound water in the dough. Water is a solvent for solutes like salt, sugar, yeast and additives. It stimulates fermentation activity of the yeast.

The presence of Calcium and Magnesium ion determines hard and soft water. The lathering capacity of soap is used for testing hardness of water. The amount in parts per million (PPM) of calcium carbonate and pH of the water are important factors to be considered.

A water of medium hardness (50-100 ppm) calcium carbonate is suitable for dough. This mineral strengthens the gluten in the dough making.

Hard water (above 200 ppm Calcium Carbonate) retards fermentation by tightening the gluten structure, calcium carbonate interferes in absorption of water. Hard water with more than pH 7.5 has negative effective on gluten. This limitation can be overcome by an increase of yeast and the addition of acid.

Soft water (10-50 ppm) calcium carbonate, also not suitable, as they weaken the gluten strength, the dough becomes soft and sticky.

Enzymes are also affected by the pH of the medium. The optimum activity is between pH 4 to 5.

16.8.4 Salt

The chief purpose of addition of salt, is to enhance the taste and it is normally 0.5 to 3% of the flour weight, but in case of weak flour, salt improves proteins or gluten strength as it increases farinograph value, mixograph peak height, binding and hardness.

16.8.5 Fermentation

Leavening agents like bakers yeast *Saccharomyces cerevisiae* converts the sugar and moisture and releases carbon dioxide. The colour and flavour of flat bread changes when baking soda is used (refer 16.2.3). Fermentation of sour dough affects the dough properties. Short proofing time is best for flat bread and baked immediately. Baking depends upon rheological, physical and chemical properties of the dough.

Table 16.1: Traditional Flatbreads of World

Region	Country	Name	Description	Ingredients
Africa	Ethiopia/ Somalia/ Eritrea	*Injera*	Similar to pancake or crumpet	Teff flour
	Morocco	*Khubz*	Rolled like pizza	
	Mali	*Ngome*	Flatbread	Millet, water, and vegetable oil
Mediterranean/ Middle east	Egypt	*Aish Mehahra*	Flatbread	5–10% fenugreek seeds and maize
		Balandi	Pocket bread/sandwich bread	Wheat flour/whole wheat flour
	Iran	*Barbari*	Persian flatbread	Wheat Flour
	Armenia	*Lavash*	Paper thin and rehydrated before use	Wheat Flour
	Israel	*Matzo*	Thin bread with cracker like texture	Wheat Flour
		Pita	Flatbread with less fermentation time	Flour, salt, yeast, and water
	Iran	*Sangak*	Flatbread	Whole-wheat flour
Southeast Asia	Thailand	*Khanom buang*	Flatbread	Rice flour
	Malaysia/ Singapore	*Roti canai*	Circular and flat	Wheat flour

(Contd...)

Europe	Russia	*Blintz/blini*	Thin pancake	Wheat flour
	Italy	*Ciabatta*	Elongated white bread, flat like a slipper and collapsed in the middle	Wheat flour, yeast
		Focaccia	Cousin of pizza with different flavors and shape	Wheat flour, yeast etc.
		Pizza	Thin bread	Wheat flour, yeast, etc. topped with tomato sauce, olive leaves, and mozzarella cheese.
	Norway	*Lefse*	Cooked on a griddle	Flour, potato, milk, and cream
	France	*Crepes*	Very thin pancake	Wheat flour
North America	Mexico	*Pancake*	Thin flat prepared from a batter	Either yeast-raised or fermented batter
South and Central America		*Arepa*	Flat unleavened patty	Cornmeal
		Tortilla	Flat unleavened bread with crisp texture	Corn flour or wheat flour
China		*Sanchuisanda (Green onion pancake)*	Baked on Ashes	All purpose flour, oil, and minced scallions (green onions)

16.8.6 Flatbreads of India

Varied forms of flatbreads are seen in different regions of Indian Sub-Continent, from Kashmir to Kanyakumari. They assume local flavour, texture changes, cultural practice and local dialect. Nomenclature of these breads also depends upon the accompanying dishes with which, it is consumed. Hence, India's flatbreads are more versatile and varied. Example: *Junka-Bhakri* is typical of Maharashtra; *Makki-ka roti-Sarsongka Sag* is popular in Punjab. *Bhakri* and *rotis* denote method of preparation is slightly different. *Rotis* depend on single main cereal or multiple millets mixed with cereals. Single cereal is *Akki* and *Jolada Roti*, multiple millets like ragi, jowar and pearls, and are mixed with wheat. These are mixed together and variation are innumerable. Some of these are presented here.

Bhakri: is rustic simple version of *chapati*. The dough is divided into equal proportion, rolled round, baked on Tawa, brushing with water and flipped to the other side. Popped short while on live fire. Then the perfect *bhakri* is served hot.

Table 16.2: Traditional flatbreads of India

Region	Name	Description	Ingredients
South India	*Adai*	Pancake	Millet dough or rice dough
	Appam	Pancake	Fermented rice batter and coconut milk

(Contd...)

Telangana	*Vedmi, Holige /Obbattu, Poli, Puranachipoli, God poli, Pappubakshalu, Bakshalu, Bobbattu, Oliga.*	Stuffed sweet flat bread	Maida/ whole wheat, channadal, sugar/jaggery
Rajasthan, Uttar Pradesh and Madhya Pradesh	*Baati*	Hard, Unleavened bread, ball shaped	Wheat flour, water, salt
Maharashtra, western and central India—Rajasthan, Gujarat, Malwa, Goa, Northern Karnataka	*Bhakri / Rotis*	Round flat unleavened bread	Sorghum, pearl millet flour, water, salt, wheat, rice
North India	*Bhatoora*	Fluffy deep fried unleavened bread	Maida, water, yogurt, salt.
South India	*Chapati*	Unleavened flatbread	Wheat flour, water, salt
North India	*Cheela*	Pancake	Pulse(dal) flour, sometimes vegetables (finely chopped, water, salt).
Gujarat	*Dhebra/ Thepla*		Whole wheat flour, chickpea, flour, black gram dhal flour, fenugreek leaves, water, salt
North India	*Kachori*	Unleavened bread, deep fried. Triangle shape	Maida, water, salt, filled with lentils.
North India	*Khakra*	Unleavened, thin crisp flatbread	Moth bean, wheat flour, oil
North India	*Kulcha*	Leavened bread	Maida, water, salt
North India	*Luchi*	Deep fried flat bread	Maida, water, salt
North India	*Naan* *Peshwari naan* *Kema naan* *Butter naan*	Flatbread baked on a *tandoor* Filled with nuts and raisins Stuffed with minced meat *Naan* topped with nigella seeds and greased with butter	Wheat flour, salt, yogurt, and water
North India	*Paratha* *e.g. Aloo Paratha, Gobi Paratha*	Stuffed unleavened flat bread.	Wheat flour, water, salt
Kerala, South India	*Parotta*	Oven baked layered leavened flat bread	Wheat flour/Maida, water, salt.

(Contd...)

Maharashtra, North Karnataka	*Thalipeeth*	Baked unleavened flatbread	Mix of whole wheat flour, bajra flour, Jowar flour, black gram dhal,
Karnataka	*Akki Rotti*	Unleavened thin, round flatbread	Rice flour, water, salt
Karnataka	*Ragi roti*	Unleavened thin, round flatbread	Finger millet flour, water, salt
Kashmir, Hyderabad	*Sheermal*	Leavened, baked in oven	Fermented with fresh yeast, sugar, water, flour, egg, milk, ghee, salt.
Goa	*Poee*	Thick rolled, oven baked, leavened flatbread.	Whole wheat flour, maida, wheat bran, water, salt, fresh yeast
Punjab	*Makki-ka-roti*	Unleavened, round flatbread	Corn flour, water, salt
Bihar, Jharkhand, parts of Uttar Pradesh	*Litti*	It is a dough ball, stuffed with Sattu (chickpea flour) roasted with ghee over coal or cow dung cakes or wood	Whole wheat flour, water, salt. For filling roasted chickpea flour, herbs spices

Cysteine Hydrochloride

16.8.7 Effect of Additives

The quality of dough can be improved by the addition of additives (Refer Chapter 30). Studies (Indrani Venkateshwar Rao, 2003 and 2006) have used oxidizing and reducing agents to improve dough quality. The modification of the rheological change brought by 100 ppm of Potassium Metabisulphite and 50 ppm of Cysteine hydrochloride, or 10 ppm of protease gave quality *parotta*. However, Sodium Stearoyl Lactate (SSL), Polyoxyethylene Sorbitan Monosterate (PS-60) at a 0.5% flour weight basis gave the best product.

Enzymes such as fungal amylase, glucose oxidase, proteinase, and xylanase, rheological characteristics of the dough gave an overall quality improvement in *parotta*, but noticeable improvement was seen in case of proteinase and xylanase when these were incorporated in the dough.

Nonstarch polysaccharides called hydrocolloids have a good rheological influences in studies (P. Achayuthakan and M. Suphantharika, 2008) which have good texture, control over a moisture content or water absorption.

Hydrocolloids have a different structures, in branching flexibility, molecular weight, ionic charge which bring about desirable rheological change. Rapid-visco-analyser when pasting is tested with continued heating at 95 °C, resulted in disintegration known as brake down.

Hydrocolloid molecules reduce bound water mobility of starch chains and thereby affected retrogradation. The guar gum (GG), Xanthan gum (XG) (0.35 – 1.0% W/W) on pasting and rheological properties of waxy con starch (WCS) (6.0% W/W) was studied. Rapid visco analyser, indicated addition of GG or XG to WCS significantly increase in peak-break down and also final set back on viscosity and pasting temperature (Refer 11.43 Emulsions).

Hydroxypropyl Methylcellulose (HPMC) xanthan and k-carrageenan at 0.2 and 0.5% levels were tested for rheological changes. Dough's water absorption was increased by all hydrocolloids except in case of k-carrageenan.

Another important noticeable change in replacing hydrocolloids in the bread is, that this bread is free of gluten. Using methylated pectin, gaur gum has good volume, moisture content of the crumb, and baking efficiency was minimized. This implies that it is a useful substitute for people who are suseptible to celiac disease.

16.8.8 Baking

The final phase of flat bread is baking. The ancient nomadic method is still in practice. In Tunisia and Algeria baking bread under a layer of sand, ember and ash without tools are still in vogue.

Other traditional method of wood-fired are of two kinds: horizontal doomed oven and the vertical cylindrical oven. Doomed are medium to large sized table with masonry structures where the bread is put on horizontal floor, in vertical cylindrical oven that are smaller and portable or fixed cylindrical clay structure where bread is stuck to the vertical walls of the oven.

Other common ways of baking is to bake on fire plate, placed directly on ember, it can be stone slab clay grill, *chapatis*, *rotis* and *bhakris* are cooked on *Tava*, a metal convex griddle. The baking qualities depends on rheological physical, chemical properties of the dough. Normally there is a loss of moisture, volume increase, starch *gelatinisation*, protein *denaturation* takes place at 65°C and the final rupurting of gas cells takes place at 350°C to 550°C. The short baking limit retains moisture, otherwise, flatbreads become brittle and unpalatable. Hence, 65 to 75% moisture has to be retained.

16.8.9 Nutritive Value of *Chapati*

Chapati made from whole wheat flour is the most important single item of food for a large section of the Indian population. In the ordinary *chapati*-based Indian diet, about 50 to 80 per cent of the calorie requirement and 60 per cent of protein requirements are met. In addition, a major portion of vitamins and minerals are also derived from *chapaties*.

All the nutrients of the wheat are present in whole wheat flour from which chapaties are made. Thus, *Chapaties* have more protein, minerals, vitamins and other nutrients than white bread made out of flours of low extraction rate, from which germ and bran, which are rich in protein and minerals, are completely removed during milling. Further nutritive value of flat bread can be enhanced by using other millets, legumes, fruits and leafy green vegetables. Stuffed *parotas* with spinach and bengal gram, green gram and vegetables like cauliflower are popular dishes that have higher nutrients than of mineral and vitamins. In addition, use of Desi Ghee in the dough making increases fats-soluble vitamins. Soya, peanut and cotton seeds flours enhance protein content.

However, it does not mean that *chapati* will be nutritionally superior to white bread. It has been observed that persons fed for a long time on 100 per cent wholemeal brown bread suffered from deficiency diseases. This may be because of the higher fibre content of wholemeal flour. Also, phytic acid present in wholemeal flour, comes in the way of their utilization of minerals, particularly calcium.

Celiac disease is a systemic immune disorder. This inadaptative immune response to gluten-derived peptides. People with this genetic disorder are susceptible to develop celiac disease.

CHAPTER

17 Pulses

Pulses are the edible fruits or seeds of pod-bearing plants belonging to the family of *Leguminosae* and are widely grown throughout the world. They have a high protein content ranging from 20–40 per cent and this makes them important in human food from the point of view of nutrition. There is widespread protein-calorie malnutrition in developing countries and pulses can play an important role in bridging the protein gap. India depends greatly on pulses to meet its demand for proteins. Because of religious sentiments, meat is not used by a good section of the people and also there is not enough meat even for those who use it. Pulses are the "poor man's meat." The per capita availability of pulses has declined from 64 g per day (1951–56) to less than 40 g per day as against the FAO/WHO's recommendation of 80 g of protein per day. If we take into account the total protein nutrition derived from other protein sources such as food grains, milk and milk products, fish, etc., then 55 g per capita/day requirement of pulses may be the realistic target.

An alternate name for pulses is "legumes," which is common in many parts of the world. In India, the term "gram" is commonly used for dry legume seeds with husk, while split decorticated grains are called "dhal."

17.1 Pulse Crop

There are over 13,000 species of plants belonging to the family of *Leguminosae* and some are cultivated as crop plants whose seeds are edible. Over the years, wild varieties of legumes have been domesticated. In this process, ancient Indian and Chinese civilizations seem to have played an important part in the domestication of Bengal gram (*Cicer arietinum*) and soya bean (*Glycine max*), respectively. Some pulses are also used as cattle feed and as green manure.

The total world acreage under pulses as recorded during 2014 is about 851.91 lakh ha with production at 774.73 lakh tones and productivity of 909 kg/ha. In the world, pulses are grown in 198 countries. Beans dry was cultivated by 152 countries, which contributed about 35.93% area to total world area, Chickpea by 58 contributed about 16.41%, Peas dry by 98 contributed 8.14%, Pigeonpea by 23 contributed 8.26%, Lentils by 56 contributed 5.31% and other 25.95%. The share to world production of Beans dry was 31.64% followed by Chickpea 17.72%, Peas dry 14.44%, Pigeonpea 6.531%, Lentils 6.23% & others 23.66%.

The world production is 96 million tonnes and India's is 276.7 lakhs tonnes, 2022. India was ranked first in pulse production during the year 2022.

The main regions with high productivity are Punjab, Haryana, Western Uttar Pradesh, West Bengal delta region, coastal Andhra Pradesh, Tamil Nadu, Kerala, coastal and eastern Karnataka and some parts of Maharashtra. India has exported 6,26,654 million tonnes of pulses to the world for the worth of ₹ 5589 crores/687 USD millions during the year 2023-24. Major export destinations (2023-24) are Algeria, the USA, Pakistan, United Arab Emirates and Turkiye.

The most important pulse crop in India is groundnut or peanut (*Arachis hypogaea*), which can be put to a wide range of uses. With its high oil content, groundnut goes to a great part into oil production and it is considered in Chapter 18 under oils and fats.

Leaving aside groundnut, of the legumes which are used just as pulse, the most important pulse crop in India is Bengal gram or chana, which is grown in an area of nearly two-fifth of that under pulse cultivation and accounts for about 50 per cent of the total production of pulses. Next in importance is red gram (*Cajanus cajan*), accounting for about 11 per cent of the pulses. Some of the major pulses produced in India and their percentage of the total production of pulses is given in Table 17.1.

Table 17.1 Major pulse crops of India

Common name	Botanical name	Percentage of total production
1. Bengal gram or chickpea (chana)	*Cicer arietinum*	35
2. Red gram or tur (arhar or pigeon pea)	*Cajanus cajan*	16
3. Black gram or urad	*Phaseolus mungo* Roxb.	10
4. Greengram or mung	*Phaseolus aureus* Roxb	10
5. Moth or tepary bean	*Phaseolus aconitifolius*	2.5
6. Lentil or masur	*Lens esculenta*	7.1
7. Horsegram or kulthi	*Dolichos biflorus*	2.7
8. Peas	*Pisum sativum*	4.2
9. Khesari dhal	*Lathyrus sativus*	3.0
10. Others	—	9.4

Source: www.fas.usda.gov/wap/circular/2006.xls.

Among the others in the table, some important ones are: cowpea (*Vigna unguiculata*), cluster bean or guar (*Cyarropis tetragonoloba*), Indian bean or field bean (*Dolichos lablab*), French bean or kidney bean (*Phaseolus vulgaris*), and soya bean (*Glycine max*).

17.2 Composition

The chemical composition of edible pulse seeds depends upon the species. In general, their protein content is high and is commonly more than twice that of cereal grains, usually constituting about 20 per cent of the dry weight of seeds. The protein content of some legumes like soya bean is as high as 40 per cent. The nutritional value of legumes is not just confined to their usefulness as a source of vegetable protein. They are rich in carbohydrates and some species like groundnut and soybean are rich in oil. Pulse seeds are also sources of other nutritionally important materials, such as vitamins and minerals. However, their importance lies in their actual and potential value as a source of plant protein in human nutrition. The chemical composition of some legumes of common usage in India is given in Table 17.2.

In addition to nutritional factors, pulses contain several heat-stable and heat-labile anti-nutritional and/or toxic factors. These include enzyme inhibitors, toxic substances, factors inciting clinical disorders, factors that interfere with digestion, and flatulence-causing substances. These factors are to be reduced or eliminated to make pulse seeds more acceptable as a source of inexpensive nutritional proteins and maximize their utilization as human food.

17.2.1 Pulse Proteins

Pulse proteins are chiefly globulins but albumins are also present in a few species. Their nutritional importance depends not only on the quantity of protein but also on its quality, which in turn depends upon the amino acid composition. Pulse proteins are deficient in sulphur-containing amino acids, particularly in methionine, and tryptophan. It is only in the case of soyabean that the tryptophan level is equal to the FAO provisional pattern. All the pulses contain sufficient amounts of leucine and phenylalanine. Lysine and threonine contents are low only in groundnuts. Overall, the most satisfying pulse protein from the standpoint of the FAO provisional pattern is that of soyabean.

There are several factors that reduce the nutritional value of pulse proteins. A majority of pulse proteins have high molecular weights and are very compact molecules, and thus reduces the digestibility of the native protein. Some proteins are found complexed with carbohydrates and the carbohydrate moiety has a negative influence on the digestibility of native protein. Proteins also form complexes with phytin and polyphenols present in pulses, contributing to their low digestibility.

17.2.2 Carbohydrates

Food pulses contain about 55–60 per cent of total carbohydrates, including starch, soluble sugars, fibre and unavailable carbohydrates. Starch accounts for the major proportion of carbohydrates in legumes. The unavailable sugars in pulses include substantial levels of oligosaccharides of the raffinose family of sugars (raffinose, stachyose and verbiscose), which are notoriously known for the flatulence production in man and animals. These sugars escape digestion when they are ingested, due to the lack of α-galactosidase activity in the mammalian mucosa. Consequently, the oligosaccharides are not absorbed into the blood and are digested by the microflora of the lower intestinal tract, resulting in the production of large amounts of carbon dioxide and hydrogen and a small amount of methane. Some of the methods used in processing pulses, such as germination, soaking, cooking and autoclaving, reduce considerable amounts of oligosaccharides. Fermentation also reduces oligosaccharides, as has been observed during the fermentation of black gram and rice.

17.2.3 Lipids

Lipids form about 1.5 per cent of the dry matter in pulses except in groundnut, soyabean and winged beans. Most of the pulse lipids contain high amounts of polyunsaturated acids. These undergo oxidative rancidity during storage resulting in several undesirable changes, such as loss of protein solubility, off-flavour development, and loss of nutritive quality.

17.2.4 Minerals

Pulses are important sources of calcium, magnesium, zinc, iron, potassium and phosphorus. A major portion (80 per cent) of phosphorus in many pulses is present as phytate phosphorus. Phytin complexes with proteins and minerals and renders them biologically unavailable to human beings and animals. Processing methods, such as cooking, soaking, germination, fermentation, etc., can reduce or eliminate appreciable amounts of phytin.

Table 17.2 Composition of Pulses (per 100 gms of edible portion)

	Moisture	Protein	Ash	Fat	Fiber	Carbohydrate	Energy		Calcium	Phosphorus	Iron	B-Carotene	Thiamine	Riboflavin	Niacin	Vitamin C	Vitamin B6
	g	g		g	g	g	K Joules	K Cal	g	mg	mg	mg	mg	mg	mg		mg
Bengal gram, whole (*Cicer arietinum*)	8.56 ± 0.37	18.77 ± 0.42	2.78 ± 0.13	5.11 ± 0.11	25.22 ± 0.39	39.56 ± 0.16	1201	287	150 ± 18.3	267 ± 21.9	6.78 ± 0.75	172 ± 21.0	0.37 ± 0.040	0.24 ± 0.011	2.10 ± 0.06	–	0.36 ± 0.025
Bengal gram, dal (*Cicer arietinum*)	9.18 ± 0.58	21.55 ± 1.45	2.10 ± 0.10	5.31 ± 0.06	15.15 ± 0.17	46.72 ± 1.29	1377	329	46.32 ± 5.12	325 ± 14.0	6.08 ± 0.27	165 ± 22.8	0.35 ± 0.029	0.15 ± 0.003	1.87 ± 0.06	–	0.19 ± 0.008
Black gram, whole (*Phaseolus mungo*)	8.70 ± 0.33	21.97 ± 0.63	3.35 ± 0.03	1.58 ± 0.06	20.41 ± 0.06	43.99 ± 0.76	1219	291	86.18 ± 8.99	345 ± 36.5	5.97 ± 0.56	12.80 ± 0.50	0.32 ± 0.024	0.11 ± 0.008	1.85 ± 0.13	–	0.53 ± 0.039
Black gram, dal (*Phaseolus mungo*)	9.16 ± 0.35	23.06 ± 0.59	3.17 ± 0.02	1.69 ± 0.12	11.93 ± 0.26	51.00 ± 0.80	1356	324	55.67 ± 6.10	375 ± 43.7	4.67 ± 0.55	10.11 ± 2.10	0.21 ± 0.005	0.09 ± 0.003	1.76 ± 0.09	–	0.22 ± 0.029
Cowpea, brown (*Vigna catjang*)	9.42 ± 0.39	20.36 ± 0.59	2.90 ± 0.11	1.15 ± 0.06	11.54 ± 0.13	54.62 ± 0.49	1340	320	81.73 ± 7.63	372 ± 32.9	5.90 ± 1.26	7.08 ± 1.58	0.33 ± 0.087	0.09 ± 0.009	1.64 ± 0.03	–	0.30 ± 0.033
Cowpea, white (*Vigna catjang*)	9.32	21.25	2.83	1.14	11.7	53.77	1340	320	84.1	378	5.04	8.21	0.34	0.09	1.51	–	0.26
Field bean, black (*Phaseolus vulgaris*)	9.57	19.93	2.73	0.92	23.4	43.46	1155	276	78.16	457	4.5	–	0.35	0.07	1.88	–	0.35
Field bean, brown (*Phaseolus vulgaris*)	8.74	19.9	2.74	0.98	22.4	45.24	1184	283	75.2	429	4.99	–	0.32	0.07	2.04	–	0.37
Field bean, white (*Phaseolus vulgaris*)	8.61 ± 0.36	19.84 ± 1.04	3.09 ± 0.15	0.94 ± 0.02	22.99 ± 0.83	44.53 ± 1.42	1173	280	77.24 ± 10.17	448 ± 71.4	5.50 ± 0.72	–	0.37 ± 0.082	0.07 ± 0.009	1.96 ± 0.09	–	0.38 ± 0.017
Green gram, dal (*Phaseolus aureus*)	9.77 ± 0.67	23.88 ± 0.61	3.04 ± 0.03	1.35 ± 0.20	9.37 ± 0.38	52.59 ± 0.45	1363	326	43.13 ± 5.14	416 ± 22.4	3.93 ± 0.30	122 ± 2.7	0.35 ± 0.071	0.12 ± 0.016	1.84 ± 0.23	–	0.19 ± 0.011
Green gram, whole (*Phaseolus aureus*)	9.95 ± 0.42	22.53 ± 0.43	3.22 ± 0.04	1.14 ± 0.17	17.04 ± 0.38	46.13 ± 0.64	1229	294	92.43 ± 10.68	353 ± 33.6	4.89 ± 0.46	137 ± 33.5	0.45 ± 0.027	0.27 ± 0.011	2.16 ± 0.13	–	0.35 ± 0.034

Horse gram, whole (*Dolicus biflorus*)	9.28 ± 0.57	21.73 ± 0.29	3.24 ± 0.11	0.62 ± 0.04	7.88 ± 0.02	57.24 ± 0.50	1379	330	269 ± 34.9	298 ± 22.5	8.76 ± 1.16	58.57 ± 9.13	0.32 ± 0.002	0.24 ± 0.033	1.82 ± 0.26	–	0.21 ± 0.017
Lentil dal (*Lens culinaris*)	9.71 ± 0.48	24.35 ± 1.10	2.23 ± 0.13	0.75 ± 0.04	10.43 ± 0.39	52.53 ± 1.05	1349	323	44.32 ± 4.74	310 ± 5.3	7.06 ± 0.55	6.34 ± 0.82	0.34 ± 0.034	0.16 ± 0.005	1.81 ± 0.02	–	0.18 ± 0.022
Lentil whole, brown (*Lens culinaris*)	9.20 ± 0.77	22.49 ± 0.58	2.39 ± 0.35	0.64 ± 0.02	16.82 ± 1.30	48.47 ± 1.12	1251	299	76.13 ± 7.23	274 ± 27.4	7.57 ± 0.67	10.29 ± 1.09	0.40 ± 0.073	0.22 ± 0.026	2.54 ± 0.12	–	0.46 ± 0.022
Lentil whole, yellowish (*Lens culinaris*)	9.75	22.87	2.2	0.61	16.66	47.91	1246	298	76.66	261	7.91	12.64	0.42	0.22	2.56	–	0.47
Moth bean (*Vigna aconitifolia*)	8.14 ± 0.49	19.75 ± 0.38	3.14 ± 0.18	1.76 ± 0.09	15.12 ± 0.49	52.09 ± 0.96	1291	309	154 ± 17.0	362 ± 31.7	7.90 ± 0.17	3.57 ± 1.03	0.45 ± 0.070	0.09 ± 0.005	1.87 ± 0.08	–	0.16 ± 0.009
Peas, dry (*Pisum sativum*)	9.33 ± 0.61	20.43 ± 0.79	2.41 ± 0.09	1.89 ± 0.08	17.01 ± 0.63	48.93 ± 0.45	1269	303	75.11 ± 13.93	334 ± 18.3	5.09 ± 0.45	65.71 ± 8.07	0.56 ± 0.049	0.16 ± 0.013	2.69 ± 0.15	–	0.26 ± 0.045
Rajmah, black (*Phaseolus vulgaris*)	8.69	19.01	3.35	1.62	17.74	49.59	1247	298	134	386	6.17	1.95	0.21	0.19	2.61	–	0.23
Rajmah, brown (*Phaseolus vulgaris*)	9.68 ± 0.79	19.50 ± 0.84	3.36 ± 0.19	1.68 ± 0.07	16.95 ± 0.27	48.83 ± 0.59	1245	298	134 ± 17.6	396 ± 32.5	6.30 ± 0.61	2.16 ± 0.50	0.26 ± 0.035	0.21 ± 0.005	2.37 ± 0.12	–	0.21 ± 0.016
Rajmah, red (*Phaseolus vulgaris*)	9.87 ± 0.30	19.91 ± 1.44	3.28 ± 0.21	1.77 ± 0.04	16.57 ± 0.63	48.61 ± 0.65	1252	299	126 ± 8.1	409 ± 32.4	6.13 ± 0.77	1.60 ± 0.24	0.30 ± 0.020	0.19 ± 0.018	2.42 ± 0.15	–	0.21 ± 0.033
Red gram, dal (*Cajanus cajan*)	9.20 ± 0.61	21.70 ± 0.50	3.26 ± 0.03	1.56 ± 0.03	9.06 ± 0.30	55.23 ± 0.83	1384	331	71.73 ± 6.41	328 ± 17.2	3.90 ± 0.46	127 ± 26.3	0.45 ± 0.046	0.11 ± 0.006	2.09 ± 0.14	–	0.24 ± 0.026
Red gram, whole (*Cajanus cajan*)	9.30 ± 0.45	20.47 ± 0.72	3.53 ± 0.03	1.38 ± 0.08	22.84 ± 0.43	42.48 ± 0.77	1146	274	139 ± 11.8	312 ± 38.3	5.37 ± 1.36	149 ± 21.0	0.74 ± 0.028	0.15 ± 0.015	2.42 ± 0.18	–	0.42 ± 0.033
Soya bean, brown (*Glycine max*)	5.51 ± 0.13	35.58 ± 0.66	4.74 ± 0.31	19.82 ± 0.26	21.55 ± 0.66	12.79 ± 0.97	1596	382	239 ± 26.6	483 ± 38.9	8.29 ± 0.51	3.50 ± 1.01	0.59 ± 0.069	0.24 ± 0.002	2.12 ± 0.14	–	0.43 ± 0.012
Soya bean, white (*Glycine max*)	5.47	37.8	4.52	19.42	22.63	10.16	1579	378	195	494	8.22	2.82	0.61	0.23	2.28	–	0.45

Source: IFCT, NIN, ICMR, Hyderabad, 2017

17.2.5 Vitamins

Pulses contain small amounts of carotene, the provitamin A. Many pulses contain 50 to 300 international units of vitamin A per 100 g. Fresh pulses like peas may have a vitamin A activity considerably in excess of this figure.

The thiamine content of pulses is approximately equal to or exceeds that of, whole cereals, the average value of the vitamin being 0.4 to 0.5 mg per 100 g of pulses. Pulses are also fairly rich in niacin (about 2.0 mg/100 g). They are poor in riboflavin, and dry legumes are almost devoid of ascorbic acid.

17.3 Processing

Processing of pulses is of primary importance in improving their nutritive value. The processing methods used are soaking, germination, decortication, cooking and fermentation.

17.3.1 Soaking

Soaking in water is the first step in most methods of preparing pulses for consumption. As indicated above, soaking reduces the oligosaccharides of the raffinose family. Soaking also reduces the amount of phytic acid in pulses.

17.3.2 Germination

Germination improves the nutritive value of food pulses. The ascorbic acid content of pulses increases manifold after 48 hours of germination. Germinated and sprouted pulses have been used to prevent and cure scurvy since the 18th Century. The riboflavin, niacin, choline and biotin contents of all pulses increase during germination. The folic acid content, however, greatly decreases and the pantothenic acid value remains practically unaltered. Germination also brings about changes in the carbohydrates of the pulses, some of the starch being converted into sugars. The sprouts maybe used either as a salad or a vegetable. The germination process reduces and/or eliminates most of the anti-nutritional and toxic factors in several pulses. Also, preparations obtained from sprouted pulses, such as those of horse gram, green gram and Bengal gram, by methods similar to those used in cooking dry seeds, are more delicious.

17.3.3 Decortication

Dry pulse seeds have a fibrous seed coat (husk or skin), which often is indigestible and may have a bitter taste. In such cases, the skin has to be removed. The germ is usually removed during dehusking, and this may result in some loss of thiamine. Husked and split pulses are commonly used in India as dhals. Dhals may not be nutritionally as good as the whole seed, but their keeping qualities, cooking time and digestibility will be better.

Several methods are available for decortication. A simple method is to soak the seeds for a short time in water; the husk takes up more water than the seeds and may be easily separated by rubbing while still moist. In the alternative, the soaked grains may be dried and the husk removed by pounding and winnowing. Roasting also renders the husk easier to separate. Roasted legumes like those of Bengal gram and peas are widely used in India.

17.3.4 Cooking

Cooking destroys the enzyme inhibitors and thus improves the nutritional quality of food pulses. Cooking also improves the palatability. However, pulses should not be overcooked as this reduces the quality of proteins. Longer cooking causes a drop in the nutritive value of pulses as it results in the loss of lysine. Prolonged heating also results in loss of vitamins and consequent loss of nutritional value.

17.3.5 Fermentation

The processing of food pulses by fermentation increases their digestibility, palatability and nutritive value. Soyabean is a very valuable pulse whose proteins approach the quality of animal protein. However, it cannot be directly used as food because of the toxic substances present in the pulse. The toxic substances can be eliminated by fermentation. In South-East Asia various fermented products of soyabean (see Section 17.8) are produced and consumed on a large scale. It appears to be possible to prepare products from Bengal gram similar to those of fermented soyabean products. The preparation of idli from a blend of fermented black gram and rice has been described in Chapter 17. This fermentation process improves the availability of essential amino acids and, thus, the nutritional quality of the protein in the blend. In general, the nutritive value of the legume-based fermented foods is shown to be higher than their raw counterparts.

17.3.6 Pulse Protein Concentrates

Separation of digestible protein from the indigestible portion of pulses is of great nutritional and economic importance. Such protein extracts have been made from soyabean (Subsection 17.8.1) and groundnut cake (Subsection 19.7.1). Such concentrates are free from anti-nutritional factors and provide nutritionally valuable proteins. Efforts to obtain such protein concentrates and isolates with low or no anti-nutritional factors will help solve the protein malnutrition problem of developing countries.

17.4 Utilization of Pulses

The fruits and seeds of pulses can be utilized in a variety of ways and the nutritional value may be influenced markedly by the way in which they are used. Their use after they are subjected to some types of processing has been described above and the ways in which the unprocessed pulses are used are the following:

17.4.1 Mature Seeds

A great bulk of pulse seeds are consumed in this form. It is convenient to use them this way, as it is most economical to store the harvested crop as dry seeds (except the oil-containing legumes) without loss of nutritive value, provided the moisture content of the grains is low and the storage pests are avoided. There are, however, certain pulses, like the moth bean which becomes very hard on storage and require prolonged soaking and cooking before they are reduced to an acceptable condition for eating. The great majority of the pulses can be used as such after storage by soaking the dried seed, followed by cooking in water.

17.4.2 Fresh Seeds

Pulses which can be used as dry seeds can also be used as mature or immature fresh seeds. If the pods are tough and fibrous, the seed is separated and cooked in much the same way as dry seeds. Some of them are preferred cooked as fresh seeds as the products obtained have better taste and flavour than those of dry seeds

17.4.3 Immature Pods

Pulses which produce pods that remain fleshy for two or three weeks before the fibre becomes hard can be used as green vegetables. This is the common way in which some beans (e.g., *Phaseolus vulgaris*)

are used. The nutritional values of immature fruits are different from those of mature seeds; their protein contents are lower, but they are relatively rich in vitamins and soluble carbohydrates.

17.5 Toxic Constituents of Pulses

The seeds of pulses include both edible and inedible types. Even amongst the edible legumes, toxic principles occur and their elimination is important in order to exploit them for edible purposes. Two thermolabile factors are implicated in toxic effects. The first includes inhibitors of the enzymes trypsin, chymotrypsin and α-amylase and the second include haemagglutinins, which impede the absorption of the products of digestion in the gut. In addition, legumes also contain a goitrogen, a toxic saponin, cyanogenic glycosides and alkaloids.

The inhibitor of trypsin is a protein found in several pulses. The inhibitor suppresses the release of amino acids and thus does not make for the normal growth of animals fed with such pulses. The trypsin inhibitor may stimulate the production of extra trypsin by the pancreas and ultimately bring about its loss of activity. Haemagglutinins are also proteins and they combine with products of digestion and thus impair the efficiency of absorption of the digested products. Cyanogenic glycosides cause cyanide poisoning. On hydrolysis of the glycoside by the enzyme, β-glucosidase, hydrogen cyanide is liberated. However, a cyanide content in the range of 10–20 mg per 100 g of pulse is considered safe. Many legumes, except lima bean (*Phaseolus lunatus*), contain cyanide within this limit.

Saponins are a group of natural products possessing the property of producing lather or foam when shaken with water. These are glycosides of high molecular weight. Saponins have been reported in soyabean, sword bean (*Canavalia gladiata*) and jack bean (*Canavalia ensiformis*). Toxic saponins cause nausea and vomiting. These toxins can be eliminated by soaking prior to cooking. Alkaloids are known to occur in the seeds of many legumes but they are relatively innocuous.

Some compounds found in pulse seeds appear to fix iodine, inducing a state of iodine deficiency in the thyroid, eventually producing goitre. It is also possible that goitre is the result of blockade of iodine uptake by the thyroid in the presence of such compounds.

Two toxic substances in legumes produce serious pathological conditions. They are the factors in kesari dhal which causes lathyrism and the haemolytic factor in *Vicia faba* associated with the disease favism.

17.5.1 Lathyrism

Lathyrism is a paralytic disease affecting the lower limbs. The incidence of the disease is higher in males than females and recovery from the condition does not usually occur. The disease has been known since early times and there is a reference to it in early Indian medical writings.

Serious outbreaks of lathyrism have occurred in this country quite a few times. The disease has been associated with the consumption of kesari dhal and is commonly noticed in poor families who continuously eat considerable quantities of the dhal. Even when other crops fail, this legume thrives and thus in times of scarcity, the poor people are forced to eat this dhal. However, lathyrism develops only when the consumption of dhal is high (300 g daily), the diet does not contain adequate quantities of cereals, and it is used for a long time (6 months or more).

In lathyrism, the toxic substance interferes with the formation of normal collagen fibres in the connective tissue. The disease can be prevented by ensuring a reasonable balance between kesari dhal and other food materials and its replacement by other pulses wherever practicable.

17.5.2 Favism

Favism is haemolytic anaemia. The disease is almost entirely confined to persons living in the Mediterranean basin or of Mediterranean origin. In severe cases of favism, death may occur within 24–48 hours of the onset of the attack. Children are more liable to succumb than adults. If the victim survives the acute stage, recovery usually takes about four weeks.

Favism is brought about by eating broad beans or by inhaling the pollen of the flower. The victim suffers from an inherited biochemical abnormality that affects the metabolism of glutathione in red blood cells and is the result of decreased activity of the enzyme glucose-6-phosphate dehydrogenase. In persons with this abnormality, the red cells are more prone to injury and destruction by certain drugs, such as sulphonamide, and this raises complications in the treatment of infectious diseases.

17.5.3 Elimination of Toxic Factors

It has already been indicated that soaking, heating and fermentation can reduce or eliminate most of the toxic factors of the pulses. Correct application of heat in cooking pulses can eliminate most toxic factors without impairment of nutritional value. Cooking also contributes towards pulse digestibility. Heat causes the denaturation of the proteins responsible for trypsin inhibition, haemagglutination and the enzyme responsible for the hydrolysis of cyanogenic glycosides. The mode of application of heat is important. Autoclaving and soaking followed by heating are effective. Another way of eliminating toxic factors is by fermentation, which yields products more digestible and of higher nutritive value than raw pulses.

17.6 Pulses in Human Nutrition

Protein malnutrition is common in third world countries. Pulse protein can serve a useful purpose in alleviating this situation. The animal proteins which are nutritionally the best are available only in small quantities in poor countries and there are limitations to their supply at the present levels even in rich countries. The average daily per capita consumption of animal protein in India is 6 g which is less than one-tenth of what it is in developed countries. Therefore, vegetable proteins, and in particular pulse proteins, have an important place in meeting the protein requirements of the world.

Though compared to animal protein, pulse foods have low nutritional value, it is possible to make pulses more acceptable as a source of inexpensive nutritious protein and maximize their utilization as human food. By the processing and blending of proteins from different sources, it should be possible to produce high quality protein from plant sources with an amino acid profile as close as possible to that of good animal proteins. Such a formula can be prepared from a suitable combination of pulses, rice and oil seeds. Necessary technology has to be developed to harness the tremendous potential of pulses in human nutrition.

17.7 Some Important Pulses

Pulses from an important item of diet all over India, being a good source of protein, especially in the vegetarian diet. The nutritional quality of a diet mainly based on cereal improves with a proper intake of pulses. The nutritional status of a pulse depends upon the protein content, its biological value, digestibility, essential amino acid composition, and the vitamin and mineral content. Based on these qualities, Bengal gram and black gram have been assigned a higher order of nutritive merit; green gram, lentil and soyabean are the next best. Then follow red gram and horse gram; the rest being comparatively inferior, mainly being low in their biological value rather than their protein content.

17.7.1 Bengal Gram (*Cicer arietinum*)

Other names of this pulse are gram, chana and chickpea. This is the most important pulse crop of India, ranking fourth among the grain crops in area and production.

India ranked first in area and production in the world, followed by Pakistan, Iran and Australia. The highest productivity of 2170 kg/ha is observed in China followed by Israel, the Republic of Moldova and Bosnia and Herzegovina. India's productivity was 1261 kg/ha yields.

The world production is 16.5 million tonnes and India's is 13.75 million tonnes, 2022. The yield per unit area was 12.6 quintals per hectare and this has remained constant over 10 years. There is a need to increase the production of this pulse and other pulses by developing appropriate agricultural technology. The crop is also grown in the Mediterranean region and a few other countries.

The Bengal gram seeds vary in size and are beaked, round, semi-round, wrinkled or semi-wrinkled in shape. The seed coat is either brown, light brown, yellow, orange, black, white or green. The cotyledons are yellow or pale yellow.

The immature grain is eaten raw or boiled as a vegetable, spiced and cooked. When ripe, the grain is consumed in the form of whole grain, dhal and basin (gram flour). The whole grain is also consumed after cooking and mixing with salt or sugar or spices. Gram flour is used as one of the chief ingredients, along with ghee and sugar, in the preparation of many forms of Indian confectionery, such as Mysore-pak. Savoury items like bajias are also made out of it.

In Gujarat, *Khaman,* a fermented product prepared from coarsely ground Bengal gram dhal and salt, and cooked like dhokla, is very popular.

The proteins of the gram are deficient in tryptophan and sulphur-containing amino acids. The proteins are more digestible and better assimilated than those in other pulses. On the whole, Bengal gram protein is the best pulse protein owing to its high net-protein-utilization value.

17.7.2 Red Gram (*Cajanus cajan*)

Red gram is also known as pigeon pea, because its seeds are the favourite food of wild pigeons. It is a highly esteemed food in India, especially in the South and figures in the daily food of a considerable number of people. Its tender green pods constitute a favourite vegetable in some parts. It is largely eaten in the form of split pulse as dhal. It is consumed in various ways but most often in South India it is cooked with spices and vegetables and consumed as sambar.

Red gram is now cultivated in different parts of the world. It is a native of Africa and is being cultivated in India for a very long time. Numerous types of red gram are known which vary in colour, size and shape of pods and seeds. Some 86 different types are grown in India. These types are grouped under two distinct varieties: arhar (*C. cajan* var. *bicolour*), mostly grown in North India, and tur (*C. cajan* var. *flavus*) grown in the South.

The world production is 4.49 million tonnes and India's 4.34 million tonnes, 2022.

The seeds differ in size, shape and colour of the seed coat. Based on size, they are distinguished as large, medium and small. The seeds may be round, oval or kidney-shaped. The colour of the seed may be white, light brown, dark brown and pinkish black.

The seeds of red gram are split into dhal before marketing. Both dry and wet methods are used in making dhal. In the dry method, the seeds are dried in the sun for 3–4 days and then split in a mill. The seeds are sometimes smeared with a small quantity of vegetable oil to soften the seed coat and facilitate the milling. In the wet method, the seeds are first soaked in water for 6-10 hours. They are then mixed with red earth, heaped and left overnight. Then the seeds are dried in the sun, sieved and winnowed to remove the earth, and finally split into dhal in a pestle-and-mortar (*chakki*). This split dhal is cleaned by winnowing and treated with some oil to preserve its quality.

17.7.3 Black Gram (*Phaseolus mungo* Roxb.)

Black gram or urd belongs to the genus *Phaseolus*, which comprises 230 species, of which 20 are cultivated for their edible pods or seeds. Based on their origin, the species are divided into two groups, the Asiatic and the American. The American pulses are generally accepted as being members of the genus *Phaseolus*, while the Asiatic pulses are assigned either to the genus *Vigna* or *Adzukia*. Pulses, other than black gram belonging to this genus, which are important in India are green gram and moth.

Black gram is reported to have originated in India. It is the most highly prized of all pulses of the genus *Phaseolus*. It is cultivated in all parts of the country in an area of 3.37 million hectares.

Black gram production in the country is largely concentrated in five states viz., Uttar Pradesh (UP), Andhra Pradesh, Madhya Pradesh, Tamil Nadu, Maharashtra. These five states together contribute for about 70% of total Urad production in the country.

It has a mucilaginous material (see Subsection 16.3.1) which makes it a valuable ingredient in idli preparation. The chief proteins present in black gram are albumins and globulins (55–56 per cent). It also has prolamines and glutelins (24–25 per cent).

Germination of the black gram reduces the phytin content and increases vitamin content. By the action of proteolytic enzymes, protein degradation products are formed.

Black gram flour is the chief constituent of the highly popular wafer-biscuit known as papad. Black gram dhal is an important ingredient in the preparation of idli and dosa. It forms the main base of some fried savoury and sweet preparations, such as vada and jahangir, which enjoy popularity on account of their special sensory and textural attributes. Like mung and moth, urad dhals are fried in fat, salted and eaten as snacks.

17.7.4 Green Gram (*Phaseolus aureus*)

Green gram or mung is being cultivated in India for over 2,000 years.

India is the world's largest producer as well as consumer of green gram. It produces about 1.5 to 2.0 million tons of Mung annually from about 3 to 4 million hectares of area, with an average productivity of 500 kg per hectare. Green gram output accounts for about 10–12% of total pulse production in the country.

The seeds are used as whole seed or dhal. The protein content of the pulse is high and is easily digested. The proteins are deficient in methionine, cysteine and tryptophan.

Green gram, whole or split, is used in a variety of ways in Indian homes. Dry seeds or sprouted whole seeds are used in the preparation of curry and some savoury dishes. Sweet dishes also are made from the green gram. Split and dehusked green gram, soaked for some time, is used in the preparation of salads or fried in a little fat and salted, and is used as a snack.

17.7.5 Moth Bean (*Phaseolus aconitifolius*)

Moth bean or terapy bean is a native of India and it grows wild in the country. The seeds are small, up to 0.5 mm long, 2 to 3 mm wide, yellow or brown in colour or mottled black, somewhat uniform in shape with rounded or truncated ends. The yield of the grain is low. The grain is used either whole or split as a dhal. The whole grain, after frying, is mixed with other savoury dishes to make "dhalmoth."

It is predominantly grown in India, although it has been cultivated in the United States, Australia, Thailand and other parts of Asia. 1.5 million hectares of land is used in India for moth bean production, producing approximately 0.4 million t/ha of seeds.

17.7.6 Lentil (*Lens esculenta*)

Lentil or masur has been known in India as an article of food from the most ancient times. It is cultivated mostly in the North.

The world production is 6.7 million tonnes and India's is 1.28 million tonnes in 2022.

India ranked first in the area (18.00 lakh ha) and second in the production (11.00 lakh tonnes) with 39% of 22% of world area and production respectively. The highest productivity is recorded in Croatia (2862 kg/ha) followed by New Zealand (2469 kg/ha). Canada ranks first in production (41%) due to very high level of productivity (1633 kg/ha) as compared to India (611 kg/ha).

In 2013, Canada produced 18.805 lakh tonnes of lentil, and India produced 11.340 lakh tonnes and is the second-largest in the world production.

Germination of the pulse increases its biological value. In nutrition, lentil occupies a place second only to Bengal gram and black gram.

Lentil is mostly used as dhal in the preparation of soups flavoured with spices. Young pods are eaten as vegetables. Lentil meal mixed with barley or other cereal flour and common salt is marketed as invalid food in some countries. The whole seed is used in preparing a salted fried preparation.

17.7.7 Horse Gram (*Dolichos biflorus*)

Horse gram or kulthi is grown largely in South India. The seeds are small, flattened, light red, brown-black or mottled.

Horse gram is extensively used in South India as feed for cattle and horses in the same way as Bengal gram is used in North India. The seeds are cooked before feeding. The legume is the poor man's pulse. It is eaten by poor people, both boiled and fried. It can be eaten whole or after grinding into a meal, unlike other pulses which are consumed after splitting. Germinated seeds and seedlings are also used in cooking. The world production is 6.7 million tonnes and India's is 1.28 million tonnes in 2022.

17.7.8 Field Bean (*Dolichos lablab*)

Dolichos lablab is of Asian origin and there are two varieties: one is an annual, commonly cultivated as a garden crop; and the other, perennial in varying degrees, cultivated as a field crop. The two varieties have been designated *D. lablab* var *typicus* and *D. lablab* var *lignosus* (field bean). They are of varying colours ranging from white to green or purple. The seeds are white, yellow, brownish-purple or black.

Field bean is popular as a vegetable. The pods in most cases retain their tenderness until they attain full size; therefore, the seeds alone can be utilized. *Lablab* var *lignosus* is valued more for the seeds than the pods. Green pods are gathered at all stages of development and tender seeds eaten fried or cooked, and salted in the same manner as green pea. Ripe and dried seeds are consumed as split pulse, while seeds are sometimes soaked in water overnight and when germination starts, they are sun-dried and stored for future use.

Field Pca: Russian Federation rank first in area (22.5%) and production (26%) at Global level. Canada stands second position in area (18.8%) followed by China (13%) respectively. India occupies fourth position in area (10.6%) and fourth position in production (7%). The highest productivity is recorded in France (2,996 kg/ha) followed by Canada (2,540 kg/ha), and Russia Federation (2,244 kg/ha). While, India's productivity is only 1,318 kg/ha.

17.7.9 Pea (*Pisum sativum*)

There are two kinds of peas—the field pea and the garden pea. The field peas are small, round and tender, while the garden peas are large and smooth or wrinkled. The field pea is grown as a dry pulse, whereas the garden pea, in addition, can be harvested immature and the immaturely seeds cooked as vegetables.

Several varieties of garden peas and field peas are grown in India.

The world production is 14.17 million tonnes and India's is 1.004 million tonnes, 2022.

Peas are consumed in India in a variety of ways. The fresh ones are consumed as such or canned, curried and dehydrated. The dry ones of certain green-seeded varieties are also processed for canning. The round smooth-seeded field peas of various colours are used as pulse mostly in the split form. Dry peas are also used for making flour, which can be used as a substitute for Bengal gram flour.

The pods of some garden peas lack the parchment tissue on the inner pod walls and these are known as sugar peas. These can be chopped like those of fresh bean or the garden *lablab*, so that the entire pod can be used. However, these are hardly known in India.

17.7.10 Kesari Dhal (*Lathyrus sativus*)

Kesari dhal is grown to the greatest extent in India and to a lesser extent in a few other countries of the Eastern and Mediterranean regions. The greatest drawback to its use is the occurrence of the pathological condition of lathyrism (Subsection 17.5.1) amongst people who consume it in large quantities, as has frequently happened in India.

The pulse grows under adverse conditions and is commonly grown in paddy areas.

17.7.11 Cluster Bean (*Cyamopsis tetragonoloba*)

Cluster bean or guar is indigenous to India and has been grown from early times for vegetable and forage purposes. The main areas of cultivation of guar gum in India are Rajasthan, Gujarat, Haryana, Punjab, Uttar Pradesh, Madhya Pradesh, Tamil Nadu, Maharashtra, Karnataka, Andhra Pradesh. India is the major exporter of guar gum to the world; it exports various forms of Guar products to a large number of countries. The country has exported 4,71,700 tonnes of gaurgum to the world for the worth of ₹ 45,131.6 crores/541.7 US Million Dollars during the year 2023-24. Major export destinations (2023-24) were USA, Germany, Russia and Norway.

In India, the young tender pods are used as a favourite vegetable. The pods are also preserved after drying and salting and eaten after frying. The seeds are very mucilaginous and they find a range of uses as a thickener in food products and for sizing textile and paper products.

17.7.12 Cowpea (*Vigna unguiculata*)

Cowpea is one of the commonly used pulses in India, but is not extensively grown. Yet it is one of the pulses used from ancient times. The yield is rather low being about 400–700 kg per hectare. The seeds vary in size, shape and colour.

In India, cowpea is used whole or as dhal. It is also used as flour after husking or with the husk. The pods are used as a vegetable when tender. The seeds may be germinated and the seedlings are eaten. Cow pea is considered inferior to black gram as food it is difficult to digest.

According to the Food and Agriculture Organisation of the United Nations, as of 2012, the average ccwpea yield in Western Africa was an estimated 483 kilograms per hectare (0.195 t/acre), which is still 50% below the estimated potential production yield. In some traditional cropping methods, the yield can be as low as 100 kilograms per hectare (0.040 t/acre).

Outside Africa, the major production areas are Asia, Central America, and South America. Brazil is the world's second-leading producer of cowpea seed, accounting for 17% of annual cowpea production, although most is consumed within the country.

17.7.13 Kidney Bean (*Phaseolus vulgaris*)

This bean is known by a great many names, none of which has more than local significance. Names, such as fresh bean, snap bean, salad bean, green bean, apply to varieties used as vegetables; those that are used as pulses are denoted by such names as dry bean and navy bean. The name common bean is used because it is the most ubiquitous bean of consumption.

The bean is grown in different parts of the world. The beans vary in size, shape and colour of pods and seeds. Green pods are harvested before they become fully grown, tough and stringy. Dry beans are harvested when pods are fully ripe. The yield of green pods varies from 2,500 to 3,500 kg per hectare, while the yield of dry beans varies from 1,500 to 2,000 kg per hectare.

The beans are used as a green vegetable or dry pulse, according to the stage at which they are harvested. French bean, the most important variety used as a vegetable, has a fleshy-walled pod with less fibres in the younger stages. The dry bean is an important source of food. India produced 6.4 million tonnes.

17.7.14 Lima Bean or Butter Bean or Liam and Alec (*Phaseolus lunatus*)

It is grown as a vegetable for its mature and immature beans. It is also known as Haba bean, Burma bean, Guffin bean, Hibbert bean, Java bean, Sieva bean, Rangoon bean, Madagascar bean, Paiga, Paigya, Prolific bean, Civet bean and Sugar bean. Lima beans typically yield 2,900 to 5,000 kilograms of seed and 3,000 to 8,000 kilograms of biomass per hectare. The lima bean is palatable and nutritious, both immature as a fresh vegetable and mature as a dry pulse.

One of the most widely grown pulses in both temperate and tropical areas. Lima beans are the main pulse crop in the wet rainforest regions of tropical Africa and Latin America. Extensively grown in Liberia, Burma, and Nigeria.

17.7.15 Velvet Bean (*Mucuna pruriens*)

It is a tropical legume known by a multitude of common names, including, cowitch, cowhage, kapikachu, nescafe, sea bean, kratzbohnen, konch, yerepe (Yoruba) and atmagupta. The plant is an annual, climbing shrub with long vines that can reach over 15 m. It bears white, lavender, or purple flowers and pods that are covered in loose orange hairs which cause a severe itch if they come in contact with skin. The beans are shiny black or brown. It is found in tropical Africa, India and the Caribbean.

17.7.16 The Winged Bean (*Psophocarpus tetragonolobus*)

Also known as the Goa bean, it is a tropical legume plant native to Papua New Guinea. It grows abundantly in hot, humid equatorial countries, from the Philippines and Indonesia to India, Burma and Sri Lanka. It does well in humid tropics with high rainfall.

The winged bean plant grows as a vine with climbing stems and leaves, 3–4 m in height. The beans themselves are similar to soybeans in both use and nutritional content (being 29.8 per cent to 39 per cent protein).

The beans are used as a vegetable, but the other parts (leaves, flowers, and tuberous roots) are also edible. The tender pods, which are the most widely eaten part of the plant, can be harvested within two to three months of planting. The flowers are often used to colour rice and pastries. The flavour of the beans has a similarity to asparagus. The young leaves can be picked and prepared as a leaf vegetable, similar to spinach. The roots can be used as a root vegetable, similar to the potato, and have a nutty flavour; they are also much more richer in protein than potatoes. The dried seeds can be useful as a flour and also to make a coffee-like drink. Each of these parts of the winged bean provides a source of vitamin A and other vitamins. It is possible that, with a little genetic improvement through selective breeding, the winged bean could raise the standard of living for millions of people in poor, tropical countries.

17.7.17 Soyabean (*Glycine max*)

Soyabean or soybean is both a useful pulse and an oilseed. It is an important food crop in China, Japan and Korea. It is also cultivated in India and throughout South East Asia. From China, soyabean went to Europe in 1792 and to the United States in 1804. In the United States, more than 1,000 types of soyabean are grown essentially as an oilseed crop and the country stands first in the world, both in the area under cultivation and production (39.65 per cent of the world production).

The world production is 398 million tonnes and India's 12.99 million tonnes in 2022.

Different varieties of soyabean with different coloured seeds, varying from white, yellow and brown to black are produced. Their chemical composition depends upon the variety.

Soyabean utilization for food in China, Japan and other countries is high. In China, of the average daily consumption of legumes of 42 g per capita, 18 g are soyabean. In Japan, it was noticed that in an area where the average pulse intake was 70 g daily, 64 g were soyabean in various forms. This is because of the advanced Japanese technology in the processing and manufacture of highly acceptable and palatable soyabean products.

Soyabean, with its high protein content, could be a substitute for expensive meat products, as there is a worldwide shortage of affordable protein. It is estimated that one hectare of land used for grazing purposes will produce enough meat to satisfy one man's protein needs for 190 days; planted in wheat it will provide enough protein for 2,167 days. But that hectare, planted with soyabeans, will yield enough protein for 5,496 days. Soyabean is being used to produce a textured vegetable protein (TVP), also known as nutrinuggates, to replace meat (see Sec. 23.11). Cheap soyabean meal feeds are used for growing livestock and poultry. It is reported that soyabean has a hypoglycemic effect, hence it can be used for diabetic patients

17.8 Processed Soyabean Products

As food, soyabean may be flaked, ground or powdered, and made into a sauce, oil or meal. Some of the processed food products of soyabean are discussed below.

Soya Oil: In processing soybeans for oil extraction and subsequent soya flour production, selection of high quality, sound, clean, dehulled yellow soyabeans is very important. Soyabeans having a dark coloured seed coat, or even beans with a dark hilum will inadvertently leave dark specks in the flour, an undesirable factor when used in food products. All commercial soyabeans in the United States are yellow or yellow-brown.

To produce soyabean oil, the soyabeans are cracked, adjusted for moisture content, rolled into flakes and solvent-extracted with commercial hexane. The oil is then refined, blended for different applications, and sometimes hydrogenated. Soyabean oils, both liquid and partially hydrogenated, are exported abroad, sold as "vegetable oil," or end up in a wide variety of processed foods. The remaining soyabean husks are used mainly as animal feed.

Meal: Soyabean meal, the material remaining after solvent extraction of soyabean flakes, with a 50% soya protein content, toasted (a misnomer because the heat treatment is with moist steam), and ground, in a hammer mill, provided the energy for the American Revolution, beginning in the 1930s, of growing farm animals such as poultry and swine on an industrial scale; and more recently the aquaculture of catfish.

Flour: Defatted soya flour is obtained from solvent extracted flakes, and it contains less than 1 per cent oil. Full-fat soya flour, is made from unextracted, dehulled beans, and contains about 18 per cent to 20 per cent oil. Low-fat soya flour, is made by adding back some oil to defatted soya flour. The lipid content varies according to specifications, usually between 4.5 per cent and 9 per cent. High-fat soya flour, is produced by adding back soyabean oil to defatted flour, at the level of 15 per cent. Lecithinated soya flour, is made by adding soyabean lecithin to defatted, low-fat or high-fat soya flours to increase their dispersibility and impart emulsifying properties. The lecithin content varies up to 15 per cent.

Infant formula: Infant formulas based on soya are used by lactose-intolerant babies; and for babies that are allergic to human milk proteins and cow milk proteins. The formulas are sold in powdered, ready-to-feed, or concentrated liquid forms. It has been recommended internationally by paediatric associations that soya formulas not be used as the primary or sole source of nutrition for infants due to the high risk of several deficiencies including calcium and zinc.

17.8.1 Extracted Soyabean Proteins

Two readily digestible proteins are separated from the indigestible portion of soyabean. They are soyabean curd and soyabean milk. These products are commonly prepared and used in China and Japan. Technology for processing these products from soyabean has also been developed in this country.

Soyabean curd: A curd called "Tofu" is obtained by grinding soaked beans into an emulsion followed by cooking and straining. The curd is precipitated from the milky fluid by the addition of calcium sulphate, allowed to settle, then separated, washed and dried. The final product which has a white colour and a soft delicate structure is cut into slices or slabs. The protein content of the preparation varies from 6 to 17 per cent depending on the moisture content. The fresh curd does not keep well; drying and refrigeration prolong storage life. In China and Japan, the curd is widely used as a food for young children. Soyabean curd may be fermented to produce cheese-like products.

Soyabean milk: Soyabean milk is prepared by grinding soaked beans in a stream of water to obtain an emulsion. The emulsion is cooked for 20 min. when margarine, sugar, salt, lime and malt are added. The cooked product is then homogenized or emulsified and it may be used fresh or spray-dried. When the milk is prepared to conform to a satisfactory formula, it is very good for infant feeding, particularly for those who are allergic to cow milk, and also is a boon for persons who, because of an enzyme deficiency, are unable to digest cow milk. Since it contains less sodium than cow milk soyabean milk is better for persons with high blood pressure. Soya milk does not contain significant amounts of calcium, since the high calcium content of soyabeans is bound to the insoluble constituents and remains in the pulp. Many traditional dairy products have been imitated using processed soyabeans, and imitation products such as "soya milk," "soya-yoghurt" and "soya cream cheese" are readily available in most supermarkets. These imitation products are derived from extensive processing to produce a texture and appearance similar to the real dairy-based ones.

Proteins are also extracted from soyabean in other ways. The seeds are defatted by mechanical processes and the oil remaining in the pressed cake is extracted by solvents. The material is then heated under controlled conditions to eliminate the bitter principles and enzymes interfering with digestion or causing rancidity. The product thus obtained is very rich in protein and nutritionally valuable.

17.8.2 Fermented Products of Soyabean

Some fermented products of soyabean are soya sauce, soyabean paste, tempeh and natto. Their methods of preparation are given below:

Soya sauce: Soya sauce is prepared in a variety of forms and is produced from a long and complex fermentation with various fungi and bacteria. Soyabeans are cooked for 4 to 6 hours and cooled. They are then mixed with an equal quantity of roasted ground wheat and the mixture, under suitable conditions, is seeded with *Aspergillus oryzae.* After the initial fermentation, salt is added and the product is matured for 6 months to 3 years when further fermentation occurs. When "ripening" is complete, the product is strained. Soya sauce thus obtained contains 67 per cent moisture and 5 to 6 per cent protein.

Soyabean paste (miso): Soyabean paste is mostly a Japanese product. The fermenting agent, as in soya sauce, is *Aspergillus oryzae.* The ingredients are cooked soyabean and steamed rice or barley, and the mixture is fermented from 2 weeks to years. Miso may be white or dark. White miso is produced by the fermentation of a mixture containing a high proportion of rice or barley and the fermentation is complete in two weeks. Dark miso results from a mixture with a high proportion of bean and fermentation takes longer. The rate of fermentation is controlled by the addition of salt. The product contains 10 per cent protein and has a paste-like consistency. It is used in the preparation of soups or served with rice and other foods as dressings or a side dish.

Tempe: Tempe is an Indonesian product. The fermenting agent is the fungus *Rhizopus oryzae.* The fungus is added to cooked and mashed soyabean, and is allowed to incubate for 24 hours during which time the mould penetrates the mash. Then the ferment is exposed to air and the tempeh is ready for consumption. The fermented product contains 25 per cent or about half of the original protein content of the beans. The other half of the protein is broken down to amino acids which are readily assimilable. Tempe has a strong smell but it is a highly nutritious product.

Natto: Natto is a Japanese product similar to Tempe. The fermenting agent is *Bacillus subtilis.* The cooked soft beans are inoculated with the bacterium and the fermentation is complete in 20 hours. The finished product is grey in colour, has a mushy flavour, and rather poor keeping qualities. It is eaten with rice.

Hamanatto: Hamanatto is a Korean product. The fermentation in this case is brought about by a fungus. Soaked and steamed beans are impregnated with the mould and when the fungus covers the bean, it is dried in the sun. The dry preparation is treated with salt water and allowed to ferment for another 3 to 12 months. It is again sun-dried, and then is ready for consumption.

CHAPTER

18

Nuts

Nuts are seeds or fruits consisting of an edible, usually fat-containing, kernel and surrounded by a hard or brittle shell. Botanically, nuts are "one-seeded indehiscent fruits." They are, for the most part, the products of trees and thus once cultivated can be looked upon as a permanent form of agriculture. Nut trees often thrive in areas unsuitable for other crops and some of them give high yields, up to over 500 kg of nuts in a season. Nuts, therefore, could help improve the food resources of the world and particularly in the developing countries. The groundnut, which is a pulse crop, is considered in this chapter because of its resemblance to other nuts.

18.1 Nuts as Foods

Nuts have been the food of man from the earliest times and still are the mini-articles of diet in many parts of the world. Coconut, groundnut and chestnut form an important part of the food of people in different parts of the world. Nuts are very nutritious and supply for a given weight twice the amount of protein than any other food product. The superior quality of nut protein renders them good substitutes for animal foods.

From the food point of view, nuts may be divided into three main groups, those with a high fat or oil content, those with high protein content, and those rich in carbohydrates, the starches. Most of the common everyday dessert nuts are rich in oil. The cashew nut, walnut, pecan, etc., are examples of this class of nuts. The majority of the nuts of this group contain, on an average, 50 per cent or more of fat. Groundnut is an example of a nut with high protein content. It contains about 25 per cent protein; other nuts like almonds and pistachios are also rich in protein (about 20 per cent). Protein rich nuts also contain a high percentage of fat. The combined richness in both proteins and fats of this group of nuts explains why some nuts like groundnuts are very popular and form the basic food in some areas. Only a few nuts are rich in carbohydrates. Chestnut, for example, contains 50 per cent carbohydrates and is relatively poor in fats and proteins.

Nuts, in addition to their superior quality protein and high oil content, are also good sources of minerals. Generally, they contain about 2 per cent minerals, with a good proportion of phosphorus and potassium. Other mineral elements present in nut kernels are calcium, sodium, magnesium and iron. Nuts also contain appreciable quantities of vitamins. The chemical compositions of some common nuts are given in Table 18.1.

In spite of the food value of nuts, many people, have a reputation for being indigestible. This arises in many instances due to over-indulgence and poor mastication. Nuts are concentrated foods with little water (generally below 5 per cent) or roughage. Thus, there is a need for thorough mastication of nuts for proper digestion. Also, nuts are to be used as a part of a meal instead of something added afterwards.

Table 18.1 Composition of common nuts (per 100 g of kernel)

	Moisture g	Protein g	Fat g	Fibre g	Carbo-hydrate g	Energy		Calcuim mg	Phosph-rous mg	Iron mg	β-Carotene mg	Thiamine mg	Riboflavin mg	Niacin mg	Vitamin C mg
						K Joules	K Cal								
Almond (*Prunus amygdalus*)	4.37±0.31	18.41±0.04	58.49±0.04	13.06±0.31	3.04±0.24	2549	610	228±10.2	446±23.2	4.59±0.61		0.15±0.024	0.26±0.046	3.71±0.24	0.74±0.07
Arecanut, dried, brown (*Areca catechu*)	6.63±0.15	5.78±0.45	4.35±0.03	11.44±0.64	70.42±0.81	1467	351	61±13.25	105±8.3	2.74±0.71		0.04±0.012	0.03±0.008	0.71±0.07	
Cashew nut (*Anacardium occidentale*)	4.44±0.22	18.78±0.58	45.20±0.07	3.86±0.47	25.46±0.70	2438	583	34±2.98	500±35.3	5.95±0.44		0.61±0.042	0.03±0.017	1.03±0.06	
Coconut, kernal, dry (*Cocos nucifera*)	3.97±0.73	7.27±0.02	63.26±0.30	15.88±0.79	8.01±1.02	2611	624	32±4.51	203±6.0	3.13±0.47		0.04±0.005	0.04±0.015	0.71±0.11	
Coconut, kernal, fresh (*Cocos nucifera*)	36.14±0.36	3.84±0.04	41.38±0.42	10.42±0.28	6.30±0.43	1711	409	8±1.42	67.73±15.15	1.30±0.51	2.66±0.28	0.03±0.003	0.08±0.006	0.30±0.02	0.80±0.24
Ground nut (*Arachis hypogaea*)	6.97±0.69	23.65±0.85	39.63±0.29	10.38±0.18	17.27±0.33	2176	520	54±7.37	391±13.0	3.44±0.36	22.75±2.13	0.57±0.052	0.12±0.017	11.35±0.36	
Pistachio nut (*Pistacia vera*)	4.68±0.22	23.35±0.35	42.49±0.34	10.64±0.16	15.82±0.52	2257	540	135±22.4	537±9.2	4.50±0.63	110±10.4	0.98±0.144	0.04±0.002	0.86±0.01	
Walnut (*Juglans regia*)	3.56±0.22	14.92±0.62	64.27±0.05	5.39±0.19	10.14±0.69	2809	672	105±5.9	400±43.0	3.21±0.17	9.53±0.91	0.40±0.020	0.12±0.006	0.86±0.03	0.88±0.10

Source: IFCT, NIN, ICMR, Hyderabad, 2017

Table 18.2: Common Nuts (per 100 gms of edible portion)

Sl. No.	Food name	Moisture	Protein	Total fat	Total Fiber	CHO	Energy KJ		Thiamin	Riboflavin	Niacin	Vit.B6	Vit.C	Vit. A	Ca	Iron
		g	g	g	g	g	KJ	Kcal	mg	mg	mg	mg	mg	µg	mg	mg
1.	Almond	4.37	18.41	58.49	13.06	3.04	2549	609.22	0.15	0.26	3.71	0.09	0.74	—	228	4.59
2.	Cashew nut	4.44	18.78	45.2	3.86	25.46	2438	582.69	0.61	0.03	1.03	0.16	—	—	34	5.95
3.	Coconut Kernal Dry	3.97	7.27	63.26	15.88	8.01	2611	624.04	0.04	0.04	0.71	0.15	—	—	32	3.13
4.	Coconut Kernal Fresh	36.14	3.84	41.38	10.42	6.3	1711	408.93	0.03	0.08	0.3	0.1	0.8	2.66	8	1.3
5.	Walnut	3.56	14.92	64.27	5.39	10.14	2809	671.36	0.4	0.12	0.86	0.8	—	9.53	105	3.21
6.	Pistachio	4.68	23.35	42.49	10.64	15.82	2257	539.43	0.98	0.04	0.86	0.96	—	110	135	4.5
7.	Brazil nut#	2.95	14.32	67.1	7.5	11.74	2757	659	0.617	0.035	0.295	0.101	0.7	—	160	2.43
8.	Hazel nut##	2.75	13.57	55.75	7.7	25.78	2788	667	0.39	0.21	—	0.45	3	—	114	4.7
9.	Macadamia nuts###	1.79	10.4	71.76	8.6	19.9	3192	763.8	1.195	0.162	2.473	0.275	1.2	0.1	85	3.69
10.	Pecan##	3.08	9.13	68.81	4.5	17.74	2997	717	0.9	0.15	—	0.2	2	0.01	75	2.5
11.	Pine seed	5.32	12.55	48.79	3.79	26.77	2486	594.1	0.36	0.08	3.52	0.11	—	1.98	17	4.5
12.	Sweet Chestnut##	2.42	2.26	6.5	45.54	789	188	0.3	0.05	—	0.3	0	0	40	1	

Sources:

Calories info.com

USDA food composition and Nutrition table.com

Research gate uploaded by Angela Rodrigues

Source: IFCT, NIN, ICMR, Hyderabad, 2017

Properly masticated nuts are well assimilated and nut proteins are as easily digested as the proteins from other sources.

Nuts are used in a variety of ways. They are eaten raw, roasted, salted or cooked. Some, like almonds, are equally palatable raw or cooked. Others, like groundnuts, may be eaten raw, but are of much better flavour when cooked. Some other nuts, like cashew, are not generally eaten in the raw state. The flavour of the nuts depends on the oils they contain and these are often modified during cooking. Nuts are favoured as ingredients in salads and in stuffing for poultry. Nuts preserved in sugar syrup or crystallized are very popular. As ingredients of puddings, cakes and sweetmeats of all kinds, nuts are in universal use. Nut butter made by grinding roasted kernels, with the addition of salt, is very popular. This finds manifold uses in chocolate manufacture. Large quantities of nuts are used in ice cream. Processed foods, made out of nut flour, are rich in protein and are used as a weaning food for children. Some nut meals are also used in cake and biscuit making.

18.2 Processing of Nuts

Nuts are of a perishable nature; they lose their palatability or become inedible, if not properly processed. Nuts are marketed more and more as kernels and this requires special methods of processing, packing and storage.

Most nuts, as they grow on trees, are enveloped in a fleshy or fibrous husk. As the nut ripens and falls from the tree, the husk may or may not remain attached to it.

In some cases, as in almonds, the nut separates readily from the husk on ripening, while in some other cases the husk remains stuck to the nut. In the latter case, removal of the husks is necessary before nuts are processed. In the case of some nuts, such as walnuts, dehusking is necessary immediately after the nuts are collected, as otherwise both the colour and the quality of kernels may be affected, apart from the disfiguration of the shells. Dehusking is often carried out by hand but when large quantities of nuts are involved, it is done mechanically.

Nuts, as gathered, are dirty and they are cleaned by washing. Next, they are sundried or dehydrated in mechanical driers. Some nuts marketed in the shell are bleached to remove all the stains including those due to sun-scorch and disease, to give a uniform colour throughout. Bleaching is done by sulphur dioxide or by dipping the nuts in suitable bleaching agents. In some nuts, such as pecan, the outer rough layer is first removed by polishing in a suitable way before bleaching. Bleaching, when properly carried out, does not affect the kernel in any way.

Many nuts in the shell keep well for long periods, especially when cold stored. However, the present tendency is for nuts to be marketed more and more as kernels, ready for immediate use. Under warm humid conditions, kernels are subject to rapid deterioration and become mouldy or rancid. Therefore, special care is to be taken to store nut kernels. They are, to be thoroughly dried and packed in moisture-proof containers or sealed tins. In this condition, they could be stored for long periods (up to two years) without loss of texture, flavour and colour. When nuts are sold in the cooked or salted state, they are to be vacuum packed as soon as they are cooled as otherwise, they will absorb moisture.

18.3 Individual Nuts

Among the various nuts, the following are of importance in India:

18.3.1 Cashew nut (*Anacardium occidentale*)

The cashew nut tree is a native of Brazil. The tree was introduced into Africa through Portuguese influence and from there to India, about 400 years ago. It is cultivated mostly on the West Coast of India. The tree bears fruits consisting of a pear-shaped swollen basal portion (or pedicle) which is succulent or juicy, and bright yellow or orange in colour. It is edible and is known as cashew apple. Attached to the apple is the kidney-shaped cashew nut, greenish-grey in colour, with an oleaginous shell or pericarp which is hard, smooth and shiny. The nut contains an acrid juice which is a powerful vesicant and burns the skin. In the centre, the nut is slightly curved while the kernel is covered by a thin, reddish-brown skin or testa.

The nuts are roasted before they are shelled. Roasting also adds to the flavour and taste of the kernel. The roasting is a delicate operation; over roasting or under roasting adversely affects both the quality and recovery of the kernel. Various methods of roasting are employed to recover the maximum amount of shell oil. After roasting, the nuts are broken avoiding the breakage of kernels as far as possible. Next, the thin reddish-brown skin of the kernels is easily removed by hand after the kernels have been placed for a few hours in drying chambers. The kernels are then graded based on size and packed. There are twenty odd species known to exist. The world production is 3.93 million tonnes and India's 7,82,000 tonnes in 2023.

The kernels possess pleasant taste and flavour and are eaten raw, fried and sometimes salted or sugared. They are an esteemed dessert and are used as a substitute for almonds with which they compare very favourably. In India, cashew is used in a variety of ways in a number of food preparations. Large quantities are used in sweetmeat and confectionery preparations. Cashew is a highly nutritious and concentrated food. Its oil consists mostly of glycerides of oleic (73.8 per cent) and linoleic acids (7.7 per cent).

In addition to kernels, cashew provides many useful products. The cashew shell oil is used for waterproofing and preservation purposes in paints and lacquers. The oil polymerizes and this finds uses in various industrial manufacturers. It consists chiefly of anacardic acid (90 per cent) and cardol (10 per cent). The latter is a phenol and is responsible for the blistering action of the oil. The cashew apple is soft and juicy. When ripe it is sweet and slightly astringent. The fruit is edible and yields a delicious beverage. Since the raw juice is rich in sugar (11.5 per cent), it can be employed for the production of alcohol. A fermented liquor "kaju" is made from the cashew apples. Distilled *kaju* is "*feni*" and is quite a popular beverage in the cashew growing areas of our country.

18.3.2 Coconut (*Cocos nucifera*)

The coconut plant is a palm growing mostly along the seashores of many tropical countries. It also grows in inland places. The inland cultivation up to an elevation of 700-1,000 m has been successful in India. The most important coconut producing countries in the world are India, Sri Lanka, Malaysia, Indonesia and Philippines. In India, the coconut palm is called "Kalpa Vriksha" or the tree that provides all the necessities of life. About 30 different varieties of the coconut palm are grown in the country. The fruits from these differ from one another mainly in size, shape and colour, which are of various shades of green, yellow, brown or red.

On several grounds an origin for the coconut in a land area that is now summed, northwest of Papua New Guinea, is generally accepted. The plant and nut were fully evolved even 20 million years ago, long before man appeared. These included one from Rajasthan, which must have got there millions of years ago when the area was under the sea.

The world production is 62.4 million tonnes and India's is 13.3 million tonnes, 2022.

The fruit is ovoid, three-angled, and long, containing a single seed. The exocarp (outer husk) is thick and fibrous and encloses a hard and bony endocarp (shell). Inside the shell is a thick, white fleshy layer of the kernel commonly known as "meat." The cavity of the endosperm is large and in the unripe or tender coconut is filled with a watery fluid (coconut-water). As the nut ripens, the liquid is gradually absorbed and the thickness of the kernel increases.

Coconuts are used for several purposes. The nut has a high place in Hindu religious ceremonies. The fresh kernel is sometimes eaten directly as a food but, more often, in the grated form, it is used in the preparation of many foods such as puddings, sweets, curries and chutneys. The principal use of coconut is in the manufacture of copra from which coconut oil and coconut cake are obtained. Sometimes, shredded coconut kernel is dried to obtain desiccated coconut.

Copra: Copra is prepared from ripe nuts. It is available in two forms: ball copra and cup copra. Ball copra is obtained from mature unhusked nuts stored in the shade for 8-12 months. During this period the coconut water is absorbed and the kernel dries up. The husk and the shell are then carefully removed. Cup copra is made from fresh or stored nuts by cutting the kernel into halves and drying them in the sun or in special driers or kilns. Copra dried to 5 per cent moisture content does not deteriorate if not stored too long. If the moisture content exceeds 6 per cent, copra is liable to mould and insect attack.

Coconut oil: See Chapter 19.

Desiccated coconut: Desiccated coconut is prepared from the white part of the meat after removing the brown parings or testa. The white meat is shredded or disintegrated and dried in a hot air drier to below 2 per cent moisture. Desiccated coconut is used in the manufacture of cakes, pastries and chocolates. It is an important ingredient in a variety of Indian sweets.

Coconut water: Coconut water plays an important part in the ripening of the nut and in germination. The water of the unripe coconut is a refreshing drink and has the advantage of being sterile. Analysis of the coconut water gives the following values: water, 95.5; protein, 0.1; fat, 0.1; mineral matter, 0.4; carbohydrates, 4.0 parts per 100 g. The nut water contains calcium, 29; phosphorus, 37; iron, 0.05; and potassium, 312 mg per 100 g. The principal mineral constituent is thus potassium. The water is rich in ascorbic acid which ranges from 2.2 to 3.7 mg per 100 ml. The water from green nuts, with soft pulp, contains a still higher concentration of ascorbic acid. Many vitamins of the B-group are also present in coconut water.

Coconut sap: Coconut sap or juice is obtained by tapping or cutting the stalk of the young flower bunches of coconut. The main constituent of the fresh juice is sucrose (12.3–17.4 per cent); the juice is rich in ascorbic acid (16–30 mg/100 ml). The juice in the fresh state is sweet toddy or neera, and is used as a beverage. Sweet toddy, if carefully collected in sterile vessels, remains unfermented for considerable time. However, as usually collected, fermentation sets in. The fermented product toddy is used as a beverage and contains about 4.0 per cent alcohol. Arrack is the product obtained by the distillation of fermented toddy and contains about 35 per cent alcohol. Coconut sap when strained and evaporated gives jaggery.

18.3.3 Groundnut (*Arachis hypogaea*)

Groundnut or peanut is the most important oil crop of India. It is of Brazilian origin and is now cultivated in tropical and warm temperate regions of the world. The Portuguese were primarily responsible for the transport of groundnut from Brazil to Goa and then to the rest of Asia.

The world production is 54.3 million tonnes and India's 7.3 million tonnes in 2022. India ranked second in world production next to China in the year 2022.

Groundnut differs from other nuts in that it is formed in the ground and has to be dug out of the soil at harvest, like other root crops. The pods are stripped from the vines immediately after harvesting and are dried soon after to prevent deterioration. Inadequately dried nuts are liable to develop free fatty acids. The pods are cylindrical, reticulated and usually contain two nuts or kernels, while some varieties contain three to four nuts. The testa or the thin skin that surrounds the kernel may be white, various shades of cream and brown or brick red in colour.

Groundnuts are rich in oil and protein as also in B-vitamins and are thus of good nutritional value. Groundnut proteins are easily digested and have high biological value. Considerable quantities of groundnuts are used directly for human consumption. The nuts are eaten either raw, roasted, steamed or fried. In general, roasted nuts are preferred. They are used in numerous ways, salted, sugared or mixed with sweetmeats and other edible preparations. Like other edible nuts, groundnuts enter into various forms of confectionery. Freshly fried and salted nuts along with popped rice or maize are quite popular. In India, roasted groundnut, eaten with some jaggery, forms a cheap and sustaining food for millions of people. The principal use of groundnuts is in the production of groundnut oil.

Groundnut oil. See Chapter 19.

Groundnut flour: Groundnut flour is made from good grade kernels by lightly roasting, decuticling, removing the germ and extracting the oil by pressing, followed by partial solvent extraction. The flour has the following composition: moisture, 4.4; protein, 59.0; fat, 9.7; carbohydrates, 20,6; fibre, 2.5; and ash, 3.8 per cent. The mineral and vitamin content in mg per 100 g is calcium, 70; phosphorus, 570; iron, 10; thiamine, 0.6; riboflavin, 0.3; and niacin, 20.0. Groundnut flour mixed with other supplements like enriched wheat flour, other legume flours, skim milk powder, etc., is extensively used in the preparation of protein rich supplementary foods for feeding infants and children in developing countries. These foods are easily digested and are of special significance to our country to combat the malnutrition caused due to the lack of proteins in the diet of vulnerable sections of our population, such as pre-school and school children. The flour combined with soyabean flour is used in the manufacture of textured vegetable proteins.

Peanut butter: Peanut butter is a popular article of diet in the USA. It is gaining importance in other countries also because of its palatability and nutritive value. It has not yet made an impact on the diet of our people. Peanut butter is made from the best quality kernels. The nuts are roasted to a moderate degree and the skin and the germ are removed. The kernels are then finely ground with the addition of salt and some hydrogenated groundnut oil. The product thus obtained is peanut butter and is found acceptable for incorporation into many dishes. The preparation contains about 48 per cent fat, and, when appropriate quantities of emulsifiers are used in its preparation, it keeps well.

Groundnut milk: Groundnut milk is prepared by treating the groundnut kernel up to the grinding stage as in the preparation of peanut butter. In the preparation of the milk, the kernels are ground with seven times their weight of water with the addition of calcium hydroxide to adjust pH and phosphate to stabilize the milk. After filtration and fortification with minerals and vitamins, the milk is homogenized and used as a dietary supplement for children.

18.3.4 Almonds (*Prunus amygdalus*)

Prunus amygdalus, *badam* or vilayati-badam is indigenous to the eastern mediterranean region.

Almond or badam is the product of a tree that grows best in tropical and subtropical regions. There are two cultivated varieties of almonds, *viz., P. amygdalus* var *amara and P. amygdalis* var *dulcis*. The first one, the bitter almond, is the source of almond oil, and the second is the sweet almond. Many types of sweet almonds are grown and classified depending upon the thickness of the shell. The almond is said to be native to Central and Western Asia. In India, it is cultivated mostly in Kashmir, and to some extent, in Himachal Pradesh and Uttar Pradesh. Large quantities of almonds are imported into the country mostly from Afghanistan.

Almond fruits are long and pubescent with tough flesh. When the fruit ripens the husk or flesh splits open, exposing the nut or stone. At this stage, the fruits are harvested, cleaned off the dried skin and dried in the sun for some time. They are then bleached with sulphur dioxide, which gives the surface of the shell a bright golden colour. The nut has a thick or thin pericarp which contains a flattened, long, oval seed with a brownish seed coat. Unshelled almonds keep well for about a year, while the kernel stays well for one or more years when kept in cold storage. Of all nuts, almonds have the largest share of the world trade.

Almond kernel is often eaten fresh and it is a popular dessert nut. Kernels obtained after bleaching, roasting, frying and salting are highly esteemed. Almond milk (*badam milk*) made from crushed almonds is a refreshing drink. Almond is also used extensively in confectionery. Almond paste, consisting of a mixture of ground unroasted almonds, sugar, water and flavouring is used in large quantities by bakers and confectioners. Almond oil, extracted from sweet as well as bitter almonds, is also used in confectionery, pharmaceutical and cosmetic preparations. Almond butter consists of ground roasted kernels to which salt is added. In countries where almond is grown, green almond or nut picked before it is fully ripe and in which the kernel is very soft and tender, is eaten as dessert or is candid, preserved and pickled.

Almond kernels are a good source of fat and protein, and are considered highly nutritious. The chief almond protein is a globulin and is easily digested but its biological value is low. It is believed to be a good supplement to milk. The protein content of bitter almonds is generally higher than that of sweet almonds by about 10 per cent. Bitter almonds contains about 2.5–3.5 per cent amygdalin, a cyanogenetic glucoside, which, on hydrolysis, gives HCN (hydrogen cyanide) together with benzaldehyde. Thus, bitter almond is not used for human consumption. It is mostly used for the production of almond oil. Sweet almonds do not contain amygdalin.

Both bitter and sweet almonds give a fatty oil on cold expression. The oil yield of bitter almonds is less (about 40 per cent) when compared to sweet almonds (about 50 per cent). Yet, bitter almond is mostly used to obtain oil, as sweet almond finds lots of uses in foods. Almond oil is seldom used as food because of its high cost. It is used in the pharmaceutical and cosmetic industries. The pressed cake after the extraction of fixed oil from bitter almonds is used for the production of an essential oil.

The world production of almond is 3.6 million tonnes in 2022 and 3.9 million tonnes in 2023. In India, Jammu & Kashmir produces 9.93 kilo tonnes in 2021-22.

18.3.5 Chestnut (*Castanea sativa*)

The chestnut or sweet chestnut is a native of Southern Europe. Large quantities are produced in Spain (hence it is called Spanish chestnut), and also in Italy and France. Chestnut is also cultivated in many parts of the Himalayas. The nut contains an edible kernel. There are many varieties of sweet chestnuts and the quality of the kernel varies with the variety of chestnut.

Chestnuts may be eaten raw but are better cooked; their flavour is best after roasting or boiling for 10–15 min. with a little salt. To obtain the best flavour, the cooking should be fairly rapid and not prolonged. Nuts preserved in sugar or syrup are a delicacy.

Unlike most other nuts, chestnuts are rich in starch and sugar, and they contain small amounts of fat. They are therefore more akin to cereals in their composition and food value than nuts. Chestnut ground into flour is used in soups, fritters, porridge, stuffings and stews. In some areas the nuts are commonly used to feed livestock. The world production is 2.13 million tonnes in 2022.

18.3.6 Pistachio (*Pistacia vera*)

Pistachia vera, a small evergreen tree is found in mediterranean and further east for 4000 years for its drupes. Pistachio is a small deciduous tree and is a native of Central Asia. The pistachio nut shell is thin but of a horny texture and it splits open at one end of its own accord when the nut is ripe. The kernel may then be easily extracted. The nut shell encloses the kernel which has a characteristic green colour. The kernel is enclosed by a thin reddish-brown leathery jacket (pellicel).

Pistachio or pista is not produced in India. However, it is greatly appreciated in India and considerable quantities are imported into the country, chiefly from Afghanistan. The pleasant mild flavour of the nut combined with its colour and good keeping qualities are highly prized and make pista much more expensive than most other nuts in commerce. The green colour imparts value to the nut for ornamental purposes, particularly in grated form for fancy dishes. The nuts are used as ingredients of sweetmeats, confectionery and ice cream. Pista is also used as a dessert nut, salted or roasted.

Oil present in pistachio can be extracted by cold pressing or solvent extraction. Cold pressed oil is without much odour and is used to some extent in confectionery, as a spice oil, and in medicine. Because of the high cost of the nut itself, oil is not extracted from the nut. The solvent extracted oil is dark green in colour and turns easily rancid. The world production is 1.2 million tonnes in 2022.

18.3.7 Walnut (*Juglans regia*)

There are many varieties of walnut grown in different parts of the world, such as the European walnut (*Juglans regia*), a native of Europe, Central Asia and China; black walnut (*Juglans nigra*), a native of North America; white walnut or butternut (*Juglans cinerea*), which is also from a North American tree, and Japanese walnut (*Juglans sieboldiana*).

The European walnut is the best known variety and it occurs in India. Kashmir is the principal walnut growing State in India. It also grows in the hilly areas of Punjab, Himachal Pradesh and Uttar Pradesh. Some walnuts are also exported from India. Apart from the nut, walnut wood is also of commercial importance.

Walnut fruit has a leathery exocarp and the endocarp is hard, woody, wrinkled and two-halved, enclosing a four-lobed, corrugated oily edible kernel. When the fruit ripens, the husk splits and the nut falls to the ground. The collected nuts are cleaned, washed, dried and sometimes bleached if they are marketed as nuts themselves. Otherwise, after removing the husks, the kernels are cleaned, dried and graded according to size, colour and marketed.

The world production is 3.9 million tonnes and India's 33,000 tonnes in 2022.

The walnut has been employed as an article of food or in everyday cooking from very early times. It is one of the most widely used dessert nuts. It is also much prized in baking, confectionery and ice cream making. The younger green fruits, gathered before the nuts harden, are one of the richest sources of ascorbic acid constituting 2–2.5 per cent of the weight of immature fruit. These green fruits are used in the preparation of pickles, marmalades, chutneys, etc. Walnut oil, extracted from the nut, is greenish, yellow or almost colourless with a pleasant odour and a nutty flavour. It is rich in unsaturated fatty acids. The oil is used for edible purposes and has been used for centuries in the preparation of artists' paints. The oil also finds other industrial uses. They are a good source of phosphorous, potassium and magnesium as well as proteins and vitamin E.

18.3.8 Brazil Nut (*Bertholletia excelsa*)

The Brazil nut is the one that is always left at the bottom of the nut bowl as it is almost impossible to crack. Despite their name, the most significant exporter of Brazil nuts is not Brazil but Bolivia, where they are called *almendras*. Commercial supplies of Brazil nuts are still derived entirely from wild trees though there are concerns that they are being harvested too intensively. Brazil nuts are seeds of a large tree that grows up to 50 m (160 ft) tall in the Amazon jungle. The seeds grow in clusters of 12 to 24 inside a large pod that looks a bit like a coconut. Nutritionally, Brazil nuts are an excellent source of selenium and a good source of magnesium and thiamine. They have 14% protein, 11% carbohydrates, and 67% fat. The world production is 75,910 tonnes in 2022.

18.3.9 Hazelnut (*Corylus avellana*)

Hazelnuts (or cobnuts–a type of wild hazelnut) were collected and eaten by Mesolithic people. Although hazels grow in most parts of Britain, cobnuts are particular to Kent where they are grown on a commercial scale. Most of the world's commercially grown hazelnuts come from Turkiye. Hazelnut is also becoming popular as an addition to the range of coffees drunk by the modern cafe society with *Hazel latte* becoming popular. The popularity of Hazelnut liqueur, based on vodka, is now increasing especially in Eastern Europe. The nuts are globe-shaped or oval, up to 2 cm long, with a hard brown shell. They tend to grow in clusters of one to four nuts, partially enclosed in a husk. In USA home production of hazelnut butter is seen as an alternative, tasty and more nutritious than its peanut butter counterpart. They are high in fibre, potassium, calcium, magnesium and vitamin E; hazelnuts are nutritious as well as tasty. The world production is 1.196 million tonnes in 2022.

18.3.10 Macadamia (*M. integrifolia*)

Macadamia is an Australian nut but it is now grown commercially in Hawaii, particularly for the American market, where it is widely used in cookies and ice cream. The Macadamia nut's kernel is extremely hard to mine out of its shell, but after some time in a warm and dry place the shell may develop big cracks. They have been described as having a taste rather like a very fine hazelnut but their texture is smoother. The nuts are a valuable food crop. Only two of the species, *M. integrifolia* and *M. tetraphylla*, are of commercial importance. The remainder of the genus possesses poisonous and/or inedible nuts, such as *M. whelanii* and *M. ternifolia*: the toxicity is due to the presence of cyanogenic glycosides. Low in carbohydrates but relatively high in fat, they are also a good source of calcium and other minerals.

In 2022, South Africa was the world's leading producer of macadamia nuts with 1,44,288 tonnes compared to Australia's 1,44,192 tonnes and global production of 2,94,914 tonnes. Macadamia is also commercially produced in Brazil, California, Hawaii, Costa Rica, Israel, Kenya, New Zealand, Colombia, Guatemala and Malawi.

18.3.11 Pecan (*Carya illinoinensis*)

Pecan is a native to North America, where they were an important food source for the native Indian tribes of Southern USA. The fruit is an oval to oblong nut, 2.6–6 cm long and 1.5–3 cm broad, dark brown with a rough, husk 3–4 mm thick, which splits off at maturity to release the thin-shelled nut. Pecan nuts are edible, with a rich, buttery flavour. They can be eaten fresh or used in cooking, particularly in sweet desserts but also in some savoury dishes. One of the most common desserts with the pecan as a central ingredient is the pecan pie, a traditional Southern US recipe. Pecans are still used in abundance in America, especially in cakes, breads and cookies. Pecans belong to the same family as walnut and have the same distinctive texture and brain-like shape, but a slightly sweeter taste. They are particularly high in vitamins A, B and E, calcium, phosphorous, magnesium, potassium and zinc.

18.3.12 Pine Nuts (*Pinus koraiensis*)

Pine nuts are the seeds that grow inside the cones of the stone pine tree and are widely used in Mediterranean regions and the Americas. In Asia, two species are widely harvested, Korean Pine (*Pinus koraiensis*) in Northeast Asia and Chilgoza Pine (*Pinus gerardiana*) in the western Himalayas. Four other species, Siberian Pine (*Pinus sibirica*), Siberian Dwarf Pine (*Pinus pumila*), Chinese White Pine (*Pinus armandii*) and Lacebark Pine (*Pinus bungeana*) are also used to a lesser extent. When first extracted from the pine cone, pine nuts are covered with a hard shell (seed coat), thin in some species and thick in others. Pine nuts are an essential component of pesto and are frequently added to meat, fish, and vegetable dishes. Pine nuts contain about 31 grams of protein per 100 grams of nuts, the highest of any nut or seed.

Russia is the largest producer of *Pinus sibirica* nuts in the world followed by Mongolia which produces over 10,000 tonnes of forest grown nuts annually, the majority of the harvest is exported to China. Afghanistan is an important source of pine nuts, behind China and Korea.

18.3.13 Sweet Chestnut (*Castanea sativa*)

Sweet chestnuts are believed to have originated in Spain and were brought to Britain by the Romans, hence they are also known as Spanish chestnuts. They grow in clusters enclosed in a spiny case. They are delicious eating on their own, roasted over hot coals, or can be used in all sorts of delicious dishes, including the traditional stuffing for Christmas dinner. Chestnuts have a high starch content so in Europe they are often made into flour and used for cakes and fritters. In France, they are preserved in sugar as marrons glaces. Their high level of tannic acid means they should not be eaten raw.

18.3.14 Butternut (*Juglans cinerea*)

Also occasionally known as the White Walnut, is a species of walnut native to the Eastern United States and Southeast Canada, from southern Quebec west to Minnesota, south to northern Alabama and southwest to northern Arkansas. The fruit is a nut, produced in bunches of 2-6 together; the nut is oblong-ovoid, 3-6 cm long and 2-4 cm broad, surrounded by a green husk before maturity in mid-autumn. Butternut grows quickly, but is rather short-lived for a tree, rarely living longer than 75 years. The nuts are usually used in baking and making candies, having an oily texture and pleasant flavour. The husks are also used to make a yellowish dye.

CHAPTER

19

Oils and Fats in Foods

Oils and fats have been used by man in food preparations for many centuries now. In the past, butter or ghee was used because it added richness of flavour and colour to the food preparation. Today, in addition to butter, many oils and fats of animal and vegetable origin and many products developed from them are consumed by man. He also consumes fats in invisible forms. Many foods contain large amounts of fats that are not apparent in their appearance, e.g., avocados contain 16 per cent, egg yolk 31 per cent, chocolate 35 per cent, beef (some cuts) 41 per cent, almonds 58 per cent, and cheese 32 per cent fat.

19.1 Nutritional Importance of Oils and Fats

Oils and fats are important sources of our energy requirements. Weight for weight, they furnish 2.25 times more energy than proteins and carbohydrates. Thus, they help reduce the bulk of the food we take. Besides being an important source of energy, oils and fats are excellent sources of fat-soluble vitamins A, D, E and K, and play a part in the biosynthesis of several long-chain alcohols.

Oils provide the essential fatty acid, linoleic acid, which is needed for human health. Excessive intake of saturated fatty acids increases the level of serum lipids and the incidence of arteriosclerosis and heart disease. A high level of consumption of unsaturated acids is thus necessary for normal health. Fatty acid composition of oils commonly used in India is given in Table 19.1.

Table 19.1 Fatty acid composition of commonly used oils

Oil	Saturated	Mono-unsaturated	Polyunsaturated
Coconut (*Cocus nucifera*)	91	8	1
Cottonseed (*Gossypium*)	34	26	40
Groundnut (*Arachis hypogaea*)	20	54	26
Mustard (*Brassica nigra*)	6	73	21
Niger* (*Guizotia abyssinic*)	12	35	55
Palm** (*Elaeis guineensis*)	80	13	7
Safflower (*Carthamus tinctorius*)	11	13	76
Sesame (*Sesamum idicum*)	14	46	40
Soyabean (*Glycine max*)	15	25	60
Sunflower (*Helianthus annuus*)	8	34	58

Source: Proceedings on Symposium on Oils and Fats, CFTRI, Mysore, 1976.

* Wealth of India, CSIR, New Delhi, Vol. IV, 2005.

** Wealth of India, CSIR, New Delhi, Vol. III, 2001.

Table 19.2 Composition of Oil Seeds (per 100 gms of edible products)

Name of Oil Seeds	Moisture	Protein	Fat	Fiber	Carbohydrate	Energy		Calcium	Phosphrous	Iron	B-Carotene	Thiamine	Riboflavin	Niacin	Vitamin B6	Bio-tin	Vitamin C
	g	g	g	g	g	K Joules	K Cal	mg	mg	mg	mg	mg	mg	mg	mg	µg	mg
Gingelly seeds, white (*Sesamum indicum*)	3.30 ± 0.28	21.70 ± 0.44	43.05 ± 0.04	16.99 ± 0.30	10.83 ± 0.50	2174	520	1283	754	15.54	12.94 ± 1.55	0.36 ± 0.047	0.07 ± 0.009	3.94 ± 0.14	0.62 ± 0.029	3.46 ± 0.46	–
Gingelly seeds, black (*Sesamum indicum*)	4.51 ± 0.44	19.17 ± 0.64	43.10 ± 0.03	17.16 ± 0.19	10.29 ± 0.74	2124	508	0.02	568	13.9	13.09 ± 2.67	0.34 ± 0.027	0.10 ± 0.009	3.12 ± 0.26	0.64 ± 0.034	3.06 ± 0.39	–
Gingelly seeds, brown (*Sesamum indicum*)	3.62 ± 0.32	21.61 ± 0.71	43.22 ± 0.08	17.21 ± 0.18	9.76 ± 1.01	2161	517	0.02	613	14.95	5.41 ± 0.57	0.27 ± 0.025	0.08 ± 0.009	3.05 ± 0.45	0.49 ± 0.033	3.48 ± 0.24	–
Mustard seeds (*Brassica juncea*)	5.67 ± 0.48	19.51 ± 0.23	40.19 ± 0.21	14.10 ± 0.66	16.80 ± 0.71	2132	510	402 ± 54.0	715 ± 82.1	13.49 ± 2.95	36.72 ± 7.07	0.55 ± 0.065	0.33 ± 0.010	3.80 ± 0.41	0.24 ± 0.019	1.45 ± 0.36	–
Linseeds (*Linum usitatissimum*)	5.48 ± 0.28	18.55 ± 0.15	35.67 ± 0.70	26.17 ± 0.39	10.99 ± 0.86	1857	444	257 ± 14.0	445 ± 20.1	5.44 ± 0.69	1.05 ± 0.03	0.28 ± 0.018	0.05 ± 0.001	1.09 ± 0.05	0.35 ± 0.020	21.25 ± 0.49	–
Niger seeds, black (*Guizotia abyssinica*)	4.65 ± 0.59	18.92 ± 1.61	38.61 ± 0.41	10.93 ± 0.05	22.98 ± 2.64	2144	513	572 ± 37.1	461 ± 9.5	18.19 ± 0.22	2.15 ± 0.81	0.46 ± 0.043	0.23 ± 0.031	1.14 ± 0.09	0.45 ± 0.061	2.37 ± 0.11	–
Niger seeds, Grey (*Guizotia abyssinica*)	5.66 ± 0.29	18.34 ± 2.11	39.53 ± 0.26	10.96 ± 0.14	20.59 ± 1.85	2128	509	375 ± 58.1	474 ± 93.5	19.61 ± 5.77	8.49 ± 0.83	0.38 ± 0.064	0.35 ± 0.042	0.88 ± 0.15	0.34 ± 0.025	2.40 ± 0.29	–
Safflower seeds (*Carthamus tinctorius*)	5.24 ± 0.16	17.66 ± 0.54	30.87 ± 0.98	13.49 ± 0.45	30.18 ± 1.20	1981	474	211 ± 14.5	644 ± 56.5	4.06 ± 0.42	2.07 ± 0.58	0.85 ± 0.019	0.15 ± 0.006	1.12 ± 0.02	0.93 ± 0.072	17.37 ± 2.17	–
Sunflower seeds (*Helianthus annuus*)	3.53 ± 0.29	23.53 ± 0.56	51.85 ± 0.07	10.80 ± 0.13	6.85 ± 0.99	2453	587	176 ± 27.0	752 ± 118	5.85 ± 1.09	8.15 ± 1.18	0.59 ± 0.064	0.13 ± 0.027	1.60 ± 0.27	0.94 ± 0.150	2.44 ± 0.18	–

Source: IFCT, NIN, ICMR, Hyderabad, 2017

Essential fatty acids from fats are components of membranes of living cells. They are also used by the body to make prostaglandins involved in a large variety of vital physiological functions. They also play a role in immunity. Decreased availability of essential fatty acids can also lead to impaired growth and diminished mental and physical capacities.

Fats are slow in leaving the stomach and hence retard digestion. This delays the pangs of hunger. There is, however, no difference in the digestibility of different fats that are ordinarily constituents of foods; they are utilized to the extent of 95–98 per cent. The difference in digestibility that does exist is related to the melting point of the fat. Those which melt below 43°C are completely digested while those melting above 43°C are more slowly digested and less completely absorbed.

Oilseeds are also rich in proteins (Table 19.2) and oilseed cake obtained after the extraction of oils from seeds can be processed to produce protein rich foods. Such foods are in the market and have helped solve the protein deficiency of vulnerable sections of our population, like infants, children and pregnant mothers.

Despite these well-known merits of oils and fats, the consumption of dietary fat in India is very low. Our per capita intake is of the order of 4–5 kg per annum as against 40–50 kg consumed in the advanced countries. Much of our malnutrition, particularly amongst children, is due to low intake of fats. The FAO/WHO expert group has recommended that 30–35 per cent of our total calorie requirements must be met by oils and fats and the ratio of saturated to polyunsaturated fatty acids should be 1:1. The minimum nutritional requirement of fat specified by the Indian Council of Medical Research is 20 kg per capita per annum. The average dietary consumption of oils and fats in India is thus about 1/4 to 1/5 of the nutritional requirements. Immediate steps are to be taken to increase the availability of oils and fats and its consumption in India to meet the energy needs of our population.

19.2 Functions of Oil and Fats in Foods

In addition to their nutritional function, oils and fats have other uses which derive principally from their distinct physical properties. They contribute to the tenderness, flavour, colour and texture of food products. They also serve as the chief ingredients in preparing foods that form emulsions and as cooking media.

19.2.1 Tenderness

One of the most important functions of oils and fats is to tenderize baked products. Large quantities of them find use in the preparation of baked products, such as breads, cakes, biscuits, cookies, etc. Their function is particularly important in pastry and bread which have little or no sugar to contribute to tenderness. In the absence of oils and fats, the gluten strands will be held firmly together as a solid mass. Fats, being insoluble in water, interfere with gluten development during mixing. Thus, fats act as shortenings in the preparation of baked products. Fat absorbed on flour proteins interferes with hydration and thus the development of a cohesive gluten structure.

Butter, margarine, a blend of vegetable and animal fats and hydrogenated fats or oils, are used as shortening agents. Hydrogenated oils used as shortening agents are partially hydrogenated as complete hydrogenation would make them too hard. Super glycerinated shortenings are used for baking. These are fats to which some 2.5 per cent monoglycerides and diglycerides have been added, to promote the emulsification of fat in water and improve the baking properties.

Different shortening agents are used in the baking of different products. The usual fat used, if any, in yeast bread is butter or margarine. In biscuits, a hard fat must be used so that the fat can be distributed in small pieces to give the desired flakiness to the biscuits. Muffins require that the fat be fluid during mixing. Shortened cakes are made using a plastic fat that combines readily with the ingredients in the flour mixture. Chiffon cakes are formulated with the use of oil. Butter and commercial shortenings are used in the preparation of cookies. Thus, the type of fat used as shortening in making pastries depends on the type of product desired. Butter is usually used in puff pastry.

Fats also contribute to the incorporation and retention of air in the form of small bubbles in the batter. Carbon dioxide and steam diffuse into these air cells during baking. Thus, fats contribute to the grain and volume of the baked products.

19.2.2 Flavour

Some fats influence the flavour of the food. Fats that are used for seasonings, table use and salad dressings, possess distinctively pleasing flavours. Butter, margarine, pecan fat and olive oil are commonly used for salad dressings. Cottonseed oil, corn oil, groundnut oil and soyabean oil lack flavour and are used for salad dressing when a bland flavour is required. All fats, flavoured or bland, act as solvents for the flavour of the foods to which they are added. For example, the flavour of onions, celery, pepper and other flavoured foods, when cooked, is extracted by fats.

19.2.3 Texture

Fats have textural effects in foods. They affect the smoothness of crystalline candies and frozen desserts through the retardation of crystallization and the gelatinization of starch in starch-thickened mixtures. They contribute to the juiciness of meats and the foam structure of whipped cream.

19.2.4 Emulsion

Fats constitute one of the essential constituents in food emulsions. Prominent among the natural food emulsions are milk, cream and egg yolk. In most food emulsions, oil is the dispersed or discontinuous phase and water is the dispersion medium or continuous phase. For the stabilization of the emulsion, an emulsifying agent is required. Various substances commonly used as emulsifiers are egg yolk, whole egg, gelatin, starch paste, vegetable gum, casein and fine powders, such as those of paprika and mustard.

Salad dressings, such as mayonnaise, French dressings and cooked salad dressing are permanent or semi-permanent emulsions of oil-in-water. Occasionally a single food, such as vinegar or sour cream, may be used as salad dressing. They may also be a simple mixture of oil and vinegar.

Mayonnaise: This is a semi-solid emulsion of vegetable oils (corn oil or cottonseed oil), egg yolk or whole egg, vinegar and seasonings. Vinegar reduces the tendency of the oil to become rancid. Mustard is frequently used in making mayonnaise as a flavouring material (which also stabilizes the emulsion) and other spices are added for taste. The oil content of mayonnaise is as high as 75 per cent.

French dressing: French dressing is an emulsion of vinegar, vegetable oils, salts and spices. The emulsion is not as stable as mayonnaise and contains about 35 per cent oil. Commercial French dressings are stabilized by adding powdered paprika, eggs, tomato sauce and other materials.

Cooked salad dressings: They are made from fat (butter, margarine or cream) or salad oil, egg, vinegar, starch and seasonings. Fruit juice or milk may be used in place of vinegar. The liquid ingredients are thickened with egg and added to water and starch heated to boiling point. Cooked dressings contain less than 30 per cent oil.

19.3 Processing of Oil and Fats

Oils and fats do not occur free in nature. They occur in animal tissues, and in the seeds and fruits from which they are isolated, refined and processed for specific use. Fats are extracted from animal tissues chiefly by rendering and from other sources by pressing and solvent extraction.

19.3.1 Rendering

In this process, fat from animal tissues is extracted by heat. Chopped or minced tissues are heated with water (wet rendering) or in its absence (dry rendering). In the former method, it is more common to use steam which results in the good disintegration of cells and efficient separation of fat. In dry rendering, the tissue is heated with steam in vacuum containers. An improved technology involves the division of the fatty tissues into fine particle size after which flash heating is applied for 15 secs. The product is then pulverized and centrifuged. This method gives a high yield and a bland and stable product.

19.3.2 Pressing

In India, oil has been obtained by processing oil seeds in village "ghanis" (made of pestle-and-mortar) driven by bullocks, from time immemorial. Power ghanis are now replacing non-power units. About 20 per cent of the total production of edible oil in the country is by the ghani sector. The predominance of this sector is because the consumer prefers the natural flavour and taste in ghani pressed oils.

The modern method of oil extraction by pressing is by the use of high-pressure expellers. In this process, the oil-bearing material is cleaned, tempered and dehulled, crushed or flaked and then passed through the expeller, when the oil separates. The deoiled cake is a good cattle feed. About 80 per cent of the oil in the country is produced by this method.

19.3.3 Solvent Extraction

Extraction of oil from expellers is not a very efficient method. Pressed cakes contain appreciable quantities of oil. Therefore, it is now common to extract oils by solvent extraction or by a combination of pressure and solvent extraction. With materials containing a low percentage of oil, solvent extraction is the only practical method of removing oil. Various organic solvents could be used, but the most commonly employed solvent is hexane. After extraction of the oil, the solvent is removed from the oil. The residue after solvent extraction (the protein-rich, deoiled meal) can be processed as edible flour. About one-tenth of the oil produced in the country is obtained from solvent extraction.

19.3.4 Refining

Oils extracted by the above methods are crude and contain many other constituents like free fatty acids, unsaponifiable matter, gums, waxes, mucilaginous matter, a variety of colouring matter, metallic contaminants, undesirable odoriferous constituents, etc. In refining, the suspended particles are removed by filtration or centrifugation. The free fatty acids are removed by alkali treatment. When the free fatty acid content is high as in palm oil (5 per cent), it is removed by blowing steam through hot oil under vacuum. This results in both as deacidification and deodorization. Any remaining free fatty acids are removed by neutralization. Pigments are removed by bleaching using adsorbents like activated earth or carbon or, in special cases, chemical bleaching agents. Finally, the oil is deodorized by injecting steam through the heated fat kept under reduced pressure. Techniques for continuous bleaching and deodorizing are available.

19.3.5 Hydrogenation

Refined oil on storage can become rancid. The unsaturated fatty acid components of the oil undergo deteriorative changes with time. To overcome this and to obtain fats of desired properties, refined oils are hydrogenated. Hydrogenation is brought about by passing hydrogen under pressure through hot oil in presence of catalysts like nickel. The properties of the final product are affected by temperature, rate of mixing with hydrogen, nature of the catalyst, and pressure of hydrogen. However, hydrogenation will bring about some isomerization of oleic acid to its *trans* isomer, eladic acid, which has some effect on the fluidity of cell membranes. The fat obtained will be neutral in flavour with a high enough smoking temperature to make it useful for frying and having shortening power. Hydrogenated fats used as shortenings may be mixed with mono- and diglycerides to improve their emulsification properties.

19.3.6 Vanaspati

Hydrogenated oil is known as vanaspati in India. It contains 95 per cent hydrogenated oil to which 5 per cent of a liquid oil is added. In earlier days, groundnut oil was used for hydrogenation and sesame oil as the liquid component. With the shortage of oil in the country, more and more non-traditional oils are being used in the vanaspati industry. In 2000's onward, vanaspati production in India was rapid growth and reaching 1.2 million tonnes by 2020's.

19.4 Animal Fats

Oils and fats are essential ingredients of foods. Several animal and vegetable fats are used in food preparations. Their use depends upon the properties of the fats, their availability, and the culture of the area of its use. The animal fats used are butter and lard, and those of vegetable origin, are the oils obtained generally from oilseeds and other vegetable sources like cereal brans.

19.4.1 Butter

Butter, because of its pleasing flavour and good shortening qualities, has for a long time been an important fat component in food preparations. It is made from milk fats. For an account of butter see Chapter 21.

19.4.2 Lard

Lard is an animal fat from hogs. It is very popular in Western countries as a low cost, flavourful substitute for butter in frying and baking. It is obtained by the heat rendering of fatty tissues. The quality of lard depends upon the part of the body of the animal from which the fat is obtained and the feed given to the animal. Lack of uniformity in some of the physical properties of lard, such as flavour and granular structure, and susceptibility to the development of rancidity, come in the way of its use.

These are overcome by modifying the fat in several ways, including bleaching, homogenization, deodorization, addition of the emulsifiers, and addition of antioxidants. In the present day, lards are obtained for specific purposes.

19.4.3 Margarine

Margarine, used as a substitute for butter, is made from vegetable oils or a mixture of vegetable and animal fat by hydrogenation. Appropriately hydrogenated fat is blended with cultured skim milk and salt. To simulate butter, yellow colouring matter, diacetyl for butter flavour, and vitamins A and D, are added. For emulsification, mono and diglycerides, and sodium benzoate as a preservative, are added. Like butter, margarine contains 80 per cent fat. Some special-purpose margarines contain only about 40 per cent fat and high water content. Margarine, like butter, can be whipped resulting in a volume increase of 50 per cent. Such a product is lower in calories on a volume basis and is used as spreads when diet foods are required.

Vanaspati, produced in this country, could easily be converted into margarine by incorporating suitable colour, flavour materials, milk fats and vitamins. It can also be tailored to meet consumer demands, such as appealing appearance and flavour, anti-splattering properties for use in frying, and attractive physical structure. However, present rules do not permit the addition of colours, etc., to vanaspati. On account of increased bread consumption in the country, it is estimated that the gap in bread spread fat is in the region of 12,000 tonnes per annum. Margarine could fill in the gap and, therefore, it is desirable to enable its manufacture in the country. This would go a long way to help the weaker sections of society who can use this in place of butter.

The world production of Margarine, short was 17 million tonnes and India produced 0.65 million tonnes in 2021. America is the largest producer with 4.4 million tonnes and Asia produced 4.57 million tonnes in 2021.

19.5 Vegetable Oils

The world's consumption of vegetable oils has increased tremendously in recent years. India depends primarily on oilseeds to meet her fat requirements. Despite the development of the dairy industry, butter is not available in the country in sufficient quantity and at a reasonable price. Other animal fats like lard are not used because of religious sentiments. Thus, our fat requirements are met by oilseeds, which constitute the second largest agricultural crop in the country after food grains. Till 1964, we were net exporters of oilseeds but unfortunately, the situation has changed now.

During 2005-06, oilseeds were cultivated in an area of 23 million hectares with a production of about 26 million tonnes. The productivity of oilseeds as a whole was about 9 quintals per hectare with castor seed topping the list (11.7 quintals per hectare), followed by rapeseed-mustard (11.5 quintals per hectare), groundnut (10.4 quintals per hectare) and soyabean (8.1 quintals per hectare). The edible oil extracted from edible oilseeds would be around 5 million tonnes against the demand of about 6.7 million tonnes. During 2022-23, 16.4 tonnes of oil were imported at a cost of ₹ 1.38 lakh crores.

The major source of oil in India is from groundnut, mustard, cottonseed, coconut and sesame. These supply over 90 per cent of the total supply of edible oils. The production of these and other edible oils for the three years ending with 2005 is given in Table 19.3. Other minor sources of edible oils are niger, safflower and rice bran.

Table 19.3 Production of important oils in India (million tonnes)

Oil	1994–95	1995–96	1996–97	2004–05	2020–21
Coconut *Cocus nucifera*	0.400	0.460	0.430	0.550	2.61
Groundnut *Arachis hypogaea*	1.680	1.420	1.710	1.616	1.60
Mustard *Brassica nigra*	1.730	1.970	1.980	2.590	3.60
Sunflower *Helianthus annus*	0.504	0.450	0.460	0.404	0.083
Sesame *Sesammumindicum*	0.229	0.370	0.290	0.220	0.088
Soyabean *Glycine max*	0.480	0.660	0.600	1.202	1.90

Source: www.fas.usda.gov/wap/circular/2006 oil.xls

19.6 Sources of Edible Oils

A brief account of the sources of edible oils in the country is the following:

19.6.1 Groundnut (*Arachis hypogaea*)

In developing countries, groundnut mostly goes into the production of oil and, to a certain extent, in the manufacture of confectionery. In India, about 50 per cent of the total edible oils produced is groundnut oil. The world production of groundnut oil was 4.75 million tonnes and India produced 1.60 million tonnes in 2019.

When groundnut is not properly stored it gets contaminated with the fungus *Aspergillus flavus,* resulting in the production of the toxic substance aflatoxin (see Chapter 28). Consumption of oil from fungal infected nuts is a health hazard and it is advisable to avoid its use. When the moisture content of groundnut is more than 8 per cent, there is a danger of fungal infection. Groundnuts should be dried to the safe moisture level soon after harvest and stacked where the relative humidity may not exceed 70 per cent, as this will help maintain the moisture content of dried nuts.

Groundnut oil is a clear amber coloured liquid extensively used in cooking and as salad oil. It is one of the most important fats used for making margarine. Large quantities of groundnut oil are used in the manufacture of vanaspati, though it is being replaced by some non-traditional oils of late. It is also used in preserving fish, as in the case of tinned sardines.

The residue left after the oil extraction of groundnuts is groundnut cake and this is used for the preparation of groundnut flour and for feeding cattle and other farm animals.

19.6.2 Rapeseed-Mustard

There are a large number of species of mustard, such as black mustard, rape, etc., cultivated in India and other countries of the world. The seeds closely resemble each other. The cultivated rapeseed mustard in the country is a mixture of three species, *Brassica compestris*, *Brassica juncea* and *Brassica nigra.* In 2005–06, the area under cultivation was 7.3 million hectares with a production of 0.93 million tonnes.

The world production of rapeseed oil was 26.6 million tonnes and India produced 2.5 million tonnes in 2020.

19.6.3 Sesame (*Sesamum indicum*)

Sesame or gingelly is one of the oldest oilseeds in the world. It is said to be native to India though its origin is sometimes traced to Central Africa and sometimes to Indonesia. Gingelly oil is one of the most important oils of domestic consumption in India.

India is the largest producer of sesame accounting for 36 per cent of the world's production. It was grown in about 1.8 million hectares and its annual production in 2004–05 was 680 thousand tonnes. It is grown in almost all parts of the country. The yield was 37.7 quintals per hectare.

The seeds are edible as such and are also fried and eaten. The decorticated seeds contain about 25 per cent oil and are used for extracting oil. The oil is extracted both by the old-fashioned ghani and in modern mills. When clean oil is required, the seed coat of gingelly seed is removed by soaking the seed in water and then rubbing off the seed coat, which is loosened by steeping in water. Most of the oil produced in India is locally consumed.

The world production of Sesame oil was 1.01 million tonnes and India produced 88,700 tonnes in 2021.

19.6.4 Cottonseed (*Gossypium*)

Cottonseed is a by-product of ginning cotton (*Gossypium*). Generally, the proportion of cotton to cottonseed is 3 to 1. On account of the huge production of cotton in India, cottonseed is an important commercial product. The seeds are of two types; the fuzzy, i.e., consisting of outer fluff or fuzz, and the non-fuzzy. The fuzzy seeds have to be delinted (removal of fuzz) before the extraction of oil. Both types of seeds are dehulled before processing. Cottonseed oil is extracted by two different methods, decorticated and non-decorticated. The fuzzy seeds are considered to possess better properties for processing into edible oils. The decorticating and dehusking method of processing yields high-grade edible oils. The undecorticated method gives oil with poor bleachability and involves considerable loss of oil.

The world production of cottonseed oil was 41.62 million tonnes and India produced 11.25 million tonnes in 2021. Asia produced 30.78 million tonnes.

19.6.5 Coconut (*Cocos nucifera*)

Coconut is used for two important purposes, viz., for use as an edible product and for the preparation of oil. Coconut oil is made from dried coconut meal or copra. The copra is milled both in ordinary rotary mills and in modern machinery. The recovered oil percentage varies from 57 to 75. Unlike other oils, coconut oil is poor in unsaturated acids. Oleic and linoleic acids are present only to the extent of about 9 per cent. The remaining 91 per cent is saturated fatty acids, characterized by the presence of a high percentage of lauric (C_{12}) and myristic (C_{14}) acids. Coconut oil is more easily absorbed than other oils, and for this reason, it is used extensively for edible purposes. The major industrial uses for coconut oil are in the manufacture of soap, vanaspati, margarine, pharmaceutical preparations, etc. Coconut cake obtained after extraction of the oil is a valuable foodstuff for cattle.

The world production of coconut oil was 2.61 million tonnes and India produced 0.34 million tonnes in 2020. Asia produced 2.34 million tonnes.

19.6.6 Sunflower (*Helianthus annuus*)

Sunflower is an important oilseed crop in temperate countries like Russia, Canada, and elsewhere. It is an important non-traditional crop that has been recently introduced to India. It was cultivated in an area of 0.15 million hectares, and in 2022-23, the production of sunflower seeds was 0.25 million tonnes.

Some important advantages of sunflower as a commercial oilseed crop are that it is a short duration crop, it can be cropped at any time of the year, the oil yield is high per unit area, crushing and extraction of oil is easy, and the quality of oil for edible purposes is high.

The world production of Sunflower oil was 51.9 million tonnes and India produced 2 million tonnes in 2022.

19.6.7 Soyabean (*Glycine max* Merr)

It is the most important oilseed crop of the world, though it has only a minor role in India. Soyabean oil is the world's leading vegetable oil in terms of both production and consumption. It is obtained from the raw bean by solvent extraction and is processed into a refined product that has several uses. It is used in vanaspati, salad oil, mayonnaise, sandwich spreads, baby food, cake mixes, and non-dairy creamers.

Soyabean oil has considerable nutritional importance. It has a high polyunsaturated fatty acid composition next only to sunflower oil. It has both n-6 and n-3 fatty acids and hence has a considerable plasma cholesterol-lowering effect. Being a vegetable oil, it has no dietary cholesterol content and a low plant sterol content. It is also reported to have anti-tumourigenic and blood sugar-lowering effects. It is a good source of vitamin E.

19.6.8 Niger (*Guizotia abyssinica*)

Niger is grown in most parts of India, but it is an oilseed of minor importance. The seeds contain about 40 per cent oil. Niger seed oil is a clear pale yellow oil that is edible and is used largely as a substitute for gingelly oil.

19.6.9 Flaxseeds (*Linum usitatissimum*)

Flaxseeds are known as *Linum usitatissimum* with its species name meaning "most useful." That would describe the versatility and nutritional value of this tiny little seed. Flax seeds are slightly larger than sesame seeds and have a hard shell that is smooth and shiny. Their colour ranges from deep amber to reddish-brown, depending upon whether the flax is of the golden or brown variety. While whole flaxseeds feature a soft crunch, the nutrients in ground seeds are more easily absorbed. The warm, earthy and subtly nutty flavour of flax seeds combined with an abundance of omega-3 fatty acids makes them an increasingly popular addition to the diets of many a health conscious consumer. Whole and ground seeds and oil are available throughout the year.

Flaxseed oil is rich in *alpha-linolenic acid*, an omega-3 fat that is a precursor to the form of omega-3 found in fish oils called *eicosapentaenoic* acid or EPA. Alpha-linolenic acid or ALA, in addition to providing several beneficial effects of its own, can be converted in the body to EPA, thus providing EPA's beneficial effects. For this conversion to readily take place, however, depends on the presence and activity of an enzyme called *delta*-6 *desturase*, which, in some individuals, is less available or less active than in others. In addition, the *delta-6 desaturase* function is inhibited in diabetes and by the consumption of saturated fat and alcohol. For these reasons, higher amounts of ALA-rich flaxseed oil must be consumed to provide the same benefits as the omega-3 fats found in the oil of cold-water fish.

The following Table 19.7 shows the nutrients for which flaxseed is either an excellent, very good or good source. Next to the nutrient name is found the following information: the amount of the nutrient that is included in the noted serving of this food; the % Daily Value (DV) and, the food's World's Healthiest Foods Rating.

The world production of Linseed oil was 7,21,900 tonnes and India produced 64,000 tonnes in 2021. China is the largest producer with 2,25,500 tonnes of production in 2021.

19.6.10 Oil from Other Sources

The gap between the supply and demand of vegetable oils in India is widening. As there are limitations to increased production of oil from traditional sources, alternative sources have to be developed. Of these, rice bran and oil palm are of great importance.

Table 19.4 Nutritional profile of flax seeds

Nutrient	Amount	DV(%)	World's Healthiest Foods Rating
Omega-3 fatty acids	3.51 g	140.4	Excellent
Manganese	0.64 mg	32.0	Very good
Dietary fibre	5.41 g	21.6	Very good
Magnesium	70.14 mg	17.5	Good
Folate	53.86 mcg	13.5	Good
Copper	0.20 mg	10.0	Good
Phosphorus	96.49 mg	9.6	Good
Vitamin B-6 (pyridoxine)	0.18	9.0	Good

Source: http: // www.whfoods.com.

Rice bran: Rice bran has not yet been exploited in the country to the fullest possible extent as a source of vegetable oil. From 2004–05, the country produced 6,00,000 tonnes of rice bran oil of technical non-edible grade. Though a lot of work has been done in the country to develop the production of rice bran oil, we have yet to develop designs that could be widely used in the rice mill for total exploitation of bran oil.

Oil palm: Red oil palm is an important new source of edible oil and can narrow the gap in our requirements. At present oil palm is cultivated on about 90,000 hectares. In 2005 India produced 70,000 tonnes of oil palm. The great attraction of oil palm is the fantastic yields of oil per unit area, nearly 4 tonnes per hectare. Palm oil accounts for nearly 40 per cent of Indian oil imports and it has found consumer acceptability as a substitute for traditional edible oils.

There are about 25 varieties of oil seeds of tree-origin in the country capable of producing about 3 million tonnes of edible oil; 40 per cent of this is from sal, a forest tree (*Shorea robusta*). Hardly 5 per cent of the available seeds from tree sources are collected at present. The minor and tree origin oil seed potential has not been fully exploited in our country. These sources could provide a sizable quantity of edible oils and reduce the gap between demand and supply.

19.7 Nutritional Food Mixes from Oilseeds

Malnutrition among the poorer sections of the population in several countries is widespread. In our country, the FAO has estimated that over 201 million persons are under-nourished. Because of economic, social and cultural factors, protein-rich and protective foods, such as milk and other animal foods are not available in adequate quantities to the poorer groups of population in India and other developing countries. Amongst the most vulnerable segments of the population, from the nutritional point, are infants and young children. About 2.3 per cent of all children of India, between the ages of 1 and 5 years, suffer from very severe forms of diseases like kwashiorkor and marasmus. Protein-calorie malnutrition has been an important cause of infant and child mortality. Hence, the development of low-cost processed protein enriched foods based on vegetable proteins is necessary. References have been made in Chapters 17 and 18 as to how pulses and nuts could be important sources of proteins, when properly processed. This section deals briefly with the development in India of the processing and utilization of oilseeds to produce nutritional food mixes.

19.7.1 Processing of Oilseeds for Food Use

India is one of the major oilseed producing countries in the world. The country produces the largest quantities of groundnut and sesame. It has also substantial quantities of cottonseed, rapeseed-mustard and coconut. It is estimated that the oilseeds in the country could provide as much as 1.7 million tonnes of proteins, which is more than what is now available through animal products like milk, egg, meat and fish. Based on oilseeds, several food products have been developed in the country which have helped improve the diets of people, particularly children.

The first step in the production of quality food from oilseeds is to obtain edible flours and protein concentrates from them. Good raw material is selected, and after removing extraneous matter, the seeds are dehulled. The dehulled kernels are then milled under optimal conditions to recover oil and a high-quality protein-rich edible grade meal. Several oilseeds contain anti-nutritional and toxic substances. These must be eliminated or inactivated during processing. Protein concentrates are obtained from different processes to suit different seeds.

Groundnut flour is the most widely used material to produce protein enriched foods. In combination with pulses and cereals, many high-protein supplementary foods have been developed. Groundnut proteins also have been isolated and several products based on them developed. Edible flours and protein concentrates have also been obtained from sesame, cottonseed, mustard-rapeseed, coconut, sunflower and soyabean and used in the production of supplementary foods.

19.7.2 Protein Rich Foods

Nutritive food mixes developed in the country are of two types: (i) protein-rich foods containing about 40–45 per cent protein based on blends of oilseed meals and pulses, and fortified with essential vitamins and minerals, and (ii) protein enriched cereal foods, containing 17–25 per cent proteins based on blends of cereals, oilseed meals and pulses.

Amongst the first type, the Indian Multipurpose Food (MPF) is important. The preparation consists of groundnut flour and Bengal gram flour in the ratio of 3 : 1, fortified with vitamins and minerals. Various formulations of MPF are prepared by the addition to the basic mix of seasoning and spice mixture, or flavours or skim milk powder. Similarly, protein-rich foods have been prepared based on groundnut, coconut and Bengal gram flours, groundnut and soyabean flours, and groundnut, sesame and Bengal gram flours. Incorporation of these foods in high-cereal diets has proved to be a valuable supplementary diet for school children.

19.7.3 Protein Enriched Cereal Foods

Some of the cereal-based protein enriched foods developed in the country are: (i) balanced malt food, (ii) enriched macaroni products, (iii) nutro biscuits, and (iv) bal-ahar. Malt foods are prepared by blending 40 per cent cereal malt, 40 per cent groundnut flour, and 10 per cent each of Bengal gram flour and skim milk powder. Enriched macaroni products are blends of groundnut flour (30 per cent), wheat flour (30 per cent), and tapioca flour (40 per cent), or a blend of wheat flour (75 per cent), and groundnut flour (25 per cent). Nutro biscuits are made from a blend of 40 per cent wheat flour, 30 per cent groundnut flour, and 15 per cent each of sugar and shortening. Bal-ahar contains a blend of cereal flours (60 per cent), and groundnut flour (30 per cent). All these preparations are fortified with vitamins and minerals, All these food mixes help considerably in making up the deficiencies in the diet of children and improving their nutritional status.

CHAPTER

20

Spices

India has been famous for its many and varied spices for many centuries. The word "India" conjures up a vision, in the minds of foreigners, of land of spices, among other things. India is considered to be the "home of spices." Even before the Christian era, tracers, and explorers from various parts of the world came to India to exchange their valuable merchandise for Indian spices. Even today, spices play a very important part in our national economy. The world trade in spices in 2019 was about 13 million tonnes, worth 20 billion US dollars. India, during that year, exported 1.53 million tonnes valued at 3.73 billion US dollars.

A diet composed of just the nutritive components may be quite insipid. To be palatable it should have flavour. In other words, man does not live by bread alone! The spice of his food life is concerned with what goes with his bread. The food is to be seasoned by the addition of flavouring agents, which include spices and condiments. According to the International Organization for Standardization, there is no clear-cut division between spices and condiments and so they are clubbed together. A spice is a dried seed, fruit, root, bark or vegetative substance used in nutritionally insignificant quantities as a food additive for flavouring. A condiment is a substance applied to food, usually in the form of a sauce, powder, or spread, to enhance or improve the flavour. Although at most forty different spice plants are of global importance (economically and culinarily), many more are used as condiments locally, in the region of their natural occurrence.

There are about 70 species of spices grown in different parts of the world. Many of them are grown in India. Spices can be classified in different ways, such as, according to their botanical families, economic importance, method of cultivation or which part of component of the plant, such as seeds, leaves, bark, etc. Each system has its own merits and demerits. A method of classification depending on the origin and active principle present in the spices is as follows:

1. Pungent spices: pepper, ginger, chillies, mustard.
2. Aromatic fruits: cardamom, nutmeg, mace, fenugreek, anise, fennel, caraway, dill, celery, cumin, coriander, etc.
3. Aromatic barks: cinnamon, cassia.
4. Phenolic spices containing eugenol: clove, allspice (pimento)
5. Coloured spices: paprika, saffron, turmeric

Spices are mostly used as flavouring agents in several foodstuffs, such as *curries*, bakery products, pickles, processed meats, beverages, liqueurs, etc. They enhance or vary the flavours of foods. Spices are also flavour disguisers; they help mask the off-flavour of foods that, if unspiced, have to be thrown away. Some spices possess anti-oxidant properties while others are used as preservatives in some foods like pickles and *chutneys*. Others, like cloves and mustard, possess strong anti-microbial

Table 20.1 Composition of Spices and Condiments, Dry (per 100 gms of edible portion)

	Moisture	Protein	Fat	Fiber	Carbohydrate	Energy	Energy	Calcium	Phosphorous	Iron	Thiamine	Riboflavin	Niacin	Vitamin B6	Biotin	Vitamin C
	g	g	g	g	g	K Joules	K Cal	mg	mg	mg	mg	mg	mg	mg	µg	mg
Asafoetida (*Ferula assa-foetida*)	9.42 ± 0.56	6.34 ± 0.53	1.26 ± 0.02	5.13 ± 0.33	71.95 ± 0.71	1387	332	266 ± 41.4	69.09 ± 15.60	15.68 ± 4.51	0.82 ± 0.037	0.01 ± 0.006	0.43 ± 0.05	0.02 ± 0.003	2.27 ± 0.34	–
Cardamom, black (*Elettaria cardamomum*)	6.69 ± 0.47	6.69 ± 0.31	2.80 ± 0.24	23.46 ± 0.58	52.53 ± 1.51	1132	271	378	132	8	0.05 ± 0.015	0.13 ± 0.047	0.52 ± 0.11	0.20 ± 0.021	4.76 ± 0.88	–
Cardamom, green (*Elettaria cardamomum*)	11.24 ± 0.51	8.10 ± 0.41	2.60 ± 0.15	23.10 ± 0.14	47.76 ± 0.47	1067	255	312	117	8	0.12 ± 0.016	0.07 ± 0.013	1.13 ± 0.13	0.15 ± 0.007	4.94 ± 0.39	–
Chillies, red (*Capsicum annum*)	14.57 ± 0.42	12.69 ± 0.22	6.40 ± 0.04	31.15 ± 0.04	29.46 ± 0.62	990	237	99.83 ± 6.61	280 ± 57.5	6.23 ± 0.79	0.46 ± 0.036	0.83 ± 0.009	6.94 ± 0.55	0.42 ± 0.009	0.92 ± 0.04	–
Cloves (*Syzygium aromaticum*)	26.49 ± 0.68	5.86 ± 0.21	8.41 ± 0.15	34.52 ± 0.48	18.73 ± 0.39	781	187	567 ± 70.8	83.10 ± 18.56	9.41 ± 2.10	0.53 ± 0.122	0.22 ± 0.022	1.15 ± 0.12	0.03 ± 0.003	2.41 ± 0.23	–
Coriander seeds (*Coriandrum sativu*)	8.72 ± 0.47	10.66 ± 0.33	17.47 ± 0.22	44.81 ± 2.36	12.98 ± 2.62	1125	269	718 ± 43.0	293 ± 54.4	17.64 ± 6.74	0.19 ± 0.018	0.23 ± 0.022	1.20 ± 0.16	0.39 ± 0.010	1.20 ± 0.22	–
Cumin seeds (*Cuminum cyminum*)	10.59 ± 0.51	13.91 ± 0.50	16.64 ± 0.15	30.35 ± 0.71	22.62 ± 1.05	1274	305	878 ± 78.0	382 ± 6.4	20.58 ± 4.24	0.52 ± 0.055	0.13 ± 0.022	2.87 ± 0.38	0.13 ± 0.006	0.76 ± 0.14	–
Fenugreek seeds (*Trigonella foenum graecum*)	7.82 ± 0.37	25.41 ± 0.24	5.72 ± 0.02	47.55 ± 0.54	10.57 ± 0.57	983	235	135	435	8.47	0.28 ± 0.029	0.14 ± 0.026	1.19 ± 0.10	0.77 ± 0.128	1.54 ± 0.29	–
Mace (*Myristica fragrans*)	20.06 ± 0.70	6.24 ± 0.27	24.41 ± 0.20	20.31 ± 0.23	26.51 ± 0.81	1488	356	174 ± 3.5	110 ± 17.7	22.69 ± 6.87	0.13 ± 0.020	0.13 ± 0.033	0.92 ± 0.11	0.30 ± 0.041	1.80 ± 0.27	–
Nutmeg (Myristica fragrans)	15.55 ± 0.55	6.30 ± 0.24	36.52 ± 0.04	11.99 ± 0.18	27.64 ± 0.70	1940	464	148 ± 12.1	207 ± 37.2	2.33 ± 0.20	0.04 ± 0.015	0.05 ± 0.011	0.51 ± 0.06	0.10 ± 0.008	1.59 ± 0.27	–
Omum (*Trachyspermum ammi*)	9.71 ± 0.18	15.89 ± 0.61	21.11 ± 0.08	20.58 ± 0.04	24.53 ± 0.68	1495	357	1034 ± 144	329 ± 57.7	13.65 ± 2.29	0.30 ± 0.032	0.23 ± 0.024	1.23 ± 0.19	0.24 ± 0.006	1.78 ± 0.30	–
Pepper, black (*Piper nigrum*)	13.18 ± 0.40	10.12 ± 0.40	2.74 ± 0.02	33.16 ± 0.29	36.22 ± 0.45	910	218	405 ± 40.9	144 ± 14.8	11.91 ± 3.48	0.06 ± 0.012	0.09 ± 0.013	0.85 ± 0.02	0.27 ± 0.013	3.49 ± 0.38	–
Pippali (*Piper longum*)	10.95 ± 0.48	10.53 ± 0.45	2.27 ± 0.02	34.14 ± 0.60	35.70 ± 0.45	906	217	414 ± 66.2	181 ± 6.9	7.99 ± 2.11	0.06 ± 0.011	0.14 ± 0.030	1.06 ± 0.11	0.60 ± 0.051	2.34 ± 0.37	–
Turmeric powder (*Curcuma domestica*)	10.58 ± 0.49	7.66 ± 0.44	5.03 ± 0.07	21.38 ± 0.29	49.22 ± 0.55	1174	281	122 ± 20.9	276 ± 33.1	46.08 ± 1.83	0.06 ± 0.004	0.01 ± 0.000	1.55 ± 0.10	0.04 ± 0.002	1.46 ± 0.34	–

Source: IFCT, NIN, ICMR, Hyderabad, 2017

Table 20.2: Composition of Spices and Condiments, Fresh (per 100 gms of edible portion)

	Moisture	Protein	Fat	Fiber	Carbohydrate	Energy		Calcium	Phosphorous	Iron	Thiamine (B1)	Riboflavin (B2)	Niacin	Vitamin B6	Biotin	Vitamin C
	g	g	g	g	g	K Joules	K Cal	mg	mg	mg	mg	mg	mg	mg	µg	mg
Chillies, green-all varieties (*Capsicum annum*)	85.39 ± 0.68	2.36 ± 0.34	0.72 ± 0.05	4.77 ± 0.61	5.86 ± 0.77	177	42.32424677	18.45	59.91	1.2	0.09 ± 0.033	0.11 ± 0.038	0.89 ± 0.15	0.28 ± 0.100	0.63 ± 0.16	94.07 ± 11.67
Coriander leaves (*Coriandrum sativum*)	86.99 ± 0.41	3.52 ± 0.26	0.70 ± 0.06	4.66 ± 0.24	1.93 ± 0.27	130	31.08560497	146 ± 13.0	64.69 ± 13.00	5.30 ± 1.55	0.09 ± 0.005	0.05 ± 0.004	0.73 ± 0.03	0.19 ± 0.025	4.17 ± 0.89	23.87 ± 7.33
Curry leaves (*Murraya koenigii*)	65.33 ± 1.57	7.41 ± 0.26	1.06 ± 0.04	16.83 ± 0.78	4.51 ± 1.79	266	63.60593018	659 ± 77.4	83.29 ± 14.06	8.67 ± 0.42	0.07 ± 0.016	0.13 ± 0.008	0.85 ± 0.10	0.57 ± 0.096	1.77 ± 0.22	6.04 ± 1.36
Garlic, big clove (*Allium sativum*)	64.38 ± 0.56	6.92 ± 0.20	0.16 ± 0.02	5.22 ± 0.41	21.93 ± 0.82	518	123.8641798	20.08 ± 5.73	119 ± 10.9	1.05 ± 0.15	0.20 ± 0.029	0.25 ± 0.026	0.38 ± 0.05	0.56 ± 0.039	2.55 ± 0.34	12.62 ± 1.15
Garlic, small clove (*Allium sativum*)	64.42 ± 0.30	6.75 ± 0.24	0.14 ± 0.01	5.47 ± 0.07	21.84 ± 0.74	514	122.9076997	17.63 ± 2.77	116 ± 27.9	0.88 ± 0.21	0.20 ± 0.023	0.23 ± 0.015	0.36 ± 0.04	0.77 ± 0.112	2.54 ± 0.21	13.57 ± 0.70
Garlic, single clove, Kashmir (*Allium sativum*)	64.49	6.12	0.16	4.01	23.46	523	125.05978	19	128	1.01	0.25	0.22	0.42	0.97	2.85	15.38
Ginger, fresh (*Zinziber officinale*)	81.27 ± 0.22	2.22 ± 0.16	0.85 ± 0.03	5.36 ± 0.40	8.97 ± 0.28	230	54.9976088	18.88 ± 2.87	44.36 ± 2.16	1.90 ± 0.55	0.04 ± 0.005	0.04 ± 0.003	0.42 ± 0.05	0.20 ± 0.025	1.07 ± 0.15	5.43 ± 1.22
Mango ginger (*Curcuma amada*)	84.55 ± 0.16	1.45 ± 0.37	0.70 ± 0.03	4.74 ± 0.50	6.98 ± 0.15	177	42.32424677	13.74 ± 2.59	68.33 ± 20.13	2.31 ± 1.27	0.02 ± 0.001	0.07 ± 0.015	0.45 ± 0.01	0.18 ± 0.010	1.49 ± 0.49	1.62 ± 0.30
Mint leaves (*Mentha spicata*)	84.24 ± 0.71	4.66 ± 0.15	0.65 ± 0.05	5.89 ± 0.49	2.39 ± 0.36	155	37.06360593	205 ± 31.8	65.25 ± 16.18	8.56 ± 3.21	0.02 ± 0.005	0.19 ± 0.029	0.74 ± 0.23	0.17 ± 0.028	2.21 ± 0.43	17.16 ± 6.75
Onion, big (*Allium cepa*)	85.76 ± 0.43	1.50 ± 0.10	0.24 ± 0.03	2.45 ± 0.21	9.56 ± 0.44	201	48.06312769	21.03 ± 6.68	32.34 ± 7.63	0.43 ± 0.11	0.04 ± 0.005	0.01 ± 0.001	0.34 ± 0.10	0.10 ± 0.014	2.61 ± 0.19	6.69 ± 0.63
Onion, small (*Allium cepa*)	84.67 ± 0.12	1.82 ± 0.20	0.16 ± 0.01	1.16 ± 0.19	11.58 ± 0.37	237	56.67144907	19.92 ± 4.48	39.65 ± 9.90	0.53 ± 0.37	0.07 ± 0.012	0.02 ± 0.004	0.21 ± 0.01	0.12 ± 0.009	2.69 ± 0.63	10.96 ± 2.00

Source: IFCT, NIN, ICMR, Hyderabad, 2017

properties and, as such, prevent food spoilage. Spices were used to preserve meat for long periods when there was no refrigeration. Many spices also possess important physiological and medicinal properties.

Phytotherapy (*phyto*—Greek word for plants) is becoming popular. It is a science of using plant substances to treat or prevent illness. These plants, including their leaves, flowers, stems, rhizomes and roots are called botanicals, but the terms "herbs" and "botanicals" are often used interchangeably. Botanicals are bulk herb extracts, tinctures and capsules used for therapeutic purposes.

20.1 Composition

Spices are obtained from a large number of different plants. They are parts of plants, such as roots, buds, flowers, fruits, barks or seeds. Thus, little can be said in a general way about their composition. Most spices owe their flavouring properties to volatile oils and, in some cases, to fixed oils and small amounts of resins, which are known as oleoresins. In many cases, no single compound is responsible for flavours; a blend of different components, such as alcohols, phenols, esters, terpenes, organic acids, resins, alkaloids and sulphur-containing compounds, contribute to the flavour. In addition to flavour-contributing components, all spices contain the usual components of plant products, such as proteins, carbohydrates, fibre, minerals and tannins or polyphenols.

20.2 Flavouring Extracts

Spices, being agricultural commodities, are prone to spoilage by insect or microbial attack. Hence, the spice oils or oleoresins, which contain all the active principles of spices, are extracted and marketed. Spice oils are obtained by the steam distillation of ground spices. Oleoresins are obtained by the solvent extraction of ground spices or, more advantageously, the steam distilled spice. The spice oils contain only the aromatic principles, while the oleoresins contain both the aromatic and pungent principles. Various solvents like acetone, isopropanol, methanol, hexane, etc., are used as solvents. According to ISI standards, oleoresins obtained from solvent extraction should not contain more than a specified amount of solvent. The processed products of spices have several advantages—they are convenient to use, free from contamination, have better storage life, and are easy to transport. Technology has developed in India to prepare ready-to-use oleoresins from spices. In 2020-21, the country exported 16,450 tonnes of oleoresins and other spice oils worth $450 million US dollars.

20.3 Adulteration

Among food items, spices, due to their inherent nature, great demand and high price, become easy substances for gross adulteration. According to the Prevention of Food Adulteration Act, 1976 (of India), adulteration means any article of food whose quality or purity falls below the prescribed standards. Spices are generally adulterated with less expensive materials, e.g., cassia or cinnamon is mixed with a variety of different materials, such as ground hulls from various fruits, sawdust, ground fruit seeds and nut shells, and other readily available waste materials. Ground spices, such as *curry* powder, *garam masala,* chilli powder and turmeric powder are others that are easily adulterated. Therefore, ISI specifies and lays down general standards for all spices to be fit to be marketed or exported (see also Chapter 28).

20.4 Major Spices of India

Nine spices, namely, pepper, ginger, cloves, cinnamon, cassia, mace, nutmeg, pimento and cardamom, alone contribute to more than 90 per cent of the total world trade in spices. The major spices of India are pepper, cardamom, ginger, turmeric and chillies. Large quantities of these spices are exported; pepper stands first (with 41 per cent), followed, by cardamom (22.7 per cent), turmeric (8 per cent), ginger (7.6 per cent) and chillies (5.3 per cent), of our total export of spices. The remaining 15.4 per cent is contributed by other minor spices. The important minor spices grown in India are ajowan, aniseed, caraway, coriander, cumin, dill seeds, fennel, fenugreek, garlic, onion, saffron and vanilla.

20.4.1 Pepper, Black Pepper (*Piper nigrum*)

Black pepper or *kali mirch* is the dried, mature but unripe fruit or berry of a perennial climbing vine cultivated as a plantation crop. It is considered to be the "king of spices" because it is the largest used spice in the domestic and industrial sectors. Presently, its world consumption is of the order of 3,00,000 tonnes. It is one of the agricultural commodities of the country with a pronounced export bias. Nearly 80 per cent of our pepper output is exported.

The world production is 36.97 million tonnes and India produced 1.74 million tonnes, 2023.

Different varieties (24 types) of black pepper are grown in the country. It is grown only in South India, Kerala contributing 95 per cent of India's total production and Karnataka 3.5 per cent. Pepper is obtained by harvesting the spikes when the fruits are fully mature and start yellowing or become yellowish. The berries are removed from the spikes by rubbing, threshing or trampling, and sun-dried for a few days. When completely dry, the outer skin of the berries becomes dark brown to black and gets shrivelled. Before drying, if the berries are kept in boiling water for about 2 min., a glossy uniform black product is obtained on drying. Heat treatment arrests enzyme activity and the dried product has better keeping quality and a fresher aroma.

Composition: The Indian black pepper gives the following ranges of values: moisture, 8.7–14.0; total nitrogen, 1.55–2.60; ether extract (volatile and non-volatile), 4.2–15.7; carbohydrates (starch), 28.0–49.0; crude fibre, 8.7–14.0; and ash, 3.5–5.7 per cent. A considerable portion of the nitrogen in pepper is non-protein nitrogen and is due to alkaloids. The spice value of pepper is mainly due to the presence of 4–5 per cent of a group of alkaloids, piperine and related compounds (chavicine, piperidine and piperettine). Apart from the pungent constituents, pepper contains about 2.5 per cent volatile oil (pepper oil) having about 95 per cent terpene hydrocarbons and about 4 per cent oxygenated terpenes, which are responsible for the characteristic odour of the oil.

White pepper: White pepper also is obtained from the berries of *P. nigrum* by harvesting them when they have become ripe, i.e., the berries are yellowish red or red in colour. White pepper is prepared by removing the outer coating of the seeds either before or after drying. White pepper has less flavour and less pungency than black pepper, for the reason that the outer skin which also contains some of these ingredients is removed. India does not produce and export white pepper on a large scale. It is prepared by any one of the following methods.

The old indigenous method consists of steeping the ripe pepper in water for several days which results in the softening of the skin, which is then rubbed and washed off. The cores are then dried to get white pepper. Microbial action during steeping gives a bad smell to the product.

A better method involves the boiling of fully ripe pepper for a few minutes in water (just long enough to soften the skins), cooling and then rubbing off the skin manually or mechanically. On drying, this gives a very pleasant-smelling product. In the alternative, the pepper is heated in water till the blackening enzymes are inactivated is treated with sulphur dioxide and the berries are then dried. This gives a buff-coloured pepper with the skin intact. On grinding, a powder similar to traditional white pepper powder is obtained and the aroma is superior. White pepper is also prepared by the decortication of dry black pepper mechanically.

Green pepper: In recent years there has been a growing demand for canned and bottled green pepper in Western countries for garnishing meat dishes. India is producing and exporting green pepper. Immature pepper is harvested and is canned in brine or vinegar. Dehydrated green pepper is also being produced in the country for export purposes.

Pepper oil and oleoresins: The characteristic odour of pepper is due to the volatile oil present in the pericarp of pepper. This oil is obtained by steam distillation using ground black pepper or light pepper obtained during the grading of pepper. Some pepper oil of commerce is a by-product of the oleoresin industry. The quality and composition of the pepper oil vary considerably. This is generally due to a variation in the variety, grade, storage condition, and processing of pepper.

Pepper oleoresin is obtained by the solvent extraction of ground pepper and subsequent removal of solvent. It contains the oil responsible for the aroma and the resinous portion containing the pungency factors. Pepper oleoresin has the largest sales among all spice oleoresins. India in 2023 exported pepper oleoresin at 45.13 US dollars per kg.

Long pepper (Piper longum): Long pepper is cultivated in India only to a limited extent. It is derived mostly from wild plants grown in the Northern and North-Eastern parts of the country. Long pepper contains alkaloids having a pungent pepper-like taste and produces marked salivation and numbness of the mouth. It contains an essential oil with a spicy odour resembling that of pepper and ginger oils. Long pepper is used as a spice and also in pickles and preserves.

Uses: Pepper is used for a variety of purposes. It is used for relieving various types of bodily ailments. For centuries it has been used as an essential preservative for meat and other perishable foods. It is largely used in meat packing and canning, pickling, baking, confectionery and preparation of beverages. Its principal use is as a seasoning agent. Black pepper is an important component of culinary seasoning and an essential ingredient of many commercial foods.

White pepper has been in use for a long time and currently, large quantities (over 20,000 tonnes) are being produced. There is scope for the increased use of white pepper in food processing. It is chiefly used in white sauces, mayonnaise and salad dressings, where black particles are undesirable, it is also a favourite with users who prefer its mild flavour to the strong one of black pepper.

Canned and dehydrated green pepper is relished as a flavouring agent for eating with meat. Since the product has a very fresh smell of harvested green pepper and higher oil content, it has found new uses besides the garnishing of meat.

Pepper oil is used in the flavouring of foods in conjunction with other spice oils. It is used in oleoresins to bring about a balance between aroma and pungency. To a limited extent, it is used in perfumery. Pepper oleoresins are chiefly used in the processed food industries in advanced countries, and these are expanding.

20.4.2 Cardamom (*Elettaria cardamomum*)

Cardamoms or *chhota elaichi* are the dried ripe fruits of *E. cardamomum*. Two distinct varieties of cardamom based on the size of fruits are recognized. They are *E. cardamomum* var *major*, comprising the wild indigenous cardamom of Sri Lanka and cultivated to some extent in the eastern Himalayan region and *E. cardamomum* var *minor* which is indigenous to India cultivated in the Southern States of

Kerala, Karnataka and Tamil Nadu. Var *major* is the more primitive variety from which the cultivated var *minor* is derived. The minor consists of a large number of races differing in the size of the plant, leaf surface, flower and fruit.

The minor variety constitutes the second most important spice of India and is known as the "queen of spices," coming next to pepper. India is the major cardamom producing country in the world, the other important countries being Guatemala, Sri Lanka, Tanzania and Taiwan. Till recently, India was the biggest exporter of cardamom accounting for about 90–95 per cent of the world's export but of late Guatemala and other countries are competing with India and our exports have come down to about 70 per cent of world trade.

India produced 41,000 tonnes in 2022.

Processing: The cardamom fruits (capsules) are ovoid, pale green to yellow in colour, and contain 15–20 hard brownish-black, angled and wrinkled seeds, covered by a thin mucilaginous membrane. The fruits are harvested when they are just short of full ripeness. This is necessary to prevent the capsules from splitting during drying. The fruits are dried either in the sun or in a drying chamber. A certain amount of bleaching takes place during drying and the capsule attains a straw colour. The capsules are sometimes bleached by exposure to sulphur dioxide or by steeping in a dilute solution of sulphurous acid. Bleaching improves the appearance of the pericarp and keeping the qualities of cardamom. On the other hand, it reduces the percentage of volatile oil in the seeds. ISI has prescribed standards for different types of cardamom grown in the country.

Composition: Analysis of the Indian cardamom seeds gives the following range of values: moisture 7.0–10.0; ether extracts, 7.5–15.0; protein 7.0–14.0; carbohydrates, 39.0–49.0; and ash 3.8–6.9 per cent. The calcium and phosphorus contents are 0.3 and 0.4 per cent, respectively. The vitamins present (mg per 100 g) are thiamine, 1.8; riboflavin, 0.23; niacin, 2.3; and vitamin A, 175 IU.

The spice value of cardamom depends on the volatile oils (2–10 per cent) present in the seeds. Seeds stored after dehusking suffer a loss of volatile oils (about 30 per cent in 8 months), while husk-protected seeds show practically no loss. Cardamom oil of commerce is obtained by the distillation of seeds or whole fruits. It is a colourless to pale yellow liquid with a penetrating, somewhat camphoraceous odour, and a strong persistent pungent taste. The oil loses its flavour on storage. The principal constituents of the oil are the terpenes—cineole, terpineol, terpinene, limonene, sabinene and terpinyl acetate. The quality of cardamom oil is related to the terpinyl acetate content.

Uses: Cardamom seeds have a pleasant aroma, and a characteristic pungent taste. They are used as a spice and in medicine. They are the common ingredients of *curry* powder, cakes and other bakery products and sweet breads. They are also used for flavouring liquors. In West Asia, cardamom is used for flavouring coffee. About 85 per cent of India's cardamom export is to the Arab nations. It also finds use in the preparation of flavoured tea. The chewing of cardamom masks bad breath and prevents dental decay. Different systems of medicines—Ayurvedic, Allopathic and Unani—employ cardamom for the cure of many human disorders. Cardamom oil also is used in medicine and in flavouring beverages.

20.4.3 Ginger (*Zingiber officinale*)

Ginger is native to South East Asia, but the wild forms are found in India and several species are grown in Malaysia.

Ginger or *adrak* is the dried underground stem or rhizome of the zingiberaceae herbaceous plant. The rhizomes are irregular and are formed at a shallow depth in the soil. Ginger has been under cultivation in India from time immemorial and is being exported from very early times. Indian ginger is considered only second to the Jamaican variety in quality. Apart from India which is the major producer of ginger today, Taiwan, Jamaica, Nigeria and Malaysia produce and export ginger.

The world production is 4.87 million tonnes and India produced 2.21 million tonnes, 2022.

Processing: The crop is dug up for ginger in stages, depending upon the type of ginger required. The tender rhizome, sold as green ginger for the preparation of preserves or pickling, is harvested from the fifth month after sowing. The crop for dry ginger is harvested after about the eighth month. The rhizomes are marketed as such or after peeling or scraping of the epidermal layer. In the latter case, the peeled ginger is washed and then sun-dried. When white, polished rhizomes free from specks or spots are required, the peeled ginger is soaked in a solution of lime and then dried. In some cases, the lime-treated rhizomes are further treated with sulphur dioxide.

Composition: The composition (average value) of Indian dry ginger is: moisture, 6.9; protein, 8.6; fat, 6.4; fibre, 5.9; carbohydrate, 66.5; and ash, 5.7 per cent. The vitamins present are thiamine, 0.05; riboflavin, 0.13; niacin, 1.9; ascorbic acid, 12.0 mg per cent; and vitamin A, 125 IU/100g.

Ginger contains 1–3 per cent essential oil (oil of ginger) with a characteristic pleasant and aromatic odour. The oil is separated by the steam distillation of rhizomes. Since the oil is more in the epidermal tissue, unscrapped ginger is used for steam distillation. The oil is greenish to yellow in colour, becomes viscous on storage, and does not have the pungent flavour of the spice. The important constituents of the oil are monoterpenes (4 per cent), sesquiterpenes (65 per cent), and oxygenated terpenes (17 per cent).

The pungent principles of ginger are non-volatile. They are extracted from the coarsely ground, dried spice by percolation with organic solvents. On removal of the solvent, a viscous and dark brown oil (ginger oleoresin) is obtained, which retains all the pungency of the spice. The oleoresin is known by the trade name "Gingerin" and it contains besides the pungent principle, essential oils and non-pungent matter. The non-pungent substances include carbohydrates and palmitic and other fatty acids. The pungent principles are oxymethyl phenols, such as gingerol, shogaol, and related, compounds.

Uses: Ginger is one of the most important and oldest spices. It is used in dried, preserved and green forms. Because of its pleasant aroma and pungency, it is widely used as a flavouring agent in the preparation of a great variety of food products like ginger bread, confectioneries, *curry* powders, *curried* meats, pickles, soft drinks like ginger cocktail or gingerella, and carbonated drinks like ginger beer. It is also used for the preparation of oleoresin and essential oils.

Substantial quantities of green ginger are used in the country as a spice in culinary preparations. Some quantity is also used for the preparation of pickles and canned ginger. Preserved ginger is made from young fleshy rhizomes boiled in sugar and packed in syrup. The preserved ginger is used in confectionery. The production of ginger *muraba* is a traditional industry in India. Ginger is also used in the preparation of some alcoholic beverages (ginger brandy and ginger wine) and in medicine. Ginger oil finds limited use in perfumery.

20.4.4 Chillies (*Capsicum annuum*)

Chillies or *lal mirch* are the fruits of some species of the genus *Capsicum*. They are also called capsicum or red pepper. Chillies are an indispensable and common ingredient of Indian food, and especially of South Indian food. Notwithstanding such a general use at the present time, the chilli crop is not indigenous to India. It was introduced to India from its native home Brazil and the South American continent, by the Portuguese only about 400–500 years ago. Prior to its introduction, black pepper was being used to provide the necessary pungency to food. In the year 2021, India produced 18.74 million tonnes.

The genus *Capsicum*, with a wide range of varieties and many intermediate and hybrid forms, has been classified in different ways and many different common names have been applied to them. The generally accepted two main species are *Capsicum annuum* and *Capsicum frutescens*. The former is an annual and the flowers grow singly in the leaf axils, while the latter is a perennial, with flower clusters in the leaf axils. Most of the chillies grown in India belong to the species *C. annum*. There are many varieties differing mainly in the size, shape and pungency of fruits. Unripe fruits are generally green but forms differing in colour are known. The ripe fruits are generally red, but in some forms, they are yellow or orange. The long and thin to round or oblong varieties having thin and comparatively smooth pericarp are highly pungent and used as spices in the preparation of hot foods. The larger bell-shaped fruits with thick pericarps are less pungent or non-pungent and used in the green condition as a vegetable, in salads and in pickles. Paprika belongs to this group.

Bird chilli (*C. fruitescens*) is a perennial plant. It grows wild in the tropics. It bears small, conical fruits which are extremely pungent. Its capsaicin (the pungent principle) content is high (0.3 per cent), and occasionally it may be as high as 1.8 per cent. Its vitamin C content is less than in *C. annum*. Cayenne pepper is made from finely ground dried bird chilli mixed with salt (25 per cent).

Processing: The dry chilli of commerce is obtained by picking ripe and nearly ripe fruits, curing them by heaping them indoors for 2–3 days and then sun drying. Partially ripe fruits, if dried without the curing treatment, develop white patches which reduce their market value. When the fruits are partially dried they are trampled upon or rolled over to flatten them. This enables a greater quantity of the dried product to be packed in a unit volume. The yield of dried material is about 25–30 per cent of fresh weight. Chillies are sometimes smeared with suitable oil to impart glossiness.

Composition: The chemical composition of Indian red chillies is as follows: moisture, 10.0; protein, 15.0; fats, 6.2; fibre, 30.2; carbohydrate, 31.6; total ash, 6.1; calcium, 0.16; phosphorus, 0.37; and iron, 0.23 percent. Chilli powder, on solvent extraction, gives a fatty oil (9–13 per cent), which is viscous, red in colour, and has a sharp taste. On steam distillation, 0.16–0.39 per cent of a volatile oil is obtained. Chilli seeds contain 26.1 per cent oil. The protein content of fat and moisture-free seeds is 28.9 per cent. In this respect, chilli seeds resemble other oil seeds.

The pungent principle in chillies is an alkaloid called capsaicin. Capsaicin retains its pungency in a dilution of one in a million parts of water. Its content varies from zero to 1.8 per cent in bird and other hot chillies. Commercial chilli samples contain about 0.1 per cent. The colouring matter of the ripe fruits is due to carotenoid pigments.

Chillies are high in vitamin C content. The vitamin content depends on the variety, locality and stage of maturity of the fruits. Hungarian paprika contains 280 mg and Indian varieties up to 170 mg per 100 g. The green chillies contain 111 mg and dry chillies 50 mg of the vitamin per 100 g. The vitamin A content of green and dry chillies are, respectively, 454 and 576 IU per 100 g.

Uses: Dry chilli is extensively used as a spice in all types of *curried* dishes. It is the major constituent of *curry* powder made by grinding roasted dry chilli with other spices, such as coriander, cumin, turmeric, etc. Bird chilli is used in making hot sauces, such as tabasco sauce.

Chilli helps in digestion. It stimulates the taste buds which results in an increased flow of salivary amylase helping the digestion of starchy foods. Paprika and green chilli are good sources of vitamins A and C. Paprika is also used to colour and flavour dishes. Chillies find several medicinal uses.

20.4.5 Turmeric (*Curcuma longa*)

The species *Curcuma longa* is probably native to India, and is a triploid with 42 chromosomes which have originated from *C. aromatica*, a species found all over India.

Turmeric or *haldi* belongs to the ginger family and, as with ginger, it is the rhizome that finds use as a spice and for other purposes. There are about 70 species of turmeric of which 30 species occur in India. Of these, several are wild species and *C. longa* is the most important cultivated variety.

In the year 2022-23, India produced 1.16 million tonnes.

Curcuma aromatica occurs wild throughout India and accounts for 4 per cent of the area under turmeric cultivation. This variety is called *Kasturi* turmeric. The cured turmeric has a sweet fragrance and is used largely for the production of bathing powder, perfumed bathing oils and other toiletry preparations.

Processing: The turmeric rhizomes are to be cured for the development of colour and aroma. The curing consists of cooking the rhizomes in water until they become soft. Earlier, some cow dung was added during cooking to intensify the colour of the product. Addition of cow dung made the boiling water alkaline. According to the new technique, the rhizomes are boiled in lime water or soda bicarbonate solution. The well-cooked rhizomes are spread out in the open for sun drying. They are then cleaned and polished mechanically in a rotary drum. Cured and finished turmeric is brittle and has a striking yellow colour.

Composition: Analysis of Indian turmeric gives the following values: moisture, 5.8; protein, 8.6; fat, 8.9; carbohydrate, 63.0; fibre, 6.9; ash, 6.8; calcium, 0.2; phosphorus, 0.26; and iron, 0.05 per cent. The vitamin content is thiamine, 0,09; riboflavin, 0.19; niacin, 4.8 mg per cent; and vitamin A, 175 IU per 100 g.

Turmeric on steam distillation gives 1.5 per cent essential oil, which consists of 56 per cent of sesquiterpene ketones (turmerones) and 9 per cent tertiary alcohol. On solvent extraction, followed by removal of the solvent, an oleoresin containing all the aroma and flavour of turmeric is obtained. This is in great demand in food and pharmaceutical industries. The colouring matter of turmeric is due to the curcumin pigment.

Uses: Turmeric powder is used as a flavouring material and colourant in many foods to give an agreeable flavour and colour. It is a constituent of *curry* powders and prepared mustards. It is used for dyeing wool, silk and cotton. Turmeric is an anti-oxidant due to its phenolic character. Turmeric is an auspicious article in all religious observances of Hindu households. It is also used as a cosmetic and for the preparation of *kumkum* which is used by Hindu women. Like other spices, it finds many uses in the indigenous systems of medicine.

20.5 Minor Spices of India

20.5.1 Ajowan, Coriander and Cumin

Among the minor spices of India, ajowan or bishop's weed or *omum* (*Trachyspermum ammi*), aniseed or *valaiti saunf* (*Pimpinella anisum*), caraway or *shia jira* (*Carum carvi*), celery or *shalari* (*Apium graveolens*), coriander or *dhania* (*Coriandrum sativum*), cumin or *jira* (*Cuminum cyminum*), dill or *sowa*

(*Anethum graveolens*), and fennel or *saunf* (*Foeniculum vulgare*) belong to the same family (*Umbelliferae*). All these seeds are used as spices for culinary purposes. They all contain essential oils which find use as flavouring material, in medicine and in toilet preparations. In some cases, the leaves and stems are also used; celery leaves and stalks are used as salads, in soups, and as pre-dinner appetizers. The stem, leaves and fruits of coriander have a pleasant aromatic odour. The entire plant, when young, is used in preparing chutneys and sauces, and the leaves are used for flavouring curries and soups. The seeds are extensively employed as a spice in the preparation of *curry* powder, pickling spices, sausages and seasonings. Young leaves of dill also are used for flavouring soups and sauces.

Cumin: This seed is derived from the herb *Cuminum cyminum* native to Mediterranean region, whose Sanskrit names are *ajaji, Karachi, and kunchika.* It appears rather late in literary usage with Kautilua, Charaka and Sushruta around 300 BC.

In the year 2023-24, India produced 24,768 million tonnes ajwon; 6,00,000 tonnes of coriander; 5,77,270 tonnes cumin.

20.5.2 Cinnamon (*Cinnamomum zeylanicum*)

Cinnamon or *dalchini* is the inner bark of the young shoots of the cinnamon tree. The tree is an important spice tree in India and it is grown on the West Coast and Western Ghats. The quality of cinnamon depends upon the length, breadth and thickness of the bark. The bark contains 0.5 to 1.0 per cent volatile oil. The bark is extensively used as a spice in the form of small pieces or powder. It is aromatic, astringent and stimulatory. It is also used for flavouring confectionery, liquors, pharmaceuticals, soaps and dental preparations. The bark oil is also used extensively as a flavouring material.

The world production is 2,38,403 tonnes in 2021 and India in 2021 produced 6,020 tonnes cinnamon and tejpatta.

20.5.3 Fenugreek (*Trigonella foenum-graecum*)

Fenugreek or *methi* is the dried ripe fruit of an annual herb, native to South-Eastern Europe and West Asia and now cultivated in India. India is one of the major producers and exporters of fenugreek. About 40,000 hectares are under this crop, producing about 20,000 tonnes of the seeds.

Fresh tender leaves and shoots of fenugreek are rich in minerals (Ca, P, Fe) and vitamins A and C, and are eaten as vegetables. The seeds are small, hard, smooth and oblong, and yellowish-brown in colour. They contain many substances like proteins, starch, sugars, mucilage, mineral matter, volatile oil, fixed oil, vitamins and enzymes. As a spice, fenugreek adds not only to the flavour but also to the nutritive value of foods. It forms a constituent of *curry* powder. Sometimes fenugreek is used in place of black gram in the preparation of idlies. The seeds possess medicinal properties and are thus articles of medicinal value, especially for diabetic patients, as there is a significant hypoglycemic effect.

In the year 2023-24, India produced 0.25 million tonnes.

20.5.4 Garlic (*Allium sativum*)

Garlic or *lassan* is a bulb made up of several cloves enclosed within the white or pink skin of the parent bulb. It is cultivated all over India. Garlic is used practically all over the world for flavouring various dishes. In India, it is used in several food preparations, notably in chutneys, pickles, *curry* powders, *curried* vegetables, meat preparations, etc. However, its flavour is less appreciated by some people. Garlic has a strong flavour due to the sulphur-containing allicin (see Chapter 9). It has also anti-bacterial and anti-insecticide activities. Garlic is a remedy for several ailments and physiological disorders. It is said that it decreases the cholesterol content of the serum and reduces hypertension.

Garlic powder is dehydrated garlic. By proper technique, garlic powder with better colour, flavour, pharmaceutical or anti-bacterial property than garlic, can be obtained. In some countries, garlic powder has largely replaced garlic in all its uses. Garlic salt is prepared by mixing garlic powder (20 per cent), pulverized salt (78 per cent) and anti-caking agent (2 per cent).

20.5.5 Mustard (*Brassica nigra*)

Mustard seed is also known as rapeseed, is a condiment bland. Mustard greens, Indian, Chinese leaf mustard resembles headless cabbage like kale hence called as mustard cabbage. Mustard has a sharp pungent horseradish flavour and is used in soul food cuisine.

Archeological excavations in the Indus valley (Indian subcontinent) have revealed that mustard was cultivated there. That civilization existed until about 1800 BC.

It had varieties wild white mustard (*Sinapis alba*), black mustard (*Brassica nigra*), brown Indian mustard (*Brassica juncea*), white mustard (*Brassica hirta*), and wild mustard (*Brassica competris*).

Locations renowned for their mustard include *dijon* (medium-strength) and Meaux in France; Norwich (very hot) and Tewkesbury's mustard, in the United Kingdom; and Düsseldorf (hot) and Bavaria in Germany.

Mustard contains glucosinolate, isothiocyanate such as allyl isothiocyanate. Because of these, it has anti-bacterial properties and does not require refrigeration.

The world production is 8,52,808 tonnes in 2022.

The role of various types of mustard as an important oilseed crop in India has been dealt within Chapter 19. The spice value of mustard seeds is due to the thiocyanates which are present in them as glycosides and are released by the action of an enzyme, in the presence of moisture under suitable conditions. The whole seeds after drying are used in pickling, preserving and seasoning vegetables. White mustard is ground with black mustard for preparing table mustard.

20.5.6 Mace and Nutmeg (*Jaipatri and Jaiphal*)

There are two species of the same tree, *Myristica fragrans,* which is native to Indonesia. The fleshy fruit splits when ripe and exposes the mace as a scarlet fleshy covering called the aril enclosing in a network the seed, which is the nutmeg. The mace is carefully removed, flattened and dried, during which process it turns brown. The nutmeg is also dried. The most important constituent of nutmeg and mace is the volatile oil which forms 4–15 per cent of mace and 7–16 per cent of nutmeg. The oil of mace contains 93 per cent terpenes and 7 per cent aromatics. The nutmeg oil contains 84 per cent terpenes and 11 per cent aromatics. Nutmeg yields 24 to 30 per cent fixed oil, also known as nutmeg butter. Both mace and nutmeg are used for flavouring foods; generally, mace is used for flavouring savoury dishes and nutmeg for sweet dishes. The volatile oil is used for flavouring foods, dental preparations, essences, confectionery, vegetable dishes and beverages. Both have medicinal properties and are used as drugs.

The Moluccas Islands are also the source of nutmeg and mace, the first being the but and the second the scarlet aril which envelopes the but and becomes visible when the fruit is stripped away. The nutmeg in Sanskrit is *Jaiphal,* the mace is *javitri,* and the bushy, every green tree is botanically Myristica fragrans.

The world production is 2,35,000 tonnes and India's is 41,000 tonnes, 2022.

20.5.7 Onion (*Allium cepa*)

Onion is grown in practically every country of the world. In India, it is grown throughout the country. India is one of the largest producers of onion and exports considerable quantities of it. There are different varieties of onions—white, yellow and red, of varying sizes and shapes. They also differ in their pungency. The culinary uses of onions are extraordinarily numerous. They are eaten raw, fried, boiled and roasted, in soups, *curries*, and a great variety of other savoury dishes. They are the main ingredient in many pickles and *chutneys*. Its spice value is due to its sulphur compounds (see Chapter 9). Dehydrated onions, onion flakes and onion powder are also used as flavouring agents.

20.5.8 Saffron (*Crocus sativus*)

It is probably native to Greece, being recorded in the 4th century BC. Saffron or *kesar* consists of rich gold or yellowish-red stigmas of the flower of *C. sativus*. Saffron is produced in India to a limited extent and considerable quantities are imported from other countries, particularly Spain and France. It has been used as a spice, or dye (saffron yellow), a cosmetic and a medicine since classical times. Its high cost limits its uses. Saffron contains a glycoside, crocin, which is its chief colouring principle. The flavour and spice value are due to the volatile and fixed oils present to the extent of 1.4 and 13.4 per cent respectively. In India, saffron is widely used in all sweetmeats.

20.5.9 Tamarind (*Tamarindus indica*)

The ripe fruits (pulp) of the tree are used as an acidulant in some food preparations. India is the only country producing a commercial crop of tamarind (*imli*). The pulp is rich in free acids (10 per cent) and combined acids (7 per cent) and plays an important role in the preparation of foods like "*sambar*", "*rasam,*" "*curries,*" "*chutneys,*" etc. which are very popular in South India. The use of pulp is cumbersome because of fibre, seeds, etc. Tamarind juice concentrate and dehydrated tamarind powder are in the market, and these can be easily dissolved in hot water and used in culinary preparations.

In the year 2023-24, India produced 132.44 thousand tonnes.

20.5.10 Cloves (*Eugenia caryophyllus*)

The species originates from the Moluccas in eastern Indonesia, which are also called the spice island. The word *lavanga* first appears in writing in the Ramayana and Chakara Samhita.

The world production is 3,00,000 tonnes, 2022 and India produced 1,74,000 tonnes.

Cloves or *lavang* are flower buds of the clove tree. When the base of the flower buds turns reddish in colour, they are harvested and dried. Clove is the second most important spice of the world from the commercial point of view, coming next to pepper. More than 80 per cent of the world crop is in Tanzania. Some clove is produced in India but most of our requirement is met by imports. Clove buds contain 16–17 per cent essential oils, which contain 90–95 per cent eugenol. The spice value of clove is mainly due to its volatile oil. In India, cloves, both whole and ground, are a popular ingredient in spice mixtures. In medicine, clove oil is used as an aid to digestion and for its antiseptic and anti-microbial properties for the cure of toothache.

20.5.11 Mint (*Mentha arvensis*)

Mint or *pudina* is an aromatic herb. Many varieties of mint are grown in this country. Mint is an important source of peppermint oil and menthol. On steam distillation of leaves, a golden yellow volatile oil is obtained. About 50 per cent of menthol separates on cooling the oil. On removal of menthol, the remaining oil is used as peppermint oil. Dementholized oil is used for flavouring mouthwashes, toothpaste and in pharmaceuticals and medicine. The very popular use of mint in India is in the preparation of *chutney*.

20.5.12 Vanilla (*Vanilla planifolia*)

Vanilla is a plant native to Eastern Mexico and Brazil. Attempts have been made to cultivate vanilla in India but not much headway has been made so far. The country imports most of its requirements. The fruit (pods) of the plant is a long bean in which a large number of small, hard, black seeds are present. The pods are cured by dipping them in boiling water followed by a long slow drying process. During this period, the enzyme (β-glucosidase hydrolyzes the glycoside vanillin with the formation of vanilla, which has a dominant aromatic flavour. The beans are cut into small pieces and are extracted with dilute alcohol which gives the flavouring extract or vanilla essence. Vanilla is used in flavouring various confectioneries, puddings, ice creams, etc. Vanillin is made synthetically, but natural vanilla remains in demand because it contains other useful aromatic substances as well as vanilla.

The world production is 7,433 tonnes in 2023.

20.5.13 Asafoetida (*Ferula foetida*)

Hingu occurs in early Buddhist Mahavagga. Hong is the exudate of the species, namely *Ferrula asafoetida*, *F. narthex* and *F. galbaniflua* each of which shows slight differences in properties.

Asafoetida or *hing* is the gum resin exuded from the rhizome of several species of *Ferula*, some of which are grown in India. It contains gum, resin and essential oil in varying proportions, which together are responsible for the strong flavour. Therefore, in trade, compounded asafoetida is marketed using flour of corn, wheat, barley and gum as diluent. It is believed that steam volatile organic sulphur compounds predominantly contribute to the characteristic asafoetida odour. Asafoetida is extensively used in India for flavouring *curries*, sauces and pickles, in conjunction with other spices. It also finds use in the Ayurvedic and Allopathic systems of medicine .

20.5.14 Allspice or Pimento (*Pimenta dioica*)

Allspice comprises the dried unripe berries which are nearly globular, with a somewhat rough surface and a reddish-brown colour. The name "allspice" is derived from the fact that the spice is said to possess the characteristic flavour and aroma of cloves, nutmeg, cinnamon and black pepper, all combined in one spice.

The allspice tree is indigenous to the West Indies and tropical Central America. It is also reported to be cultivated in gardens in some parts of India.

Allspice owes its characteristic odour to the presence of an essential oil (3.3–4.5 per cent). In addition, it contains an acid responsible for the astringency, a soft resin with a burning taste, fixed oil (5.8 per cent), proteins (5.8 per cent), crude starch (20 per cent), and traces of alkaloids.

The berries are used as a flavouring ingredient in ketchup, soups, sauces, pickles, meats, etc. It is an important ingredient of spice mixture of *curry* powders, mincemeat *pies*, etc. The berry oil is rich in eugenol (65–80 per cent) and is used for flavouring condiments, food products and in perfumery. The oil can replace ground spice in all preparations. The pimenta leaf also contains an oil, but it is inferior in flavour and odour to the berry.

CHAPTER

21 Milk and Milk Products

The story of milk goes back to the beginning of civilization itself. Cattle were domesticated even in prehistoric times and milk was one of the most essential of all foods. Because milk is one of the most complete single foods available in nature for health and promotion of growth, the cow is considered as a sacred animal and even worshipped in India.

Milk is the normal secretion of the mammary gland of mammals. Its purpose in nature is to provide good nourishment for the young of the particular species producing it. Man has learnt the art of using milk and milk products as food for his well-being and has increased the milk-producing function of the animals best adapted as a source of milk for him. The cow is the principal source of milk for human consumption in many parts of the world; other animals as sources of milk for human beings are the buffalo, goat, sheep, camel, mare, etc. In India, more milk is obtained from the buffalo than the cow. Some amount of goat milk also is consumed.

India has the largest livestock population in the world and ranks high in milk production.

In the last three decades, world milk production has increased by more than 50 per cent, from 500 million tonnes in 1983 to 769 million tonnes in 2013. India is the world's largest milk producer, with 18 per cent of global production, followed by the United States of America, China, Pakistan and Brazil. The countries with the highest milk deficits are China, Italy, the Russian Federation, Mexico, Algeria and Indonesia. Milk production in India, 2023-24 was 239.3 million tonnes.

India now has indisputably the world's biggest dairy industry—in terms of milk production; last year India produced close to 146.31 million tonnes of milk, 50% more than the US. The dairy sector in India has shown remarkable development in the past decade and India has now become one of the largest producers of milk and value-added milk products in the world. Uttar Pradesh, Maharashtra, Himachal Pradesh, Madhya Pradesh, Punjab, Rajasthan and Tamil Nadu are the major production area of Dairy Products in India. India's Export of Dairy products was 63,738 tonnes to the world for the worth of ₹ 2,269.9 crores/$272.6 US Million dollars during the year 2023-24. Major export destinations (2023-24) are United Arab Emirates, Saudi Arabia, United States, Bhutan and Singapore.

21.1 Composition of Milk

Milk from different sources, regardless of breed or even species, will contain the same classes of constituents. They are milk fat (3–6 per cent), protein (3–4 per cent), milk sugar (~5 per cent), and ash (~0.7 per cent). Water accounts for the balance of 85.5–88.5 per cent. All the solids in milk are referred to as "total solids" (11.4–14.5 per cent) and the total solids without fat is known as "milk solids-not-fat" (MSNF) or "solids-not-fat." The price of milk depends on its fat content and, to a lesser extent, on its solids-not-fat content.

There are quantitative differences in the constituents of milk from different sources; the widest variations occur with fat, next with protein, followed by milk sugar, and minerals (ash). The average composition of milk from various sources is given in Table 21.1. It is seen from the table that goat milk is next in importance to cow milk as human food. Buffalo milk is high in fat content, and human milk is low in protein content when compared to cow milk. The variations in the composition of milk from various sources become important in milk-processing operations.

Table 21.1 Composition of milk from various species (per cent)

	Water	Fat	Protein	Lactose	Ash
Buffalo	82.14	7.44	4.78	4.81	0.83
Cow	87.27	3.66	3.47	3.66	0.69
Goat	84.14	6.00	4.03	6.00	5.02
Human	87.47	3.76	2.14	3.76	0.31
Ass	89.88	1.50	2.04	1.50	0.49

The composition of milk from various sources given in Table 21.1 is the average value. The yield of milk and its composition, from the same source, vary depending upon many factors. These include the breed of the animal, its age, the stage of lactation, the time of milking, the time interval between milking seasons of the year, feed of the animal condition of the animal, and so on. For different classes and designations of milk, the milk fat and MSNF content, according to the Prevention of Food Adulteration (PFA) Standards, is given in Table 21.2.

Table 21.2 PFA Standards for different classes and designations of milk in India

Class of milk	Milk fat	Milk solids-not-fat (MSNF)
Cow milk	4.0	8.5
Mixed milk	4.5	8.5
Standardized milk	4.5	8.5
Recombined milk	3.0	8.5
Toned milk	3.0	8.5
Double toned milk	1.5	9.0
Skimmed milk	Not more than 0.5	8.7
Full cream milk	6.0	9.0

21.1.1 Milk Fat

Milk fat or butterfat is of great economical and nutritive value. Practically all dairy products, with the exception of those made from skim milk, contain an appreciable amount of milk fat. The flavour of milk and, to a large extent, of other dairy products is due to milk fat. It exists in milk in the form of minute globules in a true emulsion of oil-in-water type, the globules being the dispersed phase. The fat globules are invisible to the naked eye but are readily seen under a microscope. Each globule of fat is surrounded by a very thin layer of protein, phospholipids and neutral lipids.

Fat globules vary widely in size from 2 to 10 μm, and in numbers 3×10^9 per ml. The size of the globules depends on the breed of the animal producing the milk and the lactation period. During the first part of the lactation period, the fat globules are relatively large and as lactation progresses the granules become larger. The size of fat globules is of some practical importance in cream separation, cheese making, and the handling and transport of milk. When milk stands undisturbed, the fat globules rise because their specific gravity is less than that of the aqueous portion of the milk. The rise and clustering of fat globules are also attributed to the activity of some components of the whey protein system. The larger fat globules come to the surface of milk more quickly. Thus, the gravity separation of cream, the size of milk fat globules is important. In cheese making, if the fat globules are large, they will move up quickly before the coagulated milk could check their movement, and as a result, the loss of milk fat in whey is somewhat large. In milk transport, large fat globules churn more readily after being transported some distance and show the formation of butter granules on the surface.

Milk fat is a mixture of several different glycerides. They contain about 64 different fatty acids ranging from 4 to 26 carbon atoms. Milk contains considerable amounts of short-chain fatty acids, C_4–C_{10}, which collectively contribute to the characteristic flavour of dairy products. Saturated acids account for 62 per cent and unsaturated acids for 37 per cent of milk fat. The remaining one per cent is due to a large number of acids whose concentration is less than 0.1 per cent. Of the unsaturated acids, 3.8 per cent constitute polyunsaturated acids.

Other lipid materials present in milk are phospholipids, sterols, carotenoids and fat-soluble vitamins. Together, they constitute about 1 per cent of the total lipid material. Carotenes are responsible for the yellow colour of milk fat.

Since milk fat is a mix of several glycerides it does not have a true melting point. However, a majority of the glycerides of milk fat solidify at 10–12°C. High-melting glyceride fractions exhibit distinct polymorphic forms when a rapidly chilled specimen is slowly warmed. Milk fat will absorb volatile odour very readily. Because of this property, butter, milk and cream should not be stored near the source of volatile odours, which might contribute to the off-flavour of these products.

21.1.2 Milk Proteins

Milk proteins are synthesized in the mammary gland of the animal. Milk normally contains about 0.5 per cent of nitrogen of which 95 per cent constitutes milk protein and 5 per cent non-protein nitrogen. Milk protein is a heterogeneous mixture that can be separated based on the solubility at specific values of pH and in presence of salt solutions. Casein, which constitutes 80 per cent of the total nitrogen in milk, is precipitated on the acidification of milk or skim milk to pH 4.6 at 20°C. The remaining proteins of skim milk, called whey (serum) proteins, can be resolved into lactoglobulin and lactalbumin based on their solubility in solutions half-saturated with ammonium sulphate. The protein fraction of milk also contains minor proteins like protease-peptone and milk enzymes. The distribution of nitrogen in the milk of Indian cattle is given in Table 21.3.

Casein: None of the protein fractions of milk is homogeneous. Whole casein is a heterogeneous group of proteins, consisting of three principal components α_{si}-casein (~55 per cent); β-casein (~25 per cent), and χ-casein (~15 per cent); there are also γ-casein (~5 per cent) and several minor proteins, α_{si} –casein is precipitated by low concentration of calcium ion (calciumsensitive fraction), while χ-casein is soluble (calcium-insensitive fraction). Also, χ-casein is the site of the primary action of the enzyme rennin. The caseins exist as genetically controlled polymorphic forms, differing in one or more amino acid residues. Thus, α_{si} casein has 4, β-casein, 6, χ-casein, 2; and γ-casein, 4 polymorphic forms.

Table 21.3 Nitrogen distribution in milk of Indian cattle (as per cent total nitrogen)

Constituent	Buffalo	Cow
Protein	88.8 – 95.5	92.9 – 94.8
Casein	71.6 – 83.5	76.0 – 77.5
Albumin	8.3 –17.2	11.2 – 11.4
Globulin	3.9 – 8.2	2.9 – 5.5
Proteose –peptone	—	2.5 – 2.6
Nonprotein nitrogen	4.6 –11.2	5.2 – 7.1

Source: *Ganguli, Milk Proteins, Indian* Council of Agricultural Research (ICAR), New Delhi, 1974, p.19.

Casein is a phosphoprotein and also a glycoprotein. The phosphorus groups in casein are covalently linked predominantly with serine residues. The calcium content of the whole casein is about 8.2 per cent, χ- casein containing more than β- and γ-caseins. The sulphur content of casein is also about 0.8 per cent. The γ-casein has higher sulphur content when compared with other fractions of casein. Carbohydrates are present to the extent of 5.7 per cent in casein, sialic acid constituting more than 50 per cent of them. Other carbohydrates present in casein are galactose, glucose, mannose and glucosamine.

The amino acid composition of casein and its fractions shows the highest concentration of glutamic acid when compared with other amino acids. Other amino acids like proline, aspartic, leucine, lysine and valine are also present at a relatively higher level in casein. In addition, casein is also a good repository for the essential amino acids. Buffalo milk casein is poorer in arginine, lysine, threonine and valine than cow milk. Goat milk casein also shows a lower content of arginine, isoleucine and valine when compared with cow milk casein, but is richer in histidine and proline.

In normal milk, all the casein components are in the form of colloidally dispersed micelles. They range in size from 80 to 300 nm and are composed of discrete subunits of about 10–20 nm in size. The subunits are associated with calcium ions and/or complex calcium phosphate salt bridges. As a result of various investigations, two models have been proposed for casein micelles. According to one model. α_{si}- and β-caseins associate stoichiometrically in rosette configurations, which in turn inter-associate to form a micellar core with χ-casein oriented at the peripheral layer. According to the other, the subunits have uniform composition, consisting of α_{si} -and β-casein complexes covered with a layer of χ-α_{si} casein complex. Some experimental observations favour the first model while some others favour the second.

Rennin (rennet), an enzyme secreted by the fourth stomach (abomasum) of young calves, brings about the coagulation of milk. The coagulation is due to the change in the physicochemical status of casein as a result of the cleavage of a particular peptide bond (between phenylalanine and methionine) in the κ-casein fraction. This results in the release of a peptide, The remaining protein is no longer soluble and it cannot act as a stabilizing agent for micellar proteins. Hence, an insoluble casein gel is formed. Next, rennin acts as a general proteolytic enzyme on all the protein components.

Whey proteins: The non-casein proteins of milk are called whey proteins. These include β-lactoglobulin (~60 per cent), α-lactalbumin, serum albumin and the complex proteas-peptone fraction. The concentration of the whey protein in milks is given in Table 21.4. These proteins are heat-labile and form an associated complex when milk is heated.

Table 21.4 The Concentration of Whey proteins in milks (g/100 ml)

Whey protein	Cow	Buffalo
β-Lactoglobulin	0.30	0.37
α-Lactalbumin	0.10	0.14
Serum albumin	0.04	—
Immunoglobulins	0.08	—

Source: Ganguli, Milk Proteins, ICAR, New Delhi, India, 1974, p.95.

β-*Lactoglobulin*: This exists as several genetic variants which, depending upon environmental conditions, undergo dissociation and association. At the pH of normal milk (6.6-6.7) and 20°C, two monomeric units occur as a dimer. It contains sulphydryl groups, which can be either active or inactive depending upon the special configuration of the protein.

α.-*Lactalbumin*: This can be readily crystallized from solution and exhibits pH dependent association-dissociation phenomena and configurational changes. The protein is rich in tryptophan. It does not contain SH groups although its cystine content is high. Amongst all milk proteins, it contains more aspartic acid than glutamic acid.

α-Lactalbumin is an essential subunit of the enzyme lactose synthetase. This helps the transfer of galactose to glucose in the synthesis of lactose.

Immunoglobulins: These are similar to the immunoglobulins of blood. They consist of glycoprotein molecules that possess antibody activities. They constitute a major protein of colostrum and serve to transmit passive immunity to the new-born calf.

Minor proteins: Whey serum albumin is similar to blood serum albumin. Whey also contains small amounts of lactoferrin, an iron-binding protein, and serum transferrin, identical to blood serum transferrin.

21.1.3 Milk Sugar

Milk sugar or lactose is a reducing disaccharide, which on hydrolysis gives glucose and galactose. The complex galactose-containing biological materials required for life are thus obtained from lactose. Lactose has only about one-sixth the sweetness of sucrose and one-third to one-fourth of its solubility in water. When milk is heated lactose reacts with protein and develops a brown colour.

Lactose is acted upon by bacteria to produce lactic acid. The acid produced by the action of intestinal micro-organisms on lactose checks the growth of undesirable putrefactive bacteria and promotes the absorption of minerals. The acid fermentation is also a factor of tremendous importance in both butter and cheese manufacture, and dahi making. The very small amount of lactose that is carried into butter and cheese is entirely converted into acid and this checks the growth of undesirable micro-organisms in them.

Lactose occurs in two forms and when crystallized from whey at a temperature below 93.5°C, the hydrate of α-lactose is formed. This form is sparingly soluble and imparts a gritty feel when placed in the mouth. When crystallization takes place above 93.5°C, the anhydride of β-lactose is formed which is sweeter and more soluble than the crystals of α-hydrate. This property is of importance in the manufacture of dairy products like ice cream, and milk-based confectionery. When milk is concentrated, because of the low solubility of lactose, the sugar crystallizes out. The extent of crystallization and the relative proportion of the α- and β-forms depend on the temperature used. Care should be taken to prevent "sandiness" frequently encountered in ice creams and confectionery.

When a solution of lactose is rapidly dried, a non-crystalline "gloss" is produced which is very unstable and hygroscopic. This is likely to happen in the preparation of condensed milk and dry milk preparations if care is not taken to prevent it.

21.1.4 Ash and Salts

Milk ash is the white residue remaining after the incineration of milk at 600°C. It consists of oxides of sodium, potassium, calcium, magnesium, iron, phosphorus and sulphur, plus some chloride. In addition to these, milk contains many trace elements like copper, zinc, aluminium, molybdenum, iodine, etc., depending upon the feed of the animal.

Milk salts and milk ash are not synonymous terms. The salts of milk are phosphates, chlorides, and citrates of sodium, potassium, calcium and magnesium. Sodium, potassium and chloride are entirely ionized, whereas the phosphates and citrates of calcium and magnesium are partly in soluble form and partly as colloidal complexes in a highly labile equilibrium with the casein complex. About two-thirds of the total calcium of milk is colloidally dispersed and only one-tenth exists in ionic form. The state of equilibrium between ionic calcium and its complex forms determines the physical stability of the processed dairy products. Upon acidification, more calcium is ionized resulting in destabilization of casein. High temperature favours the complex formation and thus the stability of the casein system.

21.1.5 Enzymes

Several enzymes are present in milk. More than 25 enzymes have been identified in cow milk. They originate from the mammary tissue and gain entrance into the milk accidentally or unavoidably during the secretory process. The enzymes in milk are distributed throughout the entire system, some bound to the fat globule surface, some associated with the casein micelles, and some existing in free colloidal systems. Only a few of the milk enzymes are of interest to food scientists.

Alkaline phosphatase: This enzyme exists as lipoprotein and is distributed between the lipid and aqueous phases. The enzyme is inactivated by normal pasteurization procedures and thus its activity is tested to determine the effectiveness of pasteurization (see Subsection 21.6.2).

Lipase: More than one type of lipase occurs in milk: a "membrane lipase" adsorbed to the fat globule membrane and a "plasma lipase" which remains in the skim milk phase until activated by some form of mechanical agitation. The release of membrane material from the fat globule predisposes the fat to lipolytic attack by plasma lipase. Milk lipase is responsible for the development of rancid flavours in milk. It is inactivated by pasteurization.

Xanthine oxidase: This enzyme occurs in the fat globule membrane. It is a conjugated protein complex with FAD, iron, and molybdenum. The enzyme degradation of FAD gives FMN and riboflavin. The riboflavin content of milk may thus be due to xanthine oxidase.

21.1.6 Vitamins

Milk is a good source of both fat-soluble and water-soluble vitamins. The concentration of fat-soluble vitamins, except vitamin K, depends on the concentration of these vitamins in the feed consumed. Some milk do not contain a sufficient amount of vitamin D and this is added to fortified milk to make it a rich vitamin D source. Vitamin A is present in good quantity in milk.

Vitamin K and water-soluble vitamins are synthesized in the cow's rumen or tissues. Hence their concentration in milk is independent of feed of the animal. Milk is especially rich in riboflavin but this the vitamin is lost rapidly on exposure to light and may produce an oxidized off-flavour involving both riboflavin and protein. The concentration of niacin and ascorbic acid is relatively low in milk.

21.2 Properties of Milk

Whole milk has certain distinctive qualities of odour, taste and appearance. These qualities are related to the feed given to the animal and also to the type of milch animal. Milk is well buffered by protein and phosphates. Coagulation of milk is brought about by acidifying it. Casein, and albumin to a minor extent, are coagulated upon the addition of acid. Milk is slightly acidic with an approximate pH of 6.6 to 6.7. The specific gravity of milk is influenced by the relationship of its constituents, each of which has a different specific gravity. The average specific gravity of cow milk is 1.032.

Milk freezes at an average temperature of – 0.55°C (range – 0.5°C to – 0.61°C). The freezing point is affected by the soluble constituents, lactose and ash. Since these constituents vary only slightly in milk, the freezing point remains almost constant. This fact makes it possible to determine whether or not milk is diluted. Addition of 1 per cent (by volume) of water to milk decreases the freezing point by – 0.0055°C.

The specific heat of milk is of importance from a practical standpoint, as it gives an idea of the cost of heating and cooling of milk. The specific heat of milk at 15°C is 0.938.

Milk will form a foam when agitated. Foaming is due to the trapping of air in the liquid. The stability of foam depends on the surface tension of the liquid. Owing to its high surface tension, water does not readily foam unless an emulsifying agent is present. When milk is whipped, air is trapped as bubbles, surrounded by thin layers of protein with fat interspersed to act as a stabilizer. Because of this, freshly drawn buffalo milk foams more than cow milk. It is, therefore, of practical importance to weigh milk rather than to measure it when milk is purchased.

21.3 Effect of Heat on Milk

Heating milk to a temperature higher than that used for pasteurization (61.8°C) affects a great variety of changes in it, the changes increasing in number and degree with temperature and time.

Milk boils at 100.2°C. When it is heated up to boiling for a short time, all milk organisms are destroyed; it is good to boil milk before use in areas where pasteurized milk is not available. Some vitamins are lost with boiling even for a short duration. The loss of some of the nutritive value of boiled milk is more than compensated by the avoidance of milk-borne diseases.

When milk is heated, the heat-labile whey proteins undergo denaturation. They interact with themselves as well as with casein micelles. The mechanism of interaction is believed to be that of disulphide interchange, initiated by the sulphydryl groups of β-lactoglobulin. In the absence of micellar casein, heat-denatured whey proteins aggregate and precipitate. The whey proteins are completely denatured in one hour when heated at 77.5°C, in 30 min. at 80°C, and in 5 min. at 90°C. Casein, the principal protein, is more resistant to heat treatment with particular reference to denaturation. It is not coagulated by heating even up to 12 hours at 100°C. It is stable for one hour in fresh milk of low acidity when heated to 131° to 137.8°C. At 155°C, it is coagulated in 3 min. The resistance of casein to heat is because it is in combination with definite amounts of calcium, magnesium, phosphorus and citrate in milk. Even a slight acidity accelerates the coagulation of milk proteins. Coagulation is also influenced by different salts in different concentrations.

Generally, there is scum formation when milk is heated in an uncovered pan. A slight scum is formed at low temperature, but its formation may be prevented by covering the pan, by diluting the milk, or by the presence of fat floating on the surface. The scum gets toughened as the temperature is increased but the insoluble scum can be removed from the surface. As soon as it is removed, however, other forms. The scum contains a small amount of coagulated protein, minerals and fat globules and results from a drying out of the top of the milk. The tenacious layer of fat that forms on milk when heated is due to the breaking of the film of protein that surrounds the fat globules in unheated milk, resulting in coalescence of fat globules. Scum formation can be prevented by beating or stirring the milk while heating it. Use of a milk boiler helps prevent the formation of scum to some extent. Scum formation during the heating of milk is the principal reason for its behaviour of boiling over.

Heat has an adverse effect on the flavour and odour of milk. The "cooked" flavour of boiled milk is attributed to the loss of dissolved gases (CO_2 and O_2). Some changes that occur in the protein are also thought to influence the flavour of cooked milk.

21.4 Nutritional Importance of Milk

Milk is an established basic food. It contains all nutrients in a nearly balanced proportion to meet the demands of human nutrition. It is rich in high-quality protein, calcium, phosphorus, riboflavin and other B-vitamins. The calcium and phosphorus of milk are well utilized by the body. Without milk in the diet, it is difficult for adults and children to meet the body's need for calcium. Milk is poor as a source of vitamin D, vitamin C, and iron.

Milk proteins are one of the highest quality proteins and equal the meat proteins in nutritional efficiency. Also, cost wise, milk proteins are less expensive when compared with other proteins of equal nutritional value. The relatively minor deficiency of milk proteins is in the content of sulphur-containing amino acids cystine, cysteine and methionine. Milk proteins are rich in lysine. However, in concentrated products like evaporated milk and some milk powders, lysine is rendered unavailable.

The fat-soluble vitamins of milk are quite stable to heat and processing. However, vitamins A and E are destroyed in significant amounts in the presence of oxidizing agents. Nearly 50 per cent of thiamine also is lost with heating. Some B vitamins of milk exist partially in a free state and partially bound to proteins. The biological value of bound forms may depend on their release on ingestion.

People of certain races are intolerant of milk sugar. The intolerance results in severe diarrhoea and dehydration and is due to the lack of the intestinal enzyme lactase involved in the hydrolysis of lactose. This disorder is referred to as lactose intolerance. It is also said the disorder of lactose metabolism may be due to allergic reactions of milk proteins.

21.5 Milk Micro-organisms

Milk is an excellent medium for the growth of micro-organisms. Nearly all the changes that take place in the taste, odour or appearance after it comes from the animal are the results of the activities of milk organisms. Milk is produced from the blood constituents in the udder of the animal. As the milk passes from the udder, bacteria are picked up from the walls of the passageways, especially along the teat canal. Thus, the milk drawn directly from the udder is not sterile. In addition, bacteria are introduced to the drawn milk from the exterior of the animal's body, conditions of stabling and pasturing the animal, atmosphere, utensils and methods of handling milk. Good hygienic conditions are to be ensured at all levels of milk handling to keep the bacterial count low.

Adequate care of the milk immediately after it is drawn is necessary to prevent the many changes that are possible as a result of the growth of micro-organisms. Freshly drawn milk is to be cooled immediately to 4°C to arrest microbial growth or heated to near boiling for sufficient time to destroy them. If the raw milk is placed at room temperature, several fermentative changes will take place. First, bacteria that act principally on lactose will be active producing lactic acid, which gives milk a sour taste, and in turn, causes the precipitation of casein, a process known as "curdling." Some bacteria produce, in addition to acid, some gaseous products, while others bring about proteolysis of casein, resulting in off-flavour and unpleasant odour. There are also bacteria in milk that bring about "ropiness" in milk, i.e., in the formation of a sticky or gum-like substance.

Bacterial action in milk resulting in acid production will cease when the acid strength increases. Moulds and yeasts present in milk flourish in the acid medium. They utilize the acid and bring about chemical changes producing an alkaline condition. Finally, certain bacteria which have remained dormant during this period will decompose all the solid constituents of the milk.

Milk and milk products may transmit some disease-producing organisms to the consumer if they are not properly processed and handled. These diseases include tuberculosis, typhoid fever, scarlet fever, septic sore throat, undulant fever, gastroenteritis and diphtheria. Some of these diseases are transmitted by the milking animal and some may be introduced by bad handling of the milk.

There are also some bacteria in milk that bring about desirable changes. As a result of the activities of such organisms, volatile acids like acetic acid, diacetyl and other compounds, controlling the flavour and aroma, are formed. These organisms are important in providing the desired flavour in starters used in making butter and other fermented milk products.

21.6 Milk Processing

To ensure safe milk free from disease-producing bacteria, toxic substances and foreign flavours, fresh whole milk is to be processed before marketing. The processing helps produce milk that has an initial low bacterial count, good flavour and satisfactory keeping qualities. Milk processing operations consist of clarification, pasteurization and homogenization.

21.6.1 Clarification

Noticeable quantities of foreign materials, such as particles of dust, dirt and many other undesirable substances find their way into milk due to careless handling. To remove these, milk is generally passed through a centrifugal clarifier. The speed of the clarifier will be such that there is little separation of cream. This operation removes all dirt, filth, cells from the udder, and some bacteria. Clarification does not remove all pathogenic bacteria from milk. The clarified milk is ready for pasteurization.

21.6.2 Pasteurization

Pasteurization derives its name from Louis Pasteur, who found that the heating of liquids, especially wines, to a high temperature improves their keeping qualities. The aim of pasteurization of milk is to get rid of any disease-producing bacteria it may contain and to reduce substantially the total bacterial count for improved keeping qualities. Pasteurization of milk destroys approximately 99 per cent of all bacteria, as well as most of the yeasts and moulds. Two methods are employed for pasteurization.

In the batch process, two combinations, viz, 63°C (145 °F) for 30 min and 72°C (161°F) for 15 sec are the ones most commonly followed for commercial pasteurization and the corresponding processes are called "Holder or Batch or LTLT (low temperature-long time) method" and "HTST (high temperature-short time) method." Ultra-high temperature treatment at 93.4 °C for 3 sec. or 149.5 °C for 1 sec. is also employed. There are also methods for obtaining sterilized milk in containers.

Pasteurization is a temperature-time effect, which means the process depends on the combination of these two parameters and not on either of them alone. The following are the criteria for selecting the temperature-time combination for pasteurization:

(i) The most heat resistant pathogen, Mycobacterium tuberculosis (now *Coxiella burnetii* is considered in its place), should get killed, so that the object of killing all pathogens can be achieved with the temperature-time combination used.

(ii) The phosphatase test should be negative. In other words, phosphatase enzyme of milk should be inactivated with the temperature-time combination used.

(iii) The cream line (between the lipid and aqueous layers) should be minimally reduced, if at all, with the temperature-time combination used.

Since the most heat resistant pathogen is destroyed at a treatment slightly higher (than that required for phosphatase inactivation, pasteurization may be carried out at a temperature above that for phosphatase inactivation and yet below that for cream-line reduction. It is observed that the lower the temperature of exposure, the longer the time needed and vice-versa.

As pasteurized milk is not sterile, it must be quickly cooled after pasteurization to prevent the multiplication of surviving bacteria. The temperature and time used for pasteurization are not so high as to alter the constituents or properties of milk. Pasteurization does not produce an objectionable cooked flavour and no important change in nutritive value takes place, except for a slight decrease in the heat-labile vitamins like thiamine and ascorbic acid. The shelf life of the milk is increased by pasteurization.

The thoroughness of the pasteurization of milk is ascertained by testing for the alkaline phosphatase activity in milk. This enzyme has heat destruction characteristics that closely approximate the time-temperature exposure for proper pasteurization. The enzyme liberates phenol from phenyl phosphate. The liberated phenol gives a deep blue colour with certain organic compounds. If the milk incubated with phenyl phosphate does not give blue colour with the indicator, it means the pasteurization is complete.

21.6.3 Homogenization

The process of making a stable emulsion of milk fat and milk serum by mechanical treatment and rendering the mixture homogeneous is homogenization. This is achieved by passing warm milk or cream through a small aperture under high pressure and velocity. High-pressure homogenizers, low-pressure rotary-type homogenizers, and sonic vibrators are used for the purpose. Milk and cream have fat globules that vary from 0.1 to 20 μm in diameter. The fat globules have a tendency to gather into clumps and rise due to their lower density than skim milk. When milk is homogenized, the average size of the globule will be about 2 μm.

The decrease in the size of the fat globules increases their number and surface area. The newly formed fat droplets are no longer coated with the original membrane material. Instead, they are covered with an adsorbed layer of plasma proteins, including casein micelles, micellar subunits, and remnants of membrane material. This brings about the stabilization of the milk emulsion and thus prevents the rising of the cream.

Homogenized milk has a creamier structure, bland flavour, and a whiter appearance. It has greater whitening power when added to coffee and tea than the same milk not homogenized. A soft curd is formed when homogenized milk is coagulated, which is more easily digested than curd obtained from unhomogenized milk. In the manufacture of evaporated milk and ice cream, homogenization reduces the chance of separation of fat resulting in a smoother texture of the finished product. However, fat cannot be separated from homogenized milk efficiently. Also, homogenization accelerates the action of lipase. Therefore, if homogenization has been carried out before pasteurization, the latter operation has to be carried out quickly with homogenized milk, to prevent the rancid flavour that could develop.

Besides, the homogenization of milk after preheating to about pasteurization temperature is advisable from the microbiological point of view. Such a combination causes inactivation of natural milk lipase due to heating and thus avoids the possible lipolysis due to increased surface area of fat globules in homogenized milk.

21.7 Milk Products

The processing of milk described in the previous section is for the production of milk to be marketed as such. However, a slight departure or additional steps can be employed to produce many closely related milk products

21.7.1 Vitamin D Milk

Cow milk contains sufficient amount of vitamin D. However, the amount varies with the cow's diet. The diet of most children is deficient in vitamin D. It is, therefore, common practice to increase the vitamin D content in milk. This is done by irradiating milk with ultraviolet light which converts milk sterol (7-dehydrocholesterol) into vitamin D. A more commonly used method is to add a vitamin D concentrate, to the milk to bring it to the required potency.

To meet some nutritional requirements, milk is fortified with multi-vitamins and minerals. To meet special diet requirements, low sodium milk (containing 3 to 10 mg of sodium per 100 ml as against 50 mg in ordinary milk) is prepared by passing milk through ion exchange resins. Some persons suffer from a condition known as lactose intolerance. For persons with such a defect, the milk is treated with lactase before processing to produce low lactose milk.

21.7.2 Skim Milk

Whole milk from which fat has been removed by centrifugation is skim milk. It contains all other milk nutrients except vitamins A and D, but can be fortified by the addition of these vitamins. By varying the amount of milk fat removed from whole milk, low-fat milk (containing from 0.5 to 2.0 per cent fat) is prepared for consumers who wish to reduce their fat intake. Skim milk finds use in human food and as an animal feed. Condensed skim milk finds extensive use in the baking industry and manufacture of confectionery.

21.7.3 Concentrated Milks

Milk has large water content. This makes it a bulk food resulting in problems of storage and refrigeration. To meet these problems, methods are available to remove a considerable part of water or all of it resulting in evaporated milk (condensed milk) and dry milk, respectively.

Evaporated milk: Evaporated milk is whole milk from which more than half the water has been evaporated. In its processing, generally, raw whole milk is clarified and concentrated in a vacuum pan at a temperature of 74° -77°C. It is then fortified with vitamin D, homogenized, filled into cans, sterilized in cans at a temperature of 118°C for 15 min. and cooled. This heat-treatment gives evaporated milk a light brown colour owing to sugar protein interaction and its characteristic flavour.

Sweetened condensed milk is the product obtained from cow or buffalo milk or a combination thereof, or from standardized milk, by the partial removal of water and addition of cane sugar which is adjusted to give a sugar concentration of about 65 per cent in the water of the final product. Sweetened condensed milk, unlike evaporated milk, is not sterile. However, multiplication of micro-organisms in the product is prevented by the preservative action of sugar. It may contain added refined lactose, calcium chloride, citric acid and sodium citrate, sodium salts or orthophosphoric acid and polyphosphoric acid not exceeding 0.3% by weight of the finished product. Such addition need not be declared on the label.

Dry milk: The preservation of milk in the dry form is an old art. Whole milk can be dehydrated to about 97 per cent by spray drying and vacuum drying. Skim milk and low-fat milk are also dehydrated in large quantities to manufacture milk powder. Non-fat dry milk has vitamins A and D added to enhance its nutritive value. The low cost, and good shelf-life without refrigeration, of dry milk makes it a particularly valuable milk product. Dry milk may be substituted satisfactorily for fresh milk in most preparations. Dry milk can be reconstituted into fluid milk by mixing with the recommended quantity of water. All dried milks possess the property of taking moisture from air unless sealed in airtight, moisture-free containers.

Dry milk products were being imported into our country in large quantities. With the development of the dairy industry, these products are now being manufactured within the country. Infant foods are prepared from low-fat dry milk and fortifying them with minerals, sugar and vitamins. Buffalo milk also can be used for the production of infant foods, by reducing the fat content to about 2.5 per cent.

21.7.4 Cream

Milk fat concentrated into a fraction of the original milk is cream. In unhomogenized milk, fat globules will rise to the top to form a layer of cream. It is generally separated from milk by centrifugation. Creams containing various amounts of fat are made to meet different requirements. A mixture of milk and milk fat of 10 to 12 per cent is called half-and-half. Table cream (coffee cream) contains 18 per cent fat. Whipping cream contains 30-36 per cent milk fat. Baker's cream, heavy cream and plastic cream contain 32-40 per cent, 40 per cent and 85 per cent milk fat, respectively. The high percentage of fat helps to give a more stable foam, when whipped. The cream used for butter making usually contains from 25 to 40 per cent fat. Sour cream used in various baked products and as a salad dressing base is made by pasteurizing cream containing about 18 per cent fat at 70° to 75°C for 30 min., a procedure that kills all bacteria. The cream is then inoculated with a controlled culture of lactic acid bacteria to develop the desired acid tang in the finished product.

21.7.5 Butter

Butter consist primarily of milk fat. The process of butter making is thought to have originated in India about 2000 BC. The fat content of butter is generally about 80 per cent. Farm butter, as made in this country, may contain only 60-65 per cent fat. The non-fat components of butter consists of moisture, milk solids-non-fat and salt if added. Butter is an important dairy product in India. The total quantity of butter and ghee produced in India is estimated at 4.7 million tonnes in 2021. Most of the butter produced in the country is converted into ghee.

Desi Butter means the product obtained from milk, cream or curd of cow or buffalo or a combination thereof, without the addition of salt, colour and preservative, and intended exclusively for use in cooking or for preparation of ghee (an Indian counter part of butter oil). It should not contain more than 20 per cent of moisture and not less than 76 per cent of milk fat.

Where butter is sold or offered for sale without any indication as to whether it is table butter or desi butter, the standards of quality prescribed for table butter shall apply.

In 2020, India produced 52 per cent of the world's butter and ghee. The butter production amounted to almost 6,600 thousand metric tonnes in the country during the fiscal year 2022, growth from about 6,400 thousand metric tons in the fiscal year 2021, and 6,750 thousand metric tonnes in 2023. India's butter production is poised to grow at 6.5%.

Table 21.5 Chemical composition of typical salted Indian butter

Ingredient	Amount (%)
Milk fat	80.2
Moisture	16.3
Common Salt	2.5
Curd	1.0

Source: BIS, ISI: 3507–1966.

Butter is made from sweet or sour cream. The largest percentage of butter is made from sour cream. The cream is pasteurized at 62.8°C for 30 min. or at a higher temperature for a shorter time after which it is immediately cooled. Then a culture of desirable micro-organisms ("starter") is added. The culture consists of bacteria of two types, one of which ferments lactose producing lactic acid which, in turn, curdles the milk and the other principally attacks the citric acid of milk-producing volatile acids and products, such as diacetyl, which give the desirable flavour and aroma of butter. The cream is then allowed to ripen at 21.1°C for several hours for fermentation to take place.

The acidity of the curd determines the yield, quality and storage properties of butter. When butter is made under farm conditions, cream is fermented more or less spontaneously. In India, butter making is a cottage industry. It is mostly prepared from *dahi* (see Subsection 21.11.1) obtained from either self-souring of unprocessed milk or by the addition of a culture, generally from the previous run.

The colour of butter varies from yellowish-white to deep yellow. The yellow colour is due to carotene which the milking animal derives from its feed. The colour of the butter, thus, varies from season to season depending upon the nature of the feed of the animal. In order to have butter of uniform colour throughout the year, colouring material, mostly synthetic carotene, is added to the cream.

The ripened cream or *dahi* is next churned. Churning brings about the denaturation, by violent agitation of the fat-globule surface, the membrane; the material being eliminated in buttermilk. The fat globules clump together causing a change from an oil-in-water emulsion to a water-in-oil emulsion. For this change to be effective, the temperature should be such that there is a blending of solid and liquid fat. As churning proceeds, the cream becomes granular and definite separation of the butter and buttermilk takes place. The buttermilk is drained off from the churn and the butter is washed with water. Salt, if required, is added to the butter and worked sufficiently to bring butter into a compact mass. Butter is then cut to size, wrapped and packed.

21.8 Cheese

Making cheese from milk is of prehistoric origin and it has been an excellent method of preserving the nutrients of milk. Cheese is now manufactured on a very large scale in the West and is a very popular article of food. It is consumed as such or in cookery. Cheese is neither a common nor a popular product of consumption in India. The climatic conditions are not conducive to its preparation and it is made on a very small scale, and only in certain areas of the country.

Approximately 35% of India's total milk production is processed. Dairy processing market worth 10.2 billion USD by 2020. The Indian cheese market is presently worth around US$237 million but is expected to grow at roughly 15 to 20% annually in the coming years. Product-wise, the global market features almost 3,000 varieties of cheese, whereas only about 40 to 45 variants are marketed in India, presenting much room for the market's expansion.

The cheeses are known after their place of origin. The most common, Cheddar cheese, is the one that was originally produced in Cheddar in England. Similarly, Camembert and Roquefort cheeses originated in France, the Swiss cheese in Switzerland, and so on. There are over 800 names of cheeses but there are only a few varieties. These varieties are differentiated according to their flavour, body and texture, which, in turn, depend upon the type of milk used, manufacturing and processing method adopted, salts and seasonings added and the type of bacteria and mould species used in ripening. Cheeses are classified based on moisture content into very hard (maximum 34% moisture), hard (maximum 39% moisture), semi-hard/semi-soft (maximum 39-50% moisture) and soft (50-80% moisture). Cheeses may be ripened by bacteria (like *Lactic Streptococci, Lactobacilli, Pediococci, Brevibacterium etc*), ripened by molds (*Peneilluim spp.*) or may be unripened. The types of cheeses and their ripening culture arc given in Table 21.6.

The cheeses that are directly made from milk are "natural" cheeses as opposed to "processed" cheeses which are essentially melted or blended forms of the natural cheeses. Whey cheese is made from the whey remaining after coagulation and removal of casein.

Table 21.6 Type of cheese and ripening culture

Cheeses	Starter Composition
Cheddar	*Lactococcus lactis, S.cremoris, S.diacetyl lactis*
Swiss	*Propionibacteria shermanii*
Gouda and Dutch	*L.alactis and leuconostoc citrovorum*
Brick type	*L.lactis, S.cremoris, S.thermophilus, Brevibacterium linens*
Blue-vein	*Penicillium roqueforti and P.glaucum*
Camembert	*Penicillium camemberti*
Soft	*Geotrichum candidum*
Cottage	*L.lactis, S.cremoris, Leuconostoc sp.*
Mozzarella	*S. thermophilus or S.faecalis and L.bulgaricus*
Blue (Roquefort)	*S.lactis, Penicillium roqueforti*
Camembert	*S.lactis, Penicillium camemberti*

Source: A comprehensive Dairy Microbiology, pp.: 471,I SI: 2785–1979.

The composition of cheese varies according to its method of manufacture. The protein content varies from 20-25 per cent, fat 30-35 per cent and moisture 30-50 per cent. It also contains appreciable quantities of calcium, phosphorus and vitamins. Cheese has thus a high nutritive value. About 150 g of cheese is equivalent in food value to one litre of milk.

Cheese is made by coagulating or curdling milk with acid or rennin or both, drawing off the whey and processing the curd. Desirable flavour and texture of cheese are obtained by curing (ripening), i.e., holding it for a specified time at a specified temperature and humidity.

Manufacture of Cheddar cheese is illustrative of the cheese manufacturing process. In its preparation, raw or pasteurized milk can be used; but it is only the latter milk that is used since pasteurization destroys undesirable enzymes and most spoilage type organisms. The pasteurized whole milk is brought to a temperature of 31°C and lactic acid producing starter culture is added. The required colouring matter is also added at this stage. After about 30 min., to the mildly acidic milk, rennin solution is added, stirred and allowed to set. After another 30 min., the milk forms a firm curd. The curd is then cut with curd knives into small cubes. With the removal of whey blue-green *Penicillium-roqueforti* is inoculated prior to being hooped and pressed. The mould grows during ripening. Moulds are aerobic and so generally grow on the surface of cheeses. To permit the mould growth throughout the cheese mass, the pressed cheese is pierced when it is placed in the curing room.

Yogurt: According to FAO/WHO 1977, yogurt is a coagulated milk product obtained by lactic acid fermentation through the action of *Lactobacillus bulgaricus* and *Streptococcus thermophilus* with or without optional additions like milk powder and whey powder. The micro-organisms in the final product must be viable and abundant. The following fermentation products contribute to flavour of yogurt which include lactic acid, acetaldehyde, acetic acid and diacetyl. The various health attributes of yogurt reported by researchers include, addressing problems related to lactose intolerance, gastrointestinal disorders, maldigestion, hypocholesterolemic effect, anti-carcinogenic activity, hepatic encephalopathy and anti-bacterial activity or undesirable intestinal pathogens. The preparation of yogurt includes heat treatment of raw milk previously fortified with 1 to 1.1 per cent skimmed milk powder to 90° C for 3 minutes, cooled to 45°C, followed by the addition of *Streptococcus thermophilus* and *Lactobacillus bulgaricus* lactic cultures at 3 per cent level and then incubation at 42°C to 45°C for 4 hours. Set product is refrigerated for more than 6 hours before release for sale.

The nutritive value of yogurt is similar to that of milk, except that there is a small amount of lactic acid formed from milk lactose. Frozen yogurt is becoming popular because its caloric content is about one-third that of Ice cream. However, flavour, sugar and fruits added to the frozen product will increase the caloric content. Naturally fermented yogurt (*dahi*) has been a staple food with us from earliest times.

Bio-yogurt: Bio-yogurt is another health oriented fermented milk prepared on similar lines as yogurt except for additional probiotic culture, namely, *Bifidobacterium* species and *L. acidophilus* are used as inoculum. Incubation of the inoculated milk is also at 42°C to 45°C with a setting time of 4 hours. Bio-yogurt is shown to possess more and effective therapeutic value compared to yogurt due to inclusion of additional probiotic cultures.

Cultured buttermilk: This is made from skim milk or partially skimmed milk by mildly coagulating it with lactic acid culture (containing *Leuconostoc* species for flavours), and consumed as a beverage. This corresponds to our *lassi* (buttermilk) which is the liquid obtained after the separation of butter from *dahi*.

21.8.1 Indian Cheeses

Different types of cheeses are made in the country on a small scale. *Panir* (*paneer*) is a cheese that can be compared to Western cheese. Its growing popularity has led to its integration into the Indian cuisine.

Now, it enjoys the status of a national delicacy. Typically, *paneer* is marble white in appearance, having a slightly spongy body, close-knit texture and possessing a sweetish-acidic-nutty flavour. The regulatory standards for *chhana* and *paneer* are identical. It has been defined under the PFA Act, 1954, as follows: "Paneer means the product obtained from cow or buffalo milk or a combination thereof by precipitation with sour milk, lactic acid or citric acid. It shall not contain more than 70.0 per cent moisture, and milk fat content shall not be less than 50.0 per cent-of the dry matter. The milk fat content of skim milk *paneer* shall not exceed 13.0 per cent of the dry matter."

Decca cheese: This is made from whole milk. Milk is clotted with rennin. The cheese is made by breaking the curd into small pieces and filling into wicker baskets. A weighted board is placed on top to help drain the whey. The weights are removed after 10 to 14 days when a thin dry coat is formed on the surface due to evaporation. The cheese is then smoked with wood or cow dung smoke. It keeps well for one or two months.

Surti-cheese: This is made by precipitating the curd by methods similar to *decca* cheese preparation. The curd, without breaking, is transferred to small wicker baskets to drain whey. Then the curd is immersed in acid whey containing salt which makes it firm and salty. The cheese is drained dry. It has a short keeping period of 10 to 14 days.

Bandal cheese: Bandal cheese is a cream cheese similar to *surti* except that it is smoked. It is made from cream. It contains approximately 50 per cent fat, 10–15 per cent protein and 40 per cent moisture. Its keeping quality is lower than that of the smoked *decca* cheese.

Channa: This is a very popular form of cheese prepared by the addition of lemon juice or acid whey from earlier batches of preparation to boiling milk, containing 4–5 per cent fat. Citric acid may be used for curdling milk. After the coagulation is completed, whey is separated by filtering through a thick cloth. Then the bag containing the precipitate is pressed between boards to squeeze out the remaining whey. *Channa* is used in cooking and preparation of Indian confectionery like *rosogolla* and *sandesh*. The chemical composition of *channa* and *paneer* are given in Table 21.7.

Table 21.7 Typical chemical composition of channa and paneer

	pH	Moisture (%)	Protein (%)	Fat (%)	Lactose (%)	Ash (%)	Salt (%)
Channa (Cow milk)	5.7	53.4	17.4	24.8	2.2	2.1	0
Channa (Buffalo milk)	5.4	51.7	14.4	29.7	2.3	1.9	0
Paneer (Buffalo milk)	5.8	51.3	17.3	27.0	2.3	1.9	0

Source: Technology of Indian Milk Products, 2002, pp.: 143. ISI: 5162–1980.

21.9 Ghee

In India, about 95 per cent of the total population of milch animals is found in rural areas. Milk is perishable and because of difficulties of marketing, it is converted into a more stable product, *ghee*. Because of its keeping qualities, it is being made from very early times. About 40 per cent of the total milk produced in the country is used for *ghee* making. *Ghee* making is an important cottage industry in the country. It is produced mainly for use as food. Because of its flavour and aroma, Indians prefer to use *ghee* in place of raw vegetable oils and other cooking media. It is also used in the country for ceremonial and ritual purposes.

Ghee is the clarified butter fat obtained from cow or buffalo milk. It is produced by heat desiccation of *makkhan* (butter) 105–110°C. Heat-induced changes in milk proteins/lactose during the clarification process impart a distinctive, pleasant cooked flavour to *ghee*. The *ghee*, prepared from *makkhan* (butter), contains many of the aromatic compounds formed during the fermentation of *dahi* and its subsequent fractionation into *makkhan*. These impart a distinctive characteristic flavour. *Ghee* from cow milk has a distinct golden yellow colour, attributable to carotene. On the other hand, the *ghee* of buffalo milk is noted for its white colour with greenish tinge, attributed to bilirubin and biliverdin. During the slow cooling process after heat desiccation and subsequent storage, *ghee* develops typical white granular crystals which remain partly dispersed in the middle layer and partly in the bottom layers of clear liquid fat.

Ghee is 99.5 per cent fat. It also contains some fat-soluble vitamins. As a source of energy it is like any other fat. *Ghee* contains a small quantity of essential fatty acids. On long keeping, *ghee* becomes rancid due to the atmospheric oxidation of unsaturated fatty acids, The rancidity in *ghee*, due to hydrolysis, is not very common as the presence of moisture in *ghee* is low.

The household production of *ghee* in India is exclusively by fermenting whole milk into *dahi* (curd), churning the curd into butter, and boiling down the latter to *ghee*. Industrially, *ghee* is made by separating the cream from milk by a mechanical separator, fermenting it, churning it into butter, followed by its conversion to *ghee*. *Ghee* making at the industrial level also involves the pre stratification method. This method takes advantage of gravity settling for removing most of the moisture from butter and saves the large thermal energy required for removing moisture from butter. In this method, the cream is first churned into butter, and it is melted in a butter melting vat. It is then pumped into a vertical storage tank and left undisturbed for 30 minutes. During this period, butter stratifies into three distinct layers. The top layer consists of a curdy mass, the middle layer is of fat, and the bottom layer consists of buttermilk serum. The buttermilk serum oil is drained from the bottom of the vat and the fat layer is drawn into a double-jacketed steam kettle where it is heated to 105–110°C to drive out traces of moisture and for developing the typical *ghee* flavour. Alternatively, the cream is directly clarified to give *ghee*. With proper care and control, the curd-butter route gives excellent quality *ghee*. This is done by using boiled or pasteurized milk in curd making and seeding it with the right type and quality of organisms at the proper temperature, fermenting it to proper acidity, churning under right conditions and proper storage of butter if this is unavoidable.

In the preparation of *ghee*, butter obtained from curd or fermented cream is heated in a pan over a low fire. At about 90°C, it begins to boil when it is gently stirred. After most of the water has boiled, away, the temperature rises and at about 120°C the curd particles begin to brown and a pleasant aroma of caramelization emanates. This is taken as the end of the clarification process. The fat layer is then carefully removed from solid curd or by straining *ghee* through a muslin cloth or a strainer and allowed to cool and crystallize. In the direct cream process, cream obtained from milk is mixed with an equal volume of water and re-separated. It is then heated as in the case of butter to obtain *ghee*. Of the three processes of *ghee* making, the traditional method of obtaining it from the curd is good for household purposes. It is simple, economical and the *ghee* has the required aroma. The buttermilk obtained after the separation of butter from the curd is a nutritious by-product. A serious disadvantage of this method for industrial application is the souring of the entire volume of milk. In the other two cases, this disadvantage is overcome. In cream butter and direct cream processes, there is ten-fold reduction in bulk. However, of the different methods, the yield of *ghee* is more in the direct cream process, being about 92 per cent, as against 90 per cent in the cream butter process, and 88 per cent in the curd butter process. The chemical composition of ghee is given in Table 21.8.

Table 21.8 Chemical composition of ghee

Constituents	Cow	Buffalo
Fat (%)	99–99.5	99–99.5
Moisture (%)	< 0.5	< 0.5
Carotene (mg/g)	3.2– 7.4	–
Vitamin A (IU/g)	19–34	17–38
Cholesterol (mg/100g)	302– 363	209–312
Tocopherol (mg/g)	26– 48	18–31
Free fatty acid (%)	2.8	2.8

Source: Technology of Indian Milk Products, 2002, p.: 187, ISI:3508–1966

21.10 Ice Cream

Ice cream is a very popular product in Western countries. It is becoming popular in our country also. The demand for ice cream has recently increased, particularly in towns and cities.

21.10.1 Ingredients

Ice cream is a frozen dairy product. It contains a variety of dairy ingredients. These include whole milk, skim milk, cream, butter, butteroil (which contains 99 per cent butterfat), condensed milk products and dried milk products. Milk fat and milk solids-not-fat constitute about 60 per cent of the total solids of ice cream. These components give ice cream a rich flavour, improved body and texture. In addition to dairy products, ice cream contains sugar, stabilizer, emulsifier, flavouring material, water and air. The mixture of these ingredients, before the air is incorporated and the mixture frozen, is known as ice cream mix.

Milk and cream are sources of butterfat, proteins, and milk sugars. Butterfats, add rich flavour, smooth texture, body and good melting properties. The triglycerides in butterfat melt over a wide range of temperatures, so there is some bit of solid and some liquid butterfat. Some of the butterfat almost turns into butter while the ice cream is churned, adding to the unique texture of ice cream.

The proteins help to incorporate air into the mixture, helping to form small bubbles of air. They modify the texture of the ice cream in other ways as well, making it chewier, and giving it body. The proteins also help to emulsify the fats, keeping the fat globules suspended in the mix. The proteins coat each fat globule, keeping them from sticking together. However, making the globules stick together in chains and mesh-like structures is important in giving ice cream its texture and ability to hold air, and its ability to stay firm as the ice inside melts.

The milk sugar lowers the freezing point of the water in the ice cream. Adding extra sweeteners, such as sugar and corn syrup, also have this effect. This ensures that a portion of the water never freezes, preventing the ice cream from becoming a solid chunk of ice. Added sweeteners are inexpensive, and make-up about 15 per cent of the mix by weight. The use of high-fructose corn syrup will reduce the freezing point further than sugar, resulting in softer ice cream.

Stabilizers are used to prevent the formation of ice crystals during freezing, They form gels with the water in the formula and thereby improve the body and texture of the ice cream. Compounds generally used as stabilizers are gums, gelatin, seaweed and cellulose derivatives, such as carboxy-melhyl cellulose

Emulsifiers help disperse the fat globules throughout the mix and prevent them from clumping together during the freezing-mixing operation. They further help make the ice cream dry and stiff. Egg yolk is a natural good emulsifier. Mono and diglycerides are the commercial preparations used.

The common flavouring material used in ice cream is vanilla, followed by strawberry, chocolate and coffee. A large number of fruits and nuts are added in quantities pleasing to the taste.

21.10.2 Composition of Ice Cream

The composition of ice cream varies depending upon the ingredients used in its preparation. The percentage composition of a good ice cream is: milkfat, 12; milk solids-not-fats, sugar, 15; stabilizer, 0.2; emulsifier, 6.2, and a trace of vanilla. This composition is exclusive of air, i.e:, they are based on the weight of ice cream mix. But ice cream is a whipped product and contains a great deal of air to prevent it from being too dense, too hard and too cold in the mouth. The total solids work up to about 38.4 per cent, the remainder would be water. If ingredients, such as nuts, fruits, chocolate and additional flavour are added, the composition, of course, changes.

Different flavours of ice cream in varied forms, such as cups, cones, candies, etc., have hit the markets time and again. The most popular ones include Black Raspberry, Blueberry, Butter Krunch, Butter Pecan, Butterscotch, Cherry Vanilla, Chocolate Chip, Chocolate Walnut, Coconut, Coffee, Ginger, Grapenut, Lemon, Maple Walnut, Mocha Chip, Orange Pineapple, Peanut Butter, Pistachio, Strawberry Cheesecake, Black Currant, etc.

The latest trend in ice cream is balancing healthful ingredients with the need for a little decadence. The current advances in ice cream and frozen desserts are in areas related to health. Probiotics (healthy bacteria that aid digestion) in ice cream, as well as ice creams with greatly reduced carbohydrates and fats are some of the most promising research being done. Another area is introducing omega-3 and omega-6 fatty acids into ice creams. Researchers and others are in the early stages of successfully creating ice creams that incorporate these acids found in high concentrations in fish oil and that still taste good to consumers in preliminary tests.

21.10.3 Preparation of Ice Cream

In the preparation of ice cream, the liquid constituents are heated to 43°C, sugar and dry ingredients are added to the warm liquid, which helps dissolve them. The mix is now pasteurized at 71°C for 30 min. or HTST pasteurized at 82°C for 25 secs. The hot mix from the pasteurizer is next homogenized. This helps to improve the body and texture of ice cream. The homogenized mix is cooled to 4.4°C. The cooled mix is aged for 4 to 24 hours. Ageing helps melted fat to solidify and stabilize, and milk proteins to swell, resulting in the increased viscosity of the mix. These changes help in whipping and incorporation of the required amount of air into ice cream.

The aged mix and air are passed through a freezer. The freezer will be provided with special mixing elements, which beat the ice cream mix and subdivide air cells and evenly distribute it to give a frozen foam. Also, the temperature of the mix comes down to –5.5°C. Freezing must be quick to prevent the growth of large crystals that would coarsen the texture of the ice cream. As the air is whipped into the semi-frozen mixture there is a swelling of the volume, which is known as overrun. At –5.5°C all the water will not be frozen and the semi-solid ice cream is put into containers in which the ice cream is sold. The containers, with the ice cream, are then placed in hardening rooms where the temperature is about – 34°C. At this temperature, the remaining water freezes and makes ice cream stiff, when it is ready for sale.

For making ice cream in homes, a metal container with a paddle inside is used. The ice cream mix is passed into the container and placed in an outside container, usually made of some poor conductor of heat, such as wood, containing a freezing mixture of ice and salt in the proportion of one part of salt to six parts of ice. The mixture is then agitated with the paddle. This helps the cooling and incorporation of air in the mixture.

21.11 Indigenous Milk Products

21.11.1 Dahi

This is India's most important milk product. Of the total quantity of milk converted into milk products, about 15 per cent is used for *dahi* making.

Dahi is reported to have a better nutritive value than milk. Though there is no increase in the fat or protein content of milk during fermentation, the digestibility of *dahi* is more than that of milk. The calcium and phosphorus contents of *dahi* are more easily assimilated. *Dahi* contains more vitamins than milk.

During curd formation, the lactose of milk is converted into lactic acid. There is some breakdown of protein increasing the non-protein nitrogen. The fat globules coalesce and distribute themselves on the top. Physically, during *dahi* formation, milk proteins are jellied and a thin exudate of clear serum on the curd is seen.

The organisms involved in *dahi* formation belong to the group of *Lactobacillus* and *Streptococci.* Some strains used are *L. casei*, *L. bulgaricus*, *L. brevis*, *L. lactis* and *S. thermophilus*. Each of these organisms produce different levels of acidity. The formation of consistently good quality *dahi* depends upon the use of the right type of starter. A starter culture containing a combination of *Lactobacillus* and *Lactococcus* organisms gives good results. Starters containing yeasts, moulds and gas-forming organisms spoil the quality of *dahi*. When they are present, a product with a homogeneous texture or good aroma will not be obtained. There will be cracks and gas bubbles and the curd will be of poor quality and taste.

The method of preparation and quality of *dahi* depends upon whether it is consumed as such or used for the preparation of butter. *Dahi* can be made either from whole milk or skim milk. When whole milk is used, it has a creamy layer on top, the rest being made up of a homogeneous body of curd. The creamy layer can be removed for butter making before consuming curd as such or converting it into *lassi*.

In the preparation of *dahi* for consumption as food, milk is brought to a boil in order to destroy viable organisms, cooled to the body temperature and seeded with *dahi* from an earlier batch. The quantity of seed depends upon the season of the year and severity of the climate. About 5-10 per cent of the volume of milk is added as starter during cold weather. Lesser quantities are required during summer. Milk is then kept in a warm or cool place, depending upon the season. After 6 to 24 hours, depending upon the climatic conditions, a smooth homogeneous product having an acidity of 0.9 to 1.0 per cent acid is formed. Now, a starter for making *dahi* in a short time is available.

In the preparation of *dahi* for butter making, raw milk is used in some parts of the country. It is allowed to undergo natural fermentation by atmospheric bacteria or by the addition of a small quantity of buttermilk from the previous batch of raw-milk-curd. The result is a type of *dahi* with gas bubbles and a mouldy flavour, separating into two distinct layers—serum at the bottom and cake of curd on top. This is a very undesirable form of making curd. The buttermilk obtained after separating butter from such a *dahi* will not be fit for use as a beverage. It is always good to use boiled and cooled milk in *dahi* making even if it is required only for butter making.

Dahi is used in the preparation of beverages (*lassi*) by beating it with water and adding sugar or salt and spices. *Dahi Kusum* is a delicious dish comparable to ice cream. It is made by beating the milk, and sweetening, flavouring and colouring it before seeding with starter. *Sreekhand* is a semi-dry mass of *dahi* sweetened with sugar. It is made by suspending curd in a muslin bag until all the whey is drained off. It is then sugared and coloured.

21.11.2 Khoa

Khoa is a semi-solid obtained from milk by evaporating it in open pans. This is an important milk product and is extensively used in the preparation of Indian sweetmeats throughout the country. It is estimated that 5–7 per cent of the total milk produced in the country is converted into *khoa*. About 3,00,000 tonnes of *khoa* are produced annually. *Khoa* formation lengthens the keeping quality of milk, and makes it less susceptible to bacterial growth.

In the preparation of *khoa*, milk is boiled in a small shallow, round-bottomed iron pan over a steady fire. To prevent scorching, milk is cautiously stirred in a circular motion with a scraper. When milk becomes viscous, the rate of stirring is increased to maintain a uniform consistency. The pan is removed from the fire and the product is worked up with the flattened end of the scraper by alternately spreading it into thin layers and collecting repeatedly until it retains its shape. After cooling, it becomes solid. The yield is about 20 per cent of the weight of milk used.

Khoa is a compact mass of very small uniformly sized granules. It is white in colour (slightly brown if caramelization has taken place during heating), has a sweet taste and a pleasant odour. It keeps well for 2–3 days in hot weather and 4-5 days in cold weather. The addition of sugar prolongs its life to 3–4 months.

During the preparation of *khoa*, milk proteins are coagulated. This is accelerated by the incorporation of air and frothing during stirring. Because of appreciable homogenization during vigorous boiling, when coagulation of protein sets in, all the fat globules are entrenched in the coagulant. Similarly, water is dispersed and therefore *khoa* does not appear to be wet. Lactose will be present as an anhydrous sugar in *khoa* when it is hot and its crystallization on cooling is not favoured because of the high viscosity of the products. There is a decrease in vitamin A and some water-soluble vitamins of milk in *khoa* formation.

The composition of *khoa* depends on the nature of the milk used. Buffalo milk *khoa* contains more fat (about 46 per cent) than that of cow (35 per cent). The protein and lactose content of cow milk *khoa* are more than in *khoa* from buffalo milk. *Khoa* is the base for several sweets like *burfi*, *peda*, etc., and many other sweets that have emerged from time to time. A number of bacterial colonies is the cause for deterioration of *khoa*, which increases with the period of storage. With sufficient care, it is possible to keep it for long periods without the contamination of moulds and bacteria. Also, it is fortunate that *khoa* is only an intermediate in the preparation of other products, in which process there is a destruction of micro-organisms.

21.11.3 Rabbri

This product is prepared by heating milk in a wide pan. The milk is slowly heated and brought to a boil. During this process milk is not stirred. The scum that forms on the surface of the milk is peeled off from time to time using thin bamboo sticks and placed on the cooler parts of the pan. This is continued until about one-fifth to one-eighth part of the original quantity of milk is left. The pan is then removed from the fire, the scum that has collected on the sides of the pan is separated without injuring the flakes, and the whole mass is gently mixed. Sugar is then added to about 25-30 per cent and the product allowed to cool. The weight of *rabbri* will be a quarter to a third of the milk used.

This product is a great delicacy. It contains about 20 per cent fat, 17 per cent lactose, 10 per cent casein, and 20 per cent cane sugar. Buffalo milk gives a better product than cow milk, because of its higher fat content.

21.11.4 Mallai

This is made by simmering large quantities of milk until a thick layer of milk fat and coagulated protein forms on the surface. This is skimmed and laid aside to cool. This process is repeated twice by when most of the fat is removed. The yield is about 20-25 per cent of the milk used.

The product is smooth, white and tastes like clotted cream. The preparation is consumed with or without the addition of sugar.

21.11.5 Kheer

This is a partially desiccated product of milk. Its preparation is like that of *khoa*, but the boiling is stopped when the milk is evaporated to about half its original volume. Sugar is added to the concentrated milk and the product resembles sweetened condensed milk. The product cannot be preserved long and is meant for consumption after preparation.

21.12 Milk Substitutes

Milk, cream and other dairy products are expensive and are not available in the required quantities in developing countries. Therefore, substitutes for milk and milk products are made from vegetable sources. The substitute can be produced at a lower cost than natural milk, and carefully formulated with emulsifiers, vitamins and minerals, they could be nutritionally important. Fluid milk is being produced in our country and other developing countries from soyabean (Subsection 17.8.1) and groundnut (Subsection 19.6.1). Fluid milk of excellent quality can be prepared from skim milk and vegetable fat. These milk could be pasteurized, homogenized and marketed like ordinary milk.

Substitutes for butter, ice cream, coffee whitener, and whipped toppings can be obtained by the proper processing and modification of vegetable fats.

CHAPTER

22 Eggs

The eggs of many species of birds have been in use as an item of food from prehistoric times. But the most commonly preferred for table use are hen's eggs which are considered in this chapter.

An average Indian diet is seriously deficient in important proteins of animal origin. It is now widely recognized that the easiest and most practical method of removing this inadequacy in our diet is to supplement it with eggs. There is a misconception among people that egg is non-vegetarian. But practically all the eggs sold in the market are infertile (lifeless) and, therefore, they may be termed vegetarian eggs. Vegetarians who have no objection to take milk should have no objection to take eggs. The prejudices against the consumption of eggs are disappearing, particularly in urban areas. However, there is still a need to popularize the consumption of eggs.

In 2022, world production of chicken eggs was 93.8 million tonnes. The largest four producers were China at 34.9 million, the United States at 6.6 million, India at 6.2 million, and Japan at 2.5 million.

The egg production in the country has increased from around 83 billion nos. in 2015-16 to around 138.38 billion in 2022-23 registering a growth of about 6.19%. The per capita availability of eggs has increased from 61 in 2013-14 to 81 in 2022-23.

Table 22.1 Egg production–Growth rate

S.No.	Year	Egg production (in billion numbers)	% annual egg production growth rate
1.	2011–12	66.45	5.4%
2.	2012–13	69.73	4.94%
3.	2013–14	74.75	7.2%
4.	2014–15	78.48	4.99%
5.	2015–16	82.93	5.66%
6.	2016–17	88.13	6.28%

The poultry meat production in the country has increased to nearly 3.46 million tons during the year 2016-17 from 3.26 million tonnes during the year 2015-16 at around 6% growth rate.

World Egg production: India is currently 2nd in egg production in the world (as per FAO 2022).

Table 22.2

S.No.	Country	Eggs, hen, in shell (in Million Tonnes)
1.	China	34.9
2.	India	6.2
3.	U.S.A.	6.1
4.	Indonesia	2.4
5.	Brazil	2.3
	World total	**91.3**

Egg Production Targets 2022-23

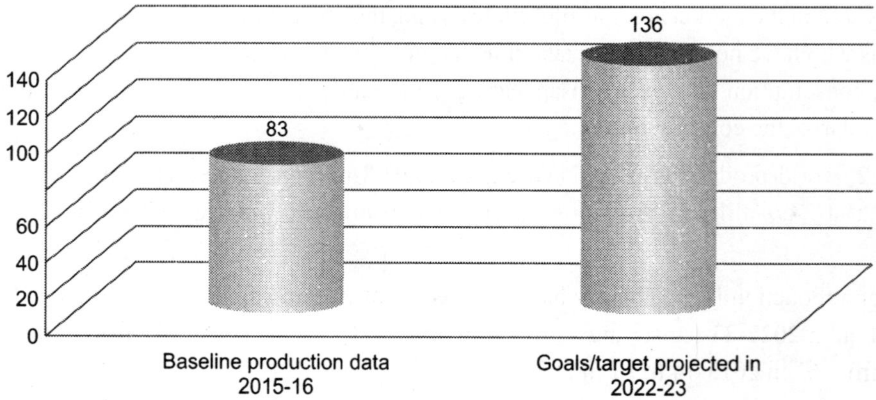

Fig. 22.1 Taking 7% CAGR and adding 2% for exports

22.1 Nutritive Value

Eggs have an excellent nutritive value. They contain 12–14 per cent proteins, which are well balanced with respect to all the essential amino acids. The egg proteins are easily digested and their quality is comparable to that of meat. As the cost of eggs is very much lower than meat, poultry and fish, it can be afforded by nearly all people. The lipids of egg constitute 10–12 per cent and they are composed of a high percentage of unsaturated fatty acids. Much of the calorie (about 80 kcal per egg) contribution is due to the fat contained in yolk. Minerals are present to the extent of 1 per cent in egg. They include iron, phosphorus, calcium and sulphur. The yolk is a particularly important source of iron (1.42 mg per egg); practically the whole of iron is present in a form in which it can be easily utilized.

Eggs are an excellent source of vitamin A which, again, is present in the yolk. The yolk is also a good source of vitamin D which is not commonly found in other foods. Egg yolk is second only to fish oil in this respect. The quantity of vitamin D depends upon the amount of direct sunshine the layers get. The egg is also a good source of B vitamins. The yolk of the egg also contains about 250 mg of cholesterol, a fact which makes it necessary for some people on special diets to restrict their intake of eggs. Thus, with its rich protein, lipid, mineral and vitamin content and good storage qualities, eggs are more useful as food than even milk.

22.2 Structure

A fully formed egg has a shell, two membranes, albumen or the white of the egg, yolk or the yellow of the egg, and the germinal disc. The various elements are arranged with great precision and their total organization is essential to the specific function of each part.

The shell of the egg is made of calcium carbonate (calcite) deposited in an organic matrix and it forms the protective covering of the inner contents of the egg, along with the two membranes. The matrix fibres have significant influence on shell strength and pass through calcite, instead of surrounding it. The matrices are made up of protein-polysaccharide complexes. An eggshell is brittle and easily breaks. It is porous and contains thousands of small holes (7,000–17,000 per egg) which allow gases to pass in and out of the egg for the developing embryo, in the case of a fertilized egg. The small holes are covered with a thin layer of a gelatinous material (mucoprotein) called the cuticle or bloom. The cuticle seals off the pores of the shell to some extent and helps avoid excessive evaporation from the inner contents of the egg. It also restricts the entry of micro-organisms into the egg and thus protects its inner contents from various infections. The cuticle is soluble in water and easily removed by washing (buffing) which results in hastening the deterioration of egg quality.

The shells of some eggs are white while those of others are brown. The pigmentation of the shell depends on the breed of the hen and has no bearing on the quality of the egg, though eggs with white shells are preferred. Eggs also show great variety in the surface characteristics of their shells. Some are glossy, others dull, some smooth, and some rough.

Within the shell are an inner and an outer membrane that also protects the quality of the egg. Both the membranes are porous and composed of fibres. The outer membrane which is thicker (48 μm) than the inner one (22 μm) is firmly attached to the shell. The outer membrane has six layers of fibres, whereas the inner has three. The inner membrane is attached to the outer and the two membranes are loosely attached to one place, usually at the broad end of the egg. The membranes are composed of protein-polysaccharide.

The eggs contain little or no air cells when it is laid. After being laid, because of the lower temperature of the outer surrounding of the egg than when it was in the hen's body, there is a contraction of the inner contents of the egg. This results in air being drawn into the shell leading to a small air-cell formation between the shell membranes, usually at the large end of the egg.

The white of the egg consists of three layers: two areas of thin white encompassing one area of thick white. The yolk is enclosed in a sac called the "vitelline membrane." Immediately beyond this is another membranous layer known as the chalaziferous layer. The yolk is connected to the thick or firm albumen by two twisted rope-like extensions of the chalaziferous layer called chalazae. The chalazae strive to anchor the yolk in the white and keep it centred in the egg.

The yolk carries the indistinct germinal disc or germ spot which, under suitable conditions, develops into a chick. Beneath the germ spot extends a white column called the latebra. The yolk itself is layered into sections of white and yellow yolk, but these are not readily discernible.

In infertile eggs, the female reproduction nucleus is not fertilized by union with the sperm of the cock. These are incapable of producing chicks, and are, therefore, sometimes called "lifeless" eggs. Infertile eggs are produced when a male bird is not kept with the laying hens. Sometimes even when the laying hens are mated or artificially inseminated, a small percentage of the eggs laid may be infertile.

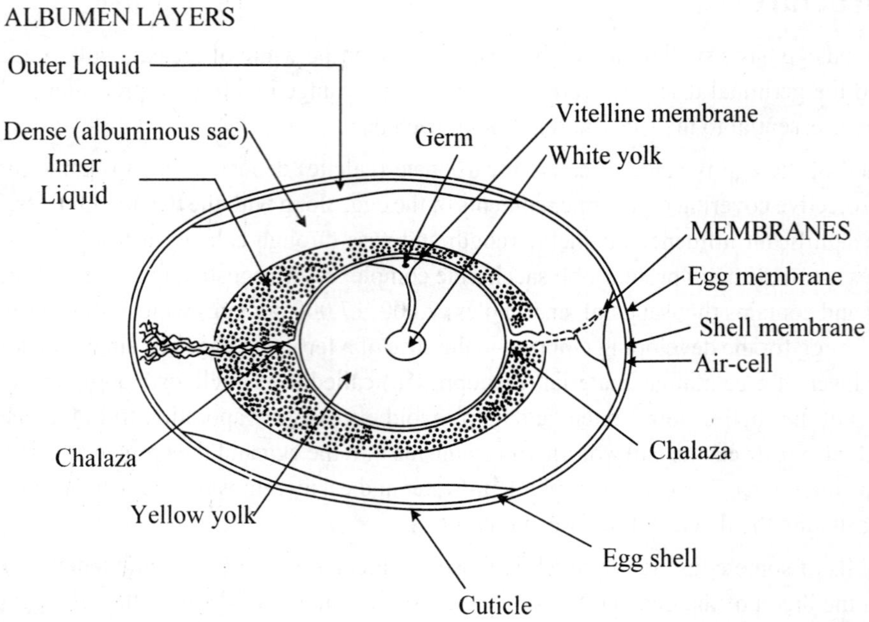

Fig. 22.2 Structure of hen's egg

22.3 Composition

The shell of the egg contributes 8–11 per cent of its weight. Egg contains about two parts white (56–61 per cent) to one part yolk (27–32 per cent) by weight. The whole egg contains about 65 per cent of water, 12–14 per cent protein, 10–12 per cent fat, and 1 per cent minerals. The compositions of the egg white and the yolk differ considerably (Table 22.3). The lipid content of albumen is negligible when compared to yolk. The carbohydrate in albumen is present in combined and free states, the latter form is mostly glucose. Proteins and lipids are the major constituents of yolk with a minor amount of carbohydrates. The amount of yolk lipid varies from 32–36 per cent, its constituents being approximately 68 per cent triglycerides, 28 per cent phospholipids, 5 per cent cholesterol, and minor amounts of other lipids. The yolk is rich in fat-soluble vitamins.

Table 22.3 Composition of the edible portion of hen's egg (in per cent)

Composition	Whole Egg	Egg White	Egg Yolk
Ash	1.0	0.82	1.5
Fat	10.5	0.05	31.6
Protein	13.4	10.00	16.7
Water	73.7	87.77	49.0

Source: *The Indian Journal of Home Science*, Vol.7, 1973, p. 104.

Table 22.4 Composition of edible portion of whole eggs from different birds based on 100 g by weight

Component	Chicken	Quail	Duck	Turkey	Goose
Unit of calories	147	158	185	171	185
Total Fat	9.9 g	11.1 g	13.8 g	11.9 g	13.3 g
Saturated Fat	3.1 g	3.6 g	3.7 g	3.6 g	3.6 g
Cholesterol	423 mg	844 mg	884 mg	933 mg	852 mg
Carbohydrate	0.8 g	0.4 g	1.5 g	1.2 g	1.3 g
Protein	12.6 g	13.1 g	12.8 g	13.7 g	13.9 g
Vitamin A	487 IU	543 IU	674 IU	554 IU	650 IU
Calcium	53 mg	64 mg	64 mg	99 mg	60 mg
Iron	1.8 mg	3.6 mg	3.8 mg	4.1 mg	3.6 mg
Sodium	140 mg	141 mg	146 mg	151 mg	138 mg

22.3.1 Egg white Proteins

Egg white contains many proteins frequently referred to as albumen. All egg white proteins are globular. These globular proteins are important for the foaming properties of egg white. Some of the well-studied egg white proteins are the following:

Ovalbumin: This is the main protein constituting 55 per cent of the proteins of egg white. This is a phosphoglycoprotein and is composed of three components A_1, A_2 and A_3, which differ only in phosphorus content. A_1 has two phosphates per molecule, A_2 has one, and A_3, has none. All the forms contain sulphydryl and disulphur groups. The relative proportion of A_1, A_2 and A_3 components is about 35 : 12 : 3. The carbohydrate components of ovalbumin are mannose and glucosamine in the ratio of 5 : 3. Ovalbumin in solution is readily denatured simply by mechanical agitation but is resistant to thermal denaturation. At pH 9 and 62°C, only 3–5 per cent ovalbumin is denatured.

Conalbumin: This constitutes 13 per cent of the proteins of egg albumen. It consists of two forms neither of which contains phosphorus or sulphur. Conalbumin is more easily heat coagulated and less susceptible to surface denaturation than ovalbumin. The protein easily binds metallic ions, such as Fe^{3+}, Al^{3+}, Cu^{2+} or Zn^{2+}, forming heat-stable complexes.

Ovomucoid: Ovomucoid constitutes about 10 per cent of the egg white proteins. It exists in three forms, all of which are trypsin inhibitors. The carbohydrate moiety of the protein contains hexoses (galactose and mannose), glucosamine and sialic acid. The protein contains eight disulphide linkages. It is resistant to heat denaturation in acid media but is rapidly denatured in alkaline solutions.

Ovomucin: This protein is responsible for the thickness of albumen. Its content in the thick layers of albumen is about four times more than in thin layers. It is insoluble in water but is soluble in dilute salt solutions. The protein consists of three components. Purified ovomucin in solution is resistant to heat denaturation. Between pH 7.1 and 9.4, heating for 2 hours at 90°C does not bring about any change. Ovomucin and lysozyme can form a water-soluble complex.

Lysozyme: Lysozyme is an enzyme capable of lysing (dissolving) the cell wall of bacteria. The enzyme is much more heat-sensitive in egg albumen than when present alone. Lysozyme has four disulphide linkages and is a well-characterized enzyme.

Avidin: Avidin is composed of three components A, B and C. It binds biotin and makes the vitamin unavailable. However, avidin is easily denatured by heat and so its presence is not of concern when eggs are cooked. For this and other reasons, it is recommended that eggs be cooked before eating.

Other proteins: Egg albumen contains other proteins. Ovoglobulin is a protein consisting of two components G_1, and G_2, which are excellent foaming agents. Ovoinhibitor is another protein capable of inhibiting trypsin and chymotrypsin. A flavoprotein is also present in egg albumen.

22.3.2 Egg Yolk Proteins

The solid content of yolk is about 50 per cent. The yolk is a dispersion containing a variety of particles distributed uniformly in a protein (livetin) solution. On high-speed centrifugation, yolk separates itself into granules and a clear supernatant, called plasma. The granules, on a dry basis, contain 34 per cent lipid, 60 per cent protein, 6 per cent ash and plasma, 77–81 per cent lipid, 2 per cent ash, and 18 per cent protein.

Granules are composed of 70 per cent α- and β-lipovitellins, 16 per cent phosvitin and 12 per cent low-density lipoprotein. Lipovitellins and phosvitin have an affinity for each other and the phosvitin-lipovitellin complex is a basic unit of granules. Plasma is composed of the globular protein livetin and a low-density lipoprotein fraction.

Phosvitin: Phosvitin is rich in phosphorus and accounts for 80 per cent of the protein phosphorus of yolk. It is rich in serine (31 per cent of the total amino acid residues), and the phosphate is presumably esterified to this amino acid. Phosvitin binds tightly ferric ions and forms a soluble complex and is thus the iron carrier of yolk.

Lipovitellins: These are high-density lipoproteins. They can be separated into two fractions, the α- and β-lipovitellins. Each fraction contains 40 per cent neutral lipid and 60 per cent phospholipids. At pH values below 7, lipovitellins occur as dimers.

Livetin: This consists of three components, the α- , β- and γ-livetins. These differ in their molecular weight. α-livetin does not contain hexose or hexosamine, γ-livetin contains only hexose and γ-livetin contains both hexose and hexosamine.

Low-density lipoprotein: Low-density lipoprotein (LDL) of egg yolk has a density of 0.98. It consists of 74 per cent neutral lipids and 26 per cent phospholipids. It can be separated into two components LDL_1, and LDL_2. These fractions have very high molecular weights. They are spherical with a triglyceride core upon which phospholipids and proteins are layered.

Pigments: The colour of egg yolk varies from a pale yellow to brilliant orange depending on the amount and type of pigment present in the diet of the hen. The colour is due to the presence of carotenoids and xanthophylls. Of these, the carotenoids are converted into vitamin A in the body. Mostly, deep coloured yolks are rich in vitamin A content. Xanthophylls are responsible for the yellow colour and they are not converted into vitamin A.

Minerals: Calcium, which is the most abundant mineral in egg, is mostly concentrated in the shell. It is also present in a significant amount in yolk and in a small amount in egg white. Phosphorus is the most abundant mineral in the yolk. Eggs are an important source of easily assimilable iron. In addition to these, other minerals present in egg white and yolk in varying amounts are sodium, potassium, magnesium, sulphur and chlorine. The mineral content of the egg depends upon their concentration in the hen's diet.

22.4 Egg Quality

Egg is an excellent food for man and, as such, its quality is of very great importance. If proper care is not taken, the quality of the egg deteriorates rapidly and its food value is adversely affected. A number of factors constitute egg quality, including both external and internal factors. External factors include the size and shape of the egg and condition of the shell. Internal factors determining the quality are the size of the air-cell and condition of the albumen, yolk and the germ spot.

The size of an egg is indicated by the weight of the newly-laid eggs. Hens lay eggs of different sizes, varying from 49 to 70 g. The size of the egg depends upon the hen's inheritance, body size, stage of laying, season of laying, age, diet, and health of the bird. The indigenous (Indian hens), however, usually lay eggs weighing less than 45 g. The size does not reflect the quality and, similarly, the grade of the egg does not indicate its size. A point in favour of small eggs is that they contain a relatively higher proportion of yolk than large eggs.

Though the shell of an egg is not consumed, its condition is important because of the protection it gives to the edible portion. The factors affecting the condition of the shell are its strength, porosity, soundness, texture, colour and cleanliness. The strength of the shell depends upon its thickness which in turn depends upon the nutrition of the bird and other factors. High porosity of the eggshell will hasten the deterioration in the quality of egg contents, as it permits the evaporation of moisture and allows dissolved carbon dioxide to escape from the inner contents during the storage of eggs. A porous shell is graded lower than a shell with fine pores. The texture of the egg shell varies. This does not materially affect the quality of the inner contents. However, there should not be ridges or grooves spread over a large area of the shell. As already stated, the colour of the shell varies but has nothing to do with the quality of the edible portion of the egg. Finally, eggs must be clean. Any dirt on the egg shell means the presence of a large number of contaminating microorganisms. Eggs may be dry cleaned or wiped with a piece of moist cloth if they are slightly soiled or washed with warm water of a temperature of about 10°C higher than that of the egg.

The quality of the internal contents of the egg is determined by the size of the air cell, the denseness of the egg white and the size, distinctness, colour and mobility of the yolk. As the quality of the egg deteriorates, the size of the air cell increases, and the white becomes thinner. The yolk should be centred in the egg and its position tends to drift off centre when the egg becomes stale. Since yolk colour depends largely on the colour of the chicken feed, the colour is not an indication of the quality of the egg, though eggs with darker yolks are preferred. The yolk should be free from abnormalities, which include blood spots, embryonic development, mould growth, discolourations, and other signs of spoilage.

22.4.1 Evaluation of Egg Quality

The quality of egg in the shell is evaluated most commonly by a process known as candling. The egg is held up to a light source in a dark room and is viewed in silhouette while being rotated. Candling will reveal a crack in the shell, the size of the air cell, the firmness of albumen, the position and mobility of yolk, and the possible presence of foreign substances. Sometimes the quality of an egg is determined by dropping the egg in water. If the egg sinks it is considered good, while it is considered to be of poor quality if it floats. This is not an effective method for finding out the egg quality; it only gives a rough idea. It shows that the egg floating on water has lost weight due to dehydration.

Where it is feasible, the quality of an egg can be graded by breaking the egg out of the shell. The appearance of the shelled egg is an excellent indication of freshness. Fresh eggs have a high yolk rather than a flat yolk, i.e., the yolk index, a figure derived by dividing the height of the yolk by its diameter, is high in fresh eggs. Also, the height of the thick albumen (albumen index) indicates the quality of the egg, i.e., fresh eggs have a larger amount of thick white relative to runny thin white. This causes a stale egg to spread out over a larger area than a fresh egg.

22.4.2 Egg Grading

Eggs whose quality has been determined, are graded for marketing purposes. They are graded according to size and quality which are independent of each other. In India, eggs are graded according to weight into four grades whose weight specification is as indicated in Table 22.5. In the US, based on minimum weight, eggs are graded into six classes, as jumbo, extra large, large, medium, small, and pee wee. Grading according to size helps the buyer obtain a particular quantity of the food material for a given price.

Clean eggs with unbroken shell are graded on quality depending upon the depth of air cell, centering of egg yolk and freedom from defects, as Grade A and grade B in India. These are further subdivided based on size. In the US, eggs are classified into three groups as AA, A and B.

22.4.3 Deterioration of Egg Quality

As soon as an egg is laid, changes begin to take place that lower its quality. There is no known method by which this quality can be improved subsequently. Therefore, eggs are to be maintained in a fresh condition as far as possible. If not, their quality will deteriorate rapidly.

Table 22.5 Weight specification of hen eggs

Grade	Weight of individual egg (g)
Extra large	>60
Large	53 –59
Medium	45–52
Small	38–44

Source: Indian Standards Institution. New Delhi, India, IS: 6558–1972.

If the shell gets cracked, the inner contents of the egg get exposed to unfavourable environmental conditions resulting in loss of moisture and carbon dioxide, invasion of micro-organisms, and formation of objectionable odour. Weak shells and rough handling during packing and transport increase the chances of damage to the shell.

The evaporation of moisture from the inner contents of the egg takes place through the shell pores. The rate of loss of moisture depends upon the extent of porosity of the eggshell, environmental temperature, and humidity. The loss of water from the egg results in a decrease in the weight of the egg, an increase in the size of the air cell and a decrease in the specific gravity of the egg.

In a newly-laid egg, the albumen of the egg contains carbon dioxide and this begins to escape through the pores of the shell soon after it is laid. This results in a rise of the pH of the egg. The pH of egg white increases from 7.9 to about 9.3, in the first three days. With an increase in alkalinity, the white becomes thinner, and so it spreads more when the egg is broken out. The white may eventually become yellow and cloudy. The thinner white will not be able to keep the yolk centred in the egg. The pH of the yolk is initially about 6.3 and it increases slowly during prolonged storage. A change in pH influences its functional properties.

The changes in pH in the egg white and yolk also results in the rupture of the vitelline membrane. The mixing of the yolk and albumen results in chemical disintegration and decomposition, producing an odour inside the egg. Unpleasant odours are also absorbed by eggs if care is not taken to prevent odours in storage areas.

The contents of newly laid clean eggs are usually free from contaminating organisms. During storage, microbial spoilage sometimes takes place. Micro-organisms may be drawn in through the porous shell, the most likely contaminants being the *Salmonella* species. The chances of microbial invasion are increased if the shell is dirty. Even if the micro organisms penetrate the shell, the shell membranes, the alkaline pH of the egg, the bacteria lysing enzyme (lysozyme), the iron containing conalbumin, and the biotin binding avidin-resist their growth. However, heavy contamination overcomes the defence mechanisms and causes spoilage during storage.

In a fertile egg, the development of the germinal disc is arrested when the egg is laid. However, as soon as the egg is exposed to a temperature of 20°C or above, the embryo starts growing. The development of the embryo deteriorates the quality of the egg contents. At a temperature below 38°C, the growth of embryo is defective and it usually dies after some time. If the death of the embryo takes place before blood has been formed, a red spot appears at the place of the germinal disc (heat spot). This lowers the edible quality of the egg. If the death of the embryo occurs shortly after blood has been formed, a small red ring is produced at the surface of the yolk (blood ring). Eggs having blood rings or dead embryos are inedible.

22.4.4 Egg Storage

Eggs subjected to varying temperatures deteriorate more quickly than eggs held at a constant temperature. Therefore, for household purposes, eggs must be kept under refrigeration where they will keep well for 1–2 weeks. Storage of eggs at room temperature may cause a reduction in quality within one week.

Egg production is not uniform throughout the year; there is more production during spring. The preservation of surplus eggs produced during the peak season for use during the lean season becomes necessary. For the preservation of eggs, control of temperature, humidity and sanitary conditions are necessary. Clean eggs maintained at a temperature of –1°C and relative humidity of 80 per cent can be stored for as long as six months without any deterioration.

Some lengthening of egg storage stability can be achieved by storing eggs under carbon dioxide to minimize carbon dioxide loss. A more common method of slowing deteriorative changes in eggs during storage is to spray them with some mineral oil, preferably containing some fungicides, before storage. The mineral oil should be very clean, colourless, odourless and tasteless to prevent flavour impairment or spoilage. The deposited oil film partially closes the pores of the shell, retarding the loss of moisture, and the rise in pH resulting from the loss of carbon dioxide. Oils of vegetable or animal origin should not be used for spraying as they undergo oxidative rancidity during storage.

Another method of prolonging storage life is by a process known as thermostabilization. This consists of heating the egg in water at a temperature of 54°C for about 15 min. or in boiling water for 5 secs. before storage. This treatment coagulates a thin layer of albumen around the inside of the shell and thus seals the pores from the inside. The heat also kills some of the surface bacteria.

22.5 Egg Processing

22.5.1 Egg Freezing

Eggs, in addition to storage in the shell, maybe preserved by freezing or by the drying their contents. An egg cannot be frozen in the shell since the eggshell would crack with the expansion of liquids when frozen. Therefore, the whole of the liquid contents of the egg is frozen or it is separated into yolk and white, and frozen.

One of the important problems in freezing is the control of micro-organisms. To reduce contamination, the shells are usually washed just before the eggs are broken from the shell, and then freezing is done as quickly as possible. Because of the prevalence of *Salmonella,* which is pathogenic, it is better to pasteurize the white, yolk, or whole egg. Egg white is very sensitive to heat, being easily coagulated very near the pasteurization temperature. By heating for 2 min. at 58°C, albumen becomes turbid and viscous and loses its foaming properties. Whole egg or yolk, in contrast, can be pasteurized at 60°–61.5°C for 3.5 to 4.0 min., without significant changes in physical and functional properties. The pasteurized whole or separated eggs are placed in cans or suitable containers and frozen in a sharp freezer room with circulating air at –29°C. Freezing may take about 48 to 72 hours.

While frozen egg white retains its qualities fairly well, yolk and whole egg cannot be frozen satisfactorily. On a freezing, the yolk or whole egg becomes viscous and gummy, a condition known as "gelation" resulting in altered functional properties. Yolk gelation is due to the formation of ice crystals on the lowering of storage temperature to below – 6°C (the freezing point of yolk is about 0.58°C). Freezing also reduces the distance between reactants, such as lipoproteins, which enhances their aggregation. This is prevented by the addition of sugar, salt, or corn syrup to the egg yolk and whole egg before freezing. The sugared yolk is used satisfactorily in dessert products, confectionery and other products that tolerate sugar, while salted yolk is used in the manufacture of mayonnaise. By enzyme treatment with pepsin, it is claimed that egg yolk maintains functional properties during frozen storage.

22.5.2 Dried Eggs

Drying is another method of egg preservation and there is a demand for egg powder for the preparation of commercial egg products. The white, yolk or whole egg, after pasteurization, maybe dried by any of the several methods of drying. The most common method employed for drying eggs is spray drying. The liquid egg is forced through an atomizer as a fine spray into a drying chamber through which hot air is blown. The powdered egg is cooled, collected and packaged.

Egg-white contains traces of glucose. When the dehydrated white or whole egg is stored at temperatures much above freezing, the glucose combines with egg proteins resulting in browning. To prevent this, glucose is to be removed with glucose oxidase or by fermentation with the yeast prior to drying.

The functional properties of an egg are not adversely affected by drying. The heat coagulation properties remain practically the same. Dried eggs keep best when the moisture content is low and if they are kept in tightly sealed containers. Dried egg white is quite stable during storage. However. objectionable changes in colour, flavour, odour and solubility occur when either dried yolks or whole eggs are held at temperatures higher than 5°C. A lower temperature retards the undesirable changes, until at –18°C when very little change occurs. Dried eggs may be reconstituted before use by mixing with an appropriate quantity of water. The nutritive value of frozen eggs and dried eggs will practically be the same as shell eggs if properly stored.

Egg substitutes: Because of the high cholesterol content of egg yolk, several commercial egg substitutes have been introduced for a cholesterol-free diet. The basic principle of these substitutes is to eliminate the egg yolk and to retain the natural egg white. Various ingredients are added to egg white to simulate whole fresh egg. Egg substitutes are available in fresh, refrigerated or frozen forms. The nutritional and caloric value of the substitute depends upon the ingredients. Though they are used in various products where the whole fresh egg is an ingredient, the result is not frequently identical to the product made using fresh egg. However, for some preparations like scrambled egg and French omelette they are found quite satisfactory.

22.6 Effect of Heat on Egg Proteins

An egg finds numerous uses in food preparations because of its fundamental properties, which, in turn, depend on the proteins of the egg. Coagulation of egg proteins is valuable in many different cooking processes. Use of egg as a thickening agent, binding agent, and clarifying agent, are all based on the coagulation of its proteins when heated.

Various proteins coagulate at different temperatures. The coagulation of the undiluted proteins of an egg depends on the combination of proteins present. Egg white proteins begin to coagulate at 52°C if the heating conditions are controlled carefully. When the white is heated more rapidly, coagulation begins at 60°C and is completed at 65°C. The coagulation of egg yolk begins at 65°C and is completed at 70°C.

The rate and the extent of coagulation depend also on time and added ingredients. A rapidly heated egg mixture coagulates at a higher temperature than a slowly heated one. The egg white coagulated at a high temperature is firm and tough when compared with the soft and tender product obtained when coagulation takes place at a lower temperature. A slow rate of heating and, consequently, a lower coagulation temperature, are preferable in food preparations.

Ingredients added to eggs affect the temperature of coagulation of egg proteins. Dilution by the addition of water or milk raises the temperature of coagulation. Sugar in an egg mixture also elevates the coagulation temperature. Acids, such as cream of tartar or lemon juice, reduce the coagulation temperature by helping reduce the pH of the egg mixture to the isoelectric point. The presence of salt lowers the temperature of coagulation. Salt causes coagulation to occur because the charges of the ions neutralize the charges on the protein molecule. The presence of salt, thus, aids the coagulation of a dilute egg mixture.

22.7 Egg Foams

Eggs can be used to produce foams which are stable, to be incorporated into various foods, or to be baked alone. Egg whites foam readily to a large volume when beaten. The thin portion of egg white foams more voluminously than the thick white. On heating, the beaten proteins are stretched into films in which air is enclosed. The air trapped in the foam expands when the product containing the foam is heated till the albumen surrounding the air undergoes some denaturation at the liquid-air interface. This denaturation caused by the drying and stretching of albumen during beating makes some ovomucin components of the albumen insoluble, thus stiffening and stabilizing the foam. The volume that develops as a result of foam renders tenderness to the product. Egg white is thus utilized in making meringues, souffles, foam cakes, etc. Egg yolk also foams but the volume change is much less than that of the white. Egg yolk foam is a component of sponge cake.

22.7.1 Egg Beating

The qualities of a foam that are of interest are volume, texture and stability. The extent of beating has a distinct influence on the stability of the foam. Different stages of foam formation are recognized on the basis of the appearance of the foam when beaten in the bowl. The first stage is the foamy stage, when the egg white is beaten briefly. The bubbles are formed at the surface, but a bit of liquid remains in the bottom of the bowl. At this stage, the air bubbles are large, opalescent, and the foam is very unstable. Foam at this stage is used for clarifying, emulsifying, and thickening, of foods.

As beating is continued beyond the foamy stage, more air is beaten into the white, causing a white, more opaque appearance. Air bubbles become smaller as agitation continues and foams are soft and flow slowly if the bowl is tipped. When the beater is withdrawn from the foam, the peaks will just bend over. Such foams are suitable for folding into a batter and are used for soft meringues or for incorporation with other ingredients in most products, except chiffon cake.

On further beating, air-cells become very small and the foam becomes stiff and very white. The peaks stand up straight as the beater is withdrawn. Stability of the foam is excellent, but the foam is not easily folded into other ingredients. Foams at this stage are used for hard meringues, cakes, fluffy omelettes, souffles, Ice creams, etc.

If beating is continued beyond the stiff peak stage a dry foam is produced, which is very white but dull, and breaks into small flakes or curds when blended with other ingredients. The stability of the foam is decreased if left to stand; liquid separates at the bottom of the bowl slowly. At this stage, the whites have little utility in food preparation.

22.7.2 Factors Influencing Foaming

Many factors influence the quality of egg foam. These include the method of beating, time and temperature of beating, characteristics of the egg white, pH, and the presence of other substances, such as water, fat, salt, and sugar.

There is an optimum amount of beating that should be done for any given foam to achieve maximum stability. The danger of over-beating is less with a hand beater than with an electric blender. However, the latter type of beaters are useful in the presence of ingredients requiring longer periods of beating to obtain the required endpoint. Finer foams are obtained with beaters with fine wires or thin blades. The time of beating the egg white depends upon the type and speed of the beater. Egg white at room temperature can be beaten more readily than at refrigerator temperature, possibly because of lowered surface tension at the higher temperature.

As already stated, thin white produces more volume than thick white and is more easily beaten. Thick white becomes thinner when eggs are stored; thus stored eggs may be beaten more quickly than white from fresh eggs. The volume of the foam is less when the lysozyme content of the egg white is high.

The pH of the egg white is important for foam formation. Egg white is alkaline in comparison with other foods. The addition of an acid, such as cream of tartar or lemon juice (tartar is more effective), lowers the pH to a value close to the isoelectric pH of the proteins thus facilitating the coagulation of some proteins. The decrease of pH also increases the stability of the foam. The addition of acids to bring pH below the isoelectric pH, however, causes some hydrolysis of proteins, thus delaying foam formation and reducing the stability of the foam.

The addition of water to egg white in an amount up to 40 per cent by volume increases the volume of the foam but decreases the stability. However, volume is not the only important criterion in foam formation. Ultimately, a foam needs to be stable if it is to be useful in food preparation. For example, in the preparation of fluffy omelette water is added during the preparation of white foam to increase the volume. Unless considerable speed is used in preparing and heating the omelette, the foam will not hold up satisfactorily and a heavy layer will collect at the bottom.

The presence of fat is a strong deterrent to the formation of an egg white foam. Even if a small amount of the yolk is present in egg white, the white will not foam well because of the presence of fat in the yolk. To prepare egg white foam, the beater and the bowl must be completely free from fat.

Salt added to the egg white or whole egg before beating reduces the stability of the foam. The volume and stability of egg white decrease and whipping time increases in the presence of salt. With whole eggs the addition of salt before beating results in a foam of small volume that does not form peaks.

Sugar delays the formation of foam. Addition of 50 per cent of sugar to egg white more than doubles the time required for foam formation. More beating to the desired endpoint stretches out the proteins more and more, air bubbles become smaller and smaller, and the foam achieves a fine structure. This helps ultimately to influence the texture of any product in which the foam is incorporated.

22.8 Egg Products

Eggs serve an essential role in many products. They may be cooked without the addition of any ingredients, or they may be included in recipes. Certain properties of eggs such as colour, flavour, texture, binding, emulsifying, and foaming properties, are valuable in the preparation of many products. The egg yolk contributes colour to such items as meringues and various cream pie fillings. The emulsifying properties make eggs significant in salad dressings and in various baked products. The binding functions of the egg are accomplished as a result of the coagulation of proteins during heating. The foaming of egg whites is of importance in the development of a light structure and good volume in baked products.

Eggs and egg-containing recipes should be cooked at low to moderate temperatures as a high temperature results in toughening the proteins. The basic methods of preparing egg products include those prepared in the shell and out of the shell.

22.8.1 Egg Prepared in the Shell

Soft-cooked and hard-cooked eggs are those prepared in the shell. The criteria for a soft-cooked egg are that the white should be firm but tender and the yolk a thick liquid. In hard-cooked (hard-boiled) eggs, the white becomes an opaque tender gel and the yolk is completely coagulated. For good results, eggs are placed in boiling water (sufficient water should be used to cover the eggs) and then a simmering temperature is maintained. Eggs should be simmered for 3–5 min. for soft-cooked eggs and for 15–20 min. for hard-cooked eggs. To prevent the cracking of the shell during cooking, the egg may be lifted quickly in and out of simmering water a couple of times.

Sometimes, with hard-cooked eggs, a greenish-grey layer is obtained at the interface of the yolk and egg white. This is due to the ferrous sulphide formed by the union of iron in the yolk and hydrogen sulphide liberated from sulphur in the white. Ferrous sulphide is formed as the pH of the yolk increases. Prolonged heating or a slow rate of heating will increase the formation of ferrous sulphide. By using fresh eggs, carefully controlling the simmering temperature and rapidly cooling the hot eggs in cold water, the formation of ferrous sulphide can be significantly reduced.

22.8.2 Eggs Prepared Out of the Shell

Poached egg: A poached egg is prepared by sliding the contents of a good quality egg carefully into a pan of water heated to simmering temperature. Use of simmering water in preference to boiling water is important as, in the former case, the egg proteins will be more tender and the egg will hold its shape better. Use of an egg poacher with individual cups for each egg will eliminate the spreading of egg white. When the white is coagulated completely, the egg should be removed from water quickly. In a well prepared poached egg, the white should be uniformly coagulated in a single mass, without spreading extensively and the yolk should be thickened, being covered by a thick coating of white. No part of the yolk should be coagulated to the point where it begins to solidify.

Fried egg: The egg is fried in just enough fat to prevent it from sticking to the pan. The pan should be sufficiently hot to coagulate the egg white but not sufficiently hot to toughen it or to decompose the fat. The egg may be turned over or a small amount of water may be added and a lid placed on the pan so that the steam may speed the cooking of the upper surface. Cooking may also be speeded up by basting the top of the egg with hot fat. The white of the fried egg should be thick and compact. It should be uniformly coagulated and tender. The yolk should be unbroken and covered with a layer of coagulated white.

Scrambled egg: For scrambled egg, the yolk and white are blended until a uniform mixture is formed. A small amount (one tablespoon per egg) of milk, cream or water may be added to the mix along with salt and seasonings. The mix is then heated slowly and the egg is scraped, as it coagulates. This helps the making of scrambled egg which is moist, tender and fluffy. Further heating results in a product which is shrunken, tough and dry. Good quality scrambled eggs are obtained by cooking in a double boiler.

French omelette: A French omelette or plain omelette is prepared by beating the whole egg, with or without a small amount of liquid and flavouring material. The mixture is then cooked in a greased pan until it is coagulated. Cooking is aided by covering the pan with a lid during part of the cooking period. The omelette is then folded or rolled. Different varieties of omelette can be prepared by the use of fillings and sauces.

22.8.3 Products Based on Egg as a Thickening Agent

As egg proteins coagulate in a product, the entire product becomes more viscous. This thickening property of egg is made use of in many products, such as custards and cream pie fillings. Proper control of coagulation temperature determines the quality of the product.

Custards are of two types: (i) The soft custard or stirred custard, which gives a product of creamy consistency by being stirred while it is cooked, and (ii) baked custard, which is allowed to coagulate without stirring.

Stirred custard: The ingredients in custard are eggs, sugar, milk, salt and flavourings. The egg is blended and strained. Then milk and sugar are added and stirred. The milk used is generally scalded to approximately 85°C as it shortens the cooking time and improves the flavour and texture of the product. The custard mixture is heated over hot water, water being just below the boiling point, for the entire heating period. A slow rate of heating is essential for the preparation of a smooth viscous stirred custard. The custard is stirred continuously as it is being cooked. Stirring breaks up the gel as it is formed. When the custard reaches the desired thickness it coats a spoon evenly. Then it is poured immediately into a shallow dish placed in cold water (or ice water) so that the custard is cooled rapidly. Excessive coagulation results in curdling.

A stirred custard should have the viscosity of heavy cream and be very smooth with no suggestion of curdling. Custard is a nutritious and pleasing dessert sauce served over cakes, fruits, or various baked desserts.

Baked custard: A baked custard is made from the same recipe used for stirred custard. The stirred homogeneous mixture of custard ingredients is placed in a pan of hot water in an oven at 177°C. The water acts as an insulator to slow the rate of heat penetration to keep the outside of the custard from being over-baked before the interior is set. The baked custard should be removed from the oven when a knife inserted half-way between the edge and centre comes out clean. An over-heated baked custard becomes porous, the pores filled with watery serum.

A baked custard should be firm, yet tender, and the texture should be smooth and uniform and without porosity. When cut no syneresis should be apparent, and the colour should be uniform with no flecks of yellow or white. The filling for a custard pie is baked custard.

Cream pudding and pies: The term "cream pudding" is misleading since it is egg yolk that is added to corn starch pudding rather than cream. The preparation of these products is based on the ability of egg to bind the ingredients.

In the preparation of cream puddings and pie fillings, the starch, sugar, salt and water are boiled together until they become thick. The mixture is removed from the heat and some of it stirred carefully into beaten egg yolk. Then the yolk mixture is blended with the starch mixture and the pudding is heated over simmering water until the protein coagulates. Slow stirring is needed during this period to promote the uniform coagulation of yolk and avoid lumps.

Cream puddings and pie fillings should be smooth and feel light on the tongue, without gumminess or stickiness. When cut, the pie filling should soften slightly but not flow.

22.8.4 Egg Foam Products

Meringues: Meringues are egg white foams into which some acid and sugar are incorporated. There are two kinds of meringues soft and hard. Soft ones are used as toppings for cream pies, and hard meringues as confections in combination with fruits, ice creams or syrups.

Soft meringues are prepared by beating the egg white to the foamy stage. Then, about 25 g of sugar per egg white are added gradually and beaten until the peaks just bend over. The fine-structured meringue is spread on soft pie fillings. For maximum volume and minimum drainage, the meringue should be placed immediately on a warm filling, the edges should be carefully sealed, and then baked in a pre-heated oven. This coagulates the protein and stabilizes the foam without causing undue shrinkage.

Usually, soft meringues are baked at 177°C. A meringue is done when a pleasing medium brown colour develops on the ridges. If the meringue is under-baked, the structure is not set and results in "weeping," i.e., the foam breaks down and leaks into the surface of the filling. If over-baked the surface is tough and amber coloured droplets of syrup appear on the surface of the baked meringue. A soft meringue should be fluffy, slightly moist and tender. The surface should be fine-grained, glossy and light brown in colour.

Hard meringues contain twice as much sugar as soft ones. As a large amount of sugar delays foam formation, the first half of sugar is gradually added to form soft meringue. Then the other half is slowly added and beaten till the desired stiffness of peak is obtained. Hard meringues are baked at a lower temperature and for a longer time than the soft variety. Hard meringues should be dry, crisp and tender. They should have a delicate colour and look fluffy.

Fluffy omelettes: Fluffy omelettes are prepared by beating egg white and yolk separately and folding them together, and then baking. The egg white is beaten until the peaks just bend over. If a liquid is added it is gradually added to the white. Without delay, the beaten egg yolk is folded into beaten white until the mixture is homogeneous and cooked promptly as in the case of a plain omelette. Fluffy omelettes should be light, tender, delicately brown and cooked uniformly throughout.

Souffles: Souffles are similar to fluffy omelettes. They differ from the latter in that they contain white sauce. They may also contain other flavouring ingredients, such as grated cheese, meats, poultry, fish, pureéd vegetables, etc. In souffle preparation, yolks are added to a thick white sauce which is warm. The egg whites are beaten to form stiff peaks. Then the sauce containing the yolk is folded into the white foam until no streaks show. The mix is immediately baked in a pre-heated oven at about 175°C. Souffles should be light, tender, flavourful and pleasing brown with no layers at the bottom.

Foam cakes: The foam of egg white is important in making foam cakes like angel, chiffon and sponge cakes. Their volume and structure depend on the use of egg white foams. For the preparation of these cakes *see* Chapter 16.

22.8.5 Products based on Egg as Emulsifying Agent

Egg yolk is a good emulsifying agent. The yolk itself is an emulsion and this partly explains its outstanding emulsifying properties. Salad dressings are emulsions of oil-in-water, in which droplets of oil are suspended in an aqueous medium. This emulsion is to be stabilized in the preparation of salad dressing. Whole egg or egg yolk is frequently employed to stabilize emulsions. Various baked products, such as cheese souffles, cream puffs, and shortened cakes also rely on egg as an emulsifier.

22.8.6 Designer Eggs

"Designer eggs" are those in which the content has been modified from the standard egg.

Vitamin content: Designer eggs have been produced that contain higher concentrations of several vitamins. Two vitamins, A and E, are receiving the most interest as components of designer eggs.

Lowered cholesterol: In order for a company to claim a reduced amount of a nutrient, the product must have 25 per cent less than the normal product standards for that nutrient. A large egg contains approximately 200 - 220 mg of cholesterol.

Fat and fatty acid content: Altering the total fat content in the diet of the hen has little effect on the total fat content of the egg yolk. However, the fatty acid profile (or the ratios of the different types of fatty acids) of egg yolk lipid can easily be changed, simply by changing the type of fat used in the diet.

Different feeds, such as flaxseed (linseed), safflower oil, perilla oils, marine algae, fish, fish oil, and vegetable oil have been added to chicken feed to increase the omega-3 fatty acid content in the egg yolk. Omega-3 fatty acid-rich eggs may provide an alternative food source for enhancing consumer intake of these 'healthy' fatty acids. Evaluation of the eggs during storage indicates that the shelf life of the enriched eggs was comparable to that of typical eggs.

There are also designer eggs on the market that contain a lowered saturated to unsaturated fatty acid ratio. Canola oil is commonly used to alter the ratio of saturated to unsaturated fatty acids. Tampa Farm Services produces an egg said to contain 25% less saturated fat than regular eggs.

Mineral content: The shell contains the majority of the minerals in an egg. There are approximately 2,200 mg of calcium and 20 mg of phosphorus in the shell. There has been very little success in changing the calcium and phosphorus content of the albumen and yolk. It is possible, however, to increase the content of selenium, iodine and chromium. This has been done through dietary supplementation of the hen. These three minerals are important in human health. There has been some interest, therefore, in promoting these eggs as designer eggs.

New biotechnology is being used to develop genetically modified chickens that produce compounds that can be harvested from the eggs. These compounds include insulin for the treatment of diabetes.

22.8.7 Vegetable Egg

Oxford English Dictionary, between 1797-1888 referred to white egg shaped brinjal as vegetable egg. This is available now in the market. Indian Institute of Technology, Delhi has release on 2nd September 2019 this vegan egg from their laboratory, using protein isolation technology.

This egg is "moong" based split green gram, (*Phaseolus aureus*). The green gram has 24.0 grams protein. This vegan egg is cholesterol and gluten free and is allergy free and free from animal related diseases. Its method of cooking is similar to regular egg. It is environmental friendly. Like paneer, scrambles "*anda bhurji*", can be prepared. it is available in packages and bottles.

It needs to be further studied to know its foaming and binding qualities and whether this is a good substitute to make angel food cakes, and puffy omelettes.

Since it is a vegetable source, the biological value is similar to hatched eggs. It requires further experimental studies.

CHAPTER

23

Meat

Man has satisfied his hunger with animal food from the earliest of times. The term "meat" refers to the muscles of warm-blooded terrestrial four-legged animals, the chief ones being cattle (cow & buffalo) sheep and pigs. Meat also includes the glands and organs of these animals. Meat products include many of the by-products from animal slaughter, such as animal gut used for sausage casings, the fat from the meat used in the manufacture of lard, gelatin and others.

India produced 6.3 million tonnes of meat and ranks 5th in the world's meat production. Meat production has not received as much attention as that of milk. One of the reasons for this is the unhygienic conditions in the slaughter houses; also the population is mostly vegetarians.

India has exported 1.44 million tonnes of buffalo meat products to the world worth of ₹ 23,950 crores/2,900 million US dollars during the year 2022-23. India is the largest exporter of sheep & goat meat to the world and has exported a total of 66,949 tonnes of sheep & goat meat to the world for the worth of ₹ 749.5 crores/90.3 million US dollars during the year 2023. Major export destinations are United Arab Emirates, Qatar, and Kuwait. India exported 0.001 million tonnes of processed meat to the world for the worth of ₹ 20.6 crores/2.48 million US dollars during the year 2022-23. Major export destinations were United Arab Emirates, Qutar, Bhutan, and Maldives in 2022-23. India has exported 0.134 million tonnes of poultry products to the world for the worth of ₹ 1,516.6 crores/184.58 million US dollars during the year 2022-23. Export destinations in 2022-23 were Oman, Maldives, Indonesia, Vietnam, and United Arab Emirates.

Meat is rich in most of the nutrients required by man. This is to be expected since the tissues and body fluids of man are very similar to those of animals. Meat is rich in protein (15 to 20 per cent) and contains all the essential amino acids. It is also rich in minerals and vitamins. Phosphorus, copper and iron are present in significant amounts in meat; of particular interest is the quantity of iron and copper contained in liver. Thiamine, riboflavin and niacin occur in good amounts in all meats. The liver usually contains a useful amount of vitamin A.

23.1 Structure of Meat

Skeletal muscle is composed of long, cylindrical, multinucleated cells (fibres), varying in length from a few millimetres to several centimetres and averaging 60 μm in diameter. The fibres are arranged in a parallel fashion to form bundles, held together by connective tissues. The connective tissues merge at the terminal of the muscle to form a tendon, which in turn connects the muscle to bone.

The surface of the muscle called the "sarcolemma," is composed of three layers: an outer network of collagen fibrils, a middle amorphous layer and an inner plasma membrane. Invaginations of the plasma membrane form the transverse (T) system. The T system has the function of extending the plasma membrane into the interior of the muscle.

The semi-fluid material within the muscle cell, called the "sarcoplasm," contains soluble components, such as myoglobin, some enzymes, and some metabolic intermediates. Glycogen particles and lipid droplets also occur in some muscle cells, depending upon the state of the muscle. Sarcoplasm, in addition, contains other constituents including the contractile apparatus.

Each muscle fibre is composed of the many parallel smaller fibrils (myofibrils), constituting 60 per cent of muscle. Approximately 2,000 myofibrils, 1.0 to 3.µm in diameter, are found in an average sized fibre. The characteristic striated appearance of skeletal muscle is due to a specific repetitive arrangement of proteins in the myofibrils. When viewed under a microscope, they show alternate dark and light bands. The dark bands are termed "A (anisotropic) bands," and the light bands "I (isotropic) bands." In the centre of each of the I bands is a dark line, called the Z line. The centre of the A band called the H zone, is lighter than the rest of the A band. Usually, in the centre of the H zone there exists a darker M line. The contractile unit is called "sarcomere" and is the material located between, and including, two Z lines. The structure of skeletal muscle is shown in Fig. 23.1.

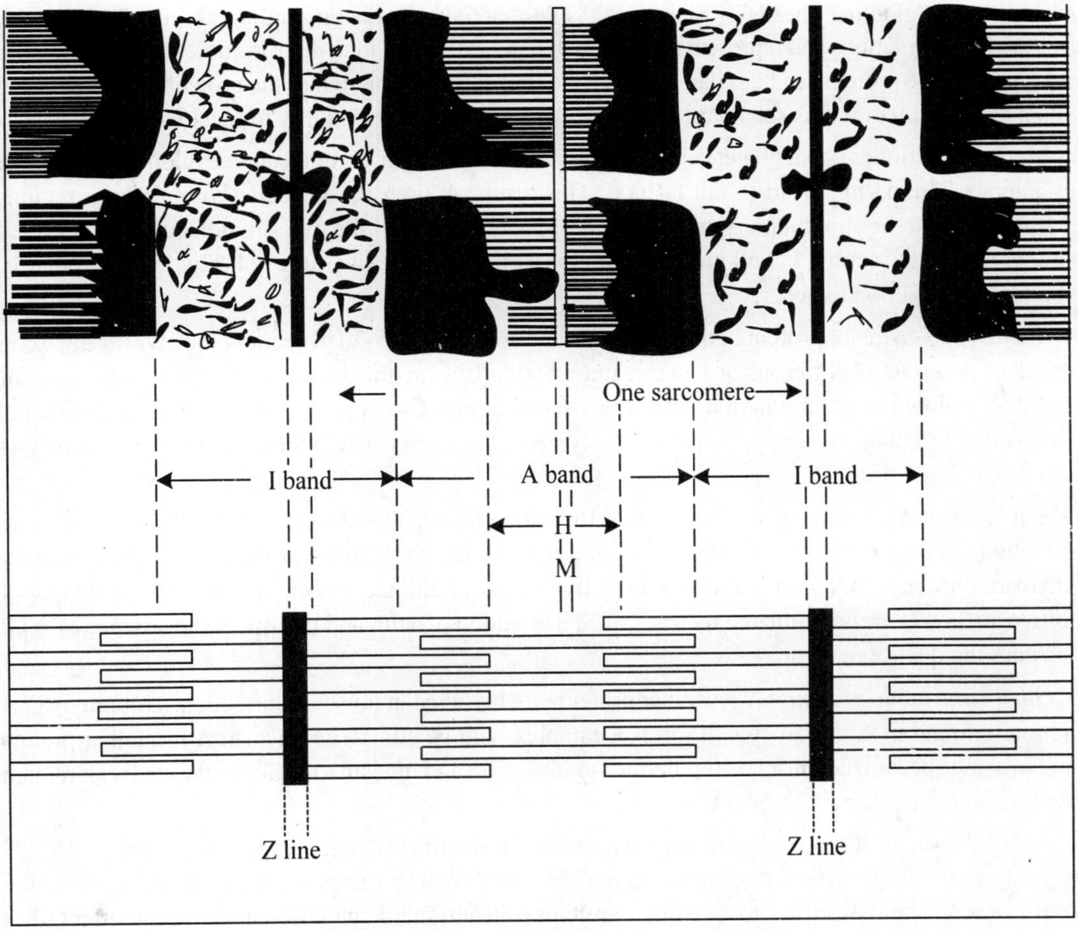

Fig. 23.1 Structure of skeletal muscle

The A band consists of thick and thin filaments, and the I band the thin filaments. The thin filaments are attached to the Z line and they extend outwards in both directions of the line. In parts of the A band, the thin filaments overlap the thick filament. The lighter zone in the A band (H zone) is the area where the thick and thin bands do not overlap, i.e., the H band consists of only thick filaments. Where the thin and thick filaments slide past each other, a contraction of the muscle occurs. During contraction, the length of the A band remains constant, while the I band and H zone both shorten.

23.2 Muscle Proteins

Muscle contains three types of proteins—contractile, soluble, and insoluble proteins. The contractile proteins are soluble in salt solutions of high concentration. The enzymes and myoglobin are soluble in water and dilute salt solutions. The insoluble fraction consists of connective tissue proteins and membrane proteins.

23.2.1 Contractile Proteins

Myosin: This is the major protein of the thick filaments. Myosin contains two heavy chains wound around each other, the carboxyl end constituting the "tail." The amino end of the heavy chain and the four light chain constitute globular "heads" which have ATPase activity and actin binding ability. The globular heads are in two fractions and represent the terminal of the extremely long myosin-molecule. The globular head region of the protein can be separated from the long tail by the action of the proteolytic enzymes on myosin and the traction thus separated retains its ATPase activity and ability to react with actin.

Myosin constitutes about 60 per cent of the myofibrils. The myosin molecules develop polarity when they interact, joining in a head-to-tail fashion. This results in myosin molecules with globular regions on either side and the straight portion in the centre. The polarities of the myosin molecules are reversed on either side of the centre, but all molecules on the same side have the same polarity. It is this polarity that allows contraction to occur.

Actin: This is a major protein of thin filaments and constitutes 15-30 per cent of the myofibrils. Actin consists of two fractions, fibrous or F actin, and globular or G actin. G actin is the monomeric form of the protein, soluble in water where it occurs as a stable dimer. Globular actin binds firmly to ATP and, in the presence of magnesium, spontaneously polymerizes to form F actin with the concurrent hydrolysis of ATP.

Actomyosin: Actin and myosin interact to form actomyosin. This interaction is responsible for muscle contraction. Actomyosin has ATPase activity but this is somewhat different from the ATPase activity of myosin. Pure myosin requires Ca^{2+} for its activity and is inhibited by Mg^{2+}. The ATPase activity of actomyosin, however, is stimulated by Mg^{2+}. The interaction of actin and myosin in the absence of ATP influences the quality of meat.

Other contractile proteins: A few other proteins are involved in muscle contraction. Tropomyosin B is a protein found in thin filaments. It forms a complex with F actin. Tropomyosin A is another protein found in some specialized muscles. It functions to lock actin and myosin together so the shell can remain closed without an expenditure of energy.

Another protein, troponin, is a component of the contractile system. Troponin-C confers calcium sensitivity to the tropomyosin-troponin-actomyosin complex, while troponin-I inhibits the contraction activity. α-actinin and β-actinin are two other proteins found in small quantities and have important roles in muscle function. These proteins are associated with filaments, α-actinin causes gelation of F actin, which is reversed by tropomyosin B. It is believed that α-actinin is also involved in the structure of the Z line. β-actinin may be associated with troponin.

Muscle contraction: The muscle is stimulated by a nervous impulse which helps the release of calcium ions from the sarcoplasmic reticulum. The released calcium interacts with the troponin-tropomyosin complex, and this results in the activation of Mg-ATP at the relaxing site of the myofibrils. The relaxing site is the inhibitory site responsible for preventing myofibrillar ATPase activity. When the inhibition is overcome, ATP is hydrolyzed by the actomyosin complex, which provides energy for systematic changes leading to muscular contraction.

When muscle contracts, the thin and thick filaments slide past each other. This helps the globular head portion of the myosin molecule to interact with actin and then pull the actin filaments parallel to the fibre axis. Maximal contraction varies from 20 to 50 per cent of the rest length of the sarcomere.

Relaxation occurs when calcium ions are removed from the sarcoplasm. This takes place through an energy-supported active transport. At reduced concentrations of calcium, myofibrils lose their capacity for the hydrolysis of ATP. Then ATP functions as a plasticizing agent, causing the separation of actin and myosin, and the sarcomeres relax to their rest length.

23.2.2 Connective Tissues

Connective tissues hold and support the muscle, through the component tendons and other tissues. They consist of various fibres, several different cell types and amorphous ground substances. The amorphous ground substances are a non-structured mixture of carbohydrates, proteins and lipids. The fibrous proteins are collagen and elastin.

Collagen: Collagen is the most abundant of all proteins in higher vertebrates-making up one-third or more of the total body proteins. It is abundant in tendons, skin, bone, the vascular system of animals, and connective tissue sheaths surrounding muscles. Collagen contributes to toughness and its partially denatured product, gelatin, is a component in many food products.

The structural unit of collagen is tropocollagen, a long cylindrical protein. It consists of three polypeptide chains wound around each other in a triple-helix (see Subsection 4.3.1). Tropocollagen molecules are linked end to end and adjacently to make collagen fibrils. The intermolecular linkages are mostly hydrogen bonds and there are some covalent linkages. The solubility of collagen decreases as intermolecular crosslinks increase.

The amino acid composition of collagen is unusual. It contains one-third glycine (distributed uniformly) and one-fourth proline and hydroxyproline. It also contains hydroxylysine. Tryptophan is absent and, from a nutritional point of view, collagen is not important.

With the increase in the age of the animal, there is an increase in the number of linkages binding the individual strands of the collagen molecule and there is also bonding between neighbouring molecules in the fibrils. The new linkages will be mostly covalent bonds. In addition to these changes, the quantity of collagen in connective tissues increases with the animal's age. These changes are responsible for the greater difficulty in the chewing of meat of older animals than those from younger ones.

Elastin: Elastin, the other principal protein found in connective tissues, consists of strands that are randomly linked and cross-linked at intervals with strong bonds. Elastin is tougher than collagen and is a constituent of the ligaments. Elastin is resistant to changes during heating; no significant changes occur in elastin when meat is cooked. However, this does not matter as the content of elastin in muscle is low.

23.3 Composition of Meat

Meat contains 15-20 per cent proteins of an outstanding nutritive value. Lean meat contains 20-22 per cent proteins. Of the total nitrogen content of meat, approximately 95 per cent is protein, and 5 per cent is smaller peptides and amino acids. The amino acid make-up of meat proteins is very good for the maintenance and growth of human tissue.

The fat content of meat varies from 5 to 40 per cent with the type, breed, feed and age of the animal. When the animal is well fed, fat deposits subcutaneously as a protective layer around the organs. Then it accumulates around and between muscles. Finally, fat penetrates between the muscle fibre bundles and this is known as "*marbling*." *Marbling* is desirable with some meats (like beef) because the amount of fat, and consequently the water holding capacity of the meat, greatly influences juiciness.

Meat fats are rich in saturated fatty acids and this likely produces certain forms of atherosclerosis. The cholesterol content of meat is about 75 mg for 100 g. The lean portion of meat contains greater proportions of phospholipids (0.5-1.0 per cent), and these are located in the membranes of the cell. The fatty acids in the lean portion of meat have a higher proportion of unsaturated fatty acids than tissue fats.

Carbohydrates are found only in very small quantities in meat. Two carbohydrates found in meat are glycogen and glucose.

Meat is an excellent source of some of the vitamins of the B complex and a good source of iron and phosphorus. Meat also contains sodium and potassium. The vitamins and minerals are found in the lean portion of the meat. The approximate composition of meat is given in Table 23.1.

Meat contains the protein hydrolyzing enzymes, cathepsins, and these are responsible for the increased tenderness of meat during ageing.

The colour of meat is due primarily to myoglobin. Variations in colour of meat depend upon the chemical state of myoglobin. Meats cured with nitrates remain pink as nitric oxide myoglobin is stable. Haemoglobin also contributes to the colour of the meat to some extent.

23.4 Post-mortem Changes in Meat

Muscle is a highly specialized tissue; it converts chemical energy to mechanical energy. Muscle requires a large outlay of energy for the contractile apparatus and this energy is derived from ATP. For long-term activity, ATP is derived by the oxidation of carbohydrates and lipids. When muscle is under heavy stress and the oxygen available not sufficient, the anaerobic glycolysis system becomes predominant. In glycolysis, glycogen is converted into pyruvate and this is then reduced to lactate. Under usual conditions, lactate enters the liver, where it is converted into glucose. The glucose is then carried back to the muscle, where eventually glycogen is resynthesized.

Table 23.1 Composition of meat of different animals per 100 g of edible portion

Name of flesh foods	Moisture (g)	Protein (g)	Fat (g)	Minerals (g)	Energy (Kcal)
Beef *Bos taurus*	74.3	22.6	2.6	1.0	114
Mutton muscle	71.5	18.5	13.3	1.3	194
Pork muscle *Sus cristatus Wagner*	77.4	18.7	4.4	1.0	114

Source : Nutritive Value of Indian Foods (NIN), ICMR, Hyderabad, India, 1984.

When the animal dies, the circulatory system ceases to work resulting in lack of oxygen. Due to glycolysis in post morterm muscle, there is an accumulation of certain waste products, especially lactic acid. Also, the ATP concentration decreases and is lost in 24 hours or less.

The increase in lactic acid concentration results in a decrease in the pH of post-mortem muscle. Also, in the absence of ATP, there is a formation of permanent links between actin and myosin, i.e., the actin and myosin bridges remain permanently fixed. The muscle passes into a state known as rigor mortis (stiffness of death). These post-mortem effects bring about changes in the quality attributes of meat, such as texture and water-holding capacity, colour and flavour. Nutritional quality, however, is not much affected.

23.4.1 Ageing of Meat

If the meat is held cold for some time after it has gone into *rigor mortis*, the muscle again becomes soft and pliable with improved flavour and juiciness (resolution of rigor). Some changes take place during this period, known as ageing or ripening. During ageing, there is progressive tenderization of meat owing to the denaturation of the muscle proteins and mild hydrolysis of denatured proteins by the intracellular proteolytic enzymes, the cathepsins. The enzymes slowly break down the connective tissues between muscle fibres as well as the muscle fibres themselves.

Ageing or ripening is done by holding meat at a temperature of 0.5° – 2°C in a cold room. Ageing may take 1 to 4 weeks. The best flavour and the greatest tenderness develop in meat aged from 2 to 4 weeks. During ageing, the humidity of the cold room is to be controlled and meat may be covered with wrapping to minimize drying and weight loss. The ageing of meat may also be affected by holding it at a higher temperature for a shorter time, usually 20°C for 48 hours. Ageing with even higher temperatures for less time is practised commercially. In such cases, ultraviolet light is used to keep down surface bacterial growth.

Beef is usually the only kind of meat that is commercially aged. Lamb and mutton are occasionally aged. Pork is never aged because of its high-fat content.

23.5 Tenderizing Meat

Tenderness is the most desired quality in meat. The amount and distribution of connective tissues and the size of both muscle fibres and bundles of fibres determine the tenderness of the meat. As already stated, the number and strength of cross-linkages between the peptide chains of collagen increase with the age of the animal, and this decreases the amount of collagen that may be solubilized during cooking thus contributing to decreased tenderness.

Cold room storage results in the natural ripening of meat with tenderizing from the meat's natural enzymes. There are several artificial methods of increasing the tenderness of meat to various extents. These include mechanical methods, the use of enzymes and salts.

The mechanical methods of tenderizing meat include pounding, cutting, grinding, needling or pinning, and the use of ultrasonic vibrations. Mechanical methods cut or break the muscle fibres and connective tissues. The pounding process breaks and tears only surface meat fibres and connective tissues. Grinding breaks and cuts all the muscle fibres and connective tissues and increases tenderness in meat. Insertion of needle-like blades into the meat increases the tenderness of certain meat cuts. Ultrasonic vibrations break the meat fibres.

The art of using enzymes for tenderizing meat is an old one. Wrapping of meat in papaya leaves before cooking results in tenderization. This is the result of the action of the enzyme papain on meat proteins. This enzyme is presently commercially available and is used extensively in meat tenderization. Other enzymes used for meat tenderization are bromelain from pineapple, ficin from figs, trypsin from the pancreas, and fungal enzymes. These proteolytic enzymes catalyze the hydrolysis of one or more meat proteins. The extent to which different proteins are hydrolyzed varies to some extent. The enzymes also hydrolyze the elastin of the connective tissues.

The effectiveness of an enzyme as a tenderizer depends upon how it is used. Commercial papain sprinkled on the surface of meat penetrates to a depth of 1 mm per hour. Penetration is improved by punching the papain treated surface. This, however, does not result in the uniform distribution of the enzyme throughout the meat. To achieve uniform tenderness, papain is injected into the veins of animals some 10 minutes before their slaughter. This results in the uniform distribution of the enzyme throughout the body of the animal by the circulating system, resulting in the increased tenderness of cooking meat. Freeze-drying meat and rehydrating it in water containing proteolytic enzymes is effective in tenderizing meat.

Tenderizing enzymes remain inactive until the meat is heated. Papain, for example, becomes active when the meat is heated to 55°C and acts on the proteins during the cooking operation until the meat temperature reaches about 82°C. Therefore, enzymes are ineffective with roasts unless the injection method has been used. Over tenderization by enzymes is not good as it changes the texture of meat and results in the loss of flavour and juiciness.

Meat may be tenderized by the use of low levels of salts. Salt increases the water holding capacity of the muscle fibres resulting in tenderness and juiciness. Salt also solubilizes the meat proteins. The tenderness of meat is improved when freeze-dried meat is rehydrated in a weak salt solution instead of water. Salts used for tenderization are sodium chloride, sodium bicarbonate, and sodium or potassium phosphate.

Another method of increasing tenderness in meat is by change of pH. Decreasing or increasing the pH of meat increases hydration and its tenderness. Soaking beef for 48 hours in concentrated vinegar increases its tenderness and juiciness.

23.6 Curing of Meat

The prime object of ageing or ripening and use of tenderizers is to increase the tenderness of meat. The curing of meat has additional objectives. Curing brings about the modification of meat that affects preservation, flavour, colour and tenderness, due to added curing agents.

Originally, curing was practised as a means of preservation before the days of refrigeration. In less developed countries, curing is still an important method of preservation. When modern methods of preservation are available, the prime purpose of curing is to produce uniquely flavoured meat products and another special purpose is to preserve the red colour of meat. Thus, cured beef (corned beef) and cured pork (ham) remain red on cooking, while in the uncured condition they become brown.

The ingredients used for curing are common salt, sodium nitrate or nitrite, sugar and spices. Salt retards microbial growth and gives flavour to the meat. Nitrite fixes the red colour of myoglobin. Nitrite has also a beneficial effect on the flavour of cured meats and an inhibitory effect on *Clostridium botulinum*. Sugar helps stabilize colour, counteract saltiness, and also adds flavour. Spices are added mainly for flavour.

During the curing process, the curing mixture may be rubbed dry on the surface of a cut of meat or the meat may be immersed in a solution of the curing agent (pickling). These processes of curing are slow when the meat cut is large. The curing ingredients may be much more rapidly and uniformly distributed throughout the meat by pumping the solution via an artery if it is intact or the cure may be injected with multiple needles into the cut of meat.

During curing by salts, the high osmotic pressure of the external fluid initially draws water and soluble proteins out of the meat. Later, salt diffuses into the meat and binds to the proteins, causing some expelled protein to diffuse back in. This causes a swelling of the meat. The salt-protein complex that forms binds water well.

Curing has also some detrimental effects during storage. The pink colour of nitrite cured meat changes to brown, in the presence of oxygen. Thus, cured meat should preferentially be packed in containers from which oxygen has been excluded. The salts of cured meat enhance oxidation of the lipid components and thus reduce shelf life. Also, there is some concern about the carcinogenic effect of nitrite, particularly when cured meat is heated to a high temperature (also see Subsection 29.5).

Smoking: A cured meat may be dried and smoked. Smoking also was originally used as a method of preservation, but today smoking is used mostly for its flavour contribution and coagulation of proteins. Ham is frequently processed by smoking. The sawdust from hardwoods is used as a fuel for smoking. Slow smoking is preferable since the extended period enables more drying to occur on the surface. Drying is responsible for much of the preservative action of smoking. The smoke contains compounds having antiseptic properties which destroy the micro-organisms present in meat. Smoking also prevents the development of rancidity in meat.

23.7 Classes of Meat

23.7.1 Beef

Various terms are used to designate meat from different types of cattle. Veal is the meat from cattle slaughtered 3 to 4 weeks after birth. The carcass of 14 to 52 weeks cattle is classified as a calf. Beef is the term applied to meat of cattle over one year old. The beef carcass is classified according to the sex, age and sexual conditions of the animals as follows:

Steer : A bovine male animal castrated at a very young age.

Heifer : A female bovine animal that has not borne a calf.

Cow : A female bovine animal that has borne a calf.

Stag : A male bovine animal that is castrated after maturing.

Calf : A male or female bovine animal up to 12 months of age, generally from 3 to 8 months of age.

The quality of meat from steer and heifer is the same if the animals are of the same grade. The quality of meat from cow and bull depends upon maturity but is generally inferior to that of steer and heifer. The quality of meat from stag varies depending upon the age at which the animal is castrated.

23.7.2 Buffalo Meat

Buffalo meat in India have a positive opening for export as these are reared without the use of hormones, antibiotics and other chemicals but on green pastures. Buffalo meat is lean, low in fat. Halal method is used for slaughtering. There is an increase in the export market for buffalo meat since 2006-2010. India produced 4.35 million tonnes in 2022.

23.7.3 Mutton

Sheep carcasses are classified under three main classes, based largely on the age of the animal.

Lamb: The flesh of young ovine animals of both sexes whose age is twelve months or under. Lamb carcasses, as a group, are distinguished from mutton carcasses by their smaller and lighter bones, lighter coloured flesh, and softer and whiter external and internal fats. The usual test for lamb carcass is the "break joint" of the foreleg. When the feet are broken off sharply from the leg above the regular joint, the break shows four distinct ridges that appear smooth, moist, and red with blood.

Yearling mutton: Carcasses of young sheep usually from 12 to about 20 months old are termed "yearling" mutton. Such carcasses are distinguished from lamb carcasses by harder and whiter bones, darker and somewhat coarser flesh, and thicker external and internal fat. The break joint of the foreleg usually breaks in ridges similar in shape to a lamb joint but the surface is rough, porous, dry, and lacks redness.

Mature mutton: This is the flesh of both the males (castrated and uncastrated) and females of the ovine species that are 20 months in age at the time of slaughter. The colour of the mature mutton ranges from light to dark red. The break joint fails to break due to the hardening and ossification of bones. Mutton has a strong characteristic flavour different from the delicate flavour of lamb. With proper preparation, however, either lamb or mutton will be acceptable to most people.

23.7.4 Pork

Pork is the meat of swine. Good quality pork is obtained from animals between the ages of 3 to 12 months before the amount of fat becomes excessive. Pork is not differentiated according to the age and size of a pig. Generally, pork has more fat than other meats. Because of this, pork is a tender cut of meat. The colour of young lean pork is highly pink and changes to rose as the animal matures. Bacon is the cut from the belly portion of hog carcass and has a high percentage of fat.

Pork obtained from animals fed on uncooked garbage may contain the hazardous organism, *Trichinella spiralis*, a worm that causes "trichimosis" in man. The organism is destroyed by smoking or cooking to an internal temperature of 58°C. Freezing to –5°C for 20 days or –28°C for 6 days (if the diameter is about 15 cm) also destroys the organism.

23.7.5 Organ Meats

These include liver, kidney, heart, sweetbread (thymus and pancreas), brain, lung, tripe (first and second stomach of the ruminants), head and tail of the animal. From the point of view of the economy, variety and nutritive value, these organ meats are less expensive and more nutritive. Some of these are tender, while others are less tender, and therefore their cooking methods vary according to tenderness.

23.7.6 Sausages

These are made of ground or minced meat. Mostly cured meat and, to a lesser extent, uncured meat are used for this purpose. There are hundreds of varieties of sausages marketed under different classes depending upon whether the ground meat is fresh or cured, and whether the sausage is cooked or uncooked, smoked or unsmoked, and dried or not during manufacture. The cooked and smoked sausages are known as table-ready-meats.

Sausages are enclosed in casings. Normal casings are made from animal intestines. As natural casings are expensive, non-uniform artificial casings made of film plastic are used now.

23.8 Cuts and Grades of Meat

Meat carcasses are commonly divided into relatively larger wholesale cuts, and these are further divided into smaller retail cuts. Distinguishing features of a cut of meat are the size, shape and location of bone, the size and shape of muscle found in the cut, and the amount and distribution of fat. The skeletal structure of beef, veal, lamb and pork is basically the same, and therefore cuts from analogous parts of different animals are similar. The carcasses of beef, being bigger in size, are cut into more number of wholesale cuts than those of other animals.

The commonly used meat in India is lamb mutton; about 70 per cent of all meat used comes from sheep and goat. The wholesale cuts of lamb are legs, loin, racks, breasts, shanks and shoulders. These cuts are related to the bones with which they are associated. Each of the wholesale cuts is further cut into retail cuts, such as chops (different types of legs), roasts, neck slices, etc. The retail cuts of other animals are similar to those of lamb.

Meat that is sold in the market must be wholesome and fit for human consumption. The Indian Standards Institution has laid down specifications to ensure this. According to this, the animals from which meat is obtained should be healthy and slaughtered in a hygienically managed slaughter house. The slaughter should be supervised by a competent authority. The animals and the carcasses thereof should be subjected to ante-mortem and post-mortem examination according to prescribed methods. The carcasses and cuts thereof should be certified as being sound and free from contagious and infectious diseases and fit for human consumption.

Apart from inspection for wholesomeness, in many countries, meats are graded for quality. Standards have been established for such grading. Two major factors used to evaluate the quality or palatability of meat are maturity and marbling. The maturity of an animal affects the texture, firmness and colour of the meat. Fine structural lean meat is usually slightly more tender than the one with a coarse texture that contributes to decreased tenderness. The tenderness of the meat of a very young animal increases as it matures to an optimum age. Marbling, which refers to the amount and distribution of fat appearing as white flecks within the lean, is an important index of quality. However, the marbling requirements now considered for good grades of meat are not as high as in previous standards, as there are no measurable differences in the eating qualities of meat with minimum marbling and those with good marbling. The quantity, consistency and character of juices, or extractives contained in muscle fibre, also contribute to the quality of meat.

Good quality lamb and mutton have a smooth covering of clear white brittle fat over most of the exterior. The lean is pinkish-red in colour in lamb and deeper red in mutton. The texture of the lean is fine-grained and velvety in appearance. The bones are porous and reddish in colour in lamb, and they are hard and white in mutton. Poor quality meats have darker flesh and the grain is coarse and fibrous. The fat layers are heavy and have a strong flavour. The quality of beef, veal and pork is determined by considerations similar to those of lamb. The grading according to ISI for lamb and beef is as follows:

Table 23.2 Grading of Lamb and Mutton and Beef

Lamb and Mutton	**Beef**
Prime	Prime
Choice	Choice
Good	Good
Commercial	Commercial
Utility	Utility
Cull	Cutter and Canner

23.9 Cooking of Meats

Cooking can make meat more tender or less tender than the original raw cut. When meat is cooked, three types of changes contribute to increased tenderness. They are the melting of fat, dissolution of collagen in hot liquids to become soft gelatin, and tissue softening and muscle fibre separation. There are also toughening influences of heating. Over-heating can cause muscle fibres to contract and meat to shrink and become tougher; evaporation of moisture occurs and dried out tissues become tougher.

There are two methods of cooking meat: dry heat and moist heat methods. Selection of the method to use for a meat cut depends upon whether it is a tender or less tender cut. Less tender cuts become more tender when prepared by moist heat methods since this provides a means for the conversion of collagen to gelatin. Moist heat methods of cooking include braising, stewing (cooking in simmering water), and pressure cooking. Tender cuts do not require the conversion of connective tissue. Then, they are cooked by dry heat methods, which include roasting, broiling, pan broiling and frying.

For any method of cooking, an appropriate cooking temperature must be chosen. Generally, a lower cooking temperature for a longer period of time is better than a higher temperature for short periods of time for any degree of doneness. This results in decreased drip loss, less shrinkage, increased juiciness, and more uniform colour throughout the cut.

Testing for doneness is an important aspect in meat cookery. This is tested by the use of a meat thermometer. The recommended temperature in the centre of cut for rare, medium and well done stages for lamb is 77°C, 79°C and 82°C respectively and for beef 60°C, 71°C and 77°C. Fresh pork is to be heated to well done stage (77°C) to destroy *Trichinella spiralis*. Moist heat methods will produce well done meats in every instance. It is not necessary to use a thermometer when employing moist heat cookery methods.

23.9.1 Dry Heat Methods

Tender cuts of beef, lamb and pork may be cooked by these methods. The use of dry heat permits the selection of the desired final interior temperature of meat.

Roasting: Roasting is one of the simplest and most commonly used methods of cooking meat. The meat is placed uncovered on a rack in a shallow pan to keep the meat out of drippings. A meat thermometer is inserted into the thickest part of the meat, taking care to see that it does not touch bones or fat. The roasting pan is placed in the centre of the oven and an oven temperature of 163°C is maintained till the desired internal temperature is indicated on the meat thermometer. This ensures the adequate browning of the meat for good flavour and good appearance. For small roasts, an oven temperature of 177°C is used. Roasts continue to cook at the centre even after they are removed from the oven. This is because heat is transmitted into the interior from the outer surface. Charts for the cooking times of various cuts of different meats are available.

It should be noted that no covering of any type is used when meat is being roasted. If a cover is placed on the roasting pan, the steam from the roasting meat is trapped inside the container and the meat cookery method becomes moist heat cookery.

Broiling: Broiling consists of cooking meat by direct radiant heat, such as the open fire of a gas flame, live coals or electric oven. In open fire or coal broiling heat comes from below, whereas in oven broiling, the heat comes from above. Broiling is applied to tender cuts that are at least 2.5 cm thick. Thinner cuts will be too dry if broiled.

To broil, meat is placed on a rack and the rack is adjusted in such a way that the top of the meat is some 5 to 10 cm from the source of heat. Shorter distances are used for thinner cuts of meat. A tray should be placed beneath the meat rack to collect the melted fat. Broiling is carried out at a temperature of 176°C until the topside is brown. At this stage, the meat is approximately half done. The broiled side is salted and turned and broiled on the other side.

Broiling is a faster method of cooking meat by dry heat than roasting. But roasting produces more juicy and tender meats than broiled meats. However, meats with unusual flavour can be obtained by broiling. by marinating meats in some types of salad dressings or juices an hour before broiling. This treatment also permits some hydrolysis of protein to occur and thus produces a small increase in tenderness.

Pan broiling: In pan broiling, heat is transferred to meat primarily by conduction from the pan or griddle. Meat is placed in a cold griddle and heated so that meat cooks slowly. Any fat that accumulates in the pan is removed so that the meat will continue to pan broil rather than pan fry. Pan broiling is the preferred method of cooking thin cuts of meats because the equipment required for cooking is simpler. A low temperature is sufficient to brown the meat. Pan broiled meat should be turned occasionally to ensure uniform heat penetration.

Frying: This is a useful method for cooking tender cuts of meat that are thin (about 1–1.5 cm thick). There are two methods of frying: pan frying and deep-fat frying. In panfrying, a small amount of fat is added to the frying pan so that the melted fat is about 0.5 cm deep. In deep-fat frying, the melted fat will be deep enough to cover the meat.

In panfrying, as with pan broiling, it may be necessary to turn meat occasionally to develop an even colour on the meat, but turning should be kept to a minimum. The temperature is to be controlled such that the meat does not develop a burned flavour and dryness. With high temperatures, fat decomposes to acrolein, which impairs the flavour of meat. With thin cuts and properly controlled temperature, the interior of the meat will be well done before the exterior becomes too brown.

In deep-fat frying also the control of temperature is very important. Too high a temperature not only causes the fat to smoke but also the meat to be underdone in the middle when the outside is a pleasing colour. If the temperature is too low, it will lengthen the frying time and result in a greasier product. A well prepared deep-fried product will have a pleasing brown exterior, done in the centre as well.

23.9.2 Moist Heat Methods

Moist heat method is used for less tender cuts of meat. The combination of moisture, heat and a long period of cooking causes meat to become tender owing to the conversion of connective tissue to gelatin. If a flavourable liquid is added, in this method of cooking, the flavour of meat also will be enhanced.

Braising: In this method of cooking, the meat is first carefully browned on all sides by broiling, pan broiling or frying. Then a small amount of water is usually added to the browned meat and the pan used for cooking is covered with a tight fitting lid and cooked with low heat until the meat becomes tender.

It is not necessary to add water in braising because steam from the water in the meat itself can provide the moisture needed for changes that take place in meat during braising. Water, when added, should be kept to a minimum. The cooking liquid from the braised meat is very flavourful and can be used for making gravy or sauce. Although water is commonly used as liquid, tomatoes and fruit juices may be added as liquids. The juices not only furnish liquid for softening the collagen but also afford a variety of flavours and may hydrolyze protein because of their acidity.

Stewing: Large pieces of tough cuts are cooked in water until tender. Meats that are to be stewed may be browned, if desired, or simmered in water with no preliminary browning at all. The meat is placed in a kettle or vessel with sufficient water to cover the meat. The vessel is then covered and heated so that the water simmers. The cooking is continued until the meat is tender.

Pressure cooking: Braising and simmering of meat takes a long time for cooking. In pressure cooking, a relatively short cooking time is required as cooking is done in steam at a temperature higher than that of boiling water. Pressure cooking brings about the same changes in meat as in other methods of cooking with moist heat. However, pressure cooked meats are less juicy and cooking losses are great.

Cooking frozen meat: Frozen meats may be cooked by the usual cooking methods either in the frozen condition or after thawing. Frozen meats take about one-and-a-half times more time to cook than unfrozen cuts of the same, size and shape. Frozen meat may be thawed in a refrigerator at room temperature or in running water. Refrigerator thawing is recommended as it results in uniform thawing and the best appearance of the meat. There are no differences in the tenderness, juiciness and flavour associated with cooking frozen or thawed cuts of meat.

23.10 Changes Produced during Meat Cooking

A number of changes take place during the cooking of meat. Heat destroys the micro-organisms that may have contaminated meat. It also brings about changes in colour, flavour and tenderness owing to changes taking place in meat fibre and connective tissue. At high temperatures, there is a considerable shrinkage of meat, toughening of protein and loss of juiciness.

Cooking brings about changes in the colour of the meat. When fresh meat is cooked, its protein pigments are denatured. Denaturation of the proteins causes a rapid release of the haem pigments from the globin part of the molecule, and the free haem is very sensitive to oxidation. On heating, therefore, red meat generally turns brown due to the oxidized pigments. However, the extent of denaturation depends upon the temperature to which meat has been cooked. The changes in the colour of the pigment in meat, when heated, are used as an index of doneness. Meat cooked to rare condition has less of oxymyoglobin denatured and is more red. Well done meat is more denatured and more brown. However, meats cured with nitrite remain red throughout cooking.

Heat treatment brings about the denaturation of most other proteins. Thus, the enzymes present in meat are inactivated. Myosin and actin are also enzymes and their inactivation brings about textural changes since the contractile proteins become tougher. However, very often this is counteracted by the concomitant conversion of the collagen of the connective tissues to gelatin. This is the reason why tough cuts of meat are cooked for a long time in the presence of water.

Ideal cooking methods for meat should minimize the hardening of contractile proteins and maximize the softening of the connective tissues. Cooking temperature and time should be adjusted so that the tenderizing effects due to the conversion of collagen to gelatin is not offset by the increasing toughness owing to an excessive coagulation of contractile proteins.

Many components of meats are responsible for its flavour. With heating, several of the components undergo changes. Proteins and free amino acids of meat, on heating, produce some volatile breakdown products. These include sulphur-containing compounds, aldehydes, ketones, alcohols, amines and others. Lipid components also break down into various volatile compounds. These volatile compounds in both the fat and lean portions of the meat, contribute to the flavour and odour of cooked meats.

During heating, meat fat melts, adipose tissue cells are ruptured, and there is a redistribution of fat. Some fat is dispersed finely in locations where collagen has been hydrolyzed. When meat is eaten warm, the melted fat serves to increase the palatability of the product by giving a desirable mouthfeel.

Meat contains a high percentage of water. Only a small percentage of this water is bound very closely to the protein of muscle tissue and the rest exists as free molecules within the muscle fibres and connective tissues. Heating reduces the water holding power of meat. The water holding capacity of meat, among other things, is related to its juiciness. The loss of water on cooking does not bring about changes in the nutritive value of proteins, and done stages are juicier than well done meats.

The nutritional value of cooked meat generally remains high. Normal cooking does not bring about changes in the nutritive value of proteins, and minerals are not lost by heat. Some minerals may be lost in meat drippings but, on the other hand, cooking dissolves some calcium from bone and so enriches the meat in this mineral. There is loss of some B vitamins during cooking. But most of the cooked meat retains more than 50 per cent of the B vitamins present in the uncooked meats.

23.11 Meat Substitutes

Meat is an important component of the food of the population of advanced countries and is the major supplier of their protein requirements. Proteins derived from meat are more expensive than vegetable proteins. In some cases, as much as ten times more vegetable protein can be obtained from farm produce than from animals that feed on them. A country with a dense population and limited amount of available land for farming cannot afford to feed animals food that is good for human consumption. Where the food supply is limited, human beings must gather their requirements of proteins and other nutrients from plants instead of allowing animals to do this for them. This necessitates the substitution of vegetable proteins for meat proteins.

The fat content of meat is high. High consumption of meat can lead to health problems, including the hazards of heart attack. Further, in many societies, there are religious beliefs of various types which forbid the use of any meat or certain types of meat. These and the limited supply of food for the world have added considerable impetus to the development of vegetable protein products.

Proteins of animals origin are of high nutritive value while those of vegetable origin are of poor quality because they lack one or more of the essential amino acids either in quantity or they are present in unfavourable proportions. However, the quality of vegetable protein may be improved if the limiting amino acids are supplemented. This can be achieved by a proper mixture of different vegetable proteins or the addition of synthetic amino acids.

The most important and abundant sources of proteins of vegetable origin are the low-fat oilseed cakes of groundnut, coconut, soya bean, cottonseed, etc. In developing countries where protein-calorie malnutrition exists, oilseed protein can help solve this problem. In India, oilseeds can provide more proteins than what is now available through animal products, such as milk, meat, eggs and fish. These proteins, with proper additives—particularly colour and flavour additives—can give products closely resembling the animal products. In addition to seed protein, leaf and yeast proteins can successfully substitute meat proteins for human consumption.

Amongst the vegetable proteins, the one that has been commercially exploited to replace meat is soya bean protein. Soya bean has a high protein content. If all the oil and most of the soluble carbohydrates are removed from soya bean, a protein content of nearly 70 per cent can be obtained, and this can be processed as a meat substitute. The defatted flour is blended with water, vitamins, flavour, and colour, and cooked. The dough is extruded at an elevated temperature and pressure and finally forced through a suitable die when the expansion of the product takes place due to a sudden release of pressure. Extrusion is used in the manufacture of granules which are marketed as textured vegetable proteins (TVP).

Textured vegetable proteins contain more protein than the meats themselves. Therefore, TVP is used as a meat extender. Because of its low cost and high nutritive value, the use of TVP as an extender in ground meat products up to 30 per cent is permitted in the US school lunch programme. TVP must be rehydrated with water before use. After rehydration, it can be used in the preparation of a variety of vegetarian and non-vegetarian dishes. Textured vegetable proteins and other vegetable protein foods are now manufactured in the country.

23.12 Gelatin

When collagen is heated, some intermolecular and a few main-chain peptide bonds are hydrolyzed. This results in the conversion of the triple helical structure of collagen to a more amorphous form known as gelatin. Thus, gelatin is a partially degraded collagen. If the collagen molecule is completely unstructured, glue, instead of gelatin, is produced.

Gelatin is prepared from the collagen of connective tissues and bones of animals. The bones are first demineralized to remove calcium and phosphorus by soaking in acid. The demineralized bone (ossein) is then hydrolyzed with alkali or acid. The commonly used method is alkaline hydrolysis with lime. About 1,500 tonnes per annum of gelatin is prepared this way in the country.

Gelatin forms a gel in water even at a concentration of one per cent. Gel formation is due to the property of large molecules to form colloidal dispersions (sols) which, in some cases, become viscous, leading to rigidity when cooled. The gel formation is due to a partial renaturation of the collagen molecule ("collagen fold"). Those parts of collagen that are rich in proline and hydroxyproline regain some of their structure, following which they can interact. When many molecules are involved, a three-dimensional structure is produced which is responsible for the gel at low temperatures. When once a gel is formed it can, without liquifying, stand a temperature higher than that required for its formation. Usually, the rigidity of a gel increases on further cooling or, sometimes, on standing. On continued standing, the gel loses water and shrinks in the syneresis process. A gelatin gel, when re-melted, sets into a gel faster than it does the first time

Different grades of gelatin and modified gelatins are used in various industries. Gelatin used for edible purposes should be pure and conform to the statutory laws laid down by the country of its use. Gelatin, with its multiplicity of properties, finds use in the commercial manufacture of food products, such as canned foods, semi-preserves, confectionery, salt products, marshmallows, Ice cream, and gelatin desserts. In its simple form, gelatin is used in the form of jellies such as jelled desserts, sponges, cream salads, etc. In our country, due to the practice of vegetarianism, gelatin is not as much used as food as in other countries. Gelatin, moreover, is a protein of low biological value as it is deficient in essential amino acids, such as tryptophan, threonine, methionine and isoleucine.

23.12.1 Gel Formation

Preparation of gelatin gel is a two-step process requiring complete dispersion of the gelatin to form a sol and chilling it to form the desired gel. Gelatin is first soaked in three to four volumes of cold water for a short time. To the soaked gelatin, hot water or the desired liquid is added in small portions, with good stirring after each addition of liquid, till a final temperature of 35°C is reached. When once all the gelatin is dispersed, on cooling to room temperature, gelatin sets into a gel. Rapid gelation by cooling in ice should be avoided as it does not give a uniformly set gel and may lose its structure when removed to room temperature. A good gelatin product will be clear, will hold its shape when cut and yet be tender. There will be no rubbery areas or small gelatinous particles in the gel.

A number of factors influence gel formation and the rigidity of the gel. They are the concentration of gelatin, temperature, molecular weight of gelatin, added substances, and the pH in certain ranges. The concentration of gelatin affects not only the firmness of the gel but also the rate of setting time. Generally, a gel of good texture is obtained with 1.5 to 2.0 per cent gelatin. If the molecular weight of gelatin is low, the rigidity of the gel is poor. Beating or mechanical stirring reduces the rigidity of the gel. The temperature has a marked effect on gelation; low temperature increases the rigidity of the gel. pH variations that are not far removed from the isoelectric pH of gelatin have very little effect on gelation. Higher acidity (due to the use of vinegar and lemon juice), however, decreases the gel forming ability of gelatin. In such cases, a higher proportion of gelatin will help give a gel of good texture. The influence of salts on rigidity is not considerable. Sugar influences the setting time as well as the gel strength. A very small amount of sugar increases the setting time of a gel, but a higher concentration of sugar decreases the setting time.

Gelatin preparations: Gelatin preparations, such as jellied fruits and vegetables, sponges and creams are very popular. If fruits and vegetables are to be combined with gelatin, the gelatin dispersion should be allowed to cool until it is ready to form a gel. Then vegetables or fruits, fresh, frozen or canned, may be added and allowed to cool further. Raw pineapple should not be used with gelatin. The enzyme bromelain present in pineapple hydrolyzes gelatin and prevents it from setting into a gel.

Gelatin forms stable foams. When gelatin is dispersed in some liquids at room temperature, the product could be whipped into a foam. On cooling, the gelatin will set in the foam and such foams are stable and firm as long as they are chilled, but the stability is lost at room temperature.

CHAPTER

24 Poultry

The term "poultry" refers to domestic fowl reared for their flesh, eggs or feathers and includes chickens, ducks, geese, turkeys, guineas, and pigeons. Of these, chicken and turkey are most commonly used for their meat.

24.1 *Desi* Birds

The present-day breeds of chicken found all over the world have descended from the jungle fowl of the Himalayan, Central and Southern parts of India. The sport of cock-fighting which was very common in India and some other Asian countries was mainly responsible for the domestication of wild birds. From these parts the domestic fowl gradually spread to other parts of Asia, and from there to other parts of the world. The turkey is considered to be of American origin.

Breeding poultry as a profession came into existence about three centuries ago but its development as an important industry all over the world has been for just about 100 years. Despite of the long tradition of poultry-keeping in India, very little was done through the centuries for the development of the industry. In our country, for several years, poultry meat was met by utilizing spent hens (after laying) and cocks that were culled from poultry groups from time to time. There was no proper poultry farming. However, during the past few decades, poultry development work has been taken up in an organized way and developed into a small-scale industry.

Till the poultry development work took place, the Indian varieties of birds were the "*desi*" breeds. They are not good from the point of egg and meat production. Their egg production is only about 53 eggs compared to the world average production of 120 eggs per hen per annum. Though their meat content is less, it is delicious. The *desi* birds have been improved.

Many imported breeds have been bred and acclimatized to India. Chief among them are the White Leghorn, New Hampshire and Rhode Island Red. Several other breeds have also been successfully introduced into the country.

These developments have resulted in a large number of poultry farms and an increase in poultry meat production. As a result of this, India has become a major global leader in poultry production. With an annual growth rate of 8 per cent in broiler production, it grew to 4.47 million tonnes in 2020. Our percent capita consumption in 2020 of poultry meat was 2,500 gins.

Table 24.1 Top 5 States in terms of poultry population

S.No.	State	Poultry Population (in million)
1.	Andhra Pradesh	161.33
2.	Tamil Nadu	117.35
3.	Maharashtra	77.79
4.	Karnataka	53.44
5.	West Bengal	52.84
6.	All others	266.45
	Total	**729.21**

24.2 Classification

Chicken are classified into different types depending on the fowl's ability to produce a product of commercial value, such as egg type, meat type, dual-purpose type, and miscellaneous type. Meat types are generally large in size with plenty of flesh but they are not good layers. The meat is tender. The dual-purpose type also yields meat of excellent quality alongside a good number of eggs.

Each kind of poultry marketed is classified based on age. Age influences tenderness and fat content, and this determines the cooking method. The classification according to Indian standards is as follows.

Broiler or Fryer: Chicken of 8 to 10 weeks of age of either sex, tender-meated with soft, pliable, is smooth-textured skin and flexible breastbone cartilage.

Rooster: A young chicken, usually 3 to 5 months of age, of either sex, tender-meated with soft, pliable, smooth-textured skin and breastbone cartilage that may be somewhat less flexible than that of the broiler or fryer.

Stag: A male chicken cock, usually under 10 months of age, with coarse skin, somewhat toughened, with darkened flesh, and a considerable hardening of the breastbone cartilage.

Stewing chicken or fowl: A mature chicken, usually more than 10 months of age, with meat less tender than that of a roaster and nonflexible breastbone tip.

Cock: A mature male chicken, usually over 10 months of age, with coarse skin, toughened and darkened meat, and hardened breastbone tip. Other forms of poultry are classified in a similar way.

24.2.1 Dark Flesh Chicken (Kadaknath)

There are three kinds of Black Meat Chicken (BMC) in the world.

Kadaknath is native to Jhabua district of Madhya Pradesh (MP), India. Silkie-Native to China, Ayyam Cemani-Native to Indonesia. Hatcheries in Madhya Pradesh produce 2.5 lakh chickens per year. Kadaknath is a premium breed and its meat is three times more compared to broiler chicken. It is one of the rarest poultry breeds of India. It is known for its popularity for its taste and special flavour. Reared by tribal communities in Bhil and Bhilala in the districts Jhabua and Dhar in the state of Madhya Pradesh. Kerala, Andhra Pradesh, Telangana and Tamil Nadu are now breeding Kadaknath.

The flesh is dark in colour and the eggs are brown in colour. It is rich in iron, hence increases blood cells and haemoglobin. It has many amino acids, Vitamin B1, B2, B6, B12, C and E, niacin, nicotinic acid, more protein, low fat and cholesterol, calcium, phosphorus, and iron.

It has medicinal value besides having high nutritive value. It is recommended to anaemic women, also advised to relieve headaches, postdelivery problems, asthma, nephritis and pulmonary problems.

Also it has great economic value since it is highly resistant for catching diseases. They can survive on kitchen waste and weighs 1.5 kgs within 6 to 7 months. The meat and egg are highly priced. The cost per kg of meat is rupees 600-700 and rupees 40-50 per egg.

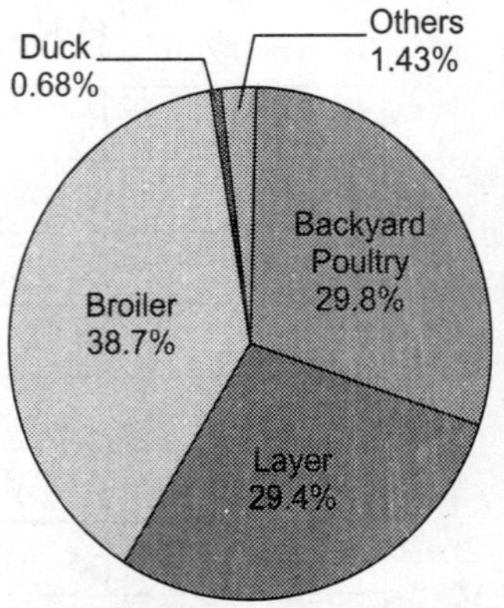

Fig. 24.1 Distribution of poultry population

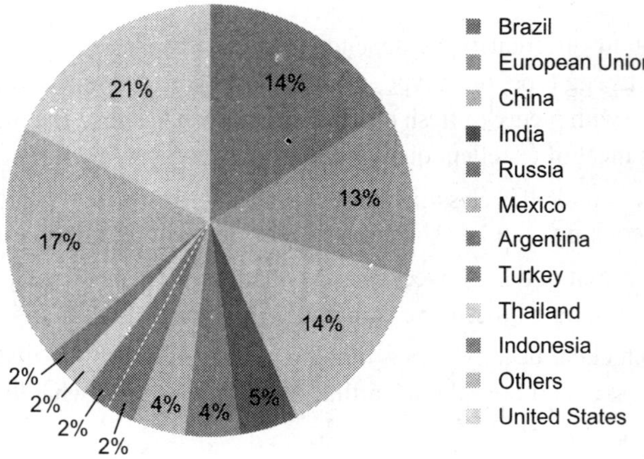

Fig. 24.2 Global share of major broiler meat producers (2016)

Market Size and Placement of Birds

The average bird placement in broiler segment is 65-70 million birds per week. Five major players (Suguna in Coimbatore, Venky's in Pune, CP, Sneha, and Shalimar in Kolkata) constitute 60 per cent of the broiler meat market. The average live wt of 1.8-2.2 kg. Broiler meat production has been growing in India at a rate of 7-8 per cent. One-third of the production is carried out by.

(credit: GAIN report, 2016)

Table 24.2 Broiler poultry – growth rate

S.No.	Year	Poultry Production (million tons)	% annual poultry production growth rate
1.	2011-12	2.48	13.22%
2.	2012-13	2.68	8.01%
3.	2013-14	1.92	–28.50%
4.	2014-15	3.05	59.16%
5.	2015-16	3.26	6.75%
6.	2016-17	3.46	6.13%

The poultry meat growth is showing fluctuations as the data collection is being standardized and now, commercial poultry and other than commercial poultry data is also gathered.

World Players in Broiler Poultry Production

World chicken meat production: India is 6th in chicken meat production in the world (as per FAO 2014) (Table 24.3).

Table 24.3 India is 6th in chicken meat production in the world

S.No.	Country	Poultry meat production (in Million Tonnes)
1.	U.S.A.	20.39
2.	China	18.19
3.	Brazil	13.00
4.	Russian Federation	3.77
5.	Mexico	2.92
6.	India	2.76
	World total	**131.12**

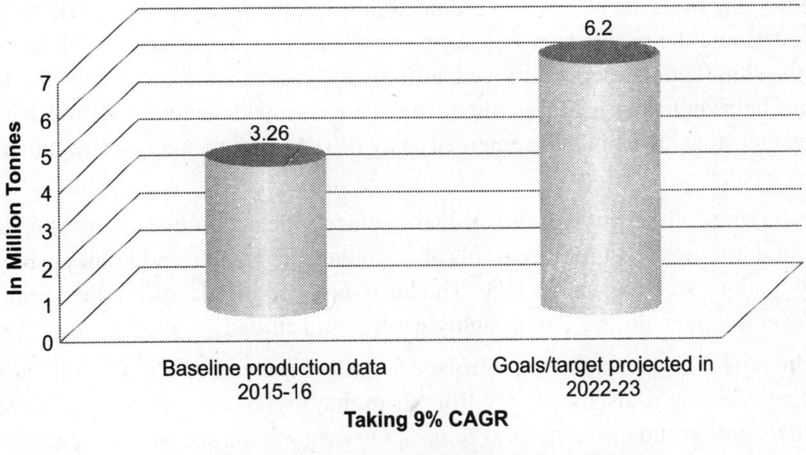

Fig. 24.3 Poultry Production Targets 2022-23

Table 24.4 Total Poultry population, share of backyard population and egg production from desi birds

S.No.	States	Total Poultry Population	Share of Poultry popn	Total Birds in Backyard	% share of Backyard Poultry	Households having Backyard Poultry	Avg birds in Backyard per Households	Egg Production from Desi/ LIT Birds	Yield from Desi Birds
		In million	in %	in million	%	in million	%	in million	Avg. Annual yield/bird (eggs in numbers)
1.	Andaman & N Island	1.17	0.16	0.72	0.31	0.29	2	52.86	116.44
2.	Andhra Pradesh	161.33	22.10	29.08	12.59	3.78	8	645.96	66

(Contd...)

3.	Arunachal Pradesh	2.25	0.31	2.22	0.96	0.14	16	27.77	132
4.	Assam	27.22	3.73	26.19	11.34	2.17	12	330.49	106
5.	Bihar	12.75	1.75	7.62	3.30	1.43	5	662.49	147
6.	Chandigarh	0.19	0.03	0.002	0.00	0.01	0	0.35	120
7.	Chattisgarh	23.1	3.16	6.29	2.72	0.97	6	159.66	97
8.	Dadra & NH	0.09	0.01	0.086	0.04	0.12	1	7.30	123
9.	Daman & Diu	0.03	0.00	0.029	0.01	0.01	4	0.00	0
10.	Goa	0.29	0.04	0.14	0.06	0.02	7	2.31	93

(BAHS, 2016 and 18th Livestock Census data)

24.3 Poultry Processing

Poultry is marketed in ready-to-cook form, i.e., the head, feet and entrails are removed (dressed chicken). Birds are generally not fed for 12 hours before slaughter to ensure that their crops are empty, which helps cleaner operations. They are killed by a method that minimizes struggle. The birds are stunned and made unconscious with a blow on the head. In large establishments, stunning is carried out by electrical stunners. The jugular vein is cut so that the bird bleeds well. Bleeding takes 1 to 3 min. and it should be complete in order to produce a product of quality.

After bleeding the birds are scalded, i.e., dipped in hot water briefly. The temperature of the scald water may be 60°C and the bird is kept in it for about 45 secs. or, more safely with less chance of the outer layer of the skin (cuticle) being removed, at 52°C for 2 min. Scalding loosens the feathers on the chicken and thus helps defeathering. Then the feathers are removed, generally by mechanical methods. Pin feathers (feathers that have not quite emerged) may be removed manually or by suitable mechanical methods.

After defeathering, *evisceration* of the bird takes place. The abdominal cavity is opened through a transverse cut, and after inspection, the entrails are removed. The lungs and kidney which are difficult to remove may be done so by a suction tube. The head, feet and oil glands are then removed from the drawn bird. The eviscerated birds are thoroughly washed and chilled.

Rapid chilling to 1.7°C is essential to control the growth of bacteria which contaminate the flesh once the skin is broken. Cooling is also necessary from the point of view of tenderness of meat. The time of onset of rigor, its duration and the tenderness of meat once rigor has gone, are influenced by the way the bird is cooled. Muscle from poultry cooled in ice-water is more tender than that held in water at higher temperatures and that cooled in air. Eviscerated and washed birds are to be promptly cooled to avoid toughening of the muscle due to lowering of pH by the accumulation of lactic acid. Poultry, like meats, goes into and out of rigor, but more rapidly than other meats. A minimum of 4-5 hours from the time the chicken is slaughtered is required until it is cooked.

Dressed chicken is graded before it is marketed. Grading takes into consideration the condition of the bird prior to the slaughter, during evisceration, and packing. Each country has set standards for grading and several grades of chicken. In India, two grades are assigned to chicken, Grade 1 and Grade 2. This is based on conformation (deformations, detract from the normal appearance), meatiness, fat covering, defeathering, cuts and tears, and discolouration.

The graded poultry is individually packed in low-moisture and low-oxygen transmission film or bags. Before sealing the packs, care is taken to expel the air between the carcass and the bag. The sealed bags may be stored under refrigeration or frozen. Refrigerated poultry has a shelf-life of only a few days (6-10 days). Frozen poultry, at –23° to –18°C, may be stored up to 9 months,

24.4 Composition and Nutritive Value

Poultry meat has a high protein content varying from 18-25 per cent, and is comparable in quality and nutritive value to other meats. It contains all the essential amino acids required for building body tissues. There is little fat on the meat of young birds, but the fat content is influenced by age, and species of poultry. In any case, the fat content of poultry is less than half that of other meats. Chicken fat is more unsaturated than the fat of red meat and this has nutritional advantages. Like other animal tissues, poultry flesh is a good source of B vitamins and minerals. The dark meat of chicken is richer in riboflavin than the light, but the light meat is richer in niacin.

Because of its high protein-to-fat ratio, poultry meat is advantageous to persons who must restrict their intake of fats. The importance of poultry in a country like ours with low nutritional standards cannot be over-emphasized. Use of poultry products in our diet will help avoid malnutrition. Another advantage of poultry in our country is that it is eaten by persons who have objection to eat beef or pork.

24.5 Poultry Cooking

Raw chicken has little or no flavour; it develops during cooking. The principles of cooking poultry are the same as for cooking meats. The cooking method is selected on the basis of the tenderness of the poultry and its fat content, both influenced mainly by the age of the bird. Moist heat methods are applied to older and tougher birds in order to make them tender and palatable. Dry heat methods are applied to young tender birds.

Table 24.5 Chemical composition of meat of different species of poultry

Species	Water (%)	Protein (%)	Fat (%)
Turkey	67.4	20.5	08.3
Guinea Fowl	65.4	20.7	10.1
Broiler	63.8	18.1	14.3
Duck	54.5	15.2	26.5
Goose	52.4	15.7	31.0

Sources: *Poultry Guide*, Vol 20, No. 11., Nov. 1983.

The changes that take place during the cooking of poultry are similar to those of other meats. To obtain tender, juicy and uniformly cooked poultry, low to moderate heat is to be used. Intense heat results in the toughening of proteins, shrinkage and loss of juiciness.

24.5.1 Broiling and Frying

Young tender poultry is cooked by broiling, frying, baking or roasting. For broiling, the bird is placed in the broiler with the skin side down. The whole bird or halves may be broiled. The broiler is placed about 10 cm from the flame or heating element and cooked at a broiling temperature of 177°C till the internal temperature of the breast muscle reaches 95°C (about 45-60 min.). Because of the low fat content of the young birds, basting with melted fat will improve the flavour, palatability and appearance of the preparation.

Frying and deep-fat frying are particularly suitable for cooking low-fat, young, tender poultry and more frequently used than broiling. The halves of the birds are frequently fried. Before frying they are coated with seasoned flour or beaten eggs and bread crumbs. They are then carefully cooked to prevent over-browning before the meat is tender. If deep-fat-fried, the bird must be steamed until the stage of doneness before being dipped in flour or egg and crumbs and fried slowly. The time required for browning in deep fat is too short to promote thorough cooking of the meat.

24.5.2 Roasting

Poultry may be roasted, stuffed or unstuffed. When the whole bird is roasted, tender parts, such as the breast, may be over-cooked before the legs and thighs are cooked to the desired state. For stuffed birds, roasting should be continued till the internal temperature of the stuffing reaches 74°C. This eliminates the possibility of bacterial food poisoning. When the poultry is roasted without stuffing, it is cooked at an oven temperature of 163 °C till the internal temperature of the thigh muscle reaches 85°C.

24.5.3 *Tandoor* Chicken

This is a well-known and popular Indian chicken dish. This is barbecued chicken. The cooking is done in a clay oven called a *tandoor*. *Tandoor* is a long earthenware pot embedded in clay and earth. Charcoal is put inside and the oven is made red-hot. Other types of ovens are also designed and used. Tender chicken, either whole or cut, is used. The skin is removed from the chicken and the flesh is pricked with a fork and sprinkled with salt. *Tandoor* sauce is then smeared on the chicken, which is then left aside for 6-8 hours. It is then cooked in the *tandoor*. Half way through the cooking time it is removed from the oven and brushed all over nicely with butter or oil, and cooked again until the chicken is fork tender. Chicken cooked this way is delicious.

24.5.4 Braising and Stewing

The older tougher birds are cooked this way. Disjointed pieces of chicken are generally braised. Usually, they are first browned by frying after which water is added and the bird simmered until it is tender. For stewing, the whole bird or cut pieces are used. They are cooked in water with seasonings and vegetables till they are tender.

CHAPTER

25

Seafoods

Fish is found abundantly in all natural waters. It is a valuable source of food and has been used by man since antiquity. With mounting population pressure, most nations are expanding their fish catching power. In addition to fishing in vast oceans, fish cultivation on a large scale is gaining major significance in many lands. Tapping the wealth of the oceans and inland waters and their efficient utilization has become urgent for the survival of the human race. About 10 per cent of the world's fish catch comes from inland fisheries.

25.1 Fish Catch

The State of World Fisheries and Aquaculture 2018 presents FAO's official world fishery and aquaculture statistics. **Global fish production** peaked at about 232.2 million tonnes in 2022, with aquaculture representing 47 per cent of the total and 53 per cent, if non-food uses (including reduction to fishmeal and fish oil) are excluded. With capture fishery production relatively static since the late 1980s, aquaculture has been responsible for the continuing impressive growth in the supply of fish for human consumption.

Table 25.1 World Fisheries and Aquaculture Production and Utilization (Million Tonnes)[a]

Category	2011	2012	2013	2014	2015	2016	2022
Production							
Capture							
Inland	10.7	11.2	11.2	11.3	11.4	11.6	11.3*
Marine	81.5	78.4	79.4	79.9	81.2	79.3	81.0*
Total capture	92.2	89.5	90.6	91.2	92.7	90.9	92.3*
Aquaculture							
Inland	38.6	42.0	44.8	46.9	48.6	51.4	59.1*
Marine	23.2	24.4	25.4	26.8	27.5	28.7	35.3*
Total aquaculture	61.8	66.4	70.2	73.7	76.1	80.0	94.4*
Total world fisheries and aquaculture	154.0	156.0	160.7	164.9	168.7	170.9	186.7*
Utilization[b]							
Human consumption	130.0	136.4	140.1	144.8	148.4	151.2	164.6*
Non-food uses	24.0	19.6	20.6	20.0	20.3	19.7	20.8*
Population (billions)[c]	7.0	7.1	7.2	7.3	7.3	7.4	8.2*
Per capita apparent consumption (kg)	18.5	19.2	19.5	19.9	20.2	20.3	20.6*

[a]Excludes aquatic, mammals, crocodiles, alligators and caimans, seaweed and other aquatic plants.
[b]Utilization data for 2014-2016 are provisional estimates.
[c]Source of population figures: UN, 2015e. http://www.fao.org/3/19540EN/i9540en.pdf page = 20
*As per FAO estimates

Total global catch in inland waters was 11.6 million tonnes in 2016, representing 12.8% of total global capture fishery production. The 2016 global catch shows an increase of 2.0% over the previous year and of 10.5% in comparison to the 2005-2014 average. The continuously increasing trend of inland fisheries production may be misleading, however, as some of the increase can be attributed to improved reporting and assessment at the country level and may not be entirely due to increased production. The improvement in reporting may also mask trends in individual countries where fisheries are declining.

25.2 Types of Fish

It is estimated that there are about 25,000 species of fish living today, varying in size from very small fish to very large sharks. They are second to insects in the largeness of population and outnumber all other vertebrates (back-boned animals), mammals, birds, reptiles and amphibians put together.

About 250 different species of fishes are used for edible purposes. Edible fish are classified into two major categories based on their anatomical differences. Fishes having vertebrae with fin-appendages, which help balance and steer the body in its movements through water, are termed finfish. The skin of these fishes is covered with protective scales and is abundantly coated with mucous. Fishes without a skeleton but covered with some type of hard shell are known as shellfish.

Shellfish are of two types; molluscs and crustaceans. The former has a soft unsegmented body while the latter has segmented bodies. The molluscs are either partially or wholly enclosed in a hard shell that is largely of mineral composition. These include oysters, clams, scallops and mussels. The crustaceans are covered with crust like shells and they include lobsters, crabs, shrimp and crayfish. Edible shellfishes are mainly saltwater fishes.

The kinds of finfish available for food are more than those of shellfish and the types differ in different locations. They are found both in saltwater and freshwater. Their flavour and quality depend partly on the water in which they are grown. Saltwater fishes have a more distinctive flavour than freshwater fishes. The common sea or marine fishes available in the country are all types of shark, salmon, mackerel, Bombay duck, ribbon fish, pomfret, sole, tuna, etc. Fishes from fresh water include sardine, mullet, catfish, perch, pearl spot, etc.

Fishes are also classified based on their fat content as lean (less than 2 per cent fat), medium (2-5 per cent fat) and fat (more than 5 per cent) fishes. Bombay duck, halibut, cod, perch and sole are examples of lean fish. Fat fish include salmon, sardine, mackerel, tuna, etc. In fish with more than five- per cent fat in the edible flesh, the flesh is usually more highly pigmented than that of the low-fat varieties which are generally white fleshed.

25.3 Composition and Nutritive Value

The composition of fish varies considerably, amongst other factors, due to variation in fat content. The fat content of fish varies from 0.1 per cent to about 25 per cent. Many factors like the season, sex and stage of maturity determine the fat content of fish. In all cases, the liver and viscera (the pyloric caecum and mesenteria) constitute the location of the fat deposit. However, fats are also encountered in muscle tissue, skin, mutt and roe (mass of eggs of fish).

The principal component of most fish oils are glycerides of fatty acids, which make up 95 per cent of the oil. Fish oils differ remarkably from vegetable oils in containing a great variety of fatty acids, especially highly unsaturated fatty acids having from four to six unsaturated linkages. The fatty-acid composition of seawater fish oil and freshwater fish oil varies, the latter containing smaller amounts of C-20 and C-22 unsaturated acids than marine fish oils, but a greater amount of C-18 unsaturated acids. Fish fat also contains cholesterol, lecithin, waxes, and fatty alcohols. The fat from fish eggs is especially high in lecithin (up to 20 per cent).

Fish is an excellent source of protein. The protein content of finfish is, on an average, about 20 per cent. The muscles of some lean fish contain exceptionally high levels of protein, when compared to the best meat. As a whole, the protein content of shellfish is lower than that of finfish.

Fish contains some glycogen, shellfish contain a higher proportion; some shellfish have 3 to 5 per cent glycogen. The sweet taste of various shellfish is due to glucose formed from the glycogen by enzymic action.

Fish is a good source of minerals. It contains more minerals than other types of meats. Fish meat is a good source of copper, sulphur and phosphorus. In general, saltwater fishes contain more iron than freshwater fishes, although Indian species of the latter group show high values. Marine fish is a dependable source of iodine. The iodine content of marine fish is nearly 30 times that of freshwater fish. Its content in marine fish varies from 0.01 to 0.5 mg per 100 g of fish meat. Iodine is essential for the prevention of goitre.

Fish oils are the richest known sources of vitamins A and D. However, there are extreme differences in the vitamin reserves of different species. Fish flesh is a fair source of thiamine, being somewhat poorer in the vitamin than most meats. In some raw fish the enzyme thiaminase is present, and this destroys the vitamin and makes it unavailable if fish is held in a raw state or consumed raw. The riboflavin content in fish flesh is as much as in beef. Red flesh has a higher content of this vitamin than white muscle. Both seawater and freshwater fish are good sources of niacin. The vitamin C content of fish is very low and does not have any nutritional significance.

Systematic investigations on the nutritive value of fish have shown that it is equal to that of meat. Fish proteins are also easily digested. The amino acid pattern of fish protein closely approximates that found in any other class of animal protein. Generally, fish meat has lysine and histidine at a high level and, occasionally, methionine and tryptophan on the low side of mammalian meat. Because of their high nutritive value, fish protein concentrates (FPC) have been developed from inexpensive and surplus fishes to combat malnutrition of people around the world (see Subsection 25.8.2).

Researchers have also found that fish rich in omega-3 oils can protect people from developing age-related macular degeneration (AMD) later in life, which is the main cause of blindness and visual impairment for people over 60. Such fish include mackerel, trout, sardines, tuna and salmon (two or more servings of fish per week are needed). Smokers have a 1.9-fold increased risk of AMD.

Fish is a good source of protein and, unlike fatty meat products, it is not high in saturated fat. It is also a good source of omega-3 fatty acids, which promotes heart health. It is recommended that fish should be eaten at least twice a week. However, some types of fish may contain high levels of mercury, PCBs (polychlorinated biphenyls), dioxins and other environmental contaminants. Levels of these substances are generally highest in older, larger, predatory fish and marine mammals. Levels of mercury and omega-3 fatty acids for various sea foods are shown in Table 25.2.

Table 25.2 Sea foods with the level of Omega-3-fatty-acids and mercury level

Sea foods	Mean mercury level in parts per Million (ppm)	Omega-3 fatty acids (grams per 3- oz.Serving)
Canned tuna (light)	0.12	0.26 – 0.73
Shrimp	ND*	0.27
Pollock	0.06	0.46
Salmon (fresh, frozen)	0.01	0.68 – 1.83
Cod	0.11	0.13 – 0.24
Catfish	0.05	0.15 – 0.20
Clams	ND*	0.24
Flounder or Sole	0.05	0.43
Crabs	0.06	0.34 – 0.40
Scallops	0.05	0.17
Lobster	0.31	0.07–0.41
Grouper	0.55	0.21
Halibut	0.26	0.40–1.00
Oysters	ND*	0.37– 1.17
Mahi Mahi	0.19	0.12
Herring	0.04	1.71 – 1.81

*ND – mercury concentration below the Level of Detection (LOD = 0.01ppm).

Source: American Heart Association Scientific Statement: Fish Consumption, Fish Oil, Omega – 3 Fatty Acids and Cardiovascular Disease, # 71– 0241 Circulation.2002; 106: 2747 – 2757.

25.4 Fish Spoilage

Fishes are highly perishable. In India, with its tropical and subtropical climate, the problem of spoilage is more acute as heat and moisture promote deterioration. Fish tissue is generally more perishable than other animal tissue and this is true even under conditions of refrigeration. Freshly caught fish at a temperature of 16°C remain good for hardly a day. On ice at 0°C, finfish may remain good for periods of up to about 14 days, but this is not true of all species. In contrast, beef may be stored at 1.7°C for several weeks. The reasons for the spoilage of fish are microbiological, physiological and chemical in origin.

25.4.1 Microbiological

The flesh of healthy live fish is bacteriologically sterile. However, there are many types of bacteria on the surface skin, gills, and the digestive tract of living fish. Generally, spoilage takes place shortly after the death of the fish when bacteria attack all the constituents of the tissues. Since these bacteria live on cold-blooded fish at a rather low ocean temperature, they are well adapted to cold and continue to grow even under common refrigeration conditions.

25.4.2 Physiological

Bacterial spoilage of fish does not begin until the fish has gone into rigor and passed out of it. For *rigor mortis* to set in, the glycogen in fish muscle must be converted into lactic acid accompanied by a decrease in pH. However, fish struggle when caught and use up virtually all of the glycogen in their muscles. When killed there is little glycogen left to be converted into lactic acid to slow bacterial growth. *Rigor mortis* in fish is comparatively shorter when compared to other animals, which are rested before slaughter to build up glycogen reserves.

25.4.3 Chemical

Fish, as taken from water, has virtually little or no odour. Yet, virtually all fish products have a fishy odour and this is an evidence of some deterioration. The fishy odour is due to the production of trimethylamine by the action of bacteria on phospholipids and choline present in fish. Also, the unsaturated fish fats undergo oxidation and become rancid, which also contributes to the smell of deteriorated fish.

25.5 Preservation and Processing

As fish is a highly perishable commodity, various methods have been devised to preserve it. Before preservation, fishes are washed with clean water to remove slime, blood stains, etc. Larger fishes are gutted (i.e., all the internal organs or viscera are removed) and the body cavity washed. The various methods adopted for preservation are drying, salting, smoking, freezing, and canning.

Sun drying is the most ancient of methods. Drying removes moisture from tissues and helps arrest bacterial and enzymatic putrefaction. In India, over 35 per cent of the total catch of sea fish is cured in the sun. This method is not hygienic, there is an appreciable percentage of loss due to putrefaction and spoilage, and the dried fish develops a peculiar odour.

Salting (pickling) is also widely used in India. The dry-salting or wet-salting method is used. In the former method, fishes are first rubbed with salt powder and then packed in tubs with dry salt powder sprinkled in between layers of fishes. After a period of about 10-20 hours, the fishes are removed, washed in brine and dried in the sun for 2-3 days.

In wet-salting, cleaned fishes are packed in large vats containing concentrated salt solutions and stirred daily till properly pickled. With large-sized fishes, longitudinal slits are made in the flesh to allow penetration of salt. After pickling for 7 to 10 days, the salty water that oozes out from the fish is allowed to drain off. Wet-salted fish is sold without drying. It does not keep for long and therefore has to be used within 3 to 4 months. In some countries fishes soaked in salt solution are taken out and smoked. Smoked fish is not popular in India.

The above methods employed for curing fish are rather crude and primitive and the products are unattractive. Case-hardening, rancidity development, colour changes, mould growth, and attack by insects and mites are some of the common defects of fishes cured by sun-drying and salting.

Chemicals, such as acids, sodium benzoate and ethylene oxide, and the antibiotic aureomycin can prolong the life of fish. However, many countries do not permit the use of these preservatives. Irradiation of fish by γ-radiations prolongs their storage life by 20–25 days. But the current methods of importance for preserving the quality fish are freezing and canning.

Freezing: Freezing can greatly extend the period of storage and is effective in keeping the fish in a condition similar to that of fresh fish, if the fish is gutted and frozen down to –29°C within two hours of its catch. In some cases, clean whole fish are frozen. Finfish are usually frozen as fillets (lengthwise cuts), steaks (crosscut section) or sticks (lengthwise or crosswise cut from fillet or steaks). Large fish are frozen by the sharp freeze, a comparatively slow freeze. Small fish, fillets and steaks are quick frozen.

This type of freezing gives a better produce. The storage life of quality frozen fish, with a low fat content, can be as long as two years.

Some undesirable changes can also take place if proper care is not taken during freezing. Slow freezing can result in protein denaturation. As the water freezes in the fish, the salt concentration of the muscle tissue increases, which causes denaturation of the protein, making it tough and rubbery. Another effect of freezing is desiccation or drying. Drying is caused by the transfer of moisture from the surface of the fish to the cold surface of the freezing equipment. Frozen fish undergo oxidative changes, and fatty fish become rancid more quickly than lean ones. Desiccation and oxidation can be prevented by properly protecting fish with suitable wrappers before freezing.

Preservation of fish by freezing is not yet widespread in India. Cold storage facilities are available in areas where fisheries are highly developed.

Canning: While high-fat fish do not store as well as low–fat fish in the frozen state, oily fish are the most suitable for canning. Salmon, tuna, sardine, herring, lobster, shrimp, etc., are canned. In the case of salmon, tuna, sardine and mackerel, additional fish or vegetable oil is commonly added to the fish prior to can closure; shrimps are canned in brine. Canning retains the natural flavour of the fish. Large quantities of certain types of fish are canned in this country mostly for export purposes.

Shellfish become dark or discoloured during canned storage. This is due to the release of hydrogen sulphide from the sulphur components of the fish, that reacts with the iron in the can to give black iron sulphide. This can be avoided by using an enamel, especially an enamel containing zinc, since the zinc sulphide formed is white in colour.

25.6 Shellfish

Shellfish are even more perishable than finfish. Lobsters and crabs, for example, are best kept alive up to the point of their cooking or freezing; otherwise they deteriorate in quality in a matter of a day or less.

25.6.1 Shrimp

India is one of the leading shrimp processing and exporting countries in the world. Shrimp should be conserved or processed within five days of being caught even though they are iced. They contain greater amounts of free amino acids than finfish and also highly active proteolytic enzymes—the cathepsins. Iced shrimp darken in colour and may become black due to enzymatic action. They, therefore, require refrigeration on being caught and quick freezing.

25.6.2 Oysters and Clams

These, when sold in shell, must be alive. Shell oyster may be held at the refrigerator temperature for only a short time before use. Oyster culture has been developed. Clams are not cultivated as are oysters. Shucked oysters (removed from the shell) are sold fresh, frozen or canned, or pressed into blocks and frozen. Oysters are nutritious food organisms, rich in protein, minerals and vitamins.

25.6.3 Crabs and Lobsters

Crabs and lobsters must be alive when cooked. There are many different types of crabs. The meat from cooked crab is squeezed out. Crab meat is canned or pressed into blocks and frozen. The lobster is dark bluish-green in colour when taken from the water but changes to red during cooking. The green colour is due to the lobster liver which is considered a delicacy. The red colour of the cooked lobster is due to the eggs of the female. The cooked meat obtained from the shells of lobsters is marketed fresh, frozen or canned, as in the case of crab meat.

Table 25.3 Inland Waters Capture Production: Major Producer Countries

Country	Production (tonnes)			% Variation		Variation, 2015 to 2016 (tonnes)
	Average 2005-2014	2015	2016	2005-2014 (overage) to 2016	2015 to 2016	
China	2 252 368	2 277 299	2 318 046	2.9	1.8	40 747
India*	1 088 082	1 346 104	1 462 063	34.4	8.6	115 959
Bangladesh	1 018 987	1 023 991	1 048 242	2.9	2.4	24 251
Myanmar*	745 483	863 450	886 780	19.0	2.7	23 330
Cambodia	422 801	487 905	509 350	20.5	4.4	21 445
Indonesia	346 722	472 911	432 475	24.7	–8.6	–40 436
Uganda	417 016	396 205	389 244	– 6.7	– 1.8	– 6 961
Nigeria	287 937	337 874	377 632	31.2	11.8	39 758
United Republic of Tanzania	305 635	309 924	312 039	2.1	0.7	2 115
Russian Federation	243 337	285 065	292 828	20.3	2.7	7 763
Egypt	248 141	241 179	231 959	–6.5	–3.8	–9 220
Democratic Republic of the Congo	224 263	227 700	229 300	2.2	0.7	1 600
Brazil*	243 213	225 000	225 000	–7.5	0.0	0
Mexico	113 854	151 416	199 665	75.4	31.9	48 249
Thailand	211 927	184 101	187 300	–11.6	1.7	3 199
Philippines	182 205	203 366	159 615	–12.4	–21.5	–43 751
Total 16 major countries	8 351 970	9 033 490	9 261 538	10.9	2.5	228 048
total other 136 countries	2 172 222	2 374 585	2 371 482	9.2	– 0.1	– 3 103
World total	10 524 192	11 408 075	11 633 020	10.5	2.0	224 945
Share of 16 major countries	79.4%	79.2%	79.6%			

*Production figures for 2015 and 2016 are FAO estimates.

25.7 Fish Cookery

Cooking methods adopted for meat are applicable for fish cooking. The muscle fibres of fish are not tough and the amount of connective tissue is small, and therefore they are more easily cooked than the meat of warm blooded animals. When sufficiently cooked, the flesh of fish can be easily separated into flakes. Thus, fish is to be carefully handled during cooking so that it does not break easily. When over-cooked, fish meat shrinks excessively and becomes tough and dry. This is true of shellfish also.

Fish is generally cooked by dry heat, such as broiling, baking and frying. Moist heat methods, such as steaming and poaching, are also used. The fat content of fish also determines the cooking method. Fish low in fat is generally fried or basted with fat. Some fishes are rich in fat and such fishes require very little additional fat in cooking.

Whole fish fillets and steaks may be baked. If the fish is thick fleshed it is scored here and there, i.e., little slits are made in the flesh on each side, so that it will hasten the cooking of the fish. The fish is then cooked at 177°C. The fish may be brushed with oil before baking to prevent over-browning.

Broiling may also be used to cook whole fish or fish cuts. The dressed fish is placed on the broiler rack and cooked at a low broiling temperature. The temperature and time of cooking depend on the thickness of the fish to be cooked. The smaller the fish, the higher should be the temperature used. If the fish is large and thick, the cooking should be conducted at a lower temperature so that the heat gradually penetrates the flesh.

Frying is one of the most popular methods of cooking fish. This method is suitable for fillets, steaks and small whole fish. The fish may be shallow or deep fried.

In shallow frying, fish is fried in a frying pan in hot butter. Before frying, the fish is soaked in lightly beaten egg or milk and rolled in flour or bread crumbs and shaken to remove the flour or crumbs not sticking to it. It is then fried till it becomes brown on each side. Next, it is removed from the pan and drained on absorbent paper.

Deep fat frying is similar to shallow frying except that the frying medium is oil. The deep fryer should be no more than half filled with oil and heated to about 195°C to 200°C. Coated fish is plunged into the oil and when cooked it rises to the surface.

Cooking fish by steaming and poaching helps preserve its delicate flavour. For steaming, the fish is kept in a covered pan and placed on a rack over boiling water and cooked until done. In poaching, fish is placed in a kettle and covered with water. It is cooked with the liquid simmering.

25.8 Fish Products

A number of products are prepared from fish. These include fish meal used as animal feed, fish flour used for protein enrichment of human food, fish oils used for feeding and industrial purposes, fish glue, is in glass—a high grade fish collagen used for the clarification of wines, beer, vinegar, etc.

25.8.1 Fish Meal

Fish meal is prepared from the parts of fish not used for human food, and sometimes the whole fish of less favoured species, by grinding the material usually with the removal of some oil, followed by dehydration. Fish meal, on an average, is composed of proteins, 55–70; fat, 2–5; minerals, 10–12; and moisture, 6–12 per cent. Fish meal is used as animal and poultry feed. Low grade fish meal is used as manure in plantations of tea, coffee and tobacco. Considerable quantities of fish meal are produced in India.

25.8.2 Fish Flour

It is possible to extract oils and fatty substances from ground fish tissues by solvent extraction to such an extent that no fishy odour or flavour remains. The fat extracted tissue, after stripping off solvent, dehydration, and milling, gives a bland highly nutritious powder rich in high quality protein and minerals.

This product, when produced under proper bacteriological and sanitary control, is good for use as human food and is known as fish flour or fish protein concentrate (FPC).

Fish flour, properly manufactured and packaged, can retain its bland and nutritive properties almost indefinitely. The flour can be incorporated at 3–10 per cent level into a variety of dishes without adverse effects upon their acceptability. Fish flour contains 85 to 90 per cent of high quality protein. It is estimated that food shortage and high quality protein needs in several areas of the world can be alleviated by fish flour, at very low cost.

25.8.3 Fish Oils

Fish oils are of two kinds, liver oils and fish body oil. Liver oil is the principal natural source of vitamin A and, to a lesser extent, vitamin D. Fishes, such as cod, halibut, tuna and shark, are good sources of fish liver oils. The oil and vitamin A content varies in different fishes. Body oil is obtained from fishes, such as sardine, herring and salmon.

Liver oil is obtained by different methods. One common method is by cooking good quality minced fish liver at 85°-95°C. This results in the disintegration of liver cells and freeing of oil. The oil floating on the steam condensate can be skimmed off or separated by centrifugation. About 300 kilolitres of shark liver oil per annum are produced in the country.

Fish body oils are produced along with fish meal. Fishes are first ground to a pulp and steamed. The oil and water get separated from the protein. The cooked flesh is then pressed. The "presscake" is worked up for fish meal. The press liquor or "stick water" is concentrated and oil recovered.

CHAPTER

26

Sugar and Confectionery

The art of making sugar (sucrose) from sugarcane had its birth in India. Early Indian scripts refer to "*gur*" (jaggery) as an article of food. From India, the making of sugar spread eastwards to Malaya and China and westwards to Persia and beyond. Indian sugar was seen in foreign markets at the close of the 15th Century. At present for the year 2023-24, India is the second largest sugar producing country in the world. Yielding approximately 31.6 million metric tonnes of sugar. The global production amounted to roughly 179.4 million metric tons. India had even earlier been the largest producer of sweetening agents out of sugarcane, when we take into consideration jaggery and *khandsari* (open pan sugar) produced in the unorganized sector of the industry.

Sugarcane is the chief source of sugar. Sugarcane belongs to the genus *Saccharum,* which consists of perennial grasses distributed in the tropical and subtropical areas of the world. The cultivated sugarcane is *Saccharum officinarum,* which is a hybrid of the wild species, *S. spontaneum,* believed to have originated in India, and *S. robustum,* a native of New Guinea. The cultivation of sugarcane spread from New Guinea to Indonesia and then to India, where it was cultivated for production of sugar for several centuries before the beginning of the Christian era. From India, sugarcane was taken to Mediterranean countries in the early centuries of the Christian era and introduced to America after it was discovered by Columbus.

Sugarcane is the world's largest crop by production quantity, with 2.04 billion tonnes produced in 2023, and Brazil accounting for 38.4% and production of India is 24.0% of the world total. In 2023. The Food and Agriculture Organization estimated it was cultivated on about 27.0 million hectares (66.8 million acres), in more than 90 countries.

The area under sugarcane in India is 5207 million hectares and production of 435.08 million tonnes with productivity of 79 tonnes/hectares. The major sugarcane growing states are Uttar Pradesh, Maharashtra, Karnataka, Tamil Nadu, Andhra Pradesh in India.

It was recognized in the 19th Century that sugarbeet (*Beta vulgaris*) is also a rich source of sugar. From the beginning of the 20th Century, sugarbeet has also become an important source of sugar. About one-third of the sugar of the world is obtained from sugarbeet. In beet, sugar is stored in the roots as distinguished from sugarcane where sugar is stored in the stem. While sugarcane is grown in the tropics, sugarbeet is a crop of the temperate zones. Sugary substances are also obtained from palmyra, date palm, coconut, sago palm, maple, etc.

26.1 Sugar from Cane

Sugarcane contains 12–15 per cent sugars (sucrose, glucose and fructose). In India, 80–90 per cent of sugarcane is used for the manufacture of three products widely used in food, viz., *gur*, open pan sugar or *khandasari,* and vacuum pan sugar or white sugar. The largest quantity, ranging between 50–60 per cent of the cane production, is used for the production of *gur*, 25–30 per cent for white sugar, and 5 per cent for *khandasari*. Only a very small quantity of refined sugar is produced in the country. The balance of about 10 per cent of sugarcane is used for chewing and sugarcane juice, which is used as a beverage, and as seed and feed. The cane juice is acidic (pH 5.0–5.4) and, in addition to sugars, contains minerals (0.4–0.7 per cent), and vitamins. The vitamins present are thiamine, 53; riboflavin 31; niacin, 49; pantothenic acid, 2,180; biotin, 22; and vitamin D, 176 μg/100 g.

26.1.1 Gur

Gur is produced throughout India and forms an important item of Indian diet. It is mainly obtained from sugarcane. *Gur* is also obtained from palmyra, date palm, and coconut. In the manufacture of *gur,* cane is crushed soon after cutting (within a day) to avoid loss of weight and sugar due to inversion. For small-scale crushing, iron crushers driven by bullocks, and for large-scale crushing, power driven crushers, are employed. Coarse suspended impurities from the juice are removed by straining and then the juice is boiled. When the juice is slowly heated up to the boiling temperature, vegetable or chemical clarificants are used to flocculate colloids present in the juice. After clarification, the cane juice is boiled vigorously to 115°–117°C (striking point) with the constant stirring, and then concentrated into a thick almost semi-solid mass which, on cooling, solidifies into *gur*. Special types of *gur* are manufactured by decolourizing clarified cane juice by the use of sodium hydrosulphite, or by activated carbon obtained from paddy husk. *Gur* is produced in different forms, viz., as lumps of various sizes and shapes.

Generally, good quality *gur* has a light colour, good flavour, hardness, crystalline structure and good keeping qualities. *Gur* contains 65–85 per cent sucrose, 10–15 per cent invert sugar, and 2.5 per cent ash. *Gur* is an article of food that is peculiarly Indian. Because of its colour and flavour, it has a special appeal in certain preparations like coconut *burfi*, groundnut toffees, *holige*, etc. It lends itself to forming moulds and, since it does not easily crystallize because of the presence of invert sugar, it is very much preferred when non-crystalline candies are prepared. It is specially used when it has to act as a binder in the preparation of groundnut and puffed rice balls and other similar products. It is more pliable than sugar which forms crystals easily or gets caramelized beyond a certain temperature, The temperature to which jaggery syrup is to be heated to get the necessary consistency for different preparations is given in Table 26.1. The consistency is determined in the same way as in the case of sugar syrups (Sub-section 26.8.1).

Table 26.1 Consistency of *Gur* jaggery syrup at various temperatures

Preparation	Temp. (°C)	Consistency obtained	Behaviour of syrup
Balls: puffed rice, groundnut and gingelly balls	110°–120°	Soft ball	Transparent
Burfies	120°– 130°	Hard ball	Transparent
Caramel	130°–145°	Brittle ball	Transparent
Butterscotch	140°–145°	Hard and cracking	Opaque
Brittle	145°–150°	Multiple needle-like thread	Opaque

Madhya Pradesh contributes about 5% gur production in India. As the major producer of Jaggery, the country has recognized as one of the leading traders and exporters of Jaggery to the world. India exported 5,16,746 tonnes of jaggery and confectionery products to the world for the worth of

₹ 3,570.8 crores/430.9 USD Millions during the year 2023-24. Major Export Destinations (2023-24) are Indonesia, USA, Kenya, United Arab Emirates and Nepal.

26.1.2 *Khandasari* Sugar

For the manufacture of *khandasari* sugar (open pan sugar or *khand*), the cane juice extraction and clarification are done in the same way as in making *gur*. The clarified juice is boiled quickly to the required consistency. The crystals that separate are removed by centrifugation and dried. Recovery of *khandasari* sugar is about 9 to 10 per cent on the weight of the cane, which is rather low. During 2024-25, 61 per cent of the cane crushed in the country was used for the production of *gur* and *khandasari* sugar.

26.1.3 Raw Sugar

In India, sugar from sugarcane is obtained in three forms. They are raw sugar, refined sugar, and white sugar.

Raw sugar is made by crushing the sugarcane and extracting the juice by pressure. The juice from the mills is dark green in colour, turbid and acidic (pH 5.0–5.4). The sucrose content varies from 10–18 per cent. The juice is strained through fine screens to remove particles of fibre and suspended matter. Next, sufficient milk of lime is added to neutralize the acids present and heated to the boiling point. The lime and heat treatment cause the coagulation of the colloidal substances (mud or scum). The hot juice is then run into clarifiers for sedimentation of mud and decantation of the clear juice. The clarified juice, which is yellow to brown in colour and contains 85 per cent water, is evaporated in multiple-effect evaporators to a syrup containing 75–85 per cent sucrose. Sugar is crystallized from the syrup in single-effect vacuum pans. The crystals are separated from massecuite (mixture of crystals and mother liquor or molasses) by centrifugation.

The raw sugar so obtained consists of brown crystals with an adhering film of molasses. It contains 96–97 per cent sucrose, 0.75 to 1.0 per cent reducing sugar, and 0.5 to 0.75 per cent of moisture, the remaining being organic non-sugars.

26.1.4 Refined Sugar

In refining, raw sugar is dissolved in water and the solution filtered through animal charcoal which adsorbs the colouring matter and some other impurities. The decolourized solution is then evaporated in multiple-effect vacuum pans as in the case of raw sugar production, until the sugar crystallizes. The massecuite is separated into crystals and syrup, and the crystals are dried in revolving drums or granulators, through which a hot current of air is drawn. In the case of refined sugar, the size of the crystals is important and the crystals are screened into granulated sugars of different coarseness.

26.1.5 White Sugar

In India, most of the sugar manufactured from sugarcane is white or direct-consumption sugar. In this case, sugar is made from cane syrup directly without the intervening step of making raw sugar. The lime-treated cane juice, obtained as in the manufacture of raw sugar, is treated with sulphur dioxide (sulphitation) or carbon dioxide (carbonation). The former process is more commonly practised in India. The rest of the process is something of a repetition of the raw sugar manufacturing processes. Sulphitation produces a near white to yellow sugar, whereas the carbonation process gives a whiter product comparing favourably with refined sugar. The recovery of sugar varies from 9.5 to 11.5 per cent.

26.2 Beet Sugar

In the manufacture of beet sugar, most of the methods employed in cane sugar manufacture are used. Beet sugar is produced in a one-stage process from beet to refined sugar, unlike cane sugar which, in many cases, is produced as raw sugar which is then refined.

Sugar present in beet is extracted by membrane diffusion operated on the counter-current principle, using the batch system or a continuous diffuser. The thin juice obtained from the diffusion process is heavily limed and carbon dioxide is passed. The precipitate formed is quickly filtered off and carbon dioxide is again passed through the clear filtrate to precipitate residual lime salts. This is followed by a second filtration, after which the carbonated juice is treated with sulphur dioxide. The sulphated juice is boiled to drive off occluded gas and again filtered to remove all the precipitate. The purified thin juice is processed to the refined sugar product in much the same manner as the process used for making refined sugar from sugarcane.

26.3 Forms of Sugar

Various forms of sugar are available for use in food preparations. Some forms are crystalline solids and others are liquids (syrups). The following are some of the solid forms, other than *gur* and *khandasari*.

Granulated sugar: This is most extensively used in food preparation because of its sweetness, colour and solubility. It is available in different granule sizes.

Cube sugar: This is granulated sugar moistened with white sugar syrup, moulded into cubes, and then dried in that shape. The cubes are convenient for sweetening tea and coffee.

Powdered sugar: Such sugar (icing sugar) is made by pulverizing granulated sugar with or without the addition of any edible starch. Starch, if added, absorbs moisture and prevents the caking of the powdered sugar. Powdered sugar is mostly used in confectionery for dressing cakes, pastries, and other bakery products.

Brown sugar: Brown sugar contains some of the molasses from which the crystals are separated, and some glucose and fructose. Some flavour substances are present in brown sugar. Because of its pleasing and distinctive flavour, brown sugar is frequently used in baked products. The darker sugar has more flavour than a light sugar. Brown sugar forms lumps during storage. To overcome this difficulty, liquid brown sugar is now available.

Rock sugar: Rock sugar (*kallu sakkare*) is made by boiling sucrose solution to a syrup consistency (110°–115°C) and pouring it into big trays. Due to slow evaporation (takes three or four days), the sugar syrup forms big slabs with a few lumps on top. This is broken into big pieces and used, generally on festive occasions.

Diamond sugar: Diamond sugar is a decorative sugar in small rectangular crystals. It is used with betel nuts and in other confectionery.

26.4 Liquid Sweeteners

Liquid sweeteners are used in confectionery in place of sucrose. They have a characteristic flavour and generally contain a mixture of sugars.

26.4.1 Molasses

Molasses is the dark coloured syrupy product resulting after the removal of crystalline sucrose by centrifugation from the concentrated clarified cane juice. It amounts to about 3.6–4.5 per cent of the cane crushed. In India, molasses is obtained as a by-product chiefly in the manufacture of direct consumption white sugar and also in *khandasari* sugar manufacture. In other countries, it is a by-product of raw sugar manufacture.

The composition of molasses depends upon the way it is obtained in the manufacture of various forms of cane sugar. Generally, it contains about 35 per cent sucrose and 15 per cent invert sugar.

Most of the molasses produced in this country is used in the fermentation industry for the manufacture of industrial alcohol and potable spirits. Molasses is also used as a flavouring agent in hookah tobacco, for feeding cattle and, indirectly, in the manufacture of vinegar and yeast. Molasses obtained during sulphitation process, which is light brown in colour with a characteristic tang and flavour, is used for edible purposes and in the manufacture of confectionery.

26.4.2 Cane Syrup

Cane syrup is similar to molasses and is obtained by simply boiling sugarcane juice to a syrupy consistency. The term "liquid sugar" is used for commercial products, such as a solution of sucrose and solutions containing varying proportions of invert sugar. They are made from raw cane sugar and their composition varies from pure sucrose to full invert sugar.

26.4.3 Corn Syrup

Corn syrup is prepared by hydrolyzing corn starch with hydrochloric or sulphuric acid with heat and pressure. The syrup is a mixture of glucose, maltose and dextrin. The composition of the syrup is variable and depends upon the extent of hydrolysis. Glucose is the principal sugar and is present to the extent of 35 per cent. The dextrin content varies from 30–35 per cent. The presence of dextrin makes the syrup inhibit crystallization of sucrose and other sugars, and thus corn syrup is used when sugar crystallization is to be controlled.

Corn syrup may also be prepared by the enzymic hydrolysis of starch. Enzyme hydrolyzed corn syrup contains a higher proportion of glucose and less dextrin than acid hydrolyzed syrup. A combination of acid and enzyme hydrolysis is sometimes used in the production of corn syrup. The syrup thus obtained contains a high percentage of maltose.

26.4.4 High Fructose Syrup

Recently, a high-fructose corn syrup has been prepared from corn syrup by the use of the enzyme glucose isomerase. The enzyme converts half of the glucose in the syrup to fructose. Because fructose has almost twice the sweetening power of glucose, less syrup is needed to achieve the desired sweetening with high-fructose corn syrup than is required when the regular corn syrup is used. High-fructose syrup contains about 42 per cent fructose and is used in the manufacture of soft drinks, candies, preserves and some baked products.

26.4.5 Maple Syrup

Maple syrup is prepared by evaporating the sap of the maple tree (*Acer saccharum*). The sap contains sucrose and the syrup has a sugar content of 64–68 per cent. The importance of the syrup is its special flavour. The sap, as it comes from the tree, has no flavour but it develops as it is evaporated into syrup. Organic acids present in the sap enter into the process of developing flavour by heat. Maple syrup is used most frequently for sweetening pancakes and waffles, and occasionally to add flavour and sweetness to baked products.

26.5 Reactions of Sugar

Sugar is extensively used in confectionery and other foods. The kind of use depends upon the reactions that it undergoes on heating and hydrolysis. The essential component contributing to the texture of confectionery is the sugar crystal. Sugar can be crystallized in different forms and sizes by varying factors influencing crystal growth.

26.5.1 Caramelization

Sugar, when heated by itself or in a highly concentrated solution, undergoes a change called caramelization (see also Subsection 2.2.3.). As dry sugar is heated, it melts to a colourless liquid and it soon develops a brown colour, giving a pleasing characteristic caramel aroma. Caramelization can be halted by the addition of water when the desired colour and flavour have developed. Sugar breaks down during caramelization and various organic acids are formed. Caramelization of sugar is useful in the preparation of confections.

26.5.2 Hydrolysis

Sugar undergoes hydrolysis with acids or enzyme (invertase) when it is converted into a mixture of glucose and fructose (invert sugar). Invert sugar can prevent or help control the degree of sucrose crystallization, because glucose and fructose crystallize more slowly than sucrose and also because a mixture of invert sugar and sucrose has greater solubility in water than sucrose. Thus, the use of invert sugar in candy preparations can alter these properties. Invert sugar, apart from limiting the amount of crystallization of sucrose, encourages the formation of small crystals, and this gives smoothness to candy. The hygroscopicity of invert sugar helps prevent more chewy candies from drying out and becoming overtly brittle. Invert sugar is sweeter than sucrose and thus has an effect upon the sweetness of candy.

26.5.3 Crystallization

The way sugar crystallizes from its solution is of great importance in the preparation of confections and other sugar-containing products. Fairly large quantities of sugar are soluble in water at room temperature and the amount dissolved increases with temperature. The amount of sugar dissolved in boiling water is about twice the amount of that dissolved at room temperature in the same volume of water. When a solution of sugar saturated at the boiling point of water is cooled, crystals of sugar start forming. The size of the crystals formed depends on the rate of formation of nuclei at which the crystals grow and the crystal growth rate around these nuclei. In the preparation of candies, the size of crystals formed and the speed of crystallization are very important in achieving the right structure. If the crystal formation is rapid, the size of the crystals is large as there are only a few nuclei on which the crystal formation can grow. Confectionery with large crystals has a grainy, almost a sandy feel on the tongue. On the contrary, if the crystals formed are small the finished product has a smooth velvety structure. Considerable care is required to prepare such confections.

Under carefully controlled conditions, a sugar solution saturated at the boiling point of water may not form crystals on cooling the solution. Thus, the solution holds more sugar than can a solution of sugar and water at the same temperature which has not been heated previously to a higher temperature. Such a solution is said to be supersaturated. The cooler the saturated solution becomes, the greater is the degree of supersaturation. A high degree of supersaturation is essential if very small crystals are to be formed. In such a case, many nuclei are available for crystal growth, and the sugar is precipitated quickly as very small crystals. The rates of nuclei formation and crystallization are influenced by a number of factors, such as the degree of supersaturation, the temperature, the time at which agitation or beating of the supersaturated solution begins to initiate crystallization, the duration of beating, and the presence of substances inhibiting crystallization.

The presence of glucose in sugar solution interferes with the crystallization of sucrose. Therefore, the addition of free glucose, corn syrup or honey to sugar solutions in candy preparations promotes the formation of many tiny crystals. In the alternative, ingredients like cream of tartar, lemon juice or vinegar, that bring about inversion, may be added to the sugar solution, causing crystallization to occur less rapidly. Fats also are useful in inhibiting the rate of growth of crystals and preventing their formation. They coat the sugar crystals and make it difficult for additional sugar to precipitate onto the existing crystals. This method is thus useful in making smooth candies and non-crystalline candies. Butter and cream are the customary fats used in candy making.

26.6 Confectionery

The art of making confectionery is an old one. Confectionery is essentially a sugar-based industry and includes sugar-boiled confectionery (candies or sweets), chocolate confectionery, and the traditional Indian sweetmeats. It is a product liked by all, especially children. Throughout the world, confectionery is recognized as an ingredient of a balanced diet and it has a wide socio-economic and health impact.

The commercial production of confectionery started in the 19th Century and its development has been phenomenal. In advanced countries, confectionery is produced on a very large scale and the annual per capita consumption is of the order of 20–25 kg, while in India it is just about 0.1 kg. The development of the organized confectionery industry in India is of recent origin. It mainly developed during the Second World War and immediate post-war years following the cessation of imports and increase in internal demand. The production of confectionery in the organized sector is of the order of about 35,000 tonnes, which is only about one-third of the installed capacity of the industry. In addition to commercial production, there is considerable production of sweetmeats in the unorganized sector. Authentic data on the number of sweetmeats produced are not available. However, the quantity of sweetmeats prepared in the country is quite large, taking into consideration the amount of *khoa* (Subsection 21.11.2), one of the raw materials used in some sweetmeat preparations, which is of the order of 35,000 tonnes per annum.

26.7 Confectionery Ingredients

A variety of ingredients are employed in the manufacture of candy. The chief among them are sugar and syrups, an account of which is given in an earlier section of this chapter. Dairy products like butter and milk—whole, condensed, evaporated, skim and dried—are used. The edible portion of fruits, such as apple, lemon, orange, pineapple, etc., and dry fruits like figs and raisins, are also used. Amongst nuts, almond, coconut, the toasted edible portion of peanuts, pecans and walnuts, find use. Other ingredients used are starch and its derivatives, fats, flavours, colours, gums, pectin and gelatin. In addition, in chocolate confectionery, cocoa products are used.

26.7.1 Starch and its Derivatives

In the confectionery industry, maize starch powder and its derivatives like liquid glucose, thin-boiling starch, dextrin, dextrose, sorbitol, and malto-dextrin, are being used in large quantities. In our country, there is negligible use of these products except for liquid glucose which is used in substantial amounts.

Liquid glucose, as indicated earlier, is obtained by the acid and/or enzyme hydrolysis of starch. The combined acid and enzyme hydrolysis gives a syrup of high dextrose equivalent (DE) and better quality. Liquid glucose is mostly used in toffee, chocolate, lollipops, lozenges, chewing gum, bubble gum, and *chikki*. It is used with sugar and the proportion between the two sweeteners depends upon the cost and the final product. Liquid glucose is more expensive than sugar. Because liquid glucose contains dextrose, maltose and dextrin, it effectively controls the crystallization of other sugars, which is a very important factor in confectionery manufacture.

Maize starch powder itself is used in the manufacture of chewing gum, pastries and panned sweets. In India, starch is generally used as a dusting powder in the confectionery industry. Starch derivatives like crystalline dextrose, sorbitol, and maltodextrin, are used in the confectionery industry because they confer special characteristics to confectionery, such as prevention of drying, improvement of shelf life, increase of nutritive value, etc. As already stated, the use of these derivatives in the confectionery industry in India is negligible.

26.7.2 Confectionery Fats

Confectionery fats can be divided into two categories: fats for general and traditional functions, and fats associated with chocolate confectionery. Fats play an important part in providing the desired textural property, which can be adjusted by the amount of fat used and how it is mixed. Fats lubricate the ingredients, thus improving their overall eating qualities, which are dependent on moisturization and tenderness. Confectionery fats should have a sharp melting point at approximately body temperature, be stable against all types of rancidity, and have an optimal solid-to-liquid ratio to ensure no waxy or oily mouthfeel of the finished product. These requirements are determined by the triglyceride composition of the fat.

Cocoa butter is an essential ingredient in the manufacture of chocolates. It has certain strong functional properties. It contracts on solidification, which makes possible the moulding of chocolate blocks and bars with attractively shaped confections. It exhibits distinct brittle fracture below 20°C. It has a sharp melting point around 30°–32°C. The completely liquid fat displays a marked tendency for supercooling, which enables enrobing of chocolate products. The melting point and solid-to-liquid ratio of cocoa fat gives the finished product excellent snap property. Attempts have been made to substitute certain fats of tree origin for cocoa butter in chocolate manufacture without much success so far. With some processing, these fats could give products with good functional characteristics.

In Indian confectioneries, certain products are deep fat fried, while in others, fats are derived from the ingredients. *Ghee* is the traditional confectionery fat. In the fresh condition, *ghee* has an attractive aroma. However, it is prone to rancidity and staleness. Because of its cheapness, *vanaspati* has almost replaced *ghee* in the preparation of confections. Indian confectionery products where the structure is furnished by *ghee* or *vanaspati* lose their structure, especially during, the summer months, owing to oil seepage. By appropriate hydrogenation, a fat of required functional properties should be obtained to overcome this defect.

26.7.3 Colours and Flavours in Confectionery

In order to introduce attractiveness and variety to confectionery, addition of colours and flavours becomes necessary. Colours are used to supplement deficiencies in colour, increase eye appeal and be suggestive of the flavour employed. For example, an orange colour to match orange flavour or a yellow colour to match lemon flavour may be used. Colours used should be harmless, readily soluble in water, and should not be affected by the action of acids, alkalis, temperature and light. The amount of colour used should be small and no artificial colour should be added when the product has a rich natural colour as in chocolate. Lemon, orange, pink, coffee and chocolate shades, are the most commonly used colours.

There are two classes of colour used in confectionery—natural and synthetic. There is much concern regarding the use of synthetic colours. Natural colours like those obtained from black and purple grapes, red beet, florets of safflower, rind of ripe fruits, and from some insects, as also turmeric and saffron, are useful as colourants. In the case of artificial colour, only the permitted colours are to be used and it is better to use only mild colours.

A wide variety of flavours are used in confectionery. They belong to three main categories: natural, synthetic and blends. Natural flavours are prepared mainly from the skins and peels of fruits, and from roots, etc. The most popular natural flavour is vanilla. Other important natural flavours are those of lemon, orange, coffee and cocoa. Synthetic flavours can be used when the desired flavours cannot be completely extracted from natural raw materials or are too expensive. A number of synthetic flavours are produced commercially. To simulate natural flavour, acids such as citric, tartaric and malic, are used. Synthetic flavours are powerful and should be used with caution. The dosage should be just sufficient to suggest the desired flavour and should not leave an intense after-taste in the mouth. There are also flavours prepared by blending natural and synthetic materials. It is better to use blends rather than any pure or synthetic flavours.

26.7.4 Gums, Pectin and Gelatin in Confectionery

Some of the softer candies, such as marshmallows, gumdrops and jellies, owe their chewiness in part to gums, pectin and gelatin. These are valuable as binders, fillers, stabilizers, and coatings. Gums, in general, are odourless and tasteless. They form viscous solutions or show jelling properties as the material cools. Gums also prevent crystal growth and emulsify fat to avoid fat separation in candies. Gums used in confectionery are gum arabic and gum tragacanth. Seaweed extracts, such as agar-agar and carrageenan, are also used. However, these are being replaced by starch and pectin. Gelatin is used in the confectionery industry because of its elastic consistency and its power of holding air and water. It also inhibits the crystallization or graining of sugar.

26.7.5 Cocoa Products

Cocoa is a very important raw material in confectionery. Because of its rich brown colour, exotic taste and aroma, it is a favourite material for bakers, ice cream producers and other food manufacturers. Its most important use is in the production of chocolate and chocolate coated or enrobed confectionery. A large variety of goods like plain chocolate, milk chocolate, flavoured chocolate, and chocolate coated nuts, fruits, wafers, and biscuits, are produced and they are very popular. For an account of cocoa and cocoa products, see Chapter 12.

26.8 Sugar-Boiled Confectionery

From boiled sugar solution, two types of confectionery are prepared—crystalline and non-crystalline (amorphous). The temperature of boiling sugar solution, the ingredients used, and the method of handling the supercooled sugar solution, determine the nature of the end product. Crystalline candies are chewed easily and they may be cut with a knife. The principal crystalline candies are fondant and fudge. Considerable care is required in the preparation of crystalline candy with a smooth and velvety structure. Amorphous candies, in contrast, have a heterogeneous structure and crack into pieces rather than being cut into desired shapes with a knife (e.g., toffee and brittles). Caramels, the softest of the amorphous candies, however, may be cut.

26.8.1 Crystalline Confectionery

Fondant and fudge are crystalline confectionery. The first step in the preparation of sugar-boiled confectionery is to dissolve the amount of sugar used completely by adding sufficient water. In crystalline or cream candy, a smooth textured, soft yet firm, product is to be obtained. This is possible by the addition of ingredients to the sugar solution, which aid in the formation of fine crystals. In the preparation of fondant, the ingredients added are acid (cream of tartar) or invert sugar and glucose or corn syrup. The candy mixture in solution is next concentrated by boiling until it reaches the appropriate doneness. Slow heating results in excess acid hydrolysis and may produce too soft a product. This principle is also used in the preparation of sugar moulds that are made in this country on festive occasions. The doneness of the candy mixture is determined by measuring the temperature of the boiling solution. For fondant, it is reached at a temperature of 113°–114°C. Another method of measuring doneness in the making of candies is by dropping a small portion of boiling syrup into very cold water, allowing the syrup to cool, and evaluating its consistency. In the case of fondant it is the softball shape. The consistency of syrup at different temperature is given in Table 26.2.

In the preparation of fondant, at the appropriate stage, the boiled solution is poured on a smooth flat surface and allowed to cool to 40°C. Then it is beaten continuously until it becomes a creamy mass. At first, the mixture becomes cloudy from the air beaten into it, and then sets into a stiff mass.

Table 26.2 Temperature of tests for syrups and candies

Product	Temp 0°C	Test	Description of test
Syrup	110 – 112	Thread	When syrup is dropped from a spoon, syrup spins a 5 cm thread
Barfi, Fondant, Fudge	112 – 115	Soft ball	Forms a soft ball when syrup is dropped into cold water; flattens on removal from water
Caramel	118 – 120	Firm ball	Forms a firm ball when syrup is dropped into cold water; does not flatten on removal from water
Divinity, *Ladu* (*Laddoo*), Marshmallow	120 – 130	Hard ball	Forms a ball hard enough to hold its shape when syrup is dropped into cold water
Butterscotch, Toffee	132 – 143	Soft crack	Forms threads which are hard but not brittle when syrup is dropped into cold water
Brittle, Glace	150 – 154	Hard crack	Forms thread which are brittle when syrup is dropped
Barley Sugar	160	Clear liquid	Sugar melts
Caramel	170	Brown liquid	Sugar melts and browns

Source: *Indian Journal of Home Science.* Vol.7, p.152.

A 24 hours ripening period in a lightly covered container softens the crystalline candy slightly and promotes smoothness.

Fondants are used in confectionery for numerous purposes. They are used to make mints. In this case, the supersaturated sugar mixture in the boiling kettle is cooled to about 71 °C and flavoured with mint. The mint quickly solidifies on further cooling. Softened fondant is used in coating fruit and nut mixtures that are moulded and sliced. Fondants are largely used as cream centres of chocolate confectionery.

The principles of making fudge do not differ from those of making fondant. Butter and milk, used in this case as ingredients, interfere with crystallization. Corn sugar and acid may also be used in addition. Fat and essence are added to the solution after it reaches the boiling point (117°C). Next, it is processed as in the case of fondant.

26.8.2 Amorphous Confectionery

It is somewhat easier to make amorphous candies than the crystalline ones. Crystallization of sugar is prevented either by cooking the solution to a high temperature so that the finished product hardens quickly before crystals have a chance to form, or by adding large amounts of interfering substances, or a combination of both. Temperatures used for making different confections vary. The final temperature of syrup for caramels is 118°–120°C. During cooking, a brown colour develops owing to the caramelization of sugar and also due to reactions of amino groups of milk proteins and reducing sugars, when milk is one of the ingredients. In the preparation of caramels, corn syrup, fats, and concentrated milk products are used as ingredients. Brittles are made merely by the melting and caramelization of sugar. Toffee is made from simple sucrose syrup with the addition of cream of tartar, vinegar or lemon juice. Flavour substances are added when the solution has cooled sufficiently. Spongy candies like marshmallows and gum drops are made using gelatin as an ingredient.

26.9 Chocolate Confectionery

Chocolate is a highly nutritive and widely appreciated confectionery. Because of its satisfying value and high energy, it is manufactured and consumed in large quantities in the Western world. In India, for some years, chocolate confectionery was a home-made fancy product, prepared from imported chocolate to cater to the sophisticated taste of foreigners and well-to-do Indians. Production of chocolate all the way from cocoa, for the first time in India, was made during World War II. However, production in the early stages depended entirely on the import of cocoa beans. The high cost of the imported cocoa and the incidence of taxation on cocoa products have made chocolate confectionery out of reach for the common man. Only about 2,000–2,500 tonnes per annum of chocolate confectionery is produced in the country.

Realizing the importance of indigenous cultivation of cocoa, the development of plantation of cocoa has been taken up in the country. At present, India is self-sufficient in respect of cocoa beans. However, the climatic conditions of the country are not conducive for the production of chocolate confectionery. The shelf-life of chocolate, particularly in the summer months, is poor. Production of chocolates that stand summer temperatures, such as sugar-coated chocolate candies, and lowering taxation on materials used in chocolate industry, are needed to increase the production of this nutritive and delightful food and bring it within the reach of many more people.

Chocolate confectionery manufacture starts with cocoa mass or bitter chocolate (see Chapter 12) from which plain or sweet chocolate and milk chocolate are obtained. In making chocolates, the ingredients—chocolate liquor, cocoa butter, sugar, and milk solids in the case of milk chocolates—are subjected to fine grinding in a melangeur, which results in the reduction of the size of the sugar crystals and other ingredients. The product at this stage will be a flaky powder. This is next "conched" or kneaded in special heated tanks provided with pressure rollers that grind and aerate the now melted mass to develop increased smoothness, viscosity and flavour. Conched liquid chocolate is tempered by stirring in a heated and then cooled kettle to promote controlled crystallization of the cocoa fat. This treatment helps obtain chocolate of uniform texture.

Tempered chocolate is used for making bars and coating candy pieces. For making bars, the thickened chocolate mass is poured into preheated moulds and, when it hardens after cooling, the bars are tapped out. The coating of small and round confections is carried out by panning. The candies are added to revolving heated pans and molten chocolate is sprayed into the pan. As the candies gently tumble, they become uniformly coated with chocolate. Then the pans are chilled with cool air to solidify the chocolate coating. Chocolate panned items frequently are further polished and glazed.

Larger candy pieces and those that are not round are coated with molten chocolate by a method known as *enrobing*. In this case, the candy centres are first "bottomed" by passing on a screen over a layer of molten chocolate. Then they pass through a tunnel in which they are showered by molten chocolate. The pieces emerging from the tunnel quickly cool, solidifying the coating.

26.10 Indian Confectionery

Indian confectionery products (sweetmeats), occupy a privileged place in our social customs, is always associated with happy and gay occasions. There are many varieties of preparations, each with its own unique texture, flavour and other sensory attributes. The types of sweetmeats differ from region to region, each region has distinct regional preferences in the products produced. Traditional Indian confectioneries are essentially cottage or home-scale preparations. Certain confections like rice pudding (*payasam*) and candy-type products based on coconut and sugar or jaggery are prepared only in households. Sweetmeats available in the market are prepared throughout the country. However, the data on the quantity of total production of sweetmeats are not available since the industry is not organized .

26.10.1 Classes of Indian Confectionery

Indian confection may be broadly classified under four groups depending on the base ingredients used:

1. *Khoa* (open pan concentrated milk)-based products like *barfi*, *pedhas*, *gulab jamun*, *kalakand*, etc.
2. *Chana* (acid-precipitated casein)-based products, like *sandesh*, *rasgulla*, *ras malai*, *cham cham*, *channa kheer*, etc.
3. Flour, sugar and fat-based products like *sohan halwa*, *soan papdi*, *mysore pak*, *laddoo*, *boondi*, *jalebi*, etc.
4. Others like walnut *burfi* and other nut candies, *sajappa*, *shrikhand*, etc.

26.10.2 Ingredients of Sweetmeats

Major ingredients used in Indian confectionery are *khoa*, *chana*, *besan* (Bengal-gram flour), sugar, *vanaspati*, *ghee*, edible oils, maida, dried fruits, and occasionally milk.

Khoa is a major raw material of Indian confectionery. It is made by the slow evaporation of milk in open kettles, with constant stirring. Its moisture content is about 30 per cent and its stability is very limited (2–4 days).

Chana is another major raw material for many Indian confections. It is prepared by precipitation of milk by the addition of aged milk whey or lactic and citric acids. For many sweetmeats, such as *rasgulla*, aged whey is preferred. The average yield of *chana* ranges from 16–18 per cent for cow milk and 22–24 per cent for buffalo milk. *Chana* contains about 50 per cent moisture and its storage life is 2 days if properly packed and stored.

26.10.3 Features and Composition of Sweetmeats

The method of preparation of sweetmeat varies very widely. Certain products are deep fat fried and immersed in sugar syrup (*jalebi*, *jamun* and *boondi*); others are boiled in sugar syrup (*rasgulla*). Sweets like *sandesh* and *sohan halwa* are obtained by a careful mixing and heating of the ingredients.

The physical forms of Indian sweetmeats vary. Products like *mysore pak*, *sandesh*, *barfi* and *peda* are solid; *kalakand* and *rabri* are semi-solid; and *rasgulla* and *jamun* are balls of protein-starch with the interstitial spaces filled with sugar syrup.

With regard to moisture content, sweetmeats show a wide variation. Some have less than 3 per cent moisture (*mysore pak*, *soan papdi*), some have 10–20 per cent (*pedha*, *barfi*, *jalebi*, etc.); others have more than 20 per cent of moisture (*rasgulla*, *shrikhand*). Similarly, they vary in their fat content. Those containing up to 5 per cent fat are *shrikhand* and *rasgulla*; about 20 per cent are *barfi*, cashew *barfi*, *sandesh*, etc.; and 25 per cent and above are *mysore pak*, *soan papdi*, etc. The sugar content of Indian sweetmeats is invariably high, lying between 35 and 55 per cent.

The shelf-life of Indian confections is poor. Those with a moisture content of about 15 per cent have a shelf-life of only 2–5 days. Storage results in loss of flavour, staleness, rancidity, discolouration, change of structure, and microbial spoilage.

ISI has laid down specification for confectionery products. Standards have also been developed for raw materials and additives. However, unpermitted colours (Rhodamine-B and Metanil Yellow) are still being used in the preparation of sweetmeats. This should be forbidden from the point of view of consumer interest. Even the use of permitted colours should be controlled as, when used in excess, they could be harmful.

Most Indian confectionery products are semi-preserved and, therefore, their microbial status is an important factor in their utilization. Market samples of various sweetmeats are found to contain pathogenic organisms. The spoilage is low in the case of products whose moisture content is low. Even though high-sugar and low-moisture contents do not favour microbial growth, there is danger of water absorption due to improper packaging. Indian sweetmeats are mostly catered without packaging. Microbial spoilage of the finished product could also be due to poor microbial quality of the raw materials used. *Khoa* is found to contain many pathogens. Proper hygienic practices are to be observed to prepare safe products.

There has been a growing demand for Indian confectionery within the country. There is also a limited export market which is expected to improve. Traditional small-scale or home-scale production can no longer be able to cope with the demands. In addition, proper quality control, standardization of the operation for large-scale handling, packaging, and long shelf-life, are to be worked out. This requires investigation both at the basic and applied levels. Some improvements at the technological level have been achieved. For example, standardized ready mixes for *jamun* and *jalebi* are in the market. Methods have been worked out for the preparation of *khoa* on a commercial scale. A process for the manufacture of *shrikhand* has been developed. Yet, more systematic and comprehensive investigations are necessary to put Indian sweetmeat production on a sound commercial basis.

26.11 Confectionery as a Source of Energy

There is calorie shortage in India, especially among the deprived groups of its population. A high percentage of our children below the age of five are under-nourished or malnourished. Considering the great appeal of confectionery, especially to children, it would appear quite natural to use this medium for meeting at least part of the shortage of calories. About 15–20 per cent of calories are sugar-derived in USA and in India it is just about a tenth or so of this amount. Consumption of sugar to provide up to 20 per cent of calorie requirements is not a health hazard. However, it can cause dental caries. It has been proved that dental caries is caused when sugar is consumed with some frequency in between meals, and when it is in a form that adheres to the tooth. Sugar consumed as a part of the meal is reported to be less carcinogenic. Therefore, promoting the use of confectionery products as a part of well balanced diets, especially for growing children, seems nutritionally sound and desirable.

Confectionery manufacture in the organized sector of the industry is quite expensive and providing even a moderate 100 Kcal per child through such confectionery is beyond the reach of the vulnerable low-income group of the population. Also, most commercial confectionery products contain mainly sugar and other sweeteners with added flavour and colour, and contain few other ingredients, such as protein and fat, that could enhance its nutritive value. On the other hand, confectionery products prepared traditionally in homes or on a cottage-scale level can provide inexpensive and nutritious sweet snacks rich in calories.

26.11.1 Chikki—A Nutritious Snack

A confection containing about 10–12 per cent of protein which is good to eat, inexpensive and with a good shelf-life could help fight malnutrition of the poor. The Indian traditional confection, *chikki*, could well serve this purpose. *Chikki* is very popular, particularly amongst children. It can be made in such a way that unit amounts of nutrition can be dispensed to children with minimum effort. It can be munched without further preparation. It can be produced hygienically on a cottage scale or industrially on a small scale. It has a shelf-life varying from 2–4 weeks, which can be increased up to 12 weeks with proper packaging.

Chikki is a jaggery-based sweet, commonly containing groundnut, but also made from puffed Bengal gram, sesame, puffed rice, coconut scrapping, and so on, either individually or in combination. In the preparation of groundnut *chikki*, groundnuts with a low fat content yield a good quality product that is also less susceptible to rancidity on storage. Groundnut is "medium" roasted on a sandbath (120°–125°C). Jaggery used should be hard yellow or brownish in colour and have a high sucrose-to-glucose ratio. The jaggery is dissolved in an adequate amount of water and filtered to remove extraneous material. The solution is heated to 145° to 150°C, cooking on a medium flame after reaching a temperature of 130°C, which imparts brittleness and a mild caramel flavour to the product. Groundnuts (or other ingredients) are transferred into the syrup and mixed thoroughly till all the nuts get coated with jaggery syrup.

The hot mass is then transferred to wooden boards dusted with starch. Using a roller, it is spread and rolled to a thickness of about 8 mm. The rolled mass is then cut into square slabs (sometimes, they are shaped into balls depending upon local consumer preference). The slabs are then removed from the board, cooled to the room temperature, wrapped in suitable wrappings, sealed and packaged in air tight tins. *Chikki* stored this way will have a shelf-life of 8–12 weeks.

Groundnut *chikki* containing equal parts of groundnut and jaggery is a good source of protein in addition to calories. 100 g of such *chikki* contains about 13 g of protein and supplies 430 Kcal of energy. Use of 32–40 g *chikki* provides 4 to 5 g protein and 155–190 Kcal. *Chikki* is a high-protein low-cost food that can be a useful supplementary diet to solve the malnutrition of young children of our country.

CHAPTER

27

Honey

Bees appeared millions of years ago, much before man appeared upon the earth. It is also known as *Madhu*. Honey hunting began 8000 years ago and was documented for its medicinal properties as back as 2100 and 2000 BC. It is seen in pre-historic cave paintings in Central India's Bhimbetka rock shelters and caves in Valencia, Spain.

Even as early as the Rigveda, the *Rbhu* brothers are credited with building artificial hives of reeds and straw, in which were fixed sections from a natural hive. The Mahabharatha has references to bee gardens, apiary keepers and pollen-yielding plants, suggesting some degree of commercialisation by then.

Honey bees the genes *Apis* is the type of bees, the beekeepers use to convert the nectar collected by bees into honey by a process of regurgitation and evaporation. Also, honey gathered depends upon types of Apis. Masika from the common honey bee (*Apis cerana* indica), Bhramara (*Apis dorsata*) Ksaudra from the dwarf ksudra bee (*Apis florea*).

Besides the above, Charaka and Sushruta mention–*Pauttika*, *chatra arghya*, *auddhalika* and *dala*, all of which have been identified in modern terms. Honey produced is further classified as Mono or Multi-floral pollen grain of flowers.

Nepal is richest in types of honey bee species. At least five different species of honeybees are found in Nepal.

- *Apis dorsata* are called the rock bee or cliff bees and are giant in size
- *Apis cerana* indica is the Indian or Asian hive bee
- *Apis florea* are the dwarf bees
- *Apis mellifera* is also known as the European or Italian honeybee, it is regarded as the medium size honeybees.
- *Apis laboriosa*, is the largest honeybee and found in higher altitudes.

27.1 Production

In 2023, global production of honey was 1.8 million tonnes, led by China with 24% of the world total. Other major producers were Turkiye, Ethiopia, Iran, India. In India, Uttar Pradesh produced 24,820 tonnes in the year 2023-24.

Table 27.1 Natural Honey Production, 2023

1.	China	tonnes	463,500
2.	Turkiye	tonnes	114,886
3.	Ethiopia	tonnes	84,591
4.	Iran	tonnes	80,389
5.	Argentina	tonnes	73,395
6.	India	tonnes	70,850
7.	Russia	tonnes	64,511
8.	Brazil	tonnes	64,189
9.	United States	tonnes	62,855

World Honey Bee Day is being celebrated every year on 3rd Saturday of August.

The sweetness of honey is due to monosaccharides, fructose, glucose and approximately the same relative sweetness of sucrose. Its chemical properties and distinctive flavours, colours and moisture contents make it an ideal sweetener in the baking industry.

27.2 Physical and Chemical Properties

The quality, of honey depends upon the water content, the type of flower and sugar contents (glucose and fructose). Fresh honey saturated cooled liquid. In supercooled honey, glucose will precipitate. The density of honey at 20 is 1.38 and 1.45 kg/l. The melting point of crystallized honey is between 40°C and 50°C. (104 and 112°F), below this temperature, honey is metastable. The ratio of fructose to glucose determines crystallization with a high percentage of glucose honey crystalizes soon after harvesting and vice versa. Also the dextrin content, water and temperature affect the rate of crystallization. At temperature 13°C to 17°C (55 and 63°F) crystallization is fastest.

Normal honey is known to be supercooled liquid. At low temperature, it will not freeze and its viscosity increases. Honey has a glass transition between –42 and –51 (–44 and –60 °F). Below this temperature, honey enters a glassy state and will become an amorphous solid and non-crystalline.

Viscosity: Honey with 20% of water has a viscosity of 20 poise. Viscosity is temperature dependent, Honey with 16% water, at 70°C (158°F), has a viscosity around 2 poise, upon cooling honey becomes more viscous (14 °C) it will reach 600 poise. It has low surface tension 50-60 mJ/m thus wettable quality is similar to water and glycerine. Both viscosity and wettability result in stickiness.

Electrolytes (acids and minerals) are present in honey. It exhibits varying degrees of electrical conductivity. Refractive index of honey can be determined by refractometer. The refractive index for honey ranges from 1.504 at 13% water content to 1.474 at 25%. Its polarizing property gives fructose a negative rotation and glucose a positive one.

Its colour varies from pale yellow to dark brown. Honey is Hygroscopic hence absorbs moisture from the atmosphere which depends upon the humidity of the atmosphere. Because of this inherent nature, it requires to be stored in sealed cartons to have a longer shelf life. Fermentation occurs in the presence of yeast. To increase shelf life honey, it is pasteurised.

Caramelized honey depends on its composition, Caramelization typically occurs between 70°C and 110°C (158 and 230°F). Presence of acids in honey, act as catalysts for caramelization and the presence of melanoidins bring about Maillard reaction. Caramelization also occurs when heated. Fructose caramelizes at these temperatures. It has in small amounts of molecular oxides and at temperatures 70°C (158°F) to 110°C (230°F). Due to Maillard reaction, darkening of honey takes place. The acids form darkened compounds are called melanoidins.

Honey has poor thermal conductivity. Honey takes substantially longer to liquefy when just above the melting point than at elevated temperatures. It takes up to 24 hours to melt 20 kg of crystallized honey, at 40°C (104°F).

The pH range of honey is 3.9-6.1. Honey has a low pH primarily due to the conversion of glucose into hydrogen peroxide and gluconic acid by glucose oxidase 3. This low pH might also contribute to the bactericidal activity of honey, demonstrated by the titration of the pH of 10-40% honey solutions from 3.4-3.5 to 7.0 combined with neutralization of other bactericidal factors (H_2O_2, MGO and bee defensin-1) reduced the bactericidal activity of honey to the same level of a honey-equivalent sugar solution.

Fermentation

Fermented honey is a beverage called honey wine. It is an alcoholic product prepared by adding yeast (*Saccharomyces cerevisiae*). Mead varieties include drinks called *metheglin* (with spices or herbs), *melomel* (with fruit juices, such as grape, specifically called *pyment*), *hippocras* (with cinnamon) and sack mead(high concentration of honey). Possibly the world's oldest fermented beverage dating to 9,000 years ago. Honey has poor thermal conductivity and takes a long time to reach thermal equilibrium.

Honey with high fructose content as in acacia has low glycaemic index of 55 and less.

27.3 Nutrition

In honey, carbohydrates as a source of saccharides have mainly fructose 38.5% and glucose (about 31%) the ratio is similar to synthetic invertase which is approximately 48% fructose, 47% glucose and 5% sucrose. Honey has besides this maltose, hence honey is nutritive sweetener with trace amounts of vitamins and minerals. It is poor in protein, has negligible 0.5%, they are present in enzymes and amino acids. It has 18 to 20 amino acids. It has other functional compounds like antioxidants, such as Chrysin and Pinobanksin, vitamin C and catalase Pinocembrin.

The oligosaccharides in honey are maltose, sucrose, melezitose, palatinose, trehalose, raffinose, isomaltose, maltulose, maltotriose, panose, erlose, turanose, gentiobiose and cellobiose. Honey has markedly increased number of *Lactobacillus* and it increases lactic acid production hence it is prebiotic.

Honey from the review has been found to contain 181 constituents. Predominantly although it contains only mono and oligosaccharides, it has bioactive constituents such as phenolic compounds, flavonoids, organic acids, carotenoid-derived compounds, nitric oxide (NO) metabolites, ascorbic acid, Maillard reaction products, aromatic compounds, trace elements, vitamins, amino acids and proteins. Some varieties of honey contain kynurenic acid (a tryptophan metabolite with neuro-active activity) which is responsible for antinociceptive and antimicrobial properties. It also has a number of enzymes such as glucose oxidase, diastase, invertase, phosphatase, catalase and peroxidase. Of all the enzymes in honey, diastase and invertase have received the most attention, Diastase is the enzyme responsible for converting starch to dextrins and sugars. Invertase is primarily responsible for converting sucrose in nector to glucose and fructose. Raw honey contains an enzyme called glucose oxidase that when combined with water, produces hydrogen peroxide, a mild anticeptic that is responsible for its antibacterial properties.

However, chromium, manganese and selenium are very important trace element present in honey. Sulphur, boron, cobalt, fluoride, iodide, molybdenum and silicon are also important elements in human nutrition. Though the RDI value is not mentioned for choline, 0.3-25 mg/kg and 0.06 to 5 mg/kg acetylcholine are present in honey which are important nutrients for cardiac, brain and cellular membrane functions.

27.4 Aroma Components

Flavours, colours of honey vary based upon the nectar the bee collects. Depending upon the nectar specific honey has specific medicinal value. The study of pollens and spores in raw honey (melissopalynology) determines the floral source of honey.

The acids present are aromatic and aliphatic. The aliphatic acids contribute greatly to the flavour of honey by interacting with the flavours. Organic acids accounts to 0.17-1.17% of the mixture, with gluconic acid formed due to glucose oxidase.

The other organic acids are formic, acetic, butyric, citric, lactic, malic, pyroglutamic, propionic, valeric, capronic, palmitic and succinic.

Table 27.2 Comparison between physio-chemical parameters or ripened and unripened honey

Parameter	Unripened	Ripened
Moisture %	19.8	18.4
Sucrose %	8.4	8.0
Fructose %	38.6	39.4
Glucose %	30.4	33.2
Reducing Sugar %	58.8	60.8
Ph	4.2	5.0
Total acidity meq/kg	26.6	23.0

Source: Journal of Food and Technology, Vol. 43(5), Oct. 2006, pp. 535-537

27.5 The Quality of Honey

The content of moisture determines the honey quality. Honey tends to ferment above 18.5% moisture, leading to spoilage. Honey containing greater than 18.5% moisture is found to be too thick in consistency and if less than 18% judged as not thick. Bees add their valuable enzymes to the honey, to reduce the moisture content and seal it with a thick film of wax when the moisture reaches 18%.

Hydroxymethylfurfural (HMF) content is used as a parameter to determine quality. HMF aldehyde is a substance produced by the chemical breakdown of fructose in the presence of acids. Good quality of honey is known to have low HMF content. High HMF content indicates that the honey has been kept for too long in heated environment. Olfactory and sensory tests are generally used for judging the quality of honey such as aroma, colour consistency and taste.

27.6 Adulterants of Honey

Food Safety and Standards Authority of India (FSSAI) has revised standards of honey. In their assessment, there is no mention of the term "Pure Honey." Honey is classified (Refer 27.7) as per floral nectar or several nectars hence, the taste of honey differs.

The Center for Science and Environment (CSE) has investigated for commercially sold honey states that 77% of samples are adulterated by sugar syrup made in China. The tests used are known as C3 and C4. These tests, test the content of sugar from corn, sugarcane or rice which are used as adulterants.

27.7 Classification

Honey is classified as per the specific floral nectar or blending several nectars which are the common polyfloral honey are from wild flowers, its taste may vary from monofloral as name suggests which is made up of a single type of flower. The beehives are kept where only one type of flower grow, such as cloves, orange blossoms, blueberry, sage tupelo, buckwheat, pine weed and sourwood. Himalayan honey from Wild Thyme, Honeydew, Eucalyptus, Indian Jujube, Horsechestnut, Babul Acacia, Wild Cherry, Multiflora, Himalayan Blackberry, Litchi, Sunflower and Mustard.

Table 27.3 Some of these Himalayan honey average quality is furnished below

Types of Honey	Energy	Moisture	F/G ratio	HMF	Diastase	Sucrose	Colour	Flavour
Wild Thyme	33 Cal/10g	18.0%	1:1	4mg/kg	52	2.7%	Golden	Pleasing
Honeydew	35 Cal/10g	18.0%	1:2	3mg/kg	40	3.6%	Dark	
Wild cherry	31 Cal/10g	18.5%	1:0	5mg/kg	20	1.9%	Pale Yellow	
Babul Acacia	39 Cal/10g	18.5%	1:4	8mg/Kg	31	3.5%	Pale Yellow	Acacia
Horsechestnut	34 Cal/10g	18.5%	1:1	4mg/kg	24	2.9%		Pleasant
Indian Jujube	38 Cal/10g	18.5%	1:3	5mg/kg	30	2.0%	Dark	Jujube
Multiflora	32 Cal/10g	18.5%	1:1	5mg/kg	30	1.9%		Strong/Sharp
Himalayan Blackberry	33 Cal/10g	18.0%	1:1	8mg/kg	25	2.1%		
Litchi	35 Cal/10g	18.0%	1:2	8mg/kg	23	2.1%		Litchi flavour
Eucalyptus	36 Cal/10g	18.0%	1:1	8mg/kg	35	2.8%		Strongly aromatic and Mouth-watering
Sunflower	33 Cal/10g	18.0%	1:1	8mg/kg	30	3%	Golden	Good
Mustard	31 Cal/ 10g	18.0%	1:0	6mg/kg	62	1.7%		
Indian Borage	30 Cal/10g	18.5%	1:0	2mg/kg	32	2.6%		Perfume
for set variety for liquid variety	40 Cal/10g	18.5%	1:6	5mg/kg	40	2.8%		Perfume

Source: http://www.brbee.co.in

1. *Honeydew honey*: The honey prepared by honey bees from honeydew instead of nectar, which are the sweet secretions of aphids or other plant sap sucking insects. Honeydew honey is dark brown colour with rich fragrance giving stewed fruit flavour but not sweet. Honeydew honey is popular in Germany, Bulgaria, Siberia, Northern California and in Greece. Precaution to be taken when using honeydew honey as it has a longer proportion of indigestible floral material and also lacks the protein rich pollen of the flowers, Hence it can cause digestive problems.
2. *Blended honey*: It is a mixture of two or more floral source honey differing in colour, density, flavour, taste and geographic origin. Hence the taste, aroma and flavour depends on the flower from which the nectar is obtained. This is the normal commercial honey
3. *Polyfloral honey*: As the name suggests it is obtained from the nectars of many different flowers. Hence known as wildflower honey. The flower blooming prevalent effects the aroma and flavour.
4. *Mono floral honey*: It is from a specific type of single flower. Their flavours, colours from the nectar have different taste. This is a controlled honey where the beehives are kept in specific area where specific flowers bloom. For example orange blossom, clover, sage, buckwheat, Tupelo, and sourwood, acacia, sunflower, cotton are examples of monofloral honey.
5. *Bastard honey*: Honey from unknown floral origins is known as Bastard honey. The source of the nectar is unknown, undisclosed, hence it is also illegitimate honey whose history is not known.

Types of honey based on processing

1. *Crystalline honey*: Has granulates of glucose. Hence it is called as granulated or candid honey set-honey.
2. *Pasteurized honey*: Pasteurized honey is pasteurized to 71.7 °C (161°F) or higher. Pasteurization destroys yeast cells and liquefies any microcrystals, it may also bring down the quality as it increases the level of hydroxymethylfurfural aldehyde (HMF) and reduces diastase activity. Heat also affects appearance, taste and fragrance.
3. *Raw honey*: Raw honey is straight from beehive contains some pollen and also particles of wax. Some prefer this honey who suffer from allergy to honey.
4. *Strained honey*: It is honey that is passed through a mesh to remove waxes and propolis without removing pollen, minerals or enzymes.
5. *Filtered honey*: It is one form in which all fine particles, pollen grains, air bubbles and other materials are removed. The honey is heated up to 65-77°C or 150-170°F to remove the above particles.
6. *Ultrasonicated honey*: It is non-thermal processing where honey is exposed to ultrasonication where most yeast cells are destroyed. This reduces the rate of honey fermentation and inhibits crystals formation.
7. *Creamed honey*: It is so called because of whipped process as spun or churned honey also called candied honey or honey fondant. This type of processed honey is smooth and spreadable.
8. *Dried honey*: Dried honey as the name suggests moisture has been extracted and is therefore solid, non-sticky granular. Dried honey is mostly used for garnishing.

Classification by processing and packaging

1. Comb honey
   - Comb honey is still in the honey beeswax comb. The standard wooden frames are cut in chunks and packed. Comb honey which is harvested traditionally is called as "cut-comb honey".
   - Chunk honey is the honey contains one or more pieces of comb honey introduced in extracted liquid honey, packed in wide mouth containers.
2. Organic honey: Organic honey adhere to the principles of organic farming and is certified by government agency or organic farming organizations. The source of nectar is organic crops.
3. Honey wine or Mead is an alcoholic beverage. Fermented honey with its natural occurring yeast gives this alcoholic flavour.

Table 27.4 Comparative biochemical quality of honey

Parameters	Raw honey	Honey processed through the developed machine	Acceptable limits
Moisture content (%)	19.07	18.4	20.0^{M}
TSS (%)	81.0	80.9	—
pH	3.25	3.35	—
Titratable acidity (%)	0.20	0.14	0.20^{M}
Reducing sugars (%)	65.83	67.44	65.0^{m}
HMF content (mg/kg)	2.64	2.81	80^{m}
Diastase activity (DN)	15.71	14.12	3^{m}

Note: Superscript M stands for maximum limit and m for minimum limit.

Source: Volume 1, Issue 4, July–August 2019, Indian Food Industry Mag, A publication of Association of Food Scientists & Technologist (India).

Table 27.5 Standard Quality Specifications for Honey

Sr. No.	Characteristics	PFA	BIS (IS 4941: 1994)			AGMARK (1984)			European Code (1969)	Codex International (1987)
			Special	A	Standard	Special	A	Standard		
1.	Specific Gravity at 27° C (min.)	—	1.41	1.39	1.37	1.40	1.35	1.35	—	—
2.	Moisture (max.) %	25	20	22	25	20	22	25	21	21
3.	Reducing Sugars (min.) %	65	70	65	60	65	65	65	65	65
4.	Sucrose (max.) %	5	5	5	5	5	5	5	5	5
5.	Ratio L/D (min.)	0.95	1	1	1	1	0.95	0.95	—	—
6.	Ash (max.) %	0.5	0.5	0.5	0.5	0.5	0.5	0.5	0.6	—

Table 27.5 (Contd...)

7.	Acidity % (as formic acid) ml eq.	0.2	0.2	0.2	0.2	–	0.2	0.2	40 ml eq/kg	40 ml eq/kg
8.	Fiehe's Test	—	–ve	–ve	–ve	–ve	–ve	–ve	—	—
9.	Aniline Chloride Test	—	—	—	—	–ve	–ve	–ve	—	—
10.	Total count of pollen and plant element/g of honey (max)	—	50,000	50,000	50,000	—	—	—		—
11.	HMF (max.) ppm	—	80	80	80	—	—	—	40	80
12.	Optical Density (max.) at 660 nm	—	0.3	0.3	0.3	—	—	—	—	
13.	Dastase No. (min.)	—	—	—	—	—	—	—	8	3
14.	Water Insoluble Matters (max.) % of pressed honey	—	—	—	—	—	—	—	—	0.1

Source: Volume 1, Issue 4, July–August 2019, Indian Food Industry Mag, a publication of Association of Food Scientists & Technologist (India).

27.8 Colour of Honey

The colour in liquid honey varies from clear and colourless (like water) to dark amber or black. The various honey colours are all shade of yellow, amber; like different dilutions or concentrations of caramelized sugar, which has been used traditionally as a colour standard. Colour varies with the botanical origin, age, and storage conditions, but transparency or clarity depends on the amount of suspended particles such as pollen. Less common honey colours are bright yellow (sunflower), reddish undertones (chestnut), greyish (eucalyptus) and greenish (honeydew). Once crystallized, honey turns lighter in colour because the glucose crystals are white.

There are several types of indigenous and traditional hives including logs, clay pots, wall niches, baskets and boxes of different sizes and shapes.

27.9 Toxic Honey

This toxic substance is identified as a poisonous compound, grayanotoxin, found in rhododendron nectar. Grayanotoxins are a group of closely related neurotoxins. They belong to a group of toxins known as diterpenes which are polyhydroxylated cyclic hydrocarbons that do not have nitrogen. Grayanotoxins are produced by *Rhododendron* species and other plants in the *Ericaceae* family. Honey made from the pollen and nectar of these plants also contains grayanotoxins and is commonly referred to as *mad honey*. Consumption of between 5 and 30 g of mad honey may cause honey poisoning. Symptoms include dizziness, weakness, excessive perspiration, nausea, and vomiting. Less commonly, low blood pressure, shock, heart rhythm irregularities, and convulsions may occur, with rare cases resulting in death.

27.10 Health Hazards

Although honey is generally safe when taken in typical food amounts, there are various, potential adverse effects or interactions it may have in combination with excessive consumption, existing disease conditions or drugs. Included among these are mild reactions to high intakes, such as anxiety, insomnia, or hyperactivity in about 10% of children. Honey consumption may interact adversely with existing allergies, high blood sugar levels (as in diabetes), or anticoagulants used to control bleeding, among other clinical conditions.

People who have a weakened immune system may be at risk of bacterial or fungal infection from eating honey, although there is no high-quality clinical evidence that this occurs commonly.

Botulism

Infants can develop botulism after consuming honey contaminated with *Clostridium botulinum* endospores.

27.11 Health Benefits

Honey is said to improve food assimilation, and useful for chronic and infective intestinal problems, such as constipation, duodenal ulcers, and liver disturbances. Honey is good for diabetics. In healthy individuals, the consumption of honey produced lower blood sugar readings than the consumption of the same quantity of sucrose. In addition to its excellent nutritional properties, honey is supposed to have medicinal properties. It naturally helps in curing a sore throat. Its antioxidants and bacteria-fighting assets also help against fighting infections that are caused by viruses, bacteria and fungi. According to doctors and scientists, buckwheat honey has the highest number of antioxidants and when consumed daily can be beneficial for boosting immunity in the long run.

Honey is the best natural moisturizer, especially for the dry skin and it is also very easy to apply. Raw honey not only unclogs pores but it also helps moisturize parched skin. It also helps cure cracked lips during winters. Also being a natural antiseptic, it is useful for the treatment of wounds, bruises, cuts, burns and other infections.

Honey not only increases brain power and memory but also makes one a healthier person altogether. Consumption of honey prevents metabolic stress and helps calm and soothe the brain, which helps in augmenting memory in the long run.

Honey is known to be one of the best home remedies for dry cough as well as wet cough. Research has also shown that drinking a tablespoon of honey can reduce irritation in the throat. Honey has antibacterial, antifungal, and antioxidant properties, which is why honey is used for healing wounds. Teeth and gum diseases like gingivitis prevents bleeding and plaque can be treated to a great extent with the regular use of honey, which reduces the duration of diarrhoea, prevents acid reflux. Fights infections.

Experimental studies on honey have shown that honey is antiseptic, antimicrobial, antipyretic, anti-inflammatory, antiallergen, antitoxic, sedative, laxative, anti-anemic, antioxidant, healing and cleansing (external and internal), moisturizing and blood-purifying. It promotes rehydration, is easily digestable, stimulates immunity, and is beneficial for all types of skins diseases.

CHAPTER

28 Cooking of Foods

Some foods like fruits, vegetables, and nuts, are eaten raw. It is good that they are consumed raw as in the uncooked condition they retain most of their nutritive value. However, most foods are cooked before they are accepted. Cooking food is the use of heat to bring about desirable changes in foods being consumed. The source of heat may be the result of combustion of wood, coal, gas or oil; by electric heating elements contained in hot plates or electric ovens; or by a microwave cooker.

28.1 Objectives of Cooking Food

Cooking of food produces improvement in flavour, texture, and appearance, and this makes the food more palatable and easily digestible. Most foods in the raw state contain harmful micro-organisms and they are destroyed during cooking.

28.1.1 Improvement of Food Quality

Cooking improves the natural flavour of food, e.g., the flavour of meat is developed and enhanced by heating; the flavour of bread develops in the crust during baking; coffee flavour is formed during the roasting of green coffee, and so on. If a blend of flavours is required, several items of food could be cooked together to bring about this. If the object is to change the flavour of a food, cooking helps achieve this by addition of required flavouring material. Cooking could also destroy the flavour of a food. In such a case, if the original flavour of a food is to be retained, there should be minimum cooking. Over-cooking results in the volatilization of flavour substances and a less desired product may be obtained. Colour and texture also influence flavour. Cooking helps develop the desired colour and texture in foods.

28.1.2 Destruction of Micro-organisms

Micro-organisms are ubiquitous in their distribution; they are found everywhere, in every environment, and adapt themselves to almost every growth condition. They make their presence known in many ways. Their action may be beneficial as in the production of cheese, pickles, leavening of bread, etc., or harmful as in food spoilage. The latter type of micro-organisms are not normally present as food contaminants. When present they cause infections or produce toxins. Infective types of bacteria, such as *Salmonella* and *Shigella*, multiply in the intestinal tract and cause disease through the infection of the host. In contrast, bacteria like *Staphylococcus aureus* and *Clostridium botulinum* produce the toxins present in the food at the time of consumption and are the direct causes of illness. Food storage under conditions that prevent bacterial growth do not provide safety against infective pathogens, but do so against toxinogenic food poisons.

Moulds also produce toxins, the mould *Aspergillus flavus* produces a toxin (aflatoxin) which, when present in food, is–a health hazard. There are many other moulds producing toxins referred to as mycotoxins. One of the most important methods of protection of food against harmful micro-organisms is by the application of heat. Cooking food to the required temperature for a required length of time can destroy all harmful micro-organisms in foods.

28.2 Methods of Cooking

Heat may be transferred to the food by conduction, convection, radiation, or by the energy of microwaves (electronic heat transfer). Conduction is the method of transfer of heat by contact. Convection is the transfer of heat as a result of the flow of a liquid or gas travelling from the hotter to a less hot part of an oven or saucepan. Radiation is the emission of heat in the form of waves from hot objects. Microwaves are a form of electromagnetic radiations similar to radio, TV, radar, light and infrared waves.

28.2.1 Conduction

In conduction, heat flows from the source to the material absorbing it. Certain materials are better conductors of heat than others. Copper utensils are the best conductors; aluminium ones conduct heat more slowly, and steel ones still more slowly. Glass is a very much less efficient conductor of heat than any of the metals. For efficient conduction to take place from a hot surface to another surface, such as the bottom of a saucepan, it is important that there is as large an area of contact as possible. Hence, the bottoms of pans should be flat and thick.

28.2.2 Convection

When a liquid or air is heated, the portions nearest to the heat become warm and less dense. They rise and are replaced by the denser material, i.e., convection currents flow from a more denser to less dense areas. The convection currents usually flow in a vertical direction, and they are hindered by solid materials. Roasting is mainly accomplished by convection. The heat source at the bottom of the oven heats the air which rises and is continuously replaced by cold air. These convection currents create uniform temperature in the centre of the oven where the food is kept, resulting in roasting.

28.2.3 Radiation

Radiation waves travel at the same speed as light rays. Like light rays they are absorbed by dull black or rough surfaces and reflected by smooth, white or metallic surfaces. Radiation waves travel through gases, clear liquids, or glass, without heating them, or through vacuum. In cooking, when heat radiations reach the food, only the surface is heated by them. They do not penetrate the food. The rest of the food is cooked mostly by conduction and also, to some extent, by convection. Radiation heat is used in broiling. The toasting of bread is essentially by radiation heat.

28.2.4 Microwave Heating

Microwaves are absorbed and penetrate the food. The energy of these electromagnetic radiations excites the water molecules (in food), which bear a positive electrical charge in one portion, and a negative charge at another position of the molecule (dipole). When the electric field of the microwave interacts with the water dipole, the water molecules begin to vibrate very rapidly in food. This vibration produces friction that creates heat within the food, thereby cooking it. The excitation of water molecules occurs as far within the food as the microwaves are able to penetrate. This is different from heating by convection methods, which transmit heat from the edges of the food to the centre. Heating of food beyond the depth of penetration of the microwaves occurs as a result of the conduction and/or convection of the heat created by microwaves.

28.3 Cooking Media

Cooking can be carried out in various media or in no media at all. Air, water, steam and fat, or combinations of these, are used as cooking media. Microwave heating involves generation of heat within the food; it is not a cooking medium.

28.3.1 Cooking in Air

Grilling, roasting and baking take place in air. Grilling consists of placing the food below or above a red-hot surface. When under the heater, the food is heated by radiation only. This results in the browning of many foods. Then the heat is more slowly conducted through the surfaces of the food downwards. As heating is mostly superficial, grilled foods are usually reversed or rotated in the oven. If the food is above the heater, heat is transmitted to the food through convection currents, as well as radiation with consequently increased efficiency.

Roasting and baking are essentially the same. They are carried out in an oven between temperatures of 120° and 260°C. Generally, the term roasting is applied to meat cooking, while baking is used for breads, cakes and biscuits. The food is cooked partially by dry heat and partially by moist heat, if the food is high in moisture content. In baking, the oven atmosphere should be moist initially so that the moisture condenses on the cold dough. This helps in heat transfer and plays a part in the formation of crust. Roasting and baking involve heat transfer from the heat source in the oven by radiation, conduction and convection. Heat is transferred directly onto the container of the food through which it is conducted to the food. Convection currents of air help keep the temperature of the oven fairly uniform. Rough and black surfaces, absorbing more radiated heat, are more efficient for baking than the bright shiny ones.

Broiling is the cooking of food by exposing it to direct heat. In this case, cooking takes place by conduction through direct contact of food with the hot broiler. Some radiation cooking also takes place in broiling.

28.3.2 Cooking in Water

Boiling, simmering or stewing involves cooking in water. In these cases the medium transferring heat is water. Water receives heat by conduction through the sides of the utensil in which the food is cooked and passes on the heat by convection currents, which equalize the temperature and become very vigorous when boiling commences. Water is a poor conductor of heat and its heat capacity is high, i.e., it requires more heat than any other liquid of the same weight to raise the temperature. The boiling point of water is 100°C but it is altered at high altitudes and in the presence of electrolytes. Pressure and a change in composition of the liquid may alter the boiling point of the liquid. Increasing the pressure as in a pressure cooker raises the temperature of the contents above the open air boiling point. Foods suitable for boiling include fish, vegetables and farinaceous foods such as pasta, eggs, meats, sauces, stocks and soups. Simmering and poaching are methods of cooking of food by immersing in a hot liquid maintained at a temperature just below the boiling point. Simmering ensures gentler treatment than boiling to prevent food from toughening and/or breaking it up. Simmering is usually a rapid and efficient method of cooking. Poaching is the process of gently simmering food in a liquid, generally water, stock or wine. Poaching is particularly suitable for fragile food, such as eggs, poultry, fish, and fruit, which might easily fall apart or dry out.

28.3.3 Cooking in Steam

Steam is the medium of cooking in steaming, "waterless" cooking and pressure cooking. Cooking by these methods involves moist heat. In steaming, food is cooked by steam from added water, while in waterless cooking the steam originates from the food itself. Cooking food wrapped in aluminium foil or in a plastic bag is a form of waterless cooking. In this case, there is the advantage of preventing the transmission of flavour from or to the sealed food. Pressure cooking is a device to reduce the cooking time by increasing the pressure so that the boiling point of water is automatically raised. While water boils at 100°C at normal atmospheric pressure, it boils at 121°C at a pressure of 1.07 kg/cm^2, which is the pressure at which food is cooked in a kitchen pressure cooker. In cooking by steam, the food is heated as a result of steam condensing on the food, and release of the large quantity of heat (latent-heat) contained in the steam. This continues until the heated food reaches the same temperature as steam.

28.3.4 Cooking in Fat

Fat is used as a medium for cooking in sauteing, shallow fat frying (pan frying), and deep fat frying. Sauteing is the cooking of food in a lightly greased pan. Only thin pieces of food (dosas, for example) are cooked this way. This prevents food from sticking to the pan. The heat is transferred to the food mainly by conduction. The food is to be turned from one side to the other to complete the cooking. In shallow fat frying, food is cooked in a larger amount of fat, but not enough to cover it. Heat is transferred to the food partially by conduction by contact with the heated pan, and partially by the convection currents of the food. This prevents local burning of food by convection away from the intense heat of the frying pan. As in sauteing, even in this case, the food must normally be turned over to ensure some degree of uniform cooking. Both sauteing and pan frying are a type of baking.

Deep fat frying is similar to boiling. Food is cooked by vigorous convection currents and cooking is uniform on all sides of the food. As fat can be heated to a much higher temperature than the boiling point of water, cooking can be rapidly completed in deep fat frying. In most foods, this high temperature results in rapid drying-out of the surface, and the production of a hard, crisp surface, usually brown, and the absorption of a fair amount of fat, which raises the calorific value of the food substantially. Fats should not be heated to the smoking point, as they decompose at that point to fatty acids and glycerol, followed by the decomposition of glycerol to acrolein, which causes irritation to the eyes and nose.

Foods may also be prepared by a combination of media. Preparation of *uppuma*, for example, involves the use of a combination of fat and water media. Some components (onions) of the preparation are first browned in a small quantity of fat, followed by the cooking of semolina in water.

28.4 Microwave Heating

Microwave cooking, which was first recognized as valuable for cooking food in 1947, is becoming more and more popular because it is a convenient and very quick method of cooking food. Microwaves do not require any medium for transfer of heat in cooking. They are generated by an electric instrument called magnetron. The energy in the Microwave electromagnetic radiation excites the water molecule in food. The positive charge in one part and negative charge in another part after food sample (E.g: Na^+ and Cl^-) in a known concentration, the ionic current creates electrical field and heat is thereby generated. There are two chief methods by which this is activated one is ionic conduction, and other is Dipolar Rotation. Both are volume metric heating, as the entire food by volume is heated.

These frequencies are of two kinds. The first one being the frequency used in Industrial, Scientific and Medical (ISM). Radio band for non-communication purpose of Microwave is more effective because its penetration is better at a lower frequency. The time frequencies being 0.915 GHz used for Industrial purposes and 2.45 GHz is used for Domestic microwave cooking.

In the Dipolar Rotation, the electric field of the Microwave energy aligns to the polarized of electric field and interacts with water diploes. This begins to vibrate and create friction. As a result, the heat generated and cooking takes place. The rotation of the speed being 2450 megacycles per second, this collision generates heat and food is cooked.

Microwaves penetrate food to a depth of 2.5 to 7.5 cm. Up to this limit of penetration of the microwaves, the food gets heated and cooked. Thus, food will heat up inside and outside at the same time. When the thickness of food is large, microwaves will heat it up throughout at the same time to the depth of their penetration and the portion of food beyond it will be heated more slowly by conduction. Food, for cooking in a microwave oven, should be kept in containers that transmit the microwave and should not absorb or reflect them. This is achieved by using paper containers, such as paper plates or cups, or utensils made of plastic, glass or chinaware, which do not contain metallic substances.

28.4.1 Advantages and Limitations

It is volumetric heating; therefore even cooking takes place, heating is quantity-wise and quality-wise is a good method of Cooking. It is a highly technical and scientific applied method of cooking.

In blanching, the loss of Ascorbic Acid is 16%, Folic Acid, Thiamine and Riboflavin is 100%, whereas in Microwave loss of Ascorbic acid is 28.8%, Folic acid is 25.7%, Thiamine is 16.9% and Riboflavin is 7.2%. Frozen Food below 0°C and unfrozen food above –0°C is a state where there are no ice residues. Here Thawing is required. Thawing in a normal condition, the temperature of the food surface rises and Microbes multiply. In Microwave, the heat reaches the core and the surface of the food. Therefore, Thawing is faster. However, energy increased absorption of the liquid goes through rigorous thawing therefore uniform thawing is not possible. This is known as "Runaway Heating". This is used only in Industries for products, like Fish, Frozen Meat, Fruits and Vegetables etc.

Tempering is a process, where a considerable amount of water in the food is in solid like ice, rest of the water has not become ice. This occurs at freezing point (–5°C to –2°C). The food product is firm so it is easy to cut, therefore tempering is an advantage and complete thawing is not required. The foods, having a high content of moisture can be dried faster in Microwave. The pressure required to expel the moisture is known as "Pumping". Where the water is expelled in the form of vapor.

Roasting Coffee beans in Microwave retains Antioxidants and reduces caffeine content. Baked products normally bring Maillard action, which improves the organoleptic appeal in the conventional method; this is not possible in Microwave. But a Gastronomist can experiment combining convention method to get the Maillard action and also utilize Microwaves benefits. Bread can be cooked in Microwave initially, as the heat penetrates evenly and then backed in a conventional oven. In case of cake, it is vice versa.

To retain natural pigments such as Chlorophyll, Anthocyanins, Betalains and Carotenoids in Microwave is advisable. These pigments undergo changes in colour due to thermal action (refer to Chapter 8). The texture and flavour of fresh vegetables fruits are retained better in the Microwave.

28.5 Solar Cooking

A solar cooker or solar oven is a way of harnessing the sun's power to cook food. A metal box forms the simplest solar cooker. A set of large mirrors or a large Fresnel lens to focus sunlight to a single point may also be added. On a sunny day, a black baking tray or cooking pot can convert hundreds of watts of light into heat, in addition to any infrared radiation. Temperatures in a typical oven can reach 200 °C (400 °F).

Cooking, using a solar oven, is not substantially different from a regular oven. There is minimal loss of nutrients and colour from foods in this form of cooking. Humanitarian organizations are promoting their use worldwide to help slow deforestation and desertification, caused by the need for firewood with which to cook. Solar cookers are in use in India in places where there is community feeding.

28.6 Changes in Cooking

When food is subjected to heat many changes occur; there is some destruction of proteins, lipids and vitamins, which is detrimental to the nutritional value of food. However, there are also some beneficial changes. Cooking is required if we have to obtain the maximum nutritive value of some foods and maintain a safe and wholesome food supply. Heat treatment is also one of the most common and effective methods of food preservation and may be used alone or in combination with other preservation techniques. Some of the changes that take place in the constituents of food during cooking are discussed below.

28.6.1 Changes in Proteins

The principal effect of heat on protein is denaturation. This results in the destruction of micro-organisms and inactivation of microbial and natural enzymes within the food. Cooking also destroys the toxic proteins and peptides, enzyme inhibitors, anti-vitamins, and other natural toxicants in food, which can seriously affect their nutritive value. Legumes contain trypsin inhibitors, haemagglutinins, and other toxic substances, which affect the digestibility and availability of sulphur-containing amino acids. These are destroyed by heat. Approximately 40 per cent of the growth depressing effect of uncooked soyabeans is due to the presence of trypsin inhibitors. Of the remaining proteins of soyabeans, their digestibility increases after cooking. Cereal grains also contain trypsin inhibitors and natural toxicants. Heat destroys these anti-metabolites in rice, wheat and oats, but has little effect in other cereals.

Cooking can also result in the interaction of protein with non-protein components of the food system; there can be interaction of protein with carbohydrate or lipid oxidation products. There can also be interprotein and intraprotein reactions in the presence or absence of oxygen. These changes in cooking result in nutritional unavailability of proteins.

There is significant loss of lysine and the sulphur-containing amino acid cysteine after heating proteins. On prolonged heating, tryptophan, methionine, and the basic amino acids, are also lost. Charring and the presence of off-odours during cooking is due to destruction of amino acids and proteins. These changes affect the palatability of the final product.

Interaction between the free amino groups of proteins with reducing sugars or carbonyl groups, formed by lipid oxidation, results in non-enzymatic browning (Maillard browning). This reaction is of importance, because it is responsible for many of the specific tastes, aromas, and colour, of foods. In this reaction, the α-amino group of the essential amino acid lysine reacts with carbonyl groups of sugar and fatty-acid oxidation compounds (see Subsection 2.4.1), which results in a decrease in the nutritive value of proteins.

28.6.2 Changes in Carbohydrates

Monosaccharides, oligo- and polysaccharides undergo many transformations when cooked in an aqueous medium. The sugars are subjected to degradation and epimerization and, of over 100 compounds that are formed by such transformations, hydroxymethylfurfural (HMF) is the most important compound. This compound and furfural are also products of non-enzymic browning reactions. But these compounds have no adverse effects.

Starch molecules, which are the main source of calories in many diets, when heated in an aqueous or moist environment, swell and rupture, and this permits greater enzymatic digestion by enzymes like amylases. Cooking thus increases the digestibility of carbohydrates. Starch, when subjected to dry heat at a temperature of 200°C or higher, breaks down, resulting in the formation of dextrin and volatile compounds like furfural and hydroxymethylfurfural (HMF).

28.6.3 Changes in Lipids

Lipids undergo hydrolytic, oxidative, polymeric or other degradative changes, which modify not only the physical properties of the lipid but also their biological properties when heated. The hydrolytic and oxidative changes result in rancidity, Hydrolytic rancidity is catalyzed in food at high temperature and pressure in an aqueous medium in the presence of acids, alkalis, and lipolytic enzymes (lipases). Hydrolytic rancidity by itself does not bring about any significant change in the nutritive value of the food. However, the objectionable flavour imparted by free fatty acids lowers the consumption of food.

Oxidative rancidity is responsible for more losses in the quality and nutritive value of lipids than any other change. This rancidity results in the formation of hydroperoxides as primary products, owing to the attack of oxygen on the unsaturated centres of lipids (see Sub-section 3.6.1). The products of oxidation exhibit strong unpleasant flavours, even when present in extremely low amounts. The oxidation of a fat at high temperature, in addition to volatile and non-volatile compounds associated with lipid oxidation at normal temperature, gives isomerization products (trans- and conjugated double bond products), cyclic compounds, dimers, and polymers. While lipids oxidized at normal temperatures exhibit no toxicity, thermally oxidized lipids have shown various detrimental effects. But the lipid or food system would be unpalatable long before the concentration of the toxic compound reaches a hazardous level.

In addition to the effect on the biological properties of lipids, thermal effects bring about physical and chemical changes also. In sauteing and shallow fat frying, the quantity of oil used is small, cooking time is short, and there is generally no reuse of fat or oil, and thus there is little concern over the nutritional effects of lipids absorbed from such cooking. In contrast, there has been a great deal of concern over deep fat fried foods. If the deep fat frying is continuous, oxidative changes are small because the fat absorbed by the food is constantly replaced. In discontinuous deep fat frying, as is common in homes, there is liberation of fatty acids due to the addition of water to the oil from the food, decreased unsaturation, and increase in peroxides, conjugated double bonds, and polymers. Such fats absorbed by foods could be toxic when consumed.

28.6.4 Changes in Vitamins and Minerals

These are lost primarily by leaching, oxidation of the water-soluble nutrients, and thermal destruction. The loss of water-soluble vitamins ranges from 0 to 60 per cent as a result of leaching and thermal destruction. In addition to losses by water and heat, ascorbic acid is lost by oxidation due to exposure to air of food during cooking. Vitamin A and carotene are water insoluble and, as such, are not lost as a result of leaching and their destruction due to oxidation is very slight. Frying and roasting cause their loss up to 40–60 per cent. Minerals also are lost on account of leaching and their losses are smaller (0 to 35 percent).

28.6.5 Changes in Colour

Colour factors in foods (see beginning of Chapter 8), such as anthocyanins, carotenoids, chlorophylls, myoglobin, etc., are affected by heat. In addition to heat, the acidity or alkalinity of the cooking medium, oxygen, and presence or absence of metals, also contribute to colour changes when heated. In some cases, the colour changes that take place in foods on cooking are desirable (as in baking), while in some other cases the changes may be undesirable (as in the prolonged cooking of cabbage). The cooking condition should be so organized as to obtain the desired colour qualities in the cooked food.

For the cooking of pulses, milk, meat, eggs, fish, and sugar, see the relevant chapters.

CHAPTER

29 Food Quality

Quality is the ultimate criterion of the desirability of any food product. The overall quality of a food depends on the nutritional and other hidden attributes, and sensory quality as assessed by means of human sensory organs. The absence of nutritional qualities and possible presence of hazardous microbes, environmental contaminants, food toxins, and chemical additives, cannot be easily judged by the consumer. Governments in many countries protect the interest of the consumer regarding nutritional and hidden attributes by stringent controls to assure good food quality and enactment of food laws regarding inspection, grading, packaging, and labelling of foods. Qualities of foods are evaluated by sensory organs—eyes, nose and mouth—or by the use of instruments.

29.1 Sensory Evaluation

Sensory evaluation consists of judging the quality of food by a panel of judges. The evaluation deals with measuring, analyzing, and interpreting the qualities of food, as they are perceived by the senses of sight, taste, touch, and hearing. By the sense of sight, the size, shape and colour of foods, and other characteristics, such as transparency, opaqueness, turbidity, dullness and gloss, can be perceived. Colours of foods contribute immeasurably to one's appreciation of them. In addition, colour is associated with other attributes, e.g., the ripeness of fruits is judged by colour. The strength of coffee and tea is judged, in part, by the colour of the beverage.

Other sensory organs, the nose and mouth, are utilized to obtain information on flavour. As has been described in an earlier chapter, flavour embraces the senses of taste, smell, and a composite sensation known as mouth-feel (see Chapter 9.4).

The sensory evaluation may be designed to reflect common preference, to maintain the quality of food at a given standard, for an assessment of process variation, cost reduction, product improvement, new market development and market analysis.

29.1.1 Selection of Panel of Judges

Actually, one extremely discriminating, pain-staking and the unbiased individual would suffice for tasting. However, human judgment is individual and is not always consistent. Physical conditions of the individual, psychological factors and environmental factors may affect one's judgment. Further, one individual may not be able to discriminate between different aspects of the food quality. For these reasons, for sensory evaluation, a panel of judges is employed. Members of the panel should be carefully selected and trained to find out differences in specific quality characteristics between different stimuli, and also direction and/or intensity of the difference. The panelists should be of sound health and average sensitivity and be conscientious individuals. The number of members in the trained panel should be small, varying from 5 to 10. The semi-trained panel should consist of 25 to 30 members. The findings in the case of an untrained panel should be based at least on 100 independent judgments.

29.1.2 Preparation of Samples

Careful sampling of the food is necessary for sensory evaluation. A well-mixed homogeneous sample, if possible, is desirable. With non-homogeneous materials, samples should be taken from the same area. Samples to be tested should be prepared by identical methods. All samples in a series should be at the same temperature. The number of samples used in any one session depends on the sensory nature of the test product and the evaluation method used.

29.1.3 Types of Tests

Different sensory tests are employed for food evaluation. The tests are grouped into four types; they are difference (discrimination) tests, rating (quantitative differences) tests, sensitivity tests, and descriptive tests. The selection of a particular test method will depend on the defined objective of the test, accuracy desired, and personnel available for conducting evaluation.

Difference tests: Difference tests are used to determine if there is any difference between or among samples. The three basic types of differences tested are simple difference, directional, and quantitative difference, and quality preference difference. The methods of difference testing commonly used are the paired comparison, duo-trio, and triangle (triad) tests.

In the paired comparison, test two samples, one standard and the other experimental are presented to the panelists to determine if the samples are different and the directional difference in a specific characteristic. The duo-trio test employs three samples, two identical and one different. The panelists are first given the reference sample and then the other two samples are given successively in random order and then asked to match one of them with the first. The triangle test also employs three samples, two identical and one different. All the three samples are presented simultaneously to the panelists, who are asked to determine which of the three is the odd sample.

Rating tests: These tests are different tests with a quantitative aspect through direction and degree of judgments using suitable defined scales or scores. A number of methods are employed for this purpose. In a ranking test, judges are asked to rank a series of samples in the increasing or decreasing order of a specified characteristic, such as flavour, odour, colour, or texture. A single sample (monadic) test is used for testing foods that have an after-taste or flavour carryover, which precludes the testing of a second sample in the same session.

In two sample different tests, a panelist is served with four pairs of samples. In two pairs, the test sample is a duplicate of the reference sample. In the other two pairs, the test sample is the test variable. The panelist is asked to judge each pair independently as to the degree of difference between the test sample and the standard, on a scale indicating no difference to large difference.

When more than one test variable is to be evaluated, the multiple sample difference test is employed. Each panelist is served 3–6 samples depending upon the number of test variables. One sample is a known standard. The panelist compares the test sample with the known standard. One test sample is a duplicate of the standard. The difference of the test sample from the standard according to the scale—none, slight, moderate, and large—is evaluated.

A hedonic rating test is used to measure the degree of pleasurable and unpleasurable experience of the food product, on a scale of 9 points from “like extremely” to “dislike extremely.”

The numerical scoring test is used to evaluate a particular characteristic of one or more samples, indicating the rating as excellent, good, fair, and poor.

Sensitivity-threshold tests: These tests measure the ability of the individual to smell, taste, or feel specific characteristics in food or beverages. The tests are most commonly used in selecting panel members for evaluating, and with materials such as spices, for assessing the intensity of odour or flavour.

Descriptive tests: These tests help identify the perceptual characteristics of a product and express them on an agreed scale. The panelists record the impact of all quality attributes in a total perspective, but not a single attribute judgment, with precision, for statistical analysis. The tests include flavour profile tests to describe the aroma and flavour intensity characteristics of food, and textural profile tests to describe the sensory manifestation of structure of inner make-up of foods, comprising concepts of texture, body, and consistency of foods.

29.1.4 Judging

The environment is an important factor in judging food. There should not be any distractions so that the judges can concentrate. Judgments should be made independently and it is preferable to have panel booths, and no communication between panel members should be allowed. The best time of the day for sensory testing is an hour after any normal meal, i.e., mid-morning or mid-afternoon when the judges are neither too well fed nor too hungry. The panel members should not smoke, chew *pan* or *supari* or take an intoxicant for at least half an hour before the test. Use of odoriferous substances (cosmetics) should be avoided. The panelists should be provided with room temperature water for rinsing between samples.

29.1.5 Results

The results of the evaluation are recorded in suitable evaluation cards prepared for different type methods. The data are tabulated, averaged, and analyzed, for the answer to the question posed in the experiment. This method may not be sufficiently trustworthy in many cases for it to be stated with confidence that the results obtained are significant. For a correct interpretation of results, a statistical analysis is necessary.

29.2 Objective Methods

The evaluation of food quality does not rely mainly on human sensory organs. Objective methods have also been developed. These methods use instruments or a standard method to evaluate food quality by physical and chemical methods. The results obtained by these methods are reproducible, can be permanently recorded, and are less susceptible to errors than the sensory methods of evaluation. Results obtained from the objective methods of evaluation should correlate with those obtained from sensory evaluation to ensure consumer acceptance. Objective evaluation includes chemical, physico-chemical, microbial, and physical methods of analysis.

Chemical methods include the determination of nutritive value of foods before and after cooking, products of food decomposition, and adulterants in food. For details of the method, one has to refer to manuals on food analysis, such as the publication of the Association of Official Analytical Chemists (AOAC). Physico-chemical methods include determinations, such as the hydrogen ion concentration by the use of a pH meter, sugar concentration, and the degree of hydrogenation of fats by a refractometer, and a qualitative analysis of sugar solution with a polarimeter. Some properties of foods that depend on the structure or the physical arrangements of their components, such as whipped cream, or meat, vegetable and fruit tissues, are examined by microscopic methods.

The most widely employed objective methods are the measurements of physical properties by the use of instruments. Measurements of the appearance and volume of foods are of importance, particularly in the evaluation of baked products. A record of size, shape, and grain (cell structure and distribution), of such foods can be recorded by photography and the volume determined by suitable methods.

29.2.1 Measurement of Colour

The importance of colour in food, the natural food colours, the changes they undergo during cooking, processing, and storage, have been considered in Chapter 8 and other chapters of this book. Natural and synthetic colours are also added to foods to bring the product to the generally accepted standard. Therefore, the colour of food is measured to identify its properties.

A number of instruments are used for colour measurement. A simple method is to match the colour of the food with coloured chips or coloured glass. Disc colourimetry is another method used. Different coloured discs are spun on a stage so that the colours merge into one colour without flickering. The test sample is placed adjacent to the spinning disc and the colours are matched. Tintometers are simple instruments used to determine the colour and its depth in foods.

For a more reliable measurement of colour, spectrophotometers are used. In the case of clear or transparent solutions, spectrophotometric measurements give quantitative results. As most foods are opaque in nature, reflectance spectrophotometry or, more commonly, tristimulus colourimetry is used. In a tristimulus system, colour is specified by three attributes: dominant wavelength, brightness and purity, according to CIE system (Commission Internationale de L' Eclairage). These three attributes refer respectively to the actual colour, the luminosity, and the strength of colour. Several colourimeters are available for the evaluation of these attributes or complete specification of colour.

29.2.2 Measurement of Texture

The texture of food is an important factor in its acceptance. The textural properties include the mechanical properties of hardness, cohesiveness, adhesiveness, chewiness, crispness, gumminess, viscosity, and elasticity (springiness). A number of instrumental methods are available to evaluate the texture of various foods.

The tenderness of meat is an important quality for consumer acceptability. One aspect of tenderness of meat is tested by measurement of structure of the meat with a penetrometer. This measurement gives an idea of how easy or difficult it is for the teeth to bite into a piece of meat. A more commonly used device to measure tenderness is an apparatus (Warner-Bratzler shear), which measures the force needed to cut the meat in simple shear, usually across the fibres, and estimate the force necessary to chew the meat.

The textures of fruits and vegetables are evaluated by a number of methods. A puncture testing is used to evaluate the firmness of fruits. It measures the amount of force required to penetrate the sample to a specific depth. A shear press is used to study the tenderness of fruits and vegetables. This consists of a rectangular box with evenly spaced slits in the bottom. A series of blades is moved through a sample of food. As the blades move, the food is compressed, sheared and extruded through the openings in the box.

Some characteristics of foods depend upon their rheological properties. Rheology is the science of flow and deformation of materials, both liquids and solids, and has three aspects: viscosity, elasticity, and plasticity.

Viscosity or consistency is an important factor in influencing the quality of a large number of food products. The acceptability of foods like salad cream, tomato products, jams, jellies, mayonnaise, syrups, and fruit pulps, depends upon their consistency. Measurement of viscosity is also important in the processing of foods. A number of instruments are available for the measurement of viscosity and the type of instrument used depends on the nature of food.

Solids do not flow. However, some solids can be deformed by force and they recover when the force is removed. This is elasticity. Gels like those of pectin, gelatin and starch, baked custard and rennet curd, are examples of elastic solids. There are a number of objective tests to determine the firmness of gels. A material that is plastic resists flow until a force is applied; but unlike elastic flow, plastic flow is not reversible.

Texture of doughs and batters determines the quality of the finished product. The consistency of batters is determined by a line-spread apparatus, which indicates the nature of dispersion of incorporated air. The consistency and stability of doughs are measured with a *farinograph*, which measures the force required to turn mixer blades at a constant speed during mixing of the dough. A micrograph also gives information similar to that of the *farinograph*.

Textures of baked products, such as pastries, cookies and crackers, are evaluated by a shortometer. The instrument measures the force required to break the product. A compressometer is used to evaluate firmness of bread crumbs or softness of a baked product. The force required to break through (shearability) a sample of a baked product is also obtained using a Warner-Bratzler shear.

Texture as perceived by human beings is a composite of characteristics. To arrive at a textural profile, different instruments have to be used. New instruments have been developed which could evaluate more than one characteristic constituting the texture of a food.

29.3 Non-nutritional Constituents and Food Safety

A diverse group of non-nutritional chemicals find their way into foods. Their presence in foods represents real or potential health risks of different characters and magnitudes to persons consuming them. The undesirable constituents that affect the safety of foods include toxicants naturally occurring in foods, toxins resulting from microbial growth, environmental contaminants—such as those arising from processing and accidental contaminants and chemical additives.

29.3.1 Naturally Occurring Toxicants

Certain plant and animal products contain natural constituents that are toxic. When foods containing them are consumed in sufficient quantities, the toxins present may prove to be hazardous.

Toxicants in plant foods: Plants are capable of synthesizing a multitude of chemicals that cause toxic reactions when consumed by men or animals. Pulses contain a number of toxic substances (Chapter 17), such as protease inhibitors, lathyrogens, and flavism agents, cyanogens, haemaglutinins and saponins. Some of these toxins are also present in other foods, e.g., protease inhibitors in cereals and potatoes. Saponins are present in spinach and asparagus. Goitrogens (which cause hypothyroidism and thyroid enlargement due to thioglucosides) are present in cabbage and related species, in rapeseed and mustard. Practically all foods contain proteins, which may act as allergens in sensitive individuals. Some varieties of mushrooms are poisonous. Oxalic acid, a constituent of rhubarb, spinach and beet, may cause oxalic poisoning in certain individuals.

Toxicants in animal foods: Tissues of marine forms of animals contain toxic chemicals and cause adverse responses when eaten. About 500 species of marine fish are known to be poisonous (*ichthyotoxism*) when eaten and many of these are among edible varieties. The toxic agents arise from blue-green algae and are then passed directly to herbivorous fish and indirectly to carnivorous species. Poisonous syndromes from their ingestion are variable in character and are usually designated by the kind of fish involved.

Shellfish have concentrated toxins from *plankton* constituting their food supply. The ingestion of shellfish (clams and mussels) results in paralytic shellfish poisoning. The toxic agent must be isolated. It is not destroyed by heating.

29.3.2 Microbial Toxins

As has been presented in previous chapters, some micro-organisms promote desirable changes in foods under controlled conditions. Use of yeasts in making breads and alcoholic beverages, and moulds and bacteria in making cheese and fermented dairy products, are examples of beneficial effects of micro-organisms. However, they also cause harmful effects and are involved in most cases of food spoilage.

Mycotoxins: Mould growth on foods, especially if they are moist, is a common observation. Some moulds, during their growth, produce toxic substances of various kinds. These substances are referred to as mycotoxins and the poisonous effect on men or animals as *mycotoxicoses*. *Mycotoxins* remain in the food long after the mould producing them has died and can therefore be present in foods that are not visibly mouldy. Further, many mycotoxins, but not all, are stable and survive the usual conditions of cooking or processing. Mycotoxin contaminated foods when eaten are thus hazardous to man. Foodgrains, especially bajra, rye and jowar, get infected with the parasitic ergot fungus, *Claviceps purpurea*. *Ergotism*, a toxicosis, results from eating grain contaminated with this fungus. Eating mouldy grains also results in alimentary toxic aleukia (ATA), a mycotoxicosis.

Aflatoxins: Mycotoxins produced by some molds, *Aspergillus flavis* or *A. parasiticus*, are known as aflatoxins. *Aspergillus* develop in many foods, particularly groundnuts and cottonseed, and their cakes and flour. Aflatoxins have been much studied. There are 14 chemically related toxins and one of them, aflatoxin B, is most frequently found in food and is the most potent carcinogen known. Liver cancer due to aflatoxin ranks high in our country.

Bacterial toxins: Just as the growth of spoilage moulds can introduce toxic substances into foods, the growth of certain bacteria can also result in production of toxic substances. These include *Clostridium botulinum*, *Staphylococcus aureus,* and *Bacillus cereus*. These produce sufficient toxins in the food to cause illness in a susceptible host. In addition to these, *Bacillus licheniformis* and *Bacillus subtilis* are organisms for which evidence of their toxin production is beginning to accumulate.

The disease caused by the toxins of *C. botulinum* is known as *botulism*. The toxins are produced after an incubation period of 18–36 hours. They act on the nervous system and are potent poisons. A concentration of less than 1.0 μg is fatal for man; death occurs in 1 or 2 days. If one survives the effect of the toxin, convalescence is slow and takes 6–8 months. The toxins produce in human beings disturbances of vision and difficulties with speaking and swallowing as the muccus membranes of mouth, tongue and pharynx usually become dry. Progressive weakness and respiratory failure set in.

The *botulism* toxins are proteins. Six serologically distinct toxins designated as A, B, C, D, E, and F, are known. The protein is produced as a single polypeptide chain and when released from the bacterial cell is cleaved by a protease producing two fragments— α and β. The toxin is probably associated with a haemagglutinin and thereby protected from proteolysis and denaturation in the gut. The toxin acts by inhibiting the release of acetylcholine from *cholinergic* nerve endings. The neurotoxin absorbed from the gut binds to nerve endings through fragment β while the α-fragment is responsible for neurotoxic effects.

The toxins causing *botulism* are thermolabile; they lose their activity on heating for 30 min. at 80°C. The cause of botulism in man is inadequately heated or cured foods. Canned foods, low in acid, could be hazardous if they have not been heated sufficiently to kill the spores of the organism which might be present.

Staphylococcal food poisoning is perhaps the most commonly experienced form of food-borne disease, but it is much less serious than botulism. To be pathogenic to man, the organism must be present in sufficient quantity, the food must support toxin production and an incubation period of 2–6 hours is required. The toxic period will last for 12–24 hours and results in nausea, vomiting, diarrhoea and abdominal pain. Severe cases will result in collapse and dehydration. However, there will be no fever.

S. aureus toxins are also proteins, single-chained and globular. At least seven serologically distinct toxins are recognized. Although termed *enterotoxins*, they are probably *neurotoxins*. They are absorbed from the gut and activate receptors on the abdominal viscera, the stimulus reaching the vomiting centre.

The toxin of *Bacillus cereus* is produced after an incubation period of 8–16 hours, and it is active for 12–24 hours. Abdominal pain, diarrhoea, vomiting, and nausea are the features of the toxin. Two or more toxins are involved in this food poisoning, one causing diarrhoea and another inducing vomiting.

29.3.3 Bacterial Food Poisoning

Over 50 genera of bacteria have been associated with food spoilage, food poisoning, food-borne diseases or general contamination. In general, gram-negative, non-aciduric, nutritionally non-fastidious bacteria are commonly associated with the spoilage of moist proteinaceous foods, related aciduric genera with acid fruit products, and lactic acid bacteria with foods rich in nutrients and fermentable carbohydrates.

Food poisoning bacteria grow in a food and infect the persons eating it. They form populations sufficiently large to colonize the gut of a susceptible individual. This situation obtains with *Salmonella* spp, *Vibrio parahaemolyticus*, *Escherichia coli, Yersinia enterocolitica, Clostridium perfringens* and *Campylobacter jejuni*. With these organisms, a casual relationship between a specific micro-organism and a specific disease exists.

Salmonella are ubiquitous, but they are more numerous in foods, such as pork, poultry and eggs, and products containing them. The illness caused by the organism is known as salmonellosis. As the multiplication of the organism in the intestine after ingestion of the food takes time, the illness starts 12–36 hours after ingestion and continues from 1–7 days. Diarrhoea, abdominal pain, vomiting and fever are caused by this type of poisoning. Infants are more susceptible to this infection than adults. Acids and temperature tend to destroy the micro-organism.

Clostridium perfringens grows in the alimentary canal, producing the poison some 8–12 hours after the ingestion of contaminated food. The symptoms of illness are diarrhoea, abdominal pain, nausea but rarely vomiting, and no fever. The toxin is a protein that is a structural component of the spore and acts on the membranes of the cells of the gut, disturbing the flow of Na^+ and Cl^- ions. The spores of the organism can withstand heating at 100°C for one hour, but there are marked variations between strains.

29.3.4 Contaminants Arising from Processing

These include residues that become part of food as a result of processing, handling, and distribution of food. Some of them are the following:

Fumigants are used to sterilize food under conditions in which steam heat is impractical. Ethylene oxide is a commonly used fumigant. This and other epoxides react with food components to produce toxic products or destroy essential nutrients. Ethylene oxide reacts with inorganic chlorides to form ethylene chlorohydrin, which is toxic.

Solvents are used for the extraction of oil from oilseeds. Solvents, like trichloroethylene that was formerly used as a solvent, react with the substance being processed, with the production of a toxic product, although the chemical used in processing it is itself non-toxic.

During processing of foods, a number of changes can be induced in their lipids. On prolonged heating, oxidative and polymerization reactions take place, and these bring down the nutritional efficiency of the processed product.

Smoking of meat and fish for preservation and flavouring is an old practice. Such foods get contaminated with polycyclic aromatic hydrocarbons (benzopyrene, for example), many of which are carcinogenic. In areas where smoked fish is consumed in plenty, the incidence of stomach cancer is high. Smoke from woods also contains many other classes of compounds such as phenols, acids, carbonyls and alcohols, most of which have toxicological activity.

Metal contaminants: Metals are one of the many unintentional contaminants of foods. They find their way into foods through air, water, soil, industrial pollution and many other routes. Metals, when present beyond small quantities, are toxic. Mercury, cadmium, lead, tin, etc., are the toxic metals present in foods.

Mercury: Toxicological effects of mercury depend on the chemical form involved. Elemental mercury and inorganic salts of mercury are much less toxic than organic mercurials. Methyl mercury is very poisonous and practically all the methyl mercury in the diet comes from fish taken from water contaminated by the industrial use of mercury. Mass poisoning due to mercury has been reported in Japan in areas where the fish consumed were caught in mercury-contaminated waters.

Cadmium: Cadmium is becoming a major environmental pollutant as the metal is extensively used in industries. The metal is readily absorbed from air, water and food, and is built up in the body. Ingested cadmium is stored in the kidney in the form of a metal-protein complex. Long-term exposure results in renal tubular damage, liver dysfunction, and testicular damage.

Lead: The human system absorbs lead not only from foods but also from water and leaded dust in the air. Lead contamination of food is due to water conveyed through lead pipes, contact with machines, equipment, packing, etc., containing lead, and lead containing sprays and dust used as pesticides of fruits and vegetables. Lead, absorbed by the human system, brings about changes in the kidney and arteries that tend to shorten life.

Other metals: Metals may enter foods from certain utensils. Enamelware of poor quality contributes antimony and galvanized utensils zinc, which are toxic. A major source of tin contamination of foods is tin plate. A variety of containers with tin plate are made for storing all types of processed foods. Canned foods, if acidic, and foods stored in tins after opening, change in colour or may develop a metallic flavour that is unpalatable. Small quantities of metal are dissolved when foods are cooked in aluminium utensils, but this does not impart harmful properties to foods. Copper is an essential trace element required by the human body but copper-contaminated foods are toxic.

Other contaminants from food processing: These include lubricants, boiling water additives, packing material, etc. Mineral oils are used as lubricants for the extrusion of foods and rapid economic production of bread by permitting it to come clearly out of the baking pan. Chemicals are added to boiler feed water to prevent scale formation as a result of hardness of water. When steam from the boiler is used in food processing, small amounts of added chemicals may be carried into the food. To strengthen paper used for food packaging, resins are used, which might migrate to the food.

In addition to the contaminants discussed above, food will contain a number of other contaminants. Further, a number of chemicals are intentionally added to foods to accomplish improvements in nutritional value, maintenance of freshness, creation of desirable properties, or aid in processing. These are considered in Chapter 30.

29.4 Food Adulteration

Adulteration of food consists of substituting it wholly or in part by any cheaper or inferior substance or of removing any of its constituents, wholly or in part, which affects adversely the nature, substance or quality of the food. According to the Indian Prevention of Food Adulteration Act (PFA), 1954, any ingredient which, when present in food, is injurious to health is an adulterant. Thus, according to the PFA definition, many of the food contaminants discussed in the previous section are adulterants and come under the purview of food adulteration.

Adulteration of foods was practised even in ancient times. It was not a serious problem then because business was on a small scale and the transactions involved a large measure of personal accountability. Later, with the increased centralization of food processing and distribution, and corresponding decline in personal accountability, intentional adulteration of food increased. Even in the early Nineteenth Century, many adulterants were used in articles like pepper, essential oils, vinegar, beverages (coffee, tea, beer, wines), butter, bread, etc. In recent years, adulteration of foods has become a serious problem the world over. In Western countries there is a rising concern over the safety of food supply and many remedial actions, both voluntary and enforced, have been taken.

The percentage of adulterated food sold in various parts of India is 30 to 35 per cent. Unfortunately, in our country, there are still no strong consumer associations to give proper education to the public at large about the various methods of food adulteration and ways to detect it. Food adulteration, apart from cheating the consumers, often results in disorders or diseases. Some of the foods commonly adulterated in India and the adulterants encountered in them are the following:

Pulses are an important component of the Indian diet. Pulses like masoor, black gram and chana, either as gram, split pulses (dhals) or gram flour, are mixed with the corresponding forms of *kesari* pulse. Consumption of *kesari* dhal for a long time produces lathyrism, which results in paralysis of the lower limbs. For an account of lathyrism see Chapter 17.

Some seeds, barks, leaves, and other matter, are dressed up to look like genuine foodstuffs for marketing as genuine products or to adulterate the pure ones. For example, roasted tamarind and date seeds are ground into coffee powder, and exhausted tea leaves or coloured sawdust are mixed into fresh tea. Exhausted bark or seeds of coffee, spices, etc., are dried, suitably coloured, and substituted for the fresh commodity. Powdered bran and sawdust may be present in wheat flour and ground spices. Strips of jute or foreign plant material may be suitably dyed to be sold as saffron. Easily obtainable seeds are substituted for cumin, cardamom, black pepper, mustard seeds, etc.

Edible oils and fats are adulterated with cheap edible and nonedible oils. Argemone seeds are obtained from *Argemone mexicana,* which grows widely in the country. The blade seeds resemble mustard and are used to mix with mustard seeds. Argemone oil itself, extracted from the seeds, is used to adulterate oils, such as coconut, sesame and groundnut. Argemone oil is poisonous and its use results in dropsy in human beings. *Orthotricresyl phosphate* is a colourless industrial chemical freely soluble in oils but insoluble in water. This is used to adulterate some oils. The chemical can cause permanent damage to the nervous system. Oils and fats are also adulterated with petroleum products, causing gastrointestinal disturbances. Other common adulterants are animal fats in *vanaspati* and *vanaspati* in *ghee*.

Stones, sand, marble, and earth, are usually found mixed in foodgrains and pulses and their flours. Talc and chalk powder are used to adulterate wheat flour, arrowroot powder, *panir,* and confectionery. Starch is used as a filler in milk, milk products and confectionery. Starch is also found in ground turmeric, coriander, mixed spices, etc. Addition of excess common salt to powdered spices, such as curry powder, is a common practice. Water is a common diluent of milk, curd, etc. It is also added to non-alcoholic beverages in more than the recommended quantities. Methyl alcohol is an adulterant of alcoholic beverages. This has resulted in a number of serious liquor tragedies in this country.

The most frequently used food adulterant in India is colouring matter. Colour is used in many foods such as milk products, confectionery (including Indian sweetmeats), soft drinks, alcoholic beverages, tea, and spices. Colours are also added to foods such as egg preparations, bakery products, fruit products, and others. More than 70 per cent of the colour containing marketed samples of foods are found to contain non-permitted colourants like coal-tar dyes and mineral pigments like lead chromate and red or yellow earth. Use of foods containing non-permitted colourants results in various health hazards.

29.5 Control of Food Quality

The governments in many countries play an important role in ensuring food quality. National official standards are set to safeguard the consumer's health and ensure fair food trade practices. In 1963, the FAO and WHO established a Commission for setting of international food standards.

29.5.1 Codex Alimentarius

The Codex Alimentarius consists of International standards set by FAO/WHO for all the principal foods, whether processed, semi-processed or raw, for distribution to the common man. It also includes standards in respect of food hygiene, food additives, pesticide residues, contaminants, labelling and presentation, and methods of analysis and sampling. A Codex Standard may be accepted by a country in its entirety, or with more stringent requirements for trade and distribution of the food within its territory. A country, which accepts Codex Standards, cannot hinder the distribution in its territory of imported foods that conform to the standards.

29.5.2 Indian Standards

In India, food standards have been prescribed based on the International Codex Alimentarius with suitable modifications to suit the country's conditions. The most important standards are those set by the Indian Standards Institution (ISI).

The ISI is responsible for preparing and promoting general adoption of standards at national and international levels. The institution has an Agriculture and Food Products Division Council and a number of Sectional Committees dealing with various commodities. The standards are formulated and revised from time to time after eliciting the opinion of interested parties, and based on the recommendations of a Technical Committee. Standards are available for a number of foods and food products like food grains and food grain products, bakery and confectionery products, processed and fresh fruits and vegetables, protein-rich food products, spices and stimulant foods like tea, coffee and cocoa. The institution has also published specifications on alcoholic and carbonated beverages, meat products and fish and fisheries products.

Chemicals used in the manufacture of food products to maintain their nutritional quality, enhance keeping quality and stability, etc., are subject to ISI standards. Before a chemical is permitted to be added, it is ensured that the substance is toxicologically safe, is added in safe dosage and is of the required purity.

The hygienic quality of food is very important. Unless the factory producing a food is governed by the strict hygienic code in respect of layout, plant and personnel, the food produced cannot be considered safe, however nutritious it may be. Therefore, ISI has prepared codes for sanitary conditions in the food processing, bakery, soft drinks, Ice cream, fruit and vegetable canning industries.

ISI has also worked out standards for sensory evaluation of foods. It safeguards the food trade interest of India, by maintaining effective liaison with organizations like the International Organization for Standardization and the Codex Alimentarius Commission.

The Indian Standards Institution operates a certification marking scheme under which manufacturers are licensed to use the ISI mark on goods produced by them in conformity with the relevant standards. The ISI mark on products has been very helpful to consumers, organized purchasers, exporters and export inspection authorities. Food products covered under the ISI Certificate mark scheme are bakery and confectionery products, cereals, pulses and their products, dairy and allied products, beverages and food additives.

In addition to ISI standards, a number of other steps have been taken by the Government of India to control the quality of foods. Some of them are the following;

The Agricultural Produce (Grading and Marketing) Act provides for the grading and marketing of agricultural and other products. The Agmark Standards, incorporate grades, 1, 2, 3 and 4, or special, good, fair and ordinary, based on physical and chemical characteristics, intrinsic as well as acquired, during processing or otherwise. The Agmark gives the consumer an assurance of quality according to the standards laid down. The grading system makes for better buying and selling of agricultural produce.

The Preventing of Food Adulteration Act, with its various amendments, provides for the prevention of adulteration of food. The Director-General of Health Services, on behalf of the Central Government or the Chief Officer in charge of Health Administration, in a State operates PFA Rules under the Act.

The Vegetable Oil Control Order stipulates that any vegetable oil product, unless it conforms to the standards of quality and offers requirements for *vanaspati* or bakery shortening or margarine, shall not be manufactured, stocked or sold. There is also an order to regulate the production, distribution and quality of solvent extracted vegetable oils and vegetable oil products.

The Fruit Products Order (FPO) lays down minimum standards relating to the quality of various fruits and vegetables. The order specifies standards of sanitation and hygiene to be followed in the factories and gives directions regarding packing, marking and labelling of containers.

The Meat Products Order provisions are meant to control production, quality and distribution of raw and processed meat.

There are thus numerous organizations in the country to control the quality of food, its production and distribution. Sometimes confusion occurs among consumers and manufacturers regarding the multiplicity of food standards, such as ISI standard, PFA standard and Agmark standard for the same product. Hence, it is felt that there is a need to have a single organization to ensure food quality control, whether it is checking for food adulteration or ensuring quality control for home consumption or export.

The trade reforms initiated by the World Trade Organisation (WTO) have transformed the business environment across the globe with the upsurge of new action in industries and governments in many countries.

Suitable strategies to conform to international quality norms are being implemented to make a dent in the competitive market. This realization has had its repercussions on the Indian Dairy Industry, an important segment of the food industry in India. Manufacturing a good food or dairy product is not enough. The product must also be free from harmful additives, microbes, and remain so during its intended shelf-life.

Excellence in food quality and safety has taken a tangible form with the advent of the ISO 9000 Quality Management System and Hazard Analysis of Critical Control Points (HACCP) standards.

The ISO 9000 standards were brought by the International Organization for Standardization (ISO) and HACCP standards by the Codex Alimentarius Commission (CAC). ISO 9000 encompasses all the activities of a company to ensure that it meets the quality objectives, while HACCP is directed towards ensuring food safety. Application of HACCP adds value to the ISO 9000 Quality Management System. A combined effect of both would provide safe and wholesome food to the consumer. Therefore the best way is to use the ISO 9000 route to manage HACCP.

CHAPTER

30

Food Additives

The great bulk of food is comprised of chemicals such as carbohydrates, fats, proteins, vitamins, minerals, water, etc. Besides, the natural components of food stuffs, additional chemicals may be incorporated, either directly or indirectly, during the growing, storage or processing of food.

30.1 What are Food Additives?

A food additive is defined as a substance or mixture of substances, other than a base foodstuff, which is present in a food as a result of any aspect of production, processing, storage, or packing. This definition includes both intentional and unintentional additives. The unintentional additives, which are not added to achieve an effect in the food but which may accidentally enter into foods as a result of their use in agricultural production, raising animals, food processing or packing, are no additives in the technical sense of the term, but they are food contaminants.

An expert committee on "food additives," made up of representatives of FAO and WHO, has defined food additives as non-nutritive substances added intentionally to food, generally in small quantities, to improve its appearance, flavour, texture, or storage properties. This definition excludes substances added primarily for their nutritive value, such as vitamins and minerals. The Codex Committee on Food Additives and Contaminants (CCFAC) establishes and endorses permitted maximum or guideline levels for individual food additives, contaminants, and naturally occurring toxicants, in food and animal feed.

Regarding additives, the committee considers technological justification and the need for proposed levels of use. It also develops and enables general risk analysis for all foods through General Standard for Food Additives (GSFA) and General Standard for Contaminants and Toxicants in Foods (GSTF).

The primary objective of establishing maximum–use levels for food additives in various food groups is to ensure that the intake of an additive from all its uses does not exceed its Acceptable Daily Intake.

A broad definition of "food additive" is any substance the intended use of which results, directly or indirectly, in its becoming a component of or otherwise affecting the characteristics of any food, and which is safe under the condition of its use. Any substance present in food, either by intentional addition or as an unintentional contaminant, has its effects on the safety of food. Some groups of intentional additives and unintentional contaminants (not covered in previous chapters) are discussed in this chapter.

30.2 Need for Food Additives

For centuries, man has recognized the effects of food additives and has used whatever was available– marigold for colour, wood ashes for leavening, the lining of calves, stomach for cheese making, etc. They were used for effects without knowing the changes they brought about. As long as the ingredient did not make one sick immediately, it was all right to use it. Today, thousands of compounds are used as food additives, whose chemical identity and structure are known. They can be obtained in a very high state of purity and, when used, bring about the desired effect in foods.

The use of food additives is imperative in the complex and integrated society in which we live. The areas of food production are separated from the areas of consumption. Additives have provided protection against food spoilage during storage, transportation, distribution, or processing. Also, with the present degree of urbanization, it would be impossible to maintain food distribution without the processing and packing with which many additives are involved.

A number of factors have led to the demand for foods with built-in preparation—"convenience" foods. A can of vegetable soup is a convenient food, since various vegetables have been cut, blended, supplemented with spices, and so on. It just requires warming up before use. There is a great demand nowadays for "instant," "heat and serve," and "ready-to-cook" convenient foods. These foods make up about 60 per cent of the food that Americans buy. Such foods result in saving considerable amounts of time and effort in food preparation at home, restaurants, etc. The "convenience food revolution" would not have been possible without food additives.

Additives permit the variety of foods that we deem desirable and which certainly are objectively important in maintaining good nutrition. Vitamins and minerals are important, among other things, for good health. Many of these chemical additives can be manufactured so that foods can be "fortified" or "enriched". Potassium iodide, for instance, added to common salt, can eliminate goitre, enriched rice or bread with B-complex vitamins can eliminate pellagra, and adding vitamin D to cow milk prevents rickets.

Many foods, particularly those with high moisture contents, do not keep well. All foods are subject to microbial attack. Fats or oily foods become rancid, particularly when exposed to humid air. The conservation of the quality of foods against agents causing such deterioration of foods requires the addition of preservatives. Additives are also used to colour foods, add flavour, impart firmness, and retard or hasten chemical reaction in food.

There is then the need for the use of food additives to maintain the nutritional quality of food, to enhance stability with resulting reduction in waste, to make food more attractive, and to provide efficient aids in processing, packing and transport. The amount of additives used should be kept to a minimum; it should conform to a standard of purity and be safe. On the other hand, food additives must not be used to disguise faulty processing and handling techniques, to deceive the customers, or if it reduces the food's nutritive value, or when the desired effect can be achieved by good manufacturing practices that are economically feasible.

Over 3,000 different chemical compounds are used as food additives. They are categorized into different groups. A few types of additives are indicated below.

30.3 Antioxidants

An antioxidant is a substance added to fats and fat-containing substances to retard oxidation and thereby prolong their wholesomeness, paiatability, and, sometimes, keeping time. An antioxidant should not contribute an objectionable odour, flavour, or colour, to the fat or to the food in which it is present. It should be effective in low concentrations and be fat soluble. Also, it should not have a harmful physiological effect.

Vegetables contain several antioxidants besides vitamins C and E, especially the flavonoids, of which quercetin in onions and apples and epigallocatechin in tea are typical examples. In one study, increasing vegetable intake by at least 400 g per day resulted in a 42% reduction in the risk of coronary heart disease. Flavonoids have become the subject of intensive research in recent years for their strong antioxidant properties. Oxidative reactions are also implicated in the development of diabetes, and Vitamin E has been found to have a preventative role here too.

Antioxidants thus have wide-ranging life-protective properties. Vitamins C and E are the two antioxidants present in living creatures, including ourselves, which fulfill the antioxidant role, and which are also widely used as supplementary additives. These are among the safest chemicals known. A recent survey concluded vitamin C inhibits the formation of carcinogenic nitrosamines, stimulates the immune system, protects against chromosome breakage, and regenerates vitamin E as part of the antioxidant defence system.

Some antioxidants used in foods are butylated hydroxyanisole (BHA), butylated hydroxytoluene (BHT), propyl gallate (PG), and tertiary butyl hydroquinone (TBHQ), which are all phenolic substances. Thiodipropionic acid and dilauryl thiodipropionate are also used as food antioxidants. The Joint FAO/WHO Expert Committee on Food Additives has recently considered the Acceptable Daily Intakes (ADIs) of BHA and BHT and set them at 0-0.5 mg/kg body weight for BHA and 0-0.3 mg/kg body weight for BHT. Naturally occurring substances that act as antioxidants are tocopherols. The tocopherols act as biological antioxidants in plant and animal tissues, but they are rarely used as additives because they are more expensive than synthetic antioxidants.

Antioxidants function by interrupting the free radical chain mechanism involved in lipid oxidation. They are effective in small concentrations (0.01–0.02 per cent). Mixed antioxidants sometimes act synergistically. The presence of metallic ions, particularly copper and iron, promotes lipid oxidation through a catalytic action. Acidic compounds, like citric acid, complex with iron and thus, when present along with phenolic antioxidants, enhance the latter's activity.

Browning of cut fruits and vegetables is due to enzymic oxidation of phenolic substances. Antioxidants prevent this discolouration. Ascorbic acid is used as an antioxidant in this case. Acids, such as citric and phosphoric, increase the effectiveness of ascorbic acid in preventing browning.

30.4 Chelating Agents

Chelating agents or sequestrants. are compounds that form complexes with metal ions. Many metals exist in food in a naturally chelated form, such as, magnesium in chlorophylls, iron in ferritin and haemoglobin, and copper, zinc and magnesium in enzymes. When metallic ions are released due to hydrolytic or other degradative reactions, they are free to participate in reactions that lead to discolouration, oxidative rancidity, turbidity, and flavour changes in foods. Addition of chelating agents results in the complexing of these metal ions and thereby the stabilization of foods.

Compounds containing two or more functional groups, such as hydroxyl, sulphydryl, carboxyl, phosphate, etc., chelate with metals under favourable conditions. Chelators used in the food industry include sorbic acid, polycarboxylic acids (citric, malic, tartaric, oxalic, and succinic acids), polyphosphates (ATP and pyrophosphates), macromolecules (porphyrins, proteins), and EDTA. Other chelating agents, which are capable of inhibiting polyphenol oxidase, include cyanide, diethyldithiocarbomate, sodium azide and 2-mercaptobenzothiazole, carbon monoxide, mercaptobenzthiazole, dimercaptopropanol, and potassium methyl xanthate. Citric acid and its derivatives, phosphates and salts of ethylene-diamine tetra-acetic acid (EDTA) are the most popular chelating agents used in foods.

Chelating agents are not antioxidants; they serve as scavengers of metals that catalyze oxidation. They, however, are antioxidant synergists. Citric acid and its esters in propylene glycol solution are effective synergists in lipid systems. It is often used in combination with other antibrowning agents such as ascorbic or erythorbic acids and their neutral salts, for the chelation of pro-oxidants and for the inactivation of polyphenol oxidase. Recommended usage levels for citric acid typically vary between 0.1 and 0.3 per cent with the appropriate antioxidant at levels ranging between 100 and 200 ppm. Citric acid exerts its inhibitory effect on polyphenol oxidase by lowering the pH as well as by chelating the copper at the active site of the enzyme.

Polyphosphates and EDTA are used as chelating agents in canned seafoods. Seafoods contain substantial amounts of magnesium ions which sometimes react with ammonium phosphate, with the formation of glossy crystals (struvite). Iron, copper, and zinc containing seafoods react with sulphides that lead to product discolouration. These reactions are prevented by the addition of chelating agents.

EDTA is a chelating agent permitted for use in the food industry as a chemical preservative. Calcium disodium EDTA and disodium EDTA have been approved for use as food additives by the United States Food and Drug Administration.

Polyphosphates, sodium acid pyrophosphate, and metaphosphate, are chelating agents of limited cold water solubility. They have been used as antibrowning agents for fresh-peeled fruits and vegetables at concentrations as low as 0.5 to 2 per cent (final concentration in the dip solution). Sporix™, an acidic polyphosphate mixture (sodium acid pyrophosphate, citric acid, ascorbic acid, and calcium chloride), has been observed to delay the onset of oxidation and enzymatic browning in fruits and vegetables.

Various sulfated polysaccharides, including carrageenans, amylose sulfate, and xylan sulfate, were determined to be effective browning inhibitors in both apple juice and diced apples. Pectin, a naturally occurring anionic polysaccharide at a concentration of 0.5 per cent, gave between 5 and 10 per cent inhibition of apple juice browning. Carboxyl groups present in pectin are believed to be capable of chelating the copper moiety of polyphenol oxidase, thus preventing browning.

Citric and phosphoric acids are used as acidulants in soft drink beverages. These chelate with metals which otherwise promote the oxidation of flavour compounds and catalyze discolouration reactions. Chelating agents also stabilize fermented malt beverages by complexing with copper, which otherwise catalyzes the oxidation of phenolic substances, which subsequently interact with proteins to form haziness or turbidity.

30.5 Colouring Agents

These include colour stabilizers, colour fixatives, colour retention agents, etc. They consist of synthetic colours, synthesized colours that also occur naturally, and other colours from natural sources. Even though colours add nothing to the nutritive value of foods, without certain colours most consumers will not buy or eat some foods. Thus, colours are frequently added to restore the natural ones lost in food processing or to give the preparations the natural colour we expect.

Originally, many colour additives were natural pigments or dyes. For example, spinach juice or grass, marigold flower, and cochineal, were used to obtain green, yellow and red colour, respectively. This gave place to synthetic dyes obtained from coal tar. Synthetic colours generally excel in colouring power, colour uniformity, colour stability, and cost. Further, in many cases, natural colouring materials do not exist for a desired hue. Carbonated beverages, gelatin dessert, candies, and bakery goods, are some foods that are coloured with coal tar dyes. As several coal tar compounds have been shown to be potent carcinogens, the use of coal tar dyes as food additives is restricted. Many countries have severely restricted the number of coal tar dyes for use in foods, while some other countries have completely banned their use. Food colours used also include some inorganic materials, such as iron oxide to give redness, and titanium dioxide to intensify whiteness.

Several natural food colours extracted from seeds, flowers, insects, and foods, are also used as food additives. One of the best known and most widespread red pigment is bixin, derived from the seed coat of *Bixa orellana*, the lipstick pod plant of South American origin. Bixin is not considered to be carcinogenic. The major use of this plant on a world wide basis, however, is for the annatto dye, a yellow to red colouring material extracted from the orange-red pulp of the seeds. Annatto has been used as colouring matter in butter, cheese, margarine and other foods. Another yellow colour, a carotene derived from carrot, is used in margarine. Saffron has both flavouring and colouring properties and has been used for colouring foods. Turmeric is a spice that gives the characteristic colour of curries and some meat products and salad dressings. A natural red colour, cochineal (or carnum) obtained by extraction from the female insect (*Coccus cacti*), grape skin extract, and caramel, the brown colour obtained from burnt sugar, are some natural colours that are used as food additives.

Further information on colours can be found in Chapter 8.

30.6 Curing Agents

These are additives to preserve (cure) meats, give them desirable colour and flavour, discourage growth of micro-organisms, and prevent toxin formation.

Sodium nitrite has been used for centuries as a preservative and colour stabilizer in meat and fish products. The nitrite, when added to meat, gets converted to nitric oxide, which combines with myoglobin to form nitric oxide myoglobin (nitrosyl-myoglobin), which is a heat-stable pigment. The curing also contributes flavour to the meat. In addition, nitrite curing inhibits the growth of *Clostridium* and *Streptococcus* and also lowers the temperature required to kill *C. botulinum.*

It has been discovered that cooking nitrite cured meat products results in the formation of small amounts of N-nitrosamines, which are potent carcinogens. The nitrosamines are formed by the reaction of secondary and tertiary amines, through the following type of reaction.

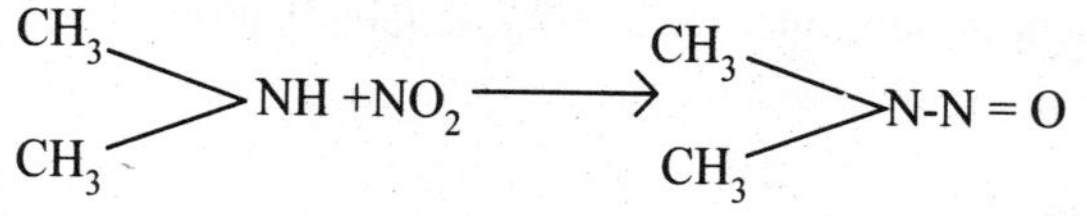

Dimethylamine N-nitrosodimethylamine

Nitrosation may also take place in foods during storage or processing, and nitrosamines may be ingested as such. There is some evidence that nitrosamines are formed under the strong acid conditions in the human stomach when nitrite cured meats are ingested.

In recent years, use of nitrite for curing has become controversial. Although the levels are low, the production of carcinogens during food manufacture or preparation cannot be ignored. As the derivation of nitrosamines is due to NO_2^- in meat, a reduction in the concentration of the curing agent used helps alleviate the problem. However, the reduction in the concentration of NO_2^- enhances the risk of food poisoning due to *Clostridium botulinum.* Recent results have shown diminished concentrations of nitrite can be used in the presence of another preservative that acts synergistically. In the presence of isoascorbate, even very dilute concentrations of nitrite significantly decrease spoilage and toxin production.

Other agents used for curing meat are ascorbates and several phosphates. Ascorbate and isoascorbate react with nitrite to give nitric oxide and thereby accelerate the rate of formation of nitrosylmyoglobin. They also stabilize colour and flavour. They inhibit the formation of nitrosamines. Through chelating iron, they may contribute also to the anti-microbial stability of cured meats.

Polyphosphates, such as sodium tripolyphosphate ($Na_5P_3O_{10}$) and sodium hexametaphosphate $(NaPO_3)_n$, where; $n = 10$ to 15, are used in meat curing. These compounds, through enhancing water retention, aid tenderness, juiciness and flavour of cured meats. They also influence texture and, by chelating metal ions, act as antioxidants. The latter property also contributes to the anti-microbial properties of cured meats.

30.7 Emulsions

Emulsifiers are a group of substances used to obtain a stable mixture of liquids that otherwise would not mix or would separate quickly. They also stabilize gas-in-liquid and gas-in-solid mixtures. They are widely used in dairy and confectionery products to disperse tiny globules of an oil or fatty liquid in water. Emulsifying agents are also added to margarine, salad dressings, and shortenings. Peanut butter contains up to 10 per cent emulsifiers.

One of the most widely used emulsifiers is lecithin which is found in milk, egg, and soyabean. Lecithin keeps, in milk, the butterfat and water phases more or less uniform. Commercial vegetable lecithin is obtained principally from soyabean. Lecithin is employed in the preparation of cocoa butter and chocolate candy. The texture and keeping qualities of bread and other fermented baking products are improved by the use of lecithin. Lecithin is a more effective emulsifying agent in combination with monoglyceryl stearate and ascorbic acid. Several mono and diglycerides and their derivatives are good emulsifying agents. In these cases, the ester groups make the molecule fat-soluble, while the alcohol group lends water solubility to another portion of the molecule. As a result, the molecule can serve as a bridge to keep fat molecules suspended in water.

In addition to these natural emulsifiers, there are many synthetic ones. These include calcium stearoyl lactylate, diglycerides, dioctyl sodium sulfosuccinate, hydroxypropyl cellulose, lecithin, monoglycerides, polysorbate 60, 65, and 80, propylene glycol, sodium hexametaphosphate, sodium lauryl sulfate, sodium stearoyl lactylate, and sorbitan monostearate.

For more information on emulsions, and their formation, properties and stability see Subsection 11.4.3.

30.8 Flavours and Flavour Enhancers

Flavouring additives are the ingredients, both naturally occurring and added, which give the characteristic flavour to almost all the foods in our diet. Flavour enhancers are not flavours themselves but they amplify the flavours of other substances through a synergistic effect. Flavour and flavour enhancers constitute the largest class of food additives. These are about 2,100 approved natural and synthetic flavours, of which more than 1,600 are synthetic ones.

Natural flavour substances, such as spices, herbs, roots, essences, and essential oils, have been used in the past as flavour additives. The flavours of such materials are not uniform. They vary with the season and area of production. In addition, natural flavours are in short supply and the amount of flavour substances in them is very tiny. It would take about a tonne of many spices to produce 1 g of the flavour substances, and in some cases only 0.1 g can be extracted. Natural food flavours are thus being replaced by synthetic flavour materials.

The agents responsible for flavour are esters, aldehydes, ketones, alcohols, and ethers. These substances are easily synthesized and can be easily substituted for natural ones. Typical of the synthetic flavour additives are amyl acetate for banana, methyl anthranilate for grapes, ethyl butyrate for pineapple, etc. Generally, most synthetic flavours are mixtures of several different substances. For example, one imitation cherry flavour contains fifteen different esters, alcohols, and aldehydes.

One of the best known, most widely used and somewhat controversial flavour enhancers is monosodium glutamate (MSG), the sodium salt of the naturally occurring amino acid glutamic acid (see also Section 9.13). This is added to over 10,000 different processed foods. This has been in use in Chinese and Japanese cooking for centuries, and was extracted from seaweeds and soyabean. About 65 years ago, a Japanese named Ikeda discovered that the flavouring from these is MSG and that it has an attractive meat-like flavour. MSG is now manufactured on a large scale all over the world, and especially in Japan.

MSG is generally recognized as safe. However, it was reported some time back that MSG injected to young mice resulted in brain damage. Also, some individuals experience symptoms often comparable to those of heart attack, when served with food containing large amounts of MSG. The matter has now been thoroughly investigated, and it has been concluded that there is no risk in its use. However, MSG which was being added to baby foods is now discontinued, as its benefits to babies are dubious.

Yeast extract has the same flavour enhancing property as MSG. It is found that, in this case, the flavour enhancing substances are the ribonucleotides. These are ten times more powerful than MSG.

30.9 Flour Improvers

These are bleaching and maturing agents; usually, they both bleach and "mature" the flour. These are important in the flour milling and bread-baking industries. Freshly milled flour has a yellowish tint and yields a weak dough that produces poor bread. Both the colour and baking properties improve by storing the flour for several months before making bread.

During storage, atmospheric oxygen oxidizes the carotenoid pigments responsible for the colour of the flour, converting them to colourless compounds. They also oxidize some of the proteins which form dough to give the latter increased strength and elasticity. These improvements can be obtained more rapidly with the use of chemical agents.

Chemical agents used as flour improvers are oxidizing agents, which may participate in bleaching only, in both bleaching and dough improvement, or dough improvement only. The agent that is used only for flour bleaching is benzoyl peroxide ($C_6 H_5 CO_2 O_2$). This does not influence the quality of the dough. Materials used both for bleaching and improving are chlorine gas, (Cl_2); chlorine dioxide, ($C1O_2$); nitrosyl chloride, (NOC1); and nitrogen di- and tetroxides, (NO_2 and N_2O_4). Oxidizing agents used only for dough improvement are potassium bromate, ($KBrO_3$); potassium iodate, (KIO_3); calcium iodate, [$Ca(IO_3)_2$]; and calcium peroxide, (CaO_2).

Benzoyl peroxide oxidation takes several hours. The gaseous agents used for bleaching and improvement act immediately upon contact with flour. Oxidizing agents used for dough improvement only remain inactive until yeast fermentation lowers the pH of the dough sufficiently to activate them. As a result of late action, they cause increase in loaf volume, improved loaf symmetry, and improved crumb and texture characteristics. The dough improving oxidizing agents oxidize sulphydryl groups (-SH) in the proteins of gluten to yield an increased number of intermolecular disulphide bonds (-S-S-), resulting in a tougher, drier, more extensible dough that gives rise to improved characteristics in finished products.

30.10 Humectants and Anticaking Agents

Humectants are moisture retention agents. Their functions in foods include control of viscosity and texture, bulking, retention of moisture, reduction of water activity, control of crystallization, and improvement or retention of softness. They also help improve the rehydration of dehydrated food and solubilization of flavour compounds.

Polyhydroxy alcohols are water soluble, hygroscopic materials that exhibit moderate viscosities at high concentrations in water and are used as humectants in foods. Some of them are propylene glycol ($CH_3 \cdot CHOH \cdot CH_2\,OH$), glycerol, and sorbitol and mannitol [$CH_2OH\,(CHOH)_4\,CH_2OH$]. Polyhydric alcohols are sugar derivatives and most of them, except propylene glycol, occur naturally.

Anticaking agents help prevent particles from adhering to each other and turning into a solid chunk during damp weather. They help free flowing of salts and other powders. These materials function by readily absorbing excess moisture, by coating particles to impart a degree of water repellency, and/or by imparting an insoluble particulate diluent to the mixture. Calcium silicate ($Ca\ SiO_3$, $X\ H_2O$) can absorb liquids in amounts two and a half times its weight and remain free flowing. In addition to absorbing water, some anticaking agents effectively absorb oils and other non-polar organic compounds.

Calcium silicate is used to prevent caking in baking powder, table salt, and other foods and food ingredients. Because it can absorb oils, calcium silicate is a useful anticaking agent in complex powdered mixes and certain spices, which contain free essential oils. Calcium and magnesium salts of long-chain fatty acids (e.g., calcium stearate) are used as conditioning agents for dehydrated vegetable products, salt, and other food ingredients in powdered form. Other anticaking agents used in food industry are sodium silicoaluminate, tricalcium phosphate, magnesium silicate, and magnesium carbonate.

30.11 Leavening Agents

Leavening agents produce light fluffy baked goods. Originally, yeast was used almost exclusively to leaven baked products. It is still an important leavening agent in bread making. When yeast is used, ammonium salts are added to dough to provide a ready source of nitrogen for yeast growth. Phosphate salts (sodium phosphate, calcium phosphate) are added to aid in control of pH.

To make light cakes, biscuits, waffles, muffins, and many other baked products, chemical leavening agents are used. Baking powders generate carbon dioxide for leavening purposes. For a further account of leavening agents *see* Chapter 16.

30.12 Nutrient Supplements

Nutrient supplements restore values lost in processing or storage, or ensure higher nutritional value than what nature may have provided. When foods are processed, there may be loss of some nutrients and additives may be added to restore the original value. For example, to produce white flour, wheat is milled in such a way as to remove the brown coloured part of the grain, which is rich in vitamins and minerals. To restore the nutritive value, thiamine, nicotinic acid, iron and calcium, are added to the flour. Similarly, vitamin C is added to canned citrus fruits to make up the loss of the vitamin during processing.

When manufactured foods are used as substitutes for natural ones, nutrients are to be added to the former to ensure that their nutritional value is at least equal to the natural product. For example, margarine is used as a substitute for butter on account of its cheapness. To ensure that the nutritional status of those who use margarine does not suffer, addition of vitamins A and D to it, at least equal to that of the natural product, is necessary,

Some foods are to be fortified by adding specified nutrients in excess of what nature provides. Milk, for instance, which is a nutritious food is low in vitamin D content. Addition of this vitamin to milk has helped some countries to reduce the incidence of rickets. Similarly, cereals, baby foods, and fruit juices, are fortified with vitamins to improve the nutritional benefits. Some proteins of foods are deficient in essential amino acids and such foods are fortified with lysine and methionine. Similarly, foods are fortified with essential fatty acids, if they are deficient in them.

Iodine deficiency causes goitre. Seafoods are a source of iodine and where these do not form part of the diet, goitre may be endemic. Iodine in the form of potassium iodide added to common salt in a controlled amount (iodized salt) is a safeguard against this disease. Similarly, fluorine in small quantities in food and water is required for normal tooth development. When there is this deficiency, controlled addition of fluoride to drinking water ensures effective protection against dental decay.

30.13 Non-nutritive Sweeteners

In many ways, sucrose is an ideal sweetener; it is colourless, soluble in water, and has a "pure" taste, not mixed with overtones of bitterness or saltiness. But it is rich in calories. Diabetics and overweights, who must restrict their intake of sugar, must have an alternative to sucrose. Thus, synthetic non-nutritive sweeteners, having less than two per cent of the calorific value of sucrose, for an equivalent unit of sweetening capacity came into use.

The first synthetic sweetening agent used was saccharin (sodium ortho benzene sulphonamide or the calcium salt), which is about 300 times sweeter than sucrose in concentrations up to the equivalent of a 10 per cent sucrose solution.

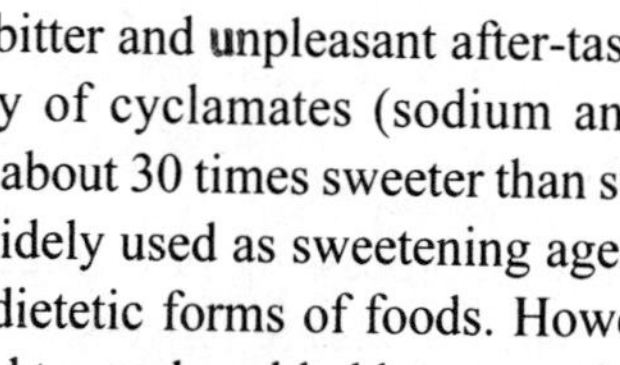

Sodium saccharin

Use of saccharin often leaves a bitter and unpleasant after-taste. Attempts to find better substitutes resulted in the accidental discovery of cyclamates (sodium and calcium salts of cyclamic acid—cyclohexane sulphamate), which are about 30 times sweeter than sucrose but have little of the after-taste of saccharin. So, cyclamates were widely used as sweetening agents in the manufacture of soft drinks, other low-calorie liquid foods, and dietetic forms of foods. However, the use of cyclamates has been banned after high dosages were found to produce bladder cancer in rats, probably from the formation of cyclohexylamine, a known carcinogen.

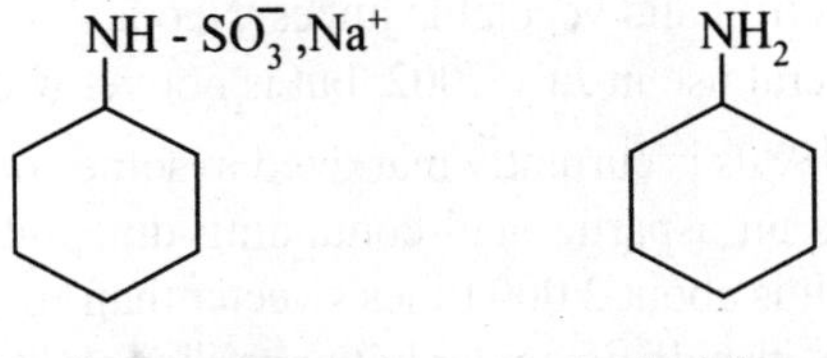

Sodium cyclamate Cyclohexylamine

Newer non-nutritive sweetening agents, ranging in sweetness from 10 to 3,000 times of sucrose have been discovered. Among them is glycyrrhizic acid, obtained from the roots of a European leguminous plant *Glycyrrhiza glabra* (licorice). The sweet taste of glycyrrhizic acid is detectable at one-fiftieth the threshold taste level of sucrose. It is used in tobacco products, confectioneries and beverages.

Acesulfame K is used in baked goods, chewing gum, gelatin desserts, and soft drinks. It is about 200 times sweeter than sugar. In 1998, the FDA allowed this chemical to be used in soft drinks, thereby greatly increasing consumer exposure. Acesulfame K is not digested, so it contributes no calories to the diet. Some animal studies suggest a possible cancer-promoting effect.

Aspartame is used in "Diet" foods, including soft drinks, drink mixes, gelatin desserts, and low-calorie frozen desserts. Aspartame is produced from two amino acids—aspartic acid and phenylalanine—and is 180 times sweeter than sucrose. Although FDA points to more than 100 scientific experiments that purportedly document the safety of aspartame, many consumers and scientists are not convinced that long-term daily intake of aspartame is completely safe, and are concerned about the growing number of foods that contain this ingredient. Aspartame intake is known to be dangerous for persons with phenylketonuria, a metabolic disorder that results in dangerously high blood levels of phenylalanine. In addition, aspartame is not recommended for use by pregnant or lactating women.

Sucralose is derived from table sugar (sucrose). It closely resembles table sugar in taste, is highly water-soluble, and is exceptionally stable at high temperatures. In 1998, the FDA approved it as a tabletop sweetener and for use in baked goods, beverages, gelatin, and frozen dairy desserts. In 1999, the FDA expanded the approved uses for sucralose, allowing it as a general-purpose sweetener for all foods. Sucralose is not absorbed from the digestive tract, so it adds no calories to consumed food. In addition, sucralose does not increase blood sugar levels.

Cyclamate was synthesized in 1937 at the University of Illinois by a student who accidentally discovered its sweet taste. Cyclamate was initially marketed as tablets that were recommended for use as a tabletop sweetener for people with diabetes and others who had to restrict their intake of sugar. In the United States, FDA banned the sale of cyclamate in 1970 after lab tests indicated that large amounts of cyclamates caused bladder cancer in rats, a disease which rats are particularly susceptible to, also caused by drinking sugar water. The findings of these studies have been challenged and some companies are petitioning to have cyclamates reapproved. Cyclamates are still used as sweeteners in many parts of the world. They are used with official approval in over 55 countries.

Neotame is the latest FDA approved non-nutritive sweetener that is between 8 000 and 13,000 times sweeter than sucrose. It is chemically similar to the popular artificial sweetener aspartame. Neotame is moderately heat stable and extremely potent and is considered to be of no danger to those suffering from phenylketonuria, as it does not metabolize into phenylalanine. The product is rapidly metabolized, completely eliminated, and does not accumulate in the body. Because only very small amounts of neotame are needed to sweeten foods, the amount of methanol derived from neotame is very small relative to that derived from common foods, such as fruit and vegetable juices. Neotame was approved by the Food and Drug Administration (FDA) for general use in July 2002, but is not yet widely used in food products,

Alitame developed in the early 1980s is currently marketed in some countries under the brand name Aclame. Like aspartame, alitame is an aspartic acid-containing dipeptide Alitame has been several distinct advantages over aspartame. It is about 2,000 times sweeter than sucrose, about 10 times sweeter than aspartame, and has no aftertaste, its half-life under hot or acidic conditions is about twice as long as aspartame's, although some other artificial sweeteners, including saccharin and acesulfame potassium, are yet more stable. Unlike aspartame, alitame does not contain phenylalanine, and can therefore be used by people with phenylketonuria. Alitame has approved for use in Mexico, Australia, New Zealand and China. Petition to permit alitame's use in the United States in 1986 by the Food and Drug Administration, but is still pending in 2006.

Dulan is about 250 times sweeter than sugar. It was an important sweetener of the early 20th century and had an advantage over saccharin in that it did not possess a bitter after-taste. Early medical tests marked the substance as safe for human consumption, and it was considered ideal for diabetics. However, an FDA study in 1951 raised many questions about its safety, resulting in its removal from the market in 1954 after animal testing revealed unspecified carcinogenic properties.

Neohesperidin dihydrochalcone sometimes abbreviated to Neohesperidin DC or simply NHDC, is derived from citrus. It is roughly 1,500–1,800 times sweeter than sugar at threshold concentrations; around 340 times sweeter than sugar weight-for-weight, NHDC is stable to elevated temperatures and to acidic or basic conditions, and so can be used in applications that require a long shelf-life. NHDC itself can stay food safe for up to five years when stored in optimal conditions. Generally recognized as a safe "flavour enhancer," it is particularly effective in masking the bitter tastes of other compounds found in citrus, including limonin and naringin. In food it is used as a flavour enhancer in concentrations of around 4–5 parts per million (ppm), and as an artificial sweetener at around 15–20 ppm. Research has shown that at strengths of around and above 20 ppm, NHDC can produce side-effects such as nausea and migraine.

5-Nitro-2-propoxyaniline, also known as P-4000 and Ultrasuss, is one of the strongest sweet-tasting substances known, about 4,000 times the intensity of sucrose. It is an orange solid that is only slightly soluble in water. It is stable in boiling water and dilute acids. Because of its possible toxicity, it is banned in the United States, although it is used in some European countries as an artificial sweetener.

The tropical African fruits, kutemfe and serendipity berry contain low-calorie sweeteners. Kutemfe contains two proteins, thaumatin I and II. On a molar basis, these substances are about 10^5 times as sweet as sucrose. The protein substance, monellin, obtained from serendipity berries, is as sweet as the sweeteners from kutemfe. But these substances are unstable to heat and lose their sweetness at pH_2 at room temperature.

30.14 pH Control Agents

These include acids, alkalis and buffers. They not only control the pH of foods but also affect a number of food properties such as flavour, texture, cooking qualities, etc. For an account of the use of these agents in foods, see Subsections 11.2.1 and 11.2.3.

30.15 Preservatives

A preservative is defined as any substance which is capable of inhibiting, retarding, or arresting, the growth of micro-organisms, of any deterioration of food due to micro-organisms, or of masking the evidence of any such deterioration. It is estimated that nearly 1/5 of the world's food is lost by microbial spoilage. Chemical preservatives interfere with the cell membrane of micro-organisms, their enzymes, or their genetic mechanisms. The compounds used as preservatives include natural preservatives, such as sugar, salt, acids, etc., as well as synthetic preservatives. Chemical preservatives are generally added after the foods are processed. The role of some preservatives is considered in this section.

30.15.1 Sodium Chloride

This has been used as a food preservative from early times. Salt stops the growth of micro-organisms and interferes with the action of proteolytic enzymes. Salt also causes food dehydration by drawing out water from the tissue cells. Salt is employed to control microbial population in foods, such as butter, cheese, cabbage, olives, cucumbers, meats, fish and bread. The amount of salt added determines the extent of protection afforded to the food. The term "brine" is used to denote the percentage of NaCl in the water phase of a food. In the preservative action of NaCl, there is synergistic action with other intrinsic factors such as pH, or extrinsic factors such as temperature, partial pressure of oxygen, etc.

30.15.2 Sugar

Sugar aids in the preservation of products in which it is used. The high osmotic pressure of sugar creates conditions that are unfavourable for the growth and reproduction of most species of bacteria, yeasts and moulds. The preservative action of moderate strength of sugars can be improved if invertase is used to increase the concentration of glucose relative to sucrose. Foods in which sugars aid preservation include syrups and confectionery products, fondant fillings in chocolate, honey, jams, jellies, marmalades, conserves, and fruits such as dates, sultanas and currants.

30.15.3 Sulphur Dioxide

Sulphur dioxide has been used in foods for long as a general preservative. It is used in the treatment of fruits and vegetables before and after dehydration to extend the storage life of fresh grapes, prevent the growth of undesirable micro-organisms during wine making, and in the manufacture of fruit juices. Sulphur dioxide is also the most useful agent for the prevention of browning reactions in dried fruits. Most cut fruits are treated with sulphur dioxide to prevent enzymic browning.

Forms in which sulphur dioxide is employed as a preservative include the gas (SO_2), the sodium or potassium bisulphites ($NaHSO_3$, or $KHSO_3$), sulphites (Na_2SO_3 or K_2SO_3,), and metabisulphite ($Na_2S_2O_5$ or K_2,S_2O_5). In aqueous solutions, sulphur dioxide and the sulphite salts form sulphurous acid (H_2SO_3) and ions of bisulphite (HSO_3^-) and sulphite (SO_3^{2-}). At low pH values (lower than 4.5), the undissociated sulphurous acid predominates and inhibits the growth of yeasts and moulds. At high values, the ion is effective against bacteria but not against yeast. The sulphurous acid anti-microbial activity may be due to the reaction of bisulphite with acetaldehyde in the cell, the reduction of essential disulphide linkages in enzymes, and the formation of bisulphite addition compounds that interfere with respiration.

One of the defects of use of sulphur dioxide is it leaves an unmistakable taste in the mouth. It also causes the breakdown of vitamin B-l, so that foods containing sulphur dioxide may not be good sources of this vitamin.

30.15.4 Nitrate and Nitrite

The role of these compounds as anti-microbial agents has already been discussed in Section 30.6.

30.15.5 Sorbic Acid

Straight chain monocarboxylic acids and α-unsaturated fatty acid analogues have anti-microbial activity. Sorbic acid (CH_3–CH=CH-CH=CH–COOH) and its sodium and potassium salts inhibit moulds and yeasts, in foods such as cheese, baked products, fruit juices, wines and pickles. The antimycotic action of sorbic acid is due to the inability of moulds to metabolize the conjugated unsaturated structure.

30.15.6 Acetic Acid

Acetic acid ($CH_3 \cdot COOH$), in the form of vinegar (4 per cent acetic acid), has been used to preserve pickled vegetables from antiquity. Acetates of sodium, potassium, and calcium, are used in bread and other baked goods to prevent ropiness and the growth of moulds, but they do not interfere with yeasts. The acid is also used in foods, such as catsup, mayonnaise and pickles, primarily for flavour, but these products also benefit from the concurrent anti-microbial action. The anti-microbial activity of acetic acid increases as the pH decreases.

30.15.7 Propionic Acid

Propionic acid ($CH_3 \cdot CH_2 \cdot COOH$) and its sodium and calcium salts exert anti-microbial activity against moulds and some bacteria. The acid finds extensive use in the bakery field, where it not only inhibits moulds effectively but is also active against the ropy bread organism *Bacillus mesentericus*. The toxicity of propionic acid to moulds and certain bacteria is related to the inability of the organisms to metabolize the three-carbon unit.

30.15.8 Benzoic Acid

Benzoic acid is widely used as an anti-microbial agent. Its sodium salt is more soluble in water than the free acid and hence it is generally used. However, once in the product, some of the sodium benzoate is converted to the acid form. The undissociated acid is the form with anti-microbial activity. The acid is most active against yeasts and bacteria, and least active against moulds. It exhibits optimum activity in the pH range 2.5–4.0, and thus is well suited for use in acid foods, such as fruit juices, carbonated beverages, pickles and sauerkraut.

30.15.9 Parabens

These are alkyl esters of p-hydroxybenzoic acid. The methyl, ethyl, propyl, and heptyl esters, are generally used. These are effective inhibitors of moulds and yeasts, but are relatively ineffective against bacteria. They are active at pH 7 and higher and have little effect on flavour.

30.15.10 Epoxides

Epoxides are cyclic ethers that destroy all forms of micro-organisms, including spores and even viruses. The epoxides used as preservatives are ethylene oxide and propylene oxide.

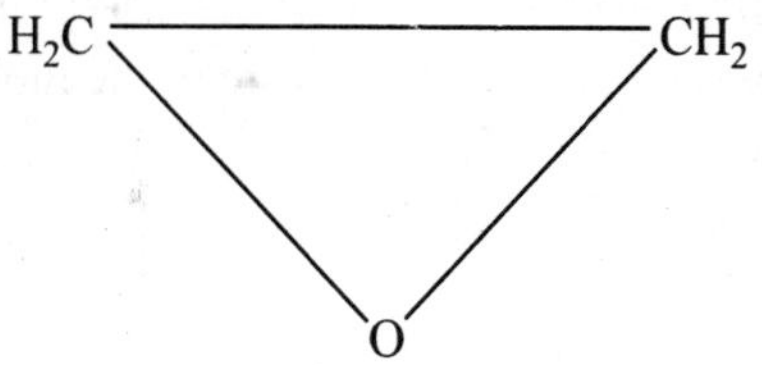

Ethylene oxide

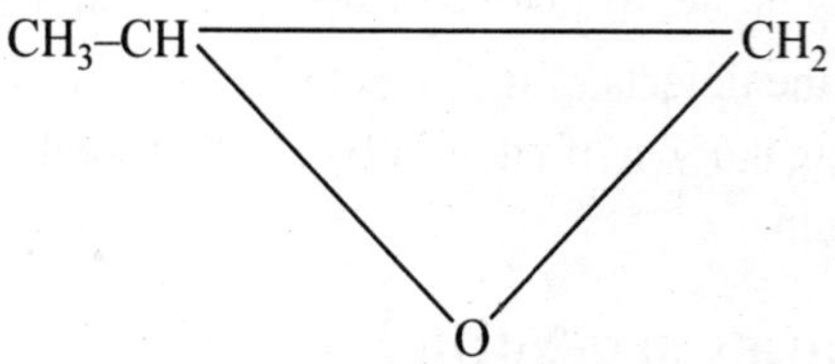

Propylene oxide

In order to achieve intimate contact with micro-organisms, the epoxides are used in the gaseous form and, after adequate exposure, the residual epoxide is removed by flushing and evacuation. Their use is limited to dry items, such as nuts and spices. Spices often contain a high microbial load and they cannot be sterilized by heat because of the instability to heat of their volatile flavour compounds. Thus, treatment with epoxides is a suitable method of reducing the microbial load of spices.

30.15.11 Antibiotics

Antibiotics are anti-microbial agents produced naturally by a variety of micro-organisms. Antibiotics are of great chemotherapeutic value in controlling pathogenic micro-organisms in living animals. Their use in food preservation could lead to the development of resistant strains of organisms, thus making their medicinal use ineffective. Therefore, the use of antibiotics as food preservatives is not permitted in certain countries, while some countries allow the limited use of relatively few antibiotics. These include nisin, pimaricin, chlortetracycline (aureomycin), and oxytetracycline (terramycin).

Nisin is used to control the growth of spore-forming bacteria of dairy products, such as cheese and condensed milk. Nisin is nontoxic to human beings and does not lead to cross-resistance with medical antibiotics. Pimaracin is an anti-fungal substance that is used to control the growth of fungi in cheese and sausages. Its toxicity in human beings is low and it is active in low concentrations of 10–100 parts per million. Chlortetracycline and oxytetracycline are used to control the growth of bacteria in fish and poultry. The residual antibiotics are destroyed by usual cooking methods.

30.15.12 Diethyl Pyrocarbonate

Diethyl pyrocarbonate ($H_5C_2O{-}\overset{O}{\overset{\|}{C}}{-}O{-}\overset{O}{\overset{\|}{C}}{-}OC_2H_5$) is used as an anti-microbial food additive for fruit juices, wines and carbonated beverages. It acts as a "cold sterilizing" agent for aqueous solutions. Its advantage is that following its action, it is readily hydrolyzed to ethanol and carbon dioxide. It is active in low concentrations (120–300 parts per million). In concentrated solutions, it is an irritant. It is likely to react with ammonia, which is ubiquitous in plant and animal tissues, forming urethane (ethyl carbamate, $C_2H_5O{-}\overset{O}{\overset{\|}{C}}{-}HN_2$), a carcinogen. Because of this, it is of limited use today. Dimethyl pyrocarbonate, a lower member of this group of compounds, may be widely used in future as a cold sterilizing agent.

30.16 Stabilizers and Thickeners

These compounds function to improve and stabilize the texture of foods, inhibit crystallization (sugar, ice), stabilize emulsions and foams, reduce the stickiness of icings on baked products, and encapsulate flavours. Substances used as stabilizers and thickeners are polysaccharides, such as gum arabic, guar gum, carrageenan, agar-agar, alginic acids, starch and its derivatives, carboxymethylcelluloses and pectin. Gelatin is one non-carbohydrate material used extensively for this purpose. Stabilizers and thickeners are hydrophilic and are dispersed in solution as colloids. These swell in hot or even cold water and help thicken food. Gravies, pie fillings, cake toppings, chocolate milk drinks, jellies, puddings and salad dressings, are some among the many foods that contain stabilizers and thickeners.

30.17 Other Additives

There are a number of food additives that provide functions other than those indicated above. Clarifying agents like bentonite, gelatin, synthetic resins (polyamides and polyvinylpyrrolidone) are used to remove haziness or sediments and oxidative deterioration products in fruit juices, beers and wines. Enzymes are added to bring about desirable changes; rennin for producing curd and cheese, papain for tenderizing meat, and pectinase for clarifying beverages. Firming agents like aluminium sulphates and calcium salts are used to keep the tissues of fruits and vegetables crisp. Freezing agents like liquid nitrogen and dichlorofluoromethane, which are extremely volatile and rapidly evaporate at ordinary temperatures, are used to chill foods. Solvents like alcohol, propylene glycol and glycerine are used to dissolve suspended flavours, colours, and many other ingredients. Packing gases, such as inert gases, are added to packets of instant foods to prevent oxidative and many other changes.

The use of additives, as well as their numbers, is increasing with years. Use of additives has helped not only to produce more food but also to protect what is produced until it is harvested, processed, marketed, bought and eaten. Use of additives has made it possible to feed an increased population and in a better way than before. In the advanced countries of the world, the use of food additives has resulted in an increase in the number of food items available from about 900 in 1941 to 7,500 in 1975.

Sugar and salt, together with other nutritive sweeteners, corn syrup and dextrose, account for about 90 per cent of 1,800 intentional additives consumed. There are some fifty-five additives that are moderately used; half of these are used as leavening agents or to control pH. Use of all other additives amounts to about 10 g per person per year. The consumption of several flavours and micronutrients may be less than 0.01 mg per person per year.

30.18 Additives and Food Safety

Although most food additives are apparently harmless, the rapidly increasing number and types of chemicals added to our food have increased concern regarding their harmfulness. Their use has provoked many emotional responses from consumers. There are those who strongly believe that essentially all chemicals in foods are bad and we should eat only natural foods. There are others who feel that there is nothing to worry about food additives, since there is no absolute proof that any chemical has harmed a human being. It thus becomes necessary to consider if food additives are safe and how to protect the consumer about unsafe additives.

There are many types of food hazards. Millions of people die every year due to microbiological hazards in the form of food-borne infections caused by unsatisfactory handling practices. There is the nutritional hazard due to suboptimal intake of several key nutrients, due to poverty, ignorance, indifference and misinformation. Then, there are the environmental pollutants due to pollution in water. Some natural foods contain toxic substances (natural toxicants). They cause harm when consumed in sufficient quantity. Pesticides applied to food crops result in pesticide residues in food, and this is a hazard. Finally, there is the hazard of food additives. Of all food hazards, microbiological and nutritional hazards are far greater than others; but are widely ignored. The hazards from food additives and others are remote and small; yet they receive the most attention of consumers, administrators and others.

The presence of synthetic additives does not necessarily mean that food is harmful and the fact that a food is completely "natural" is no guarantee of its safety. Eating halibut liver can cause vitamin-A poisoning. Cabbage, lettuce, spinach, tea, and a number of other foods, contain very small amounts of benzopyrene, a known carcinogenic chemical. Lima beans, sweet potato and tapioca contain compounds which give deadly hydrogen cyanide in the human intestine. Some vegetables (cabbage, cauliflower, turnip, Brussel sprouts, etc.) can cause goitre in some susceptible individuals. Spinach and rhubarb have high oxalic acid content, which can precipitate kidney stones. On the other hand, many synthetic food additives, such as vitamins, citric acid, etc., are identical to safe chemicals found in natural foods. So it is not a question of natural versus synthetic additives. The issue is the need and safety of the additive. The need for food additives has already been discussed at the beginning of this chapter, and tests for the safety of food additives are to be considered now.

30.18.1 Evaluation of Safety

In the evaluation of the safety of additives, it has to be proved that harmful effects have not occurred with the addition of the chemicals. As it is difficult to carry out toxicity studies with human beings, animal experiments are carried out. The simplest way to express toxicity is by the value LD_{50}, i.e., the dosage (lethal dosage) necessary to kill 50 per cent of a population of test animals under precisely stated conditions. The four following types of toxicity studies are employed:

1. Acute toxicity, or single dose experiment.
2. Sub-acute toxicity (daily ingestion for days or weeks).
3. Chronic toxicity (daily ingestion for weeks to months).
4. Studies of carcinogenicity, mutagenicity, teratogenicity and reproduction.

Acute toxicity tests: In acute toxicity studies, groups of animals (two species) are given a wide range of single doses of the additives orally or by injection into the blood stream. The LD_{50} values in a specified period of time (24 hours, 7 days) and abnormalities are seen on autopsy may provide clues to the inherent toxicity of the additive.

Sub-acute toxicity tests: In a sub-acute toxicity test, two or more species of animals (usually rats and dogs) are used. The duration of test is 90 days. The study is made at different dose levels. They vary from near zero to those sufficiently high to produce some type of adverse effect, after the study has continued for several days. Regular evaluation of the state of health of the animals is made and the physiological and biological tests are carried out. Complete autopsy and histological examination of all organ systems of these animals given high doses of additives are carried out. These studies help determine the acceptable daily intake, in milligrams per kilogram of the body weight, allowed for human being.

Chronic toxicity tests: Chronic toxicity tests are conducted in a manner similar to the sub-acute test but the duration of the test extends for 1 to 2 years. The number of animals used at each dose and the number of dose levels will be more than in the sub-acute test. Additives are administered at 10 to 100 times human allowable levels calculated from sub-acute tests. This type of test also helps determine the carcinogenicity (cancer causing) and mutagenicity (heritable changes in genetic material) of the additive. Long-term tests also help study the effect of additives on the permanent structural or functional changes induced in embryo (teratogenicity) and in reproduction, i.e., male or female fertility, litter size, litter weight and a number of the surviving young.

An additive which, according to the above evaluation procedure, is not harmful is considered safe in some countries and permitted as a food additive. The control of additives in foods is being gradually improved and tightened and testing procedures are becoming more rigorous in different economically advanced countries of the world. The laws regulating the use of additives differ in different countries. In order to try to formulate food standards on an international basis, the FAO and WHO have set up a permanent commission designated as Codex Alimentarius, to develop international and regional food standards, which include standards of food additives and contaminants, with the hope of improving food standards all over the world. The proposals of the Codex Alimentarius is highly valuable to developing nations, which as yet have few standards of their own.

Limitations of tests: Tests for safety do not solve all the problems associated with the use of food additives. Results of animal experiments, though very useful, have their own limitations. Not all biological species respond in the same way to the same compound. Further, metabolic pathways of several animals are not identical to those of man. This raises the question of which results with animals are really applicable to human beings? In addition, a chemical that has been thoroughly tested and found to be harmless may react synergistically with another chemical to produce harmful (or beneficial) effects greater than with each of the chemicals used. It is financially and scientifically not feasible to test for all synergistic reactions with the many thousands, even millions, of the natural and synthetic chemicals. Then there is the question of what is to be done when the test for safety reveals a low order of risk or leaves doubts about toxicity.

30.18.2 Safety versus Hazards

The benefits involved in the use of food additives are many, such as increased shelf-life, quality, nutritive value, and economic saving. Even if there is some risk involved in the use of a food additive, it becomes necessary to accept it if the benefits are sufficiently great. The benefit of saccharin as a sweetener, in the absence of an alternative, to diabetics and obese persons outweighs the risks. Nitrite used for meat preservation also prevents the growth of the micro-organism *Clostridium botulinum*. The banning of the use of nitrite, for its suspected adverse effect, greatly increases the toxic effects of microbes in meat. There is no such thing as an absolute safety in food additives. Even common salt, which is essential for life in small amounts, can probably kill a person if taken at one time in large quantity. Similarly, metals like copper, chromium, and zinc, are essential for life in trace amounts. These can also be toxic and mortal if ingested in large amounts. The toxic effects observed with some food additives are at levels far higher than are present in food. Factors like age, sex, weight, and nutritional status, are also to be taken into consideration in considering the hazards of an additive. Fortunately, our bodies possess a multitude of mechanisms for dealing safely with small amounts of toxic substances from any source. Thus, from a rational standpoint, the use of additives in foods should be accepted when they serve some useful purpose. As one cannot live in modern society without them, we must ensure that their use is controlled so as to gain benefits while eliminating hazards and abuses.

30.19 Unintentional Additives

The unintentional incorporation of chemicals into food is as widespread as intentional addition and may present health hazards. The sources of contamination are radioactive fall-out, thousands of chemicals used in agricultural production, animal food additives, and accidental contaminants during food processing. The last one has been considered in Chapter 28.

30.19.1 Radio-active Fallout

Radio-active fallout through nuclear explosions is a serious modern problem. Nuclear explosions inject into the stratosphere as well as into the atmosphere considerable amounts of smaller particles called fission products. These contain unstable atoms, called radio-isotopes, which spontaneously break down emitting radiations and particles that are highly injurious to living tissues. The fission products finally reach the ground through rain, snow or wind. This is known as fall-out. The fall-out matter reaches man directly in drinking water, fruits and vegetables, or indirectly through animals, which eat contaminated feed or graze on contaminated pastures.

Many of the fission-produced radio-isotopes have half-lives (length of time that has to elapse before the amount of radioactivity measured has dropped to half the original value) of less than one day. Some have a half-life of a few days (8 days for ^{131} iodine) while others are radioactive for many years. The half-life of ^{90}strontium is 28 years and that of ^{137}cesium is 30 years. Even ^{131}iodine, with a half-life of only 8-days, is hazardous for the normal functioning of thyroid. ^{90}Strontium is considered to be the most hazardous radioactive isotope. It is closely related to calcium and the body treats both strontium and calcium in exactly the same way. ^{90}Strontium induces bone cancer and leukaemia. ^{137}Cesium passes through the human body quickly but it emits radiations which, through blood, reach all tissues and can be a potential genetic danger.

30.19.2 Agricultural Contaminants

Chemicals in the form of insecticides, fungicides, herbicides (in general biocides), growth promoting substances, and protectants, etc., are extensively used in large numbers in agricultural production. Without them much food would be lost. Commercial production of some crops would be impossible if chemicals are not used. It is estimated that 23 per cent of the commercial cabbage crop and 37 per cent of the potato crop would be lost if chemicals were not used. Small quantities of chemical residues often remain in such crops.

The residues of the pesticide, DDT, has been observed in small amounts in soil, water, vegetables and animal tissues in all parts of the world. From these sources, the pesticide residues reach man. The widespread use of this chemical as an insecticide has contaminated even the air we breathe. The presence of pesticide and other residues in food is a serious international problem, WHO has attempted to control the extent of contamination by prescribing the limits of many pesticides that may be present in foods. Some countries have banned the use of chemicals like DDT.

30.19.3 Animal Food Additives

The use of some antibiotics as food additives has been considered in Subsection 30.15.11. They are also used as plant and animal additives. In some countries (particularly USA), about 80 per cent of animal feed it treated with small quantities of antibiotics for enhancing growth, improved feed utilization, and the checking of intestinal flora of animals. This has helped to produce less expensive meat and poultry. In all the cases where antibiotics have been used, residues may remain in meat. As already indicated, the presence of antibiotics in foods may result in the development of strains resistant to antibiotic drugs.

The synthetic female hormone, diethylstilbesterol (DES), is used on chicken, cattle, sheep as implants and as a daily additive to the feed. This helps the conversion of foodstuffs into meat more efficiently in such animals. On an average, the growth is one-fourth faster than in untreated animals; and the increase is more in muscle than fat. Residues of DES when present in food are potential cancer hazards.

Contamination of food in any way is bad. Just as in the case of food additives, food contamination must be considered in the light of any benefits that ensue. Use of pesticides is hazardous; but without pesticides much food would be lost. Some type of packing may result in contamination but the protection of food, requiring long-distance transport, from dirt and infection requires packing. Again, contamination of any type in very small quantities may not be harmful, and in many cases the reported hazard has not been proved conclusively.

CHAPTER

31 Food Preservation and Processing

Foods gradually undergo deterioration or spoilage from the time they are harvested, slaughtered, or manufactured. Some foods spoil rapidly; others keep for longer but limited periods. The useful storage life of some fruits, leafy vegetables, and animal foods, is less than 1–2 days at 21°C. The deteriorative changes in some foods are so rapid as to render them virtually useless in a matter of hours. These result in physiological, chemical, and biological, changes in food, rendering them unfit for human consumption.

31.1 Food Deterioration

Several causes are responsible for food deterioration. These include micro-organisms (bacteria, yeasts and moulds); activities of enzymes present in food; insects, parasites and rodents; temperature (heat and cold); moisture; oxygen, light and time. These factors are not isolated in nature. At any one time, many forms of deterioration may take place depending upon the food and environmental conditions. The deterioration owing to individual causes is discussed below.

31.1.1 Microbial Spoilage

Bacteria, yeasts and moulds spoil food after harvesting, during handling, processing, and storage. But not all micro-organisms cause food spoilage; e.g., the use of lactic acid producing bacteria in the making of cheese and fermented dairy products, and yeasts as leavening agents and for the production of wine and beer, has already been discussed. However, except the micro-organisms that are specially cultivated under controlled conditions for their beneficial effects, others that multiply on or in foods are frequently the major causes of food deterioration. They are found everywhere; they, however, are not generally found within healthy living tissues but are always present to invade the flesh of animals and plants when there is a break in their skin, or if the skin is weakened by disease or death.

Bacteria are minute unicellular plant-like micro-organisms. The length of a bacterial cell is about 1 μm and somewhat smaller than this in diameter. Bacteria are classified according to the shape of their cells. Cocci are spherical in shape, bacilli are elongated cylindrical forms, and, spirilla and vibrios are spiral. They can penetrate the smallest opening; many can pass through the natural pores of an eggshell. Bacterial spores are seed-like and they are more resistant to most processing conditions than yeast or mould spores. Bacteria, with a few exceptions, cannot grow in media as acid as those in which yeasts and moulds thrive. They multiply by cell division. Under favourable conditions, bacteria can double their number every 30 min. Some bacteria cannot tolerate oxygen (anaerobes) and some require oxygen for growth (aerobes). Some can grow in an atmosphere devoid of oxygen but manage also in the air (facultative anaerobes).

Yeasts are unicellular plants (fungi), widely distributed in nature, and they grow well in a slightly acid medium in the presence of sugar and water. They are found in fruits, cereals, and other foods containing sugar. They are also found in soil, air, on the skin and in the intestines of animals. They are somewhat larger than bacteria. The individual cell length is of about 10 μm and the diameter is about a third of this size. Most yeasts are spherical or ellipsoidal. They have been used for centuries for the leavening of bread and to bring about the fermentation of fruit juices. They can be harmful to foods if they bring about undesired fermentations.

Moulds are multicellular, filamentous fungi, having a fuzzy or cottony appearance when they grow in foods. They are larger than yeasts which they resemble in their nutritional requirements. They are strict aerobes and require oxygen for growth and multiplication. They tend to grow more slowly than bacteria. Moulds frequently thrive under conditions of acidity or of osmotic pressures that are inhibitory to most bacteria. This explains why they are frequently found growing on the surface of jams and jellies. Moulds require less free moisture for growth than yeasts and bacteria. The absence of bright light and the presence of stagnant air favour their rapid development.

Bacteria, yeasts, and moulds, multiply best between 16° and 38°C. Some grow even at 0°C and others at a temperature as high as 100°C. They alter food constituents. Some can hydrolyze starch and other complex organic matter like cellulose, lignin, and pectin; others can hydrolyze lipids and produce rancidity; still others digest proteins and produce putrid and ammonia-like odours. They can also bring about decolourization of foods, produce acids, gases or toxins. Thus, bacteria, yeasts and moulds are the most important agents in causing the deterioration of foods.

As already discussed in a previous chapter bacterial spoilage of foods could be of two types: due to food infection or intoxication. The former type of spoilage is on account of organisms present in the food at the time of consumption, which then grows in the host and cause disease, while the latter type is due to toxins produced by bacteria prior to consumption, which cause disease upon ingestion. The toxin of *C. botulinum* is produced only in anaerobic conditions, such as found in canned products and meats in airtight packages. In a frozen stage, *C. botulinum* survives but does not grow. Hence, frozen foods do not present the hazard of botulism.

31.1.2 Food Enzymes

Enzymes present in plant and animal foods continue to be present and are even intensified after harvest and slaughter. They are responsible for facilitating many changes during storage, such as the changes in colour, texture, and flavour, noticed in fresh produce after it has been harvested. Some of these changes, such as the continued ripening of tomatoes after they are picked, and natural tenderizing of meat on ageing, are desirable. But these changes can proceed too far, resulting in food deterioration if not halted, at the appropriate time. The enzymes responsible for deteriorative changes are to be inactivated by a suitable method at the appropriate time to prevent food deterioration.

31.1.3 Insects, Parasites and Rodents

Insects are particularly destructive so far as cereal grains, fruits, and vegetables, are concerned. The loss of food due to insect destruction varies from 5 to 50 per cent depending upon the care taken in the field and during storage. Insect eggs may persist in the foods even after processing as, for example, in flour. It is virtually impossible to produce and transport grains and other food commodities completely devoid of insects and insect pests. Therefore, a certain level of insect contamination in such foods is inevitable but it should be kept to a minimum by controlling the level of insect infestation. Insects in grains, dried fruits, and spices, are generally controlled by fumigation with fumigants like methyl bromide, ethylene oxide, and propylene oxide (see Subsection 30.15.10). Apart from the loss due to the food eaten by them, insects cause greater damage due to the bruises and cuts they make in foods, exposing them to microbial attack resulting in total decay.

Parasitic food spoilage occurs in some foods. Hogs eat uncooked food wastes. The parasitic nematode penetrates the hog's intestine, and finds its way into pork. The live worms can infect man if the pork is not thoroughly cooked. A parasite worm, belonging to the genus *Anisakis,* is found in fish. If such fish is eaten raw it can infect man. Another common parasitic contamination of foods is *Entamoeba histolytica,* responsible for amoebic dysentery. This organism contaminates foods when raw human excrement is used as fertilizer for crops. Infected water and poor hygiene also spread the parasite. Cooking kills most of these parasites.

Rodents contribute substantially to food shortages in countries where they are not controlled. Rats live up to 3 years and may have 3–8 litters. Apart from the fact that they consume large quantities of food, they contaminate food. Rodent's urine and droppings harbour several kinds of disease-producing bacteria, and rats spread such human diseases as typhus fever, plague, typhoid fever, etc.

31.1.4 Temperature

Heat and cold, apart from their role in food preservation, contribute to food deterioration if not controlled. The rate of chemical reaction doubles for every 10°C rise in temperature. Excessive heat brings about protein denaturation, destroys vitamins, breaks emulsions, and dries out food by removing moisture. The uncontrolled cold will also deteriorate food. The freezing and thawing of fruits and vegetables destroy their structure. Skin rupture leaves the food susceptible to microbial infection. If milk is frozen, fat will separate and milk protein will be denatured, causing it to curdle. Several fruits and vegetables are damaged even at the temperature of refrigeration (4°C). The deterioration includes off-colour development, surface biting, and various forms of decay. Bananas, tomatoes, lemons, and squash, should be maintained above 10°C for maximum quality retention.

31.1.5 Moisture

Presence or absence of excess moisture in food leads to food spoilage. Moisture is required for chemical reactions and microbial growth. Foods with a high percentage of water deteriorate fast. Perishable foods have high water content. Leafy vegetables, young shoots, juicy fruits, meats, and milk, deteriorate rapidly. Even if the moisture content is not uniform throughout the food, it exerts its influence. Surface moisture changes due to changes in relative humidity can cause lumping and caking, surface defects, crystallization, and stickiness in foods. Condensation of even small amounts of moisture can result in the multiplication of bacteria and moulds. This condensation need not come from outside. Fruits and vegetables can give off moisture from respiration and transpiration even when packed in a moisture-free package. This moisture trapped within the package is enough for the micro-organisms to grow. Even non-living foods in moisture-proof packages can give up moisture and change relative humidity in the enclosed space, which can result in microbial growth. Control of moisture in foods is thus very important from the point of view of their preservation.

31.1.6 Oxygen, Light and Time

Air and oxygen bring about a number of destructive changes in food components, such as destruction of food colour, flavour, vitamins A and C, and other food constituents. Oxygen is necessary for the growth of moulds. Oxygen is, therefore, to be excluded from food in the course of processing, by deacration, vacuum packing, or flushing containers with nitrogen or carbon dioxide and, in some cases, by the use of oxygen-absorbing chemicals.

Light destroys vitamins B-2, A and C. It also deteriorates many food colours. Not all wavelengths of natural or artificial light are absorbed by food constituents or are equally destructive. Surface discolourations of meat pigments are different under natural and fluorescent light. Foods may be protected from light by impervious packing or keeping them in containers that screen out specific wavelengths.

All the food deteriorative factors considered so far are time-dependent. The larger the time, the greater the destructive influences. All foods, fresh or processed, have their qualities at a peak at some time after they are obtained. For best quality, they should be consumed before deterioration sets in. Deterioration with time takes place with most foods, except certain foods like cheese, wine, and other fermented foods which improve with ageing up to a point.

31.1.7 Food Safety in the Home

Despite the fact that food is free from harmful levels of micro-organisms when it is brought home, there is still a danger of food spoilage due to the causes discussed above. In order to avoid it at home, standards of hygiene should be maintained in all aspects of food preservation. Personal hygiene and kitchen sanitation practice should be maintained. Foods should be appropriately stored. The temperature range favourable for growth of micro-organisms should be avoided. Foods should be kept at a temperature colder than 4°C. Hot foods should be cooled as quickly as possible to the point where they can be placed in the refrigerator.

31.2 Methods of Preservation and Processing

The holding over of food supplies from periods of plenty for supply, during seasons of little or no production, is one of the most fundamental problems tackled by man and also animals. For thousands of years, man has extensively practised food preservation. It was necessary to ensure a year-round food supply. Storing of food has become increasingly important today in the progress of economic life. Without the hoarding of food, life, as we know it today, would be impossible.

The earliest methods used for food preservation were smoking, drying, and salting. The use of ice and snow to preserve perishable foods was known to early man. Fermentation of agricultural produce also was known from early times. Barley, rice, and fruit juices, were used for alcoholic beverages. Fermented soyabean products have been used in the East from 2,000 BC. Modern methods of food preservation have developed through the centuries on the basis of practices employed in the past. Industrial processing of food started on a small scale in the 19th Century, and during this century there have been tremendous developments.

The underlying principle of all preservation techniques, whether carried out at home or commercially, is to restrict food spoilage so that food can be used safely in a palatable form at a later time. Preservation methods are designed to inhibit the growth of organisms, the removal of organisms, and killing the organisms. Food preservation should also arrest the biochemical breakdown of tissues and the transformation of their cell contents. This is achieved by heat, cold, drying, fermentation, radiation, and chemicals. Food deterioration also is brought about by any one of these techniques. The technique employed should be such that micro-organisms are killed or inhibited, biochemical attacks lowered, and ensure the food is still left unaltered.

31.3 Preservation and Processing by Heat

Of the various methods of food preservation, heat finds very wide applications. The application of heat to food is so universal that "processing" and "heating" are considered synonymous. This underlines the importance of heat in bringing about physical, chemical, and biological, modifications in foods. The purpose of heat treatment in food preservation is to kill the micro-organisms and inactivate the enzymes that become active in the subsequent storage of packed food. Various methods have been developed to achieve this purpose without bringing about other undesirable effects in foods.

31.3.1 Effect of Heat on Micro-organisms

Most bacteria, yeasts, and moulds, show a growth optimum between 16°–38°C (mesophiles). Such organisms, in general, do not grow below 5°C and above 45°C. Some organisms grow in the range of 66°–82°C (thermophiles). Most bacteria are killed in the range of 82°–93°C. However, bacterial spores and certain other heat-resistant forms can withstand prolonged exposure to 100°C. Some organisms endure this temperature for 5½ hours. However, they last only minutes at 120°C and are destroyed in moist heat at 100°C in about 15 min. The thermal death of micro-organisms in dry air is due to oxidation. Therefore, a high temperature is required for their destruction. In wet heat, cell death is due to coagulation, consisting of reactions between proteins and water; this is also accelerated by raised temperatures.

The complete destruction of micro-organisms is known as sterilization. This is achieved when organisms are exposed at 121°C to wet heat for 15 min. This can be accomplished in a pressure cooker or autoclave on a small scale or, on a commercial scale, in pressure retorts. It should be remembered, however, that for storage a food need not be completely sterile. In many cases it would be enough if it is "commercially sterile"(appertized), i.e., foods may contain a very small number of resistant bacterial spores, but these will not normally multiply in the food during storage. For most foods, a theoretical reduction to $1/10^{12}$ of the original population is considered satisfactory. Canned foods, which are commercially sterile, have a shelf-life of two years or more.

Since the heat required for complete sterilization of food also adversely affects the properties of foods, the heat treatment given should be just enough to destroy the pathogenic organisms and toxins, and ensure desired storage life. Thus, to preserve foods by heat with safety, a knowledge of the time-temperature combination required to inactivate the most heat-resistant pathogens in a particular food, and the heat penetration characteristics of the particular food, including the can or container if the food is packed, is required.

31.3.2 Thermal Death Time (TDT) Curve

An interesting aspect of the thermal death of micro-organisms (this applies to bacterial spores also) is that, at a given lethal temperature, the death rate is proportional to the number of micro-organisms still living. This is referred to as the logarithmic order of death, which means that under constant thermal conditions, the same percentage of microbial population, will be destroyed in a given time interval, regardless of the size of the surviving population. Thus, if 90 per cent of an original microbial population is killed in the first minute, 90 per cent of the remaining will be killed in the second minute and so on. The logarithmic death rate curve for an organism provides the death rate of the organism in a specific medium or food at a specific temperature. From the death rate curves at different temperatures, a death-time curve is obtained. A thermal death-time curve, for a specific organism in a specific medium or food, provides data on the destruction time for a defined population of that organism at different temperatures.

A thermal death-time curve indicate that the greater the initial microbial population in a food, the greater is the heat treatment required for its destruction. This strongly emphasizes the importance of good sanitation in food industries, even though heat is a destructive force for micro-organisms. In food preservation by heat, in addition to heat destruction of micro-organisms as indicated by the thermal death-time curve, several other factors influence the microbial population. The acid pH of the food, for example, will increase the killing of organisms by heat. Foods high in acid (having a pH of 4.6 or less), such as tomatoes or orange juice, need not be heated severely because the acid increases the killing power of heat. With acid foods, in many cases, temperature at or below 100°C for a few minutes constitutes adequate heat treatment. Certain spices and food chemicals act synergistically with heat in killing micro-organisms, and so reduce the heat treatment that must be used. As will be discussed subsequently, many other food constituents have an opposite effect on the heat sensitivity of micro-organisms and protect them against heat. Thus, thermal death-time curves, to be valid, should be established for the specific food for which a heat process is being applied. To provide a substantial margin of safety, it is better to work out the heat treatment by assuming that the food contains a heat-resistant spore and its population is large.

31.3.3 Environmental Factors

The data obtained from thermal death-time curves indicate the time and temperature required to destroy the micro-organisms. For proper preservation of food, every particle of food (within the container if the food is canned) has to reach the lethal temperature for the required time. That is, heat should penetrate the mass of food or throughout the can. Thus, the extent of heating depends upon the size and shape of the food or can, and also on the nature and consistency of the food. This involves heat transfer into the food by conduction or convection. Convection heating is far more rapid than conduction heating, and so a liquid food reaches the required temperature more rapidly than food containing free liquid and solid, which in turn is heated more rapidly than solid food.

When heat is applied from outside, the food nearest to the container (can) surface will reach the sterilization temperature sooner than the food in the centre of the can. The point in the can or mass of food that is last to reach the final heating temperature is known as the "cold point." To ensure the necessary sterilization of food, heating must be continued till the time the cold point attains the lethal temperature and remains at that temperature for the required interval. Since the time required for penetration of heat throughout the food varies depending upon the type of sterilizing unit used, size and shape of the food container, and the composition of food, it is obvious that the required heat treatment will be different for each specific case. This has to be determined to complete the sterilization requirement of food.

The required lethal effect at the cold point of the food can be achieved by various time-temperature exposures. For example, destruction of *Clostridium botulinum* in a low-acid medium is complete in 2.78 min. at 121°C or 10 min. at 116°C. Also, the temperature rise during heat penetration accomplishes some degree of microbial destruction. The cooling of sterile food is not instantaneous, and some additional microbial destruction takes place during the cooling period. These factors are to be taken into consideration in evaluating the temperature and time required for food preservation by heat.

Several constituents of food protect micro-organisms to various degrees against heat. Sugar in high concentration decreases their susceptibility to heat. Thus, canned fruit in a sugar syrup requires a higher temperature or longer time for sterilization than the same fruit without sugar. Fats and oils decrease the penetration of wet heat into the cells of micro-organisms, and heating becomes more like dry heat. Food constituents, in addition to the above types of direct protection of micro-organisms, also contribute indirectly to the penetration of heat. Fats are poor conductors of heat than water. Food consistency determines whether conduction or convection heating will take place. If starch is added as a thickener to food, it may result in the conversion of the convection heat system to a conduction system, thus slowing down heat penetration within the container or mass of food, and this too will protect micro-organisms.

31.3.4 Canning

The basic process of canning consists of placing food in a sealable container, closing, heating and cooling. This method of food preservation has been in use since early the 1800s, though the understanding of the process came much later. Large quantities of foods are canned for preservation. In advanced countries, canned foods form a significant part of the diet of the people. Most fruits and vegetables, a wide variety of meats and meat products, fish products, soups, and many other items, are all canned. A typical canning process includes the following steps:

1. Receiving, cleaning, grading, and inspecting raw commodities.
2. Blanching to inactivate enzymes.
3. Placing in the container with added brine or syrup, and deaeration of the product.
4. Heating in a retort, under 1.05 kg/cm^2 pressure, using steam for metal cans or pressurized water for glass containers.
5. Partial cooling under pressure in the retort.
6. Additional cooling by water sprays or in a cooling tank.
7. Labelling, racking and distributing.

First, the raw commodity is inspected for any treatment required before canning. Many of them require special treatment, such as washing, trimming, shelling, size grading, and so on. In commercial canning, most of these operations are carried out mechanically. The food may then be blanched to reduce surface contamination and inactivate enzymes. The blanched food is placed in the containers. Brine (1.1 to 1.6 per cent salt concentration) is added in the case of vegetables, meat, and fish, and syrup in the case of fruits. In some cases, only water is added. Oils are commonly added to fish products.

The containers generally preferred for most heat-processed foods are tin cans. Glass jars are easy to clean, corrosion-free, and transparent, but they have the disadvantage of requiring more processing time than cans of the same size. There is also the problem of breakage. As heating time is roughly proportional to volume of the container, larger containers must be heated for a longer time, and food canned in such containers will be of lower quality than those placed in smaller containers.

Heating time can be reduced by placing the food in a flexible, relatively thin pouch instead of a can or jar. It has been shown that foods processed in this manner are of comparable quality to frozen foods. The pouches can be heated for serving by simply placing them in hot water, and damage in distribution would be significantly less than with a can or glass jar. Pouch canning is gradually gaining importance.

The container with the food has to be ready for deaeration. This can be done by heating the filled cans in steam or hot water or by the use of a vacuum closing machine when the air is sucked out by a pump and the lid is sealed on while vacuum is maintained. Air and gas removal is necessary to prevent the bulging of the can due to internal pressure, oxidation of the contents, and inside corrosion of the tin plate.

The sealed containers are subjected to heating in a retort, a chamber in which canned foods are processed. Several types of retorts are used. Still, retorts are the simplest type in which the cans remain still while they are being heated. In this case, the heating time to bring the cold point to the sterilizing temperature is relatively long. The time taken for sterilization can be markedly reduced by using agitating retorts. The cans are agitated during the heating process. The mixing inside the container helps the conduction and convection processes so that heating is achieved in significantly less time, and food quality is improved. Whether still or agitating retorts are used, the high temperatures required for sterilization is commonly obtained from steam under pressure. The heating may be batchwise or continuous. The heated containers are partially cooled under pressure in the retorts to decrease the internal pressure of the container. Next, the containers are cooled in water or under a spray. Finally, they are labelled and packed for distribution.

Aseptic canning: In normal canning, heat transfer from the outside of the container to the inside will require many minutes or even hours depending upon the container size to reach the sterilization temperature. The time of sterilization can be shortened to seconds or even a fraction of a second in aseptic canning. The basic principle of this method is that food is pumped continuously through a plate-type or tubular heat exchanger, which heats it very quickly to a high temperatures, holding it at that temperature for the time required and then cooling. The food temperature employed may be as high as 150°C and sterilization takes place in 1 or 2 secs. Such rapid sterilization at high temperature is referred to as ultra-high-temperature sterilization. The sterile food is quickly cooled, placed in aseptic containers, and the lids are sealed, while in a sterile environment. The food canned aseptically retains the nutrients and the sensory attributes will be good.

With acid foods, foods sterilized as in aseptic canning, while still hot, can be filled into clean but not necessarily aseptic containers. The heat of the food and some holding time before cooling the closed container renders the containers commercially sterile. This type of canning is known as "hot pack" or "hot fill."

With low-acid food (above pH 4.6), conventional hot pack processing is not possible. In such cases, the *"flash 18"* process (pressure canning) is employed. Low-acid foods are heated above 100°C under pressure for sterility. If the food at that temperature is poured into containers for sealing at atmospheric pressure, there will be violent boiling. This is eliminated by carrying out the canning process in a chamber under a pressure of 1.05 to 1.40 kg/cm^2. Thus, low-acid foods can be pre-sterilized by high temperature for a short time. They are then transferred to cans in a pressurized room and heated for an appropriate number of minutes so that commercial sterility of non-sterile cans is obtained, and finally, the cans are sealed and cooled.

31.3.5 Pasteurization

When foods are heated in containers or by other methods to a temperature below the boiling point of water for a definite period, the process is known as pasteurization. This process serves two objectives: it destroys pathogenic organisms associated with the food and extends the product's shelf-life by decreasing the microbial population, and inactivating some enzymes. The choice of temperature and time of pasteurization will be influenced by the consideration of the purpose of the process, and the chemical and physical composition of food. Thus, milk is pasteurized at 62.8°C for 30 min. (see Chapter 21) to inactivate pathogens, and whole egg (mixture of yolk and white) at 64.4°C for 2–5 min. to control the dissemination of *Salmonella* spp. With sweetened condensed milk, a mild heat treatment is acceptable because of the moderate heat resistance of yeasts, the only organisms that can grow under conditions imposed by sugar concentration. Pasteurization is also employed in the case of beer, wines, fruit juices, and certain other foods, mostly to increase shelf-life.

Pasteurized products are not sterile. They contain vegetative organisms and spores are still capable of growth. Many pasteurized foods must be stored under refrigeration. Pasteurized milk under refrigeration can be stored for a week or more in good condition. However, at room temperature, pasteurized milk may be spoilt in a day. High-temperature, short-time treatment (HTST) using a temperature of 130°C and above for short times, i.e., a few seconds to 6 min. is used to obtain a germ-free stage.

Blanching: Blanching is a heat treatment like pasteurization. The term is usually used in conjunction with vegetable processing, where the goals are to inactivate degradative enzymes and deaerate the product before further processing rather than kill micro-organisms. If omitted, off-flavour, vitamin losses, and colour changes, occur, in the frozen storage. Blanching is usually performed by dipping the products in boiling water for two to three minutes.

31.4 Preservation and Processing by Cold

As stated earlier, the preservation of food by freezing and cold storage was known to ancient people. Tribes and nations in the temperate and cooler climates froze their harvest, thawed it when necessary and consumed it. Frozen foods were even transported over short distances to consuming centres. With the development of mechanical refrigeration systems, cold preservation of food, food processing, storage, and distribution, have become widespread. Refrigeration has also influenced agricultural practices. It has become possible to transport perishable foods for long distances from production to consumption centres, and make available seasonal foods at all times of the year.

31.4.1 Effect of Cold on Micro-organisms

While most bacteria, yeasts, and moulds, grow best at temperatures of 16° to 38°C, some micro-organisms continue to grow even at low temperatures. These are known as psychrophilic (cryophilic) organisms. These grow even at 0°C, the freezing point of water. However, lowering the temperature of foods and food products decreases the growth rate of micro-organisms and the growth and multiplicity completely stop when water freezes. In some foods, water does not freeze even at 10°C or lower temperatures, because of the lower freezing point due to dissolved salts, sugars, and other substances. The retardation of microbial and biochemical activities at low temperatures is the basis of preservation of food by cold. Cold temperature treatment, including severe freezing, only reduces the microbial activities and population, but does not kill all bacteria. Foods frozen, even for two years or more, when removed from cold storage have shown bacterial activity when thawed.

31.4.2 Types of Cold Preservation

Cold preservation of food may be categorized into two groups: refrigeration, and freezing. Household and commercial refrigerators usually run at 4.4°–7.2°C. Commercial refrigeration (cold or chill storage) may use a slightly lower temperature, depending upon the nature of the food refrigerated. Freezing refers to foods maintained in a frozen condition. For good freezing, a temperature of –18°C or below is required. Chill storage will preserve perishable foods for days or weeks depending upon the food. Frozen storage (deep freezing) will preserve foods for months or even years.

Refrigeration has certain advantages over freezing. It takes less energy to cool food to just above its freezing point than to freeze it. Refrigeration storage requires less insulation and refrigeration capacity, and refrigerated products do not suffer from texture and flavour losses caused by freezing. Finally, refrigerated products do not have to be thawed before use—a process that may take as much as 48 hours with large frozen foods.

A further distinction between refrigeration and freezing temperatures relate to microbial activity. Most spoilage organisms grow above 10°C. Some food poisoning organisms grow slowly up to 3.3°C. Cryophilic organisms grow slowly from –4.4°C to –9.4°C, provided the food is not frozen. These organisms, however, do not produce toxins or disease but cause food deterioration. There is no growth of organisms below –9.4°C, though there may not be a total destruction at that temperature.

31.5 Chill Storage

Chill storage is useful as the principal method of preservation and as an adjunct to other methods of preservation. The shelf-life of food is directly linked with the microbial rate of growth as influenced by temperature. Storage at – 1° and – 4°C can provide stability, particularly in the presence of food preservatives or a modified atmosphere.

31.5.1 Production of Low Temperature

Chill storage requires controlled low temperature. This is achieved by taking heat away from the storage area. Heat is transferred from the storage area by the principle of latent heat of vaporization. If the state is changed from liquid to gas, or from gas to liquid, without affecting its temperature, an amount of heat must be added or removed. Liquids like ammonia and freon (Cl_2F_2) are used as refrigerants. The liquid refrigerant is circulated through an expansion valve or a capillary tube and then through a heat exchanger, called an evaporator, within the storage area. In passing through the capillary tube, the refrigerant goes from relatively high pressure to a relatively low one, causing the liquid refrigerant to evaporate, thus reducing the temperature of the liquid-gas phase of the refrigerant. In the evaporator, the remaining liquid evaporates, absorbing heat from the storage area. The temperature of vaporization of the refrigerant is some 5°–6°C below the storage temperature. A compressor then pumps the refrigerant from the low-pressure cold condition to a high-pressure hot one. The hot gas flows through a condenser where heat is extracted from the refrigerant, and transforms it back to a room temperature, high-pressure liquid ready to flow again to the expansion or capillary tube. Air, water, or a combination of air and evaporating water, is used to cool the condenser.

For the construction of commercial chill storage rooms, the "refrigeration load" is to be taken into consideration. This is the quantity of heat that must be removed from the product and the storage area, in order to go from an initial temperature to the selected final temperature, and then maintain this temperature for a specific time. This depends on the storage area and other factors that may generate heat within the storage area or influence the removal of heat from the area. These include the light and electrical installations, number of people working, how often the doors, which permit the entrance of warm air, are opened, and the amount and nature of the food product stored in the refrigerated area. Also, the specific heat of food and the rate of respiration of such foods as fruits and vegetables have a bearing on the extent of refrigeration required. The heats produced from the respiration of fruits and vegetables vary considerably. Products like green beans, peas, spinach, sweet corn, and strawberries have a high respiration rate even at 0°C.

31.5.2 Air Circulation and Humidity

The heat produced due to respiration in the vicinity of the food surface in cold storage is to be transferred towards the refrigerator. This is achieved by air circulation. The humidity of the circulated air is to be controlled. If it is too moist, moisture will condense on the cold food and moulds will grow on food surfaces at the common refrigeration temperature. On the other hand, if the air is too dry there will be desiccation of food. The optimum relative humidity of the circulated air depends upon the moisture content of the foods and the ease with which they dry out. Most foods store best at a refrigeration temperature when the relative humidity of air is between 80 and 95 per cent. Dry and granular foods store well at about 50 per cent relative humidity.

When foods are to be chill stored for a long time, they are protected by packing to prevent loss of moisture. Plastic sacks or moisture-resistant coating are used for this purpose. Cheese ripened for a long time in cold storage are wax coated. Loss of moisture from stored eggs is prevented by dipping the eggs in some oil, to seal the minute pores of the eggshell. If packing is not possible, as in the case of tenderizing beef by ageing in cool rooms, ultraviolet light is employed to retard mould growth.

31.5.3 Modified Atmosphere

Continued chill storage, and biochemical changes of fruits and vegetables, even under chill storage, result in overripening, softening, and general loss in quality. These changes take place at the normal chemical composition of air (78 per cent nitrogen, 21 per cent oxygen, and 0.03 per cent carbon dioxide) and they can be arrested by using refrigeration in conjunction with a "modified atmosphere" or "controlled atmosphere". By raising the carbon dioxide and lowering the oxygen levels, foods can be stored for an extended period of time. In a modified atmosphere of 3 per cent oxygen and 3 per cent carbon dioxide, apples can be preserved in good condition for about a year at 2.8°C and 87 per cent relative humidity. For each food, there is an optimal storage temperature, relative humidity, oxygen level, and carbon dioxide level, which delay the ripening process. Modified atmosphere cold storage in gas-tight containers has enabled the shipment of even highly perishable foods like lettuce over long distances. Ramifications of controlled atmosphere can have other desirable effects on cold-stored food. For example, the presence of diphenyl vapours can inhibit mould growth in citrus foods, and the use of ethylene gas can speed up the ripening and colour development of citrus fruits and bananas.

31.6 Deep Freezing

Tremendous advances have been made in freezing food for preservation, storage, and distribution. Many foods can be frozen for twelve months or more without major changes in size, shape, texture, colour, and flavour. Frozen foods have thus attained wide acceptance by the public. At present, no form of food preservation is as well suited to provide maximum convenience as freezing. Complete meals on individual plates can be frozen and are ready for use with a single thawing-heated operation. An unlimited number of items may now be frozen in their final serving forms.

31.6.1 Changes during Freezing and Thawing

Uncontrolled freezing of food can result in the disruption of texture, breaking up of emulsion, denaturation of proteins, and many other physical and chemical changes. Substances like sugar, salt, and proteins dissolved in water lower the freezing point of water. Thus, when food is kept at a freezing temperature, where the temperature is considerably below the freezing point of water, the water component freezes first and leaves the dissolved solids in a more concentrated solution, which requires a still lower temperature to freeze it. Thus, different foods, with varying levels of water as well as the amount and nature of dissolved substances, will have different freezing points, and under a given freezing condition will require different times to reach a solidly frozen state.

When food containing water is placed in a freezer, it does not freeze uniformly. The portion of food nearest to the container freezes first and the first ice crystals are pure water. As water continues to be frozen, the concentration of dissolved solids increases, and finally a central core of highly concentrated unfrozen liquid remains. If the temperature is sufficiently low, this central core also freezes solid ultimately. In the case of solid foods, like a piece of meat at about –4°C, they appear to be solidly frozen, but they still contain about 3 per cent water in an unfrozen condition. Even at –18°C, not all of the water is completely frozen.

Small quantities of unfrozen water in frozen foods result in the deterioration of food with respect to texture, colour, flavour, and other properties. The high concentration of dissolved substances in the remaining water can cause effects of various kinds. The dissolved substances may precipitate or crystallize, imparting a gritty, sandy texture to the food; if they remain in solution, the high salt concentration or drop in pH (if the solutes are acidic) might result in protein denaturation. The disturbances in anionic and cationic concentration can disturb colloidal substances, and finally the concentration effects can cause the dehydration of adjacent tissues, resulting in loss of tissue turgor. Other effects of unfrozen water are the possibility of the growth of psychrophilic micro-organisms, and the greater action of enzymes.

The formation of ice crystals during freezing can affect the texture of many frozen foods. There is water within and between the cells of food. When water freezes rapidly, it forms minute ice crystals and clusters of crystals. In slow freezing, water within and between the cells freezes, causing physical rupture and separation of cells. If freezing is rapid, the minute crystals formed are only within the cells but not between the cells, and physical damage of the cells is less severe. Rapid cooling also minimizes concentration effects by decreasing the time of contact of solutes with food tissues during the transition from the unfrozen to the fully frozen state. For these reasons, rapid freezing is desirable for better product quality.

From the point of view of quality and economic aspects, it is best to freeze foods to –18°C or lower, and maintain them at that temperature during storage and transport. In order to achieve the best advantage of rapid freezing, many foods are frozen to temperatures somewhat below –26°C, but this increases the cost. A freezing temperature of –18°C is very safe from attack by micro-organisms as no pathogenic organisms grow below about 3.3°C and spoilage organisms below about –9.4°C. At –9.4°C, most foods retain considerable frozen water, and long storage at this temperature can result in the enzymatic deterioration of food. Even at –18°C some enzymes retain activity. However, the rates of reactions they catalyze will be extremely slow. In the case of fruits and vegetables, the enzyme activity even at –18°C is sufficient to bring about spoilage. In these cases, the enzymes are inactivated by blanching before freezing. Properly packed foods, frozen and stored at –18°C, have high-quality storage life of the order of 12 months and longer.

The kind of damage that occur to food during slow freezing also occurs during thawing. Repeated freezing and thawing is, therefore very detrimental to the quality of food. Even a fluctuation of 3°C in freezing temperature above and below –18°C, at which the food is frozen and stored, can damage many foods. Upon refreezing, water melted from small ice crystals tends to bathe unmelted crystals, causing them to grow in size. Also, if the thawing of frozen foods is slow, there is loss of quality due to concentration effects. In slow thawing, there is more time for food constituents to be in contact with concentrated solution, thus intensifying their damaging effect. Quick thawing is also desirable from the point of keeping the microbial population in check. Large volumes of frozen food can take from 20–60 hours for thawing. Since bacteria survive the thawing process, long periods and a rise in the temperatures of products will be opportune for bacterial multiplication. Use of microwave heating reduces the thawing time.

31.6.2 Methods of Food Freezing

There are three basic methods of freezing in commercial use. These are freezing in air, freezing by indirect contact with a refrigerant, and freezing by direct contact with the freezing medium. Air freezing may be by the use of still air ("sharp freezing") or an air blast. Indirect contact freezing consists of keeping food or food packages on a surface cooled by a refrigerant. In direct-contact freezing, the food or package is submerged in a cold liquid or the cold liquid is sprayed on the food or package.

Air freezing: Still-air freezing is the oldest and least expensive method of freezing. This is the type of freezing carried out in home freezers. In this method, food packs are placed in the freezer in such a way that air can circulate between the packages. The freezer is maintained in the range of –23° to –29°C. There is some air movement due to convection, and in some cases gentle air movement may also be promoted.

In air-blast freezing, food packages are carried on an open mesh belt through a tunnel, through which air at temperatures of –29°C to –46°C is forced at velocities of 10 to 15 m/s over, under, or through, the product. Under these conditions, a food packet that takes 72 hours to freeze in still-air can be frozen in about 12–18 hours. A drawback of air-blast freezing is the dehydration of food in an unwrapped condition, which is known as freezer burn. This occurs due to ice changing directly to water vapour molecules without going through the liquid state. Freezer burn results in discolouration, changes in texture, and off-flavour. Freezer burn can be minimized by pre-chilling food with air at high humidity at about –4°C, and the pre-chilled food is then moved into the colder zone where it is quickly frozen.

Indirect contact freezing: Solid foods in consumer size flat packets are placed on shallow metal plates chilled by the circulating refrigerant so that the food is in direct contact with the cold metal wall but in indirect contact with the refrigerant. The efficiency of freezing depends upon the extent of contact between the plates and the food. For this reason, the packages should be well filled or slightly overfilled to make good pressure contact with the plates. The freezing of liquids and pure¾s by indirect freezing is carried out by pumping them through tubes on the outside of which the refrigerant flows. Through appropriate mechanical devices, the frozen food is scrapped to keep the mass in motion thus enabling the continuous bringing of new portions of food into contact with the cold wall. In this method, freezing occurs in a matter of seconds.

Immersion freezing: Immersion freezing has a number of advantages. There is intimate contact between the food or package and the refrigerant. This is particularly important in freezing irregularly shaped food pieces, and immersion freezing minimizes the contact of food with air during freezing, which is desirable for foods sensitive to oxidation.

The refrigerants used for immersion freezing should be non-toxic, pure, clear, free from taste, odour, colour, or bleaching action. Low-freezing-point liquids cooled by indirect contact with another refrigerant or cryogenic liquids like liquid nitrogen, carbon dioxide, or freon, are used as refrigerants.

The low-freezing-point liquids used are solutions of sugar, salt, or glycerol. A temperature as low as –21°C can be reached with a 23 per cent sodium chloride or 62 per cent sucrose solution. With a 67 per cent glycerol-water solution, one could go down to –47°C.

Cryogenic liquids are liquefied gases of extremely low boiling point, such as liquid nitrogen (BP, –196°C), liquid carbon dioxide (BP, –79°C), and freon 12 (BP, –30°C). The most commonly used cryogenic liquid is liquid nitrogen. Its low boiling point helps very quick freezing of even large food pieces and it can give a quality unattainable by other non-cryogenic freezing methods. Further, since the cold temperature results from evaporation of liquid nitrogen, freezing by liquid nitrogen does not require a primary refrigerant to cool this medium, and liquid nitrogen is non-toxic and inert to food constituents. The operating cost of liquid-nitrogen freezing, however, is high. With liquid nitrogen, it is possible to freeze food down to –196°C, but it is seldom frozen to a temperature below –46°C. Generally, liquid-nitrogen freezing produces less dehydration loss during freezing and less drip loss during thawing than other freezing methods.

Freezing with liquid carbon dioxide is carried out in a manner similar to freezing with liquid nitrogen. Some foods frozen with this refrigerant are equal in quality to those by liquid nitrogen freezing. In such cases, use of liquid carbon dioxide for freezing is very economical. Of late, freon freezing is coming into use. The installation and operational costs of freon freezing are high, but this can be overcome by the efficient recovery of freon, which becomes vapour on contact with food, for reuse.

Packaging for freezing: Choice of packaging material is of special concern in the manufacture of high-quality frozen foods. The material should be moisture-proof and impermeable to oxygen and flavour compounds, both at freezing temperature and after thawing. It should be resistant to chemical attacks from the constituents of foods. Most foods expand on freezing. Therefore, the packaging material in which the food is frozen should have good mechanical strength, have a degree of flexibility, and should not be completely filled. Many packaging materials, such as cans, metal foils, waxed papers, plastic-coated cardboards and plastic foils, cellophane, parchment paper, etc., are all satisfactory for frozen foods. Glass is not generally satisfactory for frozen foods, due to the possibility of breakage from expansion and thermal shocks.

31.7 Drying

Food preservation by drying is one of the methods practiced since ancient times. Drying is the method nature resorts to preserve foods. Grains in the field dry sufficiently on the stalk by exposure to the sun, which requires no further drying for preservation. This is also true of legumes, innumerable seeds, and some spices. The observation of natural drying was adopted by early man to dry fruits, fish, and meat, by exposing them to the sun. Sun drying is still in use in many parts of the world for preserving certain foods, such as fruits and nuts. However, it is limited by the fact that it is feasible only under climatic conditions of high heat and low humidity.

Drying of food involves the complete removal of water under controlled conditions in such a way that the food is not altered and results in minimum changes by the drying process. Dried foods contain moisture to the extent of 1–5 per cent, and they have storage stability at room temperature for a year or longer. On reconstitution with water, dried foods are very close to and virtually indistinguishable from the original foods used in their preparation. Removal of moisture from a solid with minimum change in food material is not an easy problem. Removal of only a part of the water of foods, perhaps 1/3 to 2/3 of the water, as in the preparation of syrups, evaporated milk, tomato paste, condensed soups, etc., is not considered drying. Partial removal of water is known as concentration.

31.7.1 Advantages of Drying

Micro-organisms require water for growth, and when they are growing on food, they get water from the food. If water is removed from the food, the multiplication of micro-organisms will stop. The highest water contents at which microbial spoilage does not occur in the case of traditional dried foods are: dehydrated whole egg, 10–11 per cent; wheat flour, 13–15 per cent; dehydrated fat-free meat, 15 per cent; dehydrated vegetables, 14–20 per cent; and dehydrated fruits, 18–25 per cent. The drying of foods, thus, is primarily carried out to preserve food by controlling micro-organisms. Partial drying, as in concentration, will be less effective than total drying in food preservation. However, concentration is quite sufficient to arrest the growth and multiplication of micro-organisms in some foods.

Drying, in addition to preservation, helps decrease the weight and bulk of food, e.g., 237 ml of orange juice on dehydration yields just 28 g of solids. In some cases, the drying process may be chosen to retain the original shape and size. However, in such a case, the volume may not be affected but there is weight reduction. Drying thus results in a great economy in storage, packaging, and transport, of food. Drying also results in the production of convenience foods, such as instant coffee, instant rice, etc. In these cases, cooking steps are completed before the products are dried.

31.7.2 Drying Rate

The amount of water removed from a given weight of material during a given time interval is called the drying rate. The most important stages in dehydration are penetration of heat into the product and removal of moisture out of the product. Various factors contribute to these two stages. A large surface area of the food to be dehydrated provides more surface area for contact with the heating medium and for moisture to escape. Therefore, generally, foods are divided into small pieces of thin layers for dehydration. This also helps reduce the distances heat must travel to reach the centre of the food and moisture must travel to reach the surface to escape. Also, the greater the temperature differences between the heating medium and the food to be dried, greater is the drying rate. For any given temperature, the rate of water removal from the food is greater in vacuum than under atmospheric pressure. When the heating medium is air, it gets saturated with the moisture from the water driven from the food and this slows down subsequent moisture removal. Air in motion sweeps away moist air from the drying food surface. Thus, air velocity is also a factor that determines the drying rate.

When food is dried in the air, the drier the air, the more rapid is the rate of drying. Moist air absorbs and holds less moisture than if it were dry. Dryness also determines the extent to which a food can be dried. Dried foods are hygroscopic. Each food has its own equilibrium relative humidity; i.e., the humidity at a given temperature where food neither loses moisture to the atmosphere nor picks up moisture from the atmosphere. Below this atmosphere-humidity level, food cannot be further dried. For example, potato at 100°C and 46 per cent relative humidity level can be dried to 4 per cent moisture. If we wish to dry it down to 2 per cent moisture at the same temperature in air, then the relative humidity of air should be 15 per cent. Thus, the equilibrium relative humidity data of a food are important both from the point of view of its drying and storage.

There is a relationship between evaporation and temperature in drying. As water evaporates from the food, it results in the cooling of the food surface. This is due to the latent heat of phase change from liquid to gas. There are several important consequences of this phenomenon in food drying. Regardless of the drying temperature or heating surface, the temperature of the food will not be higher than a particular temperature as long as water is evaporating rapidly. Thus, in a spray drier, the incoming air may be at 204°C and the exit air at 121°C, but the food particles while drying may be at no more than about 71°C. As the moisture content of food decreases and evaporation slows down the particles rise in temperature. When there is no water, the incoming air and the exit air will have the same temperature (204°C). As foods are heat-sensitive, they are to be removed from the drier before this high temperature is reached.

There is also a time and temperature relationship in food preservation by drying. As food constituents are heat-sensitive, a high temperature for a short time does less damage to food than a low temperature for a long time. Also, when foods are dried, they do not lose water at a constant rate all the way down to dryness. At the beginning of drying, and for some time thereafter, water generally evaporates from the food at a rather constant rate, and then leaves with a falling-rate period of dryness. For example, 90 per cent of water from diced carrot can be removed in four hours, and the removal of the remaining 10 per cent requires another four hours.

Thus, varying conditions, such as temperature, humidity, air velocity, the direction of the air, the thickness of the food, and other factors affect the drying of food. Removal of water below 2 per cent, without damage to the product, is exceedingly difficult.

More than the physical factors, some of the properties of food components and the changes they undergo during drying determine the drying rate. Most foods are not homogeneous at the molecular level. For example, a piece of meat will have lean and fat interlaced or marbled together. Therefore, when a piece of meat is dried it will give up water at different rates in the regions of fat and lean. The drying rate in such a case can be increased by orienting the meat portion relative to the source of heat, such that moisture escapes in a line parallel to the layers of fat rather than having to pass through them.

When sugar and low-molecular-weight substances are present in foods, they elevate the boiling point of water and thus affect the drying rate. Also, during drying, the concentration of solutes becomes greater which slows down drying. The escape of water from food depends upon the condition in which it is present. Free water easily evaporates. Water loosely held, by force of adsorption to food solids, evaporates slowly. Removal of water that enters into colloidal gels, such as when starch, pectin or other gums are present, is more difficult. It is also more difficult to remove chemically bound water as in hydrates of salts. The cells of blanched or cooked foods are more permeable to moisture and dry more easily than their fresh counterparts, provided cooking does not cause excessive toughening or shrinking.

In many cases, foods are pre-treated before drying, with a view to making the structure more porous so as to facilitate transfer of moisture and thereby speed the drying rate. Porous sponge-like structures are excellent insulating bodies, and generally, slow down the rate of heat transfer into the food. The net effect of food porosity on drying rate thus depends on whether the effect of porosity is greater on speeding the escape of moisture from food or slowing the heating transfer rate. Apart from its effects on the drying rate, food porosity has the advantages of quick solubility on reconstitution but suffers from the disadvantages of increased bulk and shorter storage stability.

31.7.3 Changes during Drying

Drying bring about changes in the final product quality. One of the most obvious changes during drying of cellular as well as non-cellular foods is shrinkage. The type and extent of shrinkage depend upon the rate of drying. For example, on the slow drying of a vegetable dice, first there is surface shrinkage. With continued drying, water is removed from the deeper layers and finally from the centre, causing continuous shrinkage towards the centre with a concave appearance, and the product is dense. With quick high-temperature drying of food, the surface becomes dry and rigid long before the centre dries out. Thus, when the centre dries and shrinks it pulls away from the rigid surface layer causing internal splits, voids and honeycomb effects, and the product is less dense. Such a product absorbs water, reconstitutes quicker, more closely resembles the original material, and is thus favoured by consumers.

With foods that contain dissolved sugar and other solutes in high concentration, drying can result in shrinkage and sealing off of the surface pores and cracks. This results in trapping much of the remaining water with the food and drying rate dropping off severely. Dried food pieces may also contain voids, cracks and pores of various diameters. The shrinking and pore-clogging by the solutes is known as core hardening. Gradual drying with low surface temperature can minimize core hardening.

Some foods, which lack structure and are rich in sugar and other materials, soften when heated at the elevated temperature of drying. Even after all the water has been removed the foods will be in a thermoplastic tacky condition, giving an impression that they still contain moisture; they stick to the drier. However, on cooling, the thermoplastic solids harden into a crystalline or amorphous glass form. In this more brittle condition, they can be easily removed from the drier.

In addition to the physical changes described above, drying can bring about a range of chemical changes. These contribute to the quality of both the final product and the reconstituted food in terms of colour, flavour, texture, viscosity, nutritional value, and storage stability. Complete prevention of these changes is virtually impossible. They can be minimized by appropriate technology.

31.7.4 Methods of Drying

Methods used for food preservation by drying should produce a maximum drying rate with minimum product damage and economic drying costs. A number of drying methods are available; some are particularly suited for liquids, others for solid foods, or mixtures containing food pieces. The common drier types used for liquid and solid foods may be categorized as the air-convection drier, drum or roller drier, and vacuum drier. In the air-convection method, hot air supplies the heat for evaporation. If liquid, the food may be sprayed, or poured, into pans or on belts. Drum or roller driers are limited to their use with liquid foods, purées and mashes, that can be applied as thin films. Vacuum driers are employed to lower the temperature of drying. Freeze driers are vacuum driers where, at an extremely low temperature, water vapour directly forms ice without going through the liquid state. The above division of driers is not rigid since many driers are combinations, e.g., a drum drier can be operated in a vacuum or by blowing high-velocity healed air.

Air-convection driers: There are some common aspects of the different types of air-convection driers. They all have an insulated enclosure, a means of circulating air through the enclosure, and a means of heating this air. They also have means of supporting foods to be dried, and devices to collect dried food.

Air may be heated directly or indirectly. In the former method, air is in direct contact with combustion gases. In indirect heating, the air is heated in contact with a hot surface, which is heated by a convenient method. A direct heating method may contaminate the food product, which is not the case with indirect heating.

The simplest type of air-convection drier is the kiln drier. In this case, there is direct heating of air. This kind of drier does not generally reduce moisture to below 10 per cent. A step more advanced drier is the cabinet drier. Food loaded in trays or pans in thin layers is placed in the cabinet, and air heated by an indirect method is blown across food trays. This method is used for small-scale operations. Foods commonly dried by this method are fruits and vegetables. The drying time is of the order of 10–20 hours. For larger operations, a tunnel drier is used. Wet food carts are moved through the tunnel on a continuous belt. Drying air is blown in a direction opposite to the movement of food carts (counter-current principle). The conveyer belt itself in some cases may form a trough (belt trough drier). The belt is usually of metal mesh and heated air is blown through the mesh. Another type of air-convection drier is the fluidized bed drier. In this case, heated air is blown through food particles with just enough force to suspend the particle in a gentle boiling motion.

The most important kind of air-convection drier is the spray drier. More food is dehydrated by using this drier than all other kinds of driers put together. Spray drying is limited to liquids, low-viscosity pastes, or purées. Food in the form of a fine spray or mist is introduced into a tower or chamber along with heated air. The small droplets make intimate contact with hot air, blast off their moisture, become small particles, and drop to the bottom of the tower, from where they are removed. Drying takes place in a matter of seconds. The air temperature will be 204°C, but the food particles, never reach a temperature above 82°C as evaporation cools the food. This method of dehydration can produce a high-quality product even with heat-sensitive materials like milk, eggs and coffee.

Drum or roller drier: Liquid foods, purées, and mashes, are dried by this method. The food to be dried is applied, as a continuous thin layer, onto the surface of a revolving drum or between a pair of drums moving in opposite directions, generally heated by steam. The dried thin layer of food on the drum is scraped by a scraper blade positioned at a point on the drum. Some foods when dry are sticky and cannot be scraped off from the drum when hot. Such a sticky food becomes brittle when cold, which facilitates scraping. Providing a cold zone on a drum thus helps the drying of such foods. The drum temperature may be kept above 100°C by using steam under pressure. Generally, the drum is kept at 150°C when a film of food 1.6 mm in thickness gets dried in one minute or less. For heat resistant food products, drum drying is one of the least expensive dehydration methods. Drum-dried foods generally will have a somewhat more "cooked" character than the same material spray-dried.

Vacuum driers: This method of drying of foods is expensive but gives high-quality foods. The drying system consists of a vacuum chamber that can withstand external air pressure, and contains shelves or other supports to hold food. This kind of vacuum drier is for batch-type operation. For continuous operation, a belt drier is used. The shelves are heated electrically or by circulating a heated fluid. The food gets heated by conduction and also by radiated heat from shelves above and below. The drying chamber is evacuated by a suitable device maintained outside the vacuum chamber. The water that evaporates from the food is suitably condensed. The temperature of the food and the rate of water removal is controlled by controlling the degree of vacuum and the intensity of heat output. Liquid foods dehydrated by vacuum drying have a puffed structure and are easily dissolved in water. Because of the low temperature used, there is minimal flavour change and other kinds of heat damage in this method of drying.

Freeze-drying is used to dehydrate sensitive high-quality liquid foods, such as coffee and juices, and also solids of high value, like strawberries, shrimps, etc., having delicate flavour, colour and textural attributes, which cannot be preserved by any other drying method. In freeze-drying, water evaporates from ice without passing through the liquid stage, i.e., water from ice directly becomes water vapour. This happens at a temperature of 0°C or below, and at a low pressure of 4.7 mm of mercury or less. Frozen food is dried by keeping it in a vacuum chamber maintained at a pressure of 0.1 to 2 mm of mercury and maintaining the temperature of the chamber just below the melting point of ice. Under such conditions, water from the frozen food evaporates at the maximum rate. Since the frozen food remains rigid, the evaporation of water leaves voids behind it, resulting in a porous sponge-like dried material. After the food is dried, the vacuum is broken with inert nitrogen gas, and it is packed under nitrogen. If the vacuum is broken by admitting air, the dried product absorbs the air into its pores, resulting in impaired storage stability.

Foam-drying (puff dry) at atmospheric pressure can be employed to dehydrate foods and obtain products with qualities approaching vacuum-dried ones. This method of drying is very economical compared to the vacuum drying method and can be applied to liquid foods and purées which can be pre-foamed before drying. As foaming exposes an enormous surface area for quick moisture escape, drying of foams can be rapid at atmospheric pressure at a reduced temperature. With foods that do not whip readily, some whipping agents (vegetable proteins, gums, monoglycerides) are added prior to being whipped. Stable foams are cast in thin layers into trays or belts and dried by various heating schemes.

Solar food drying is an ideal application for solar energy. Solar radiation passes through the clear glass top of a wooden dehydrator box, then the heat trapped by the box dries the food. The dehydrator also may have an absorber plate inside, which indirectly heats food and creates a convection current of air that enters a vent at the bottom of the dryer. As the food dries, moisture is carried away with the hot air. The easiest solar food dryer to build is a "hot box." One type of solar food dryer integrates the solar collector and food drying cabinet into a compact configuration, which uses both direct heating (like the solar hot-box dryer) and indirect heating from the absorber plate. In a solar food dehydrator, foods are dried quicker on par with an electric food drier. It is relatively compact and lightweight for portability. A simple solar dehydrator can be used at the household level as it is easy to load, unload, and clean.

31.8 Concentration

Foods are concentrated for the same reasons that they are dried—preservation and reduction in weight and bulk. Nearly all liquid foods are first concentrated before drying, because of the technical and economical advantages of such processing. Many foods are better recognized as concentrates than dried ones; examples are fruit-juice concentrates, canned soups, condensed milk, etc.

Concentration may not be effective in all cases as a means of food preservation The levels of water in most concentrated foods are sufficient for microbial growth. Concentrated non-acid fruit juice and vegetable purées undergo spoilage unless they are further processed. On the other hand, concentrated sugar syrups, sauces, and jellies, are relatively free from spoilage. The solutions of sugar and salt dissolved in the remaining water give concentrates that exert high osmotic pressure and draw water from the microbial cells or prevent normal diffusion of water into the cells, and thus prevent microbial contamination. Solutions containing 70 per cent of sugar or 18–25 per cent salt prevent the growth of all micro-organisms

31.8.1 Methods of Concentration

As in food drying, one of the simplest methods of concentration is by utilizing solar energy. Salt has been manufactured by the concentration of seawater by this method from the earliest times.

Kettle evaporators: A simple method of concentration is by the use of open kettles and pans, which may be heated by direct flame or steam. High temperature and long concentration times damage most foods. However, kettle or pan concentration is used in the manufacture of syrups, as high heat is desirable to produce the colour from caramelized sugar and develop typical flavour.

Flash evaporation: Purées are concentrated by flash evaporation. Superheated steam (150°C) is injected into the food pumped into a vertical tubular steam-jacketed evaporator, where boiling occurs. The boiling mix then enters a separator from which the concentrated food is drained off.

Film evaporators: Foods are also concentrated using thin film evaporators. In this case, food is pumped into a vertical cylinder which has a rotating element that spreads the food into a thin layer on the cylindrical wall. The cylinder wall is usually heated by steam. Water quickly flashes from the thin food layer, and the concentrated food is simultaneously wiped from the cylinder wall. The product temperature may reach 83°C, but since the concentrated food will be in contact with the heated cylinder for less than a minute, the damage is minimal.

Vacuum evaporators: Heat-sensitive liquid foods are commonly concentrated at low temperatures in vacuum evaporators. Evaporation systems can be made that operate many times more effectively than single-effect evaporation. Several vacuumized vessels in series constitute multiple effect evaporators (see also Chapter 26). In this process, the first evaporator under vacuum is heated with steam. The water vapour boiled off from the food is sent to the next evaporator kept at a higher vacuum than the first. The water vapour acts as a heat source to evaporate food in the second evaporator. The water vapour from the second can next be passed to a third evaporator, having a higher vacuum than the second, and so on. Grape juice and tomato juice are concentrated in this way. This method results in energy conservation.

Freeze concentration: Concentration by freezing has been used to concentrate fruit juice. When liquid food is frozen, not all the water is converted into ice at the same time. Before the food freezes, the initially formed ice crystals are separated. By repeating this process several times on the concentrated unfrozen food, a high percentage of water can be removed. The disadvantage of this method is the unavoidable entrainment loss.

Ultrafiltration and reverse osmosis: Another method of concentration of liquid food is by ultra-filtration and reverse osmosis. The process consists of pumping liquid foods at a high pressure against selective membranes that allow water molecules to pass through them, while retaining macromolecules, salts, sugar, and other organic molecules. Membranes used in ultra-filtration are "less light" and may allow small molecules to pass through them under moderate pressure, while in reverse osmosis, the membranes are "tighter" and permeability does not allow even these molecules to pass through. In osmosis, there is the movement of water through membranes from a region of lower concentration to a region of higher concentration. In reverse osmosis, this is reversed; under pressure, there is flow of water through the membranes from a region of higher concentration to that of a lower.

The concentration of foods results in a cooked flavour and darkening of colour. Concentration aiso causes changes in organoleptic and nutritional properties of foods. Some foods cannot be concentrated beyond a certain point. When foods containing sugar are concentrated, sugar crystallizes out as concentration increases. Concentration also causes an increase in the level of salts and minerals, which results in the precipitation of proteins. This is the cause of gel formation of evaporated milk after a few weeks' or months' storage.

31.9 Fermentation

The methods of food preservation so far studied, such as application of heat, cold, removal of water, and other methods used, have the common objective of decreasing the number of micro-organisms in food or holding them in check against further multiplication. In food preservation by fermentation, in contrast, multiplication of micro-organisms and their metabolic activities are encouraged. However, the organisms that are encouraged to grow and multiply are the select groups, whose metabolic products help food preservation.

Natural fermentations have played a vital role in the preservation of foods from early times. Fruit juices exposed to air underwent natural fermentation and acquired an alcoholic flavour. Milk on standing became slightly acidic. These changes were, therefore, used as a means of preservation of otherwise perishable foods. At the same time, the changes in the texture and taste of fermented foods were found desirable. These are the principal reasons for the continued use of fermentation in food processing and preservation. The list of foods produced by fermentation is extremely long, and includes the following: cheese, curd, butter, all alcoholic beverages, pickles, sauerkraut, vinegar, bread, idli, soya sauce, coffee, tea, and cocoa.

The term "fermentation" means the breakdown of carbohydrate material by micro-organisms (or enzymes) under anaerobic conditions. In common usage, the term "fermentation" refers to both the anaerobic and aerobic breakdowns of carbohydrates and carbohydrate-like materials. Thus, the conversion of lactose to lactic acid by *Streptococcus lactis,* which takes place under anaerobic conditions and conversion of ethyl alcohol to acetic acid by the bacteria *Acetobacter aceti,* under aerobic conditions, are both referred to as fermentation. The term is used in a still broader and less precise manner to describe fermented foods.

In the fermentation of foods, a complex mixture of carbohydrates, proteins, fats, etc., undergo modifications simultaneously under the action of a variety of micro-organisms and enzymes present. Thus, the carbohydrates and carbohydrate-like materials undergo fermentation, proteinaceous materials undergo proteolysis or "putrefactive" breakdown, and lipids "lipolytic" breakdown. The nature and extent of these changes depend upon the food, types of micro-organisms present, and conditions, affecting their growth and metabolic pattern.

The preservative effect of fermentation is caused by the chemicals excreted by the micro-organisms. The principal chemicals involved are acids (especially lactic acid) and alcohol. These inhibit the growth of common pathogenic organisms in foods. The toxin producing *Clostridium botulinum*, for example, cannot grow at pH values below 4.6.

31.9.1 Benefits of Fermentation

In addition to contributing to preservation, fermentation of foods has additional benefits. Fermentation produces flavour and textural changes and fermented foods are more nutritious than their unfermented counterparts. Micro-organisms, in addition to breaking down complex compounds, synthesize several vitamins and other growth factors. In fact, the industrial production of some vitamins is largely by fermentation processes. The digestible carbohydrates and proteins of grains and seeds are enclosed in cellulosic and hemicellulosic structures, which are indigestible materials. Fermentation, especially by certain moulds, breaks down the indigestible protective coating, as they are rich in cellulose-splitting enzymes. The altered structure of the cells makes the permeability of digestive juices easy. An additional advantage of such splitting of cellulose, hemicellulose, and related materials, is that such materials are converted into simpler sugars and sugar derivatives, which increases the nutritional value of foods. In addition to the above, research has also proved health benefits associated with fermented foods to decrease fat deposition, stimulate metabolism, normalize stomach acidity, and protect the stomach and intestinal lining.

31.9.2 Microbial Activities in Foods

Microbial flora associated with foods have a broad complement of enzymes and, as already stated, bring about fermentative, proteolytic, and lipolytic changes, among others. Proteolytic organisms break down proteins and other nitrogenous compounds resulting in a putrid and rotten odour and flavour. Lipolytic organisms hydrolyze lipids giving rise to free fatty acids resulting in rancidity. These changes are undesirable in foods. On the other hand, fermentative organisms converting carbohydrates and related compounds to alcohols, acids and carbon dioxide, are not offensive to food tastes. When the concentration of their fermentative products increases, they control the growth of organisms of the proteolytic and lipolytic types. However, fermentation of food is complex and only one type of change, to total exclusion of other changes, is impossible. Thus, to obtain a product of desired quality, controlled fermentation becomes necessary.

31.9.3 Control of Fermentation in Foods

The factors that influence the growth and metabolic activities of micro-organisms in food fermentation are acidity, levels of alcohol, use of starters, and levels of oxygen and salts.

Acid: Acids when present in food, either as natural constituents, added or formed by fermentation, exert an inhibitory effect on harmful micro-organisms. However, the preservative effect of acid is lost if oxygen is available and surface moulds grow, which results in the fermentation of acids. This happens during the ripening of cheddar cheese and constitutes a defect. Some yeasts tolerate moderately high acidity and produce ammonia from the breakdown of protein. This results in the neutralization of the acid present, and permits the subsequent growth of proteolytic and lipolytic bacteria, as happens in the ripening of some types of cheese.

These types of changes also occur when raw milk is allowed to ferment. Raw milk contains many types of organisms. First, *Streptococcus lactis* grow to produce lactic acid, but its growth is inhibited when the acid concentration reaches a particular level. *Lactobacillus* bacteria, which are still more acid resistant, then grow and produce more acid until the new level becomes inhibitory to their growth. This results in milk clotting and curd formation. In the high-acid environment, acid resistant yeasts and moulds become active. The moulds oxidize acid and the yeast produces alkaline end products. These result in a decrease of the acid level, favouring the growth of proteolytic and lipolytic spoilage bacteria and resulting in an off-odour and gassy condition in the curd.

Alcohol: Alcohol is also a preservative depending upon its concentration. Yeast converts sugar to alcohol but it cannot tolerate alcohol concentration of over 12 per cent. When the alcohol content is below this level, as in beer, pasteurization of the food becomes necessary to prevent spoilage.

Use of starters: When a particular type of micro-organism is present in large numbers and is multiplying at a good rate, it keeps down the growth of other micro-organisms. This is the reason why in curd making or wine making a part from the previous batch of curd or wine is added to the fresh milk or grape juice. However, in commercial food fermentation, pure cultures are used as starters to obtain products of desired quality.

Temperature: Temperature has an effect on all microbial reactions and hence has to be controlled. In mixed fermentations, as in foods, control of temperature is all the more necessary as different organisms have different temperature sensitivity. For example, in the production of sauerkraut, three major types of organisms, which grow well at different temperatures, are involved in fermentation. In sauerkraut fermentation, therefore, an initial low temperature (about 21°C), which then is increased somewhat in the later stages of fermentation, is employed.

Oxygen: The level of oxygen determines the extent of fermentation of some foods. Thus providing or removing air or oxygen is used to encourage or inhibit a particular micro-organism. Also, an organism may have different oxygen requirements for growth than it has for fermentation activity. For example, bakers' yeast (*S. cerevisiae*) and wine yeast (*S. ellipsoideus*) both grow well and produce greater cell masses under aerobic conditions, but they ferment sugar more rapidly under anaerobic condition. Thus, for production of bakers' yeast, the yeast is grown under the aerobic condition by bubbling air through the fermenting medium. In vinegar production, there are two steps: the first step involves conversion of sugary substances to alcohol, and the second the conversion of alcohol to acetic acid. Alcohol production is an anaerobic process and its conversion to acetic acid is an oxidative fermentation. Thus, in vinegar production, initially fermentation should be anaerobic and this should be followed by generous supply of air.

Salt: Salt can also be used for controlling food fermentation. Lactic acid producing micro-organisms used in the fermentation of pickles, sauerkraut, etc., are tolerant to salt solutions of the order of 10–18 per cent. Many proteolytic and other spoilage organisms that can infest lactic bacteria are not tolerant to salt above 2.5 per cent. Similarly, salt added to cheese curd controls proteolytic organisms during the long ripening periods.

31.10 Radiation

Preservation of food by ionizing radiations is a recently developed method but has not yet gained general acceptance. As is well known, electromagnetic radiations suppress the growth of most micro-organisms. The possibilities of employing nuclear radiation to sterilize food have been extensively studied since World War II. The harmful effects on the human body of radiations from nuclear explosions have given rise to suspicion in the minds of many people about the safety of use of irradiated foods. Much work has been done on the safety and wholesomeness of irradiated products, but more careful investigations are required before allowing the irradiated food to be used on a large scale.

31.10.1 Kinds of Ionizing Radiations

There are several kinds of radiant energy emitted from different sources, which differ in wavelength, frequency, penetrating power, and in the various effects they have upon biological systems. Irradiation of foods is carried out by exposing them to high-energy radiations which penetrate them and bring about changes within them. The principal radiations used in food irradiation are gamma rays (wavelengths<2Å), emitted from excited radioactive elements (^{60}CO), and accelerated negatively charged particles, electrons (β-particles), which are emitted from a hot cathode. Gamma-rays are very similar to X-rays, except that they have much greater penetrating power. An electron beam can be accelerated to very high speeds and increased energies so that it can penetrate foods, by passing it through electronic devices.

Ultraviolet radiations are also employed in preservation; but they have a very low degree of penetration and are employed to inactivate micro-organisms on the surface of food and to treat air, water, and the surface of food processing equipment to reduce the number of micro-organisms.

31.10.2 Measurement of Radiation

Originally, the common reference for a specific radiation dose was the term "rad," which stands for radiation absorbed dose. A rad is defined as the amount of radiation that results in absorption of 100 ergs of energy per gram of irradiated material (1 joule=107 ergs). The radiation effects are related to dose by the relation:

$$n = n_o \exp(-D / D_0)$$

where n = the number of live organisms following irradiation; n_0 = initial number of organisms; D = dose radiation received (rads), and D_0 = a constant depending on type of organism and environmental factors.

However, this term "rad," has fallen out of use and has been replaced with the term "Gray" (Gy). A Gy is defined as 100 rads. So, when 1 kilogram (kg) of material absorbs 1 joule of energy, it is said to have received a radiation dose of 1 Gy. Doses are usually measured in the kiloGray, or kGy. which is equal to 1,000 Gy.

Different organisms are sensitive to irradiation to different extent as indicated below:

$10^{3-4} - 10^7$ rads — micro-organisms are killed.

$10^3 - 10^5$ rads — insects are killed.

$10^3 - 10^4$ rads — sprouting of potatoes, onions, carrots, etc., is inhibited.

$10^2 - 10^3$ rads — dose is lethal for humans.

In the case of micro-organisms, the approximate sterilizing dose is: bacterial endospores, 3.0×10^6 rads; yeasts and fungi, $\sim 5.0 \times 10^4$ rads. There are, however, some micro-organisms with exceptional resistance to irradiations; for example, *Micrococcus radiodurans* is resistant up to 55 times greater dosage than gram-negative organisms like *Escherichia coli.*

31.10.3 Mode of Action of Radiations

When gamma rays and electron beams pass through foods, there are collisions between ionizing radiations and food particles at the atomic and molecular levels, resulting in the production of ion pairs and free radicals. The reactions of these products among themselves and with other molecules result in physical and chemical phenomena, inactivating micro-organisms in foods. Thus, radiation of foods can be considered to be a means of achieving "cold sterilization" of food — a food is freed of micro-organisms without the need for high temperatures.

Water is an ubiquitous ingredient in foods. Of all the reactions brought about by ionizing radiations, the one with water is the most important in producing foods free of spoilage micro-organisms or pathogens, or containing a greatly diminished content of spoilage organisms. Ionizing radiations split water to produce hydrated electrons (e^-_{aq}), highly reactive hydrogen (H·), and hydroxyl (·CH) radicals, excited water (H_2,O), and ionized water molecules $(H_2O)^+$. Interactions between these products, or these products and other components of food containing oxygen result in the formation of highly reactive species such as hydrogen peroxide.

$$\cdot OH + \cdot OH \rightarrow H_2O_2$$

$$\cdot H + O_2 \rightarrow \cdot HO_2$$

$$\cdot HO_2 + HO_2 \rightarrow \cdot H_2O_2 + O_2$$

Hydrogen peroxide is a strong oxidizing agent and a toxicant to micro-organisms.

31.10.4 Specific Types of Radiation Treatment

While the term "irradiation" pertains to all forms of treating food products with ionizing radiation, there are specific types of radiation treatments that are used in the food industry today.

Radurization: Radurization is the process of pasteurization by the use of radiation. It is primarily used to treat foods that are high in pH and which also have a high water activity. The organisms that are targeted are usually grain-negative psychrotrophs, which are mainly spoilage organisms. Meats and fish are the foods for which this process is mainly used. It can also be used to target yeasts and moulds in foods that are low in pH and low in water activity. The treatment dose for radurization is approximately 1 kGy.

Radicidation: The process of radicidation treats the food product to destroy pathogenic organisms on the product. This process only kills vegetative cells. This means that it will not kill spores that have been produced. The dose for radicidation ranges from 2.5 –5.0 kGy. Most vegetative cells are killed by this dose. However, some cells can survive. This includes some strains of the bacterium *Salmonella typhimurium.* These strains are said to be radiation-resistant. After the dosage has been administered, the product should be stored at or below 4°C to prevent any growth of spores from the *Clostridium botulinum* organism.

Radappertization: Radappertization is a process that is not recommended for most foods. It involves treating the product to levels of radiation of approximately 30 kGy. This high level of radiation kills all vegetative cells and also destroys spores from organisms, such as *Clostridium botulinum*.

31.10.5 Uses of Radiations

Ionizing radiations may be used for sterilization of foods in hermetically sealed packs, reduction in the size of the spoilage flora on perishable foods, elimination of pathogens in foods, control of infestation in stored cereals, prevention of sprouting of potatoes, onions, etc, and retardation of the development of pickled mushrooms. The destruction of the growing point, causing tissue darkening of the sprouting areas of vegetables such as potatoes by radiations, eliminates the risk of sprouting during storage.

Irradiation does not very much affect the nutritional properties of foods. The destruction of various amounts of nutrients are of the same degree as in heat processing. Ionizing radiations can also hydrolyze and modify proteins, starch, and cellulose. Thus, irradiation can help to improve nutritive value of certain plant materials. Significant levels of toxic or carcinogenic substances are not produced in foods irradiated with sufficient dose of radiations. At appropriate dose of radiations, sterilized or pasteurized foods, are safe from microbial standpoint.

Irradiation of foods can also result in certain undesirable effects. Ionizing radiation, in excessive doses, can alter the structure of organic and biochemical compounds in food, resulting in food damage. Degradation of carbohydrates may result in loss of texture and colour. Protein degradation results in undesirable changes in colour and odour and brings about liquefaction. Egg white proteins, on irradiation, become thin and watery. Irradiation of fats results in the development of off-flavour and off-odour and the loss of the natural antioxidants. Foods irradiated with large doses of radiation might themselves become radioactive and prove harmful when consumed.

In the irradiation of foods for preservation, the control of the radiation process is very necessary. The radiation dose must be carefully controlled to destroy micro-organisms and inactivate many food enzymes. It should be sufficient to destroy the pathogenic and spoilage causing organisms. Apart from the intensity of radiation, the amount of radiation absorbed and the length of time of radiation are to be controlled. The longer the food is in the radiation path, the more it will absorb. Radiation energy must be provided in such a manner that it reaches every particle of food to ensure adequate killing of all micro-organisms.

As already stated, the use of ionizing radiations for food preservation has been adopted very slowly. This is largely due to the unacceptable flavour of some foods irradiated to sterilization stage. Also, the fear that radioactivity might be induced in a food has come in the way of its extended use. However, recent reappraisal by the WHO and the International Atomic Energy Authority has resulted in the recommendation that irradiation dose up to 1 M rad is not hazardous.

The disinfection of grains, the preservation, the prevention of sprouting of potatoes and other vegetables, are of great economic value. In less developed countries lacking refrigeration facilities, losses from insects and spoilage of food account for more than half of the total food production. In such cases, radiation of foods will be of great significance. This requires radiation facilities at a cost that developing countries can afford.

For food preservation using salt, sugar and chemicals see Chapter 30.

The role of smoke in preservation and curing of meat and fish is discussed in the relevant chapters.

CHAPTER

32

Nutrition, Health and Food Consciousness

Food is basic for the survival of life. It is needed for the body's growth, repair, and reproduction. Food provides the energy required for all life activities. Satisfaction of hunger is usually the primary criterion for adequate food intake. But, the satisfaction of hunger itself is not a safe guide for selection of proper food. Also, when the types and variety of foods available for consumption are many and constantly change, scientific knowledge of nutrients in food becomes essential. Hence, there is a need for an introduction to nutrition in a book on foods.

Good health is a major factor in our happiness and an active life. Food is vital for building strong bodies and promoting good health. The science of nutrition helps in planning a diet, which improves growth rate, longevity, and health. This is only one aspect of nutrition. In addition to material aspects, nutrition should help to promote emotional, energetic, and spiritual quality, resulting in holistic health.

Finally, the role of food is not just providing for life and health. The dynamic force of food should interact with the dynamic force of one's total being. Thus, this chapter deals with food in respect of nutrition, health, and consciousness.

32.1 Nutrition

There are different concepts of nutrition. The most commonly studied aspect is the one based on laboratory research on how the various food components of our diet are digested, absorbed, and metabolized, to carry out various activities of the body and bodily processes. So it helps to understand the various diseases which occur due to malnutrition and deficiency. The wealth of information encompassing these aspects of nutrition is many times more than that of food.

32.1.1 Diet

Diet, *Dieta* word from Latin means space of a day and *Diaita* word from Greek means as way of living. Diet, therefore, means a mixture of food in different proportions consumed at different time of a day.

Dietetics is a study of the effects of consumed food both in health and disease.

Yogic diet is qualitative diet based on "Gunas" of Sattvic food.

The three basic foods which constitute our diet are carbohydrates, fats, and proteins. Carbohydrates and fats are considered to be energy providing foods, whereas proteins are growth-promoting, substances. Mineral salts and vitamins, which are required for many metabolic activities, form the minor components of the diet. For a diet to be adequate and balanced, these foodstuffs must be ingested in the correct proportions.

Carbohydrate is the fuel on which the body functions are based. The energy produced through oxidation of carbohydrates forms the primary source of energy for the body. In terms of quantity, carbohydrates make up the bulk of the diet and consist of simple sugars like glucose, fructose, and sucrose, and starch from food grains or tubers like a potato. The sugar should form only a small portion of carbohydrate intake as large amounts lead to obesity and serious health problems.

Fat is the most concentrated source of food energy, providing, on a dry weight basis, more than twice the number of calories derived from protein or carbohydrate. Fat is taken in lesser quantity than carbohydrates. Food fat serves as a carrier for fat-soluble vitamins A, D, E and K. Fat is stored in the body to afford energy for later use, its high caloric density and low solubility provides superior qualities for purposes of storage. Dietary fats may be from plant or animal sources, but, healthwise, vegetable oils containing polyunsaturated fatty acids are preferable. The deposits of fat in adipose tissue provide both insulation and protection for the body. With the exception of the central nervous system, virtually all tissues of the body utilize fatty acids directly as a source of energy.

Protein in the diet is necessary to provide sources of nitrogen and amino acids to be utilized in the synthesis of body proteins and other nitrogen containing substances. The proteins of the body contribute to tissue structure and are involved in a variety of important metabolic functions. Proteins in excess of these needs serve as a source of energy. The nutritional value of a protein depends upon the composition of its amino acids. Vegetable foods generally contain small quantities of protein, and the amino acids present are rarely in the proportions required by animal tissues. Therefore, there is a danger of malnutrition if only one vegetable food forms the major component of the diet. However, a good vegetarian diet can be worked out, which provides the complete range of protein requirements by using a wide variety of protein-containing vegetable foods. These include cereals, legumes, nuts, fruits, and other vegetables. Most of the animal proteins contain a high proportion of essential amino acids in balanced amounts, and are termed biologically good proteins.

The minor components of food contribute about 2 per cent of the dry weight of our diet. Of these vitamins form the accessory food factors. These are complex organic components present in very small quantities in natural food and absorbed into the body from the small intestine. They possess no energy but are essential for good health and maintain the body's normal metabolic activity. If the diet is deficient in a particular vitamin, metabolic activity is impaired. This produces a disorder symptomatic of that particular vitamin deficiency. This is known as "deficiency disease." This deficiency disease can be avoided by supplementing the diet with the missing vitamin.

Mineral salts are the second important minor components of our diet. Some minerals in the form of their salts (sodium, calcium and potassium) are found in the body in large amounts, while others like zinc, copper, cobalt, manganese, and iron, are present in small amounts. Some of these metals are part of several enzymes and complex organic molecules, which play a crucial metabolic role. Our requirement of minerals is met by the foods we eat, particularly vegetables and leafy stuff, which constitute our diet. If need be, there could be an external supplement of minerals.

32.1.2 Digestion

The process by which our food is broken down from complex insoluble substances into simple soluble ones is called digestion.

Digestion starts in the mouth; when food is properly chewed, there is thorough mixing of the salivary gland secretion with food. The salivary enzyme— α-amylase—acts on the starch component of the food, breaking it into shorter components - dextrins. When food enters the stomach, its contents become acidic due to gastric secretion, and starch digestion due to enzyme ceases. Further digestion of starch into sugar takes place in the small intestine. The mucosa of the stomach possesses many tubular glands, which are lined with different types of cells, such as chief cells and parietal cells. Chief cells secrete the inactive enzymes pepsinogen and prorenin, while parietal cells secrete a 0.05% solution of HC1, which makes the pH of the stomach contents 1-2.5, ideal for the optimum activity of the stomach enzymes. The acid promotes the conversion of pepsinogen to pepsin, which hydrolyzes protein into smaller polypeptides. Hydrochloric acid converts prorenin to rennin, which in turn coagulates caseinogen, the soluble protein of milk, into the insoluble calcium salt of casein. The calcium salt is then digested by pepsin.

Relatively little digestion of fats occurs in the stomach because the pH of the stomach is too low for gastric lipase to be active. In the lower regions of the stomach, triacylglycerols (fats) are mixed with proteins, carbohydrates, gastric juice, and other substances. Partial degradation of this mixture and churning action of the stomach results in the formation of chyme. This results in the elevation of pH, which allows some gastric lipase activity to occur. Chyme then enters the duodenum, where it is mixed with pancreatic juice, which contains bile salts, pancreatic lipase, and esterase. Pancreatic lipase ultimately breaks down triacylglycerols to fatty acids and glycerol.

The pancreas is a large gland, whose cells, called acini, produce a variety of digestive enzymes that are poured into the duodenum via the pancreatic duct. They include amylase to convert amylose to maltose, lipase to convert fats to fatty acids and glycerol, trypsinogen, which, when converted to trypsin by enterokinase, digests proteins into smaller polypeptides, chymotrypsinogen, which is converted to chymotrypsin to digest proteins to amino acids, carboxypeptidases to convert peptides to amino acids, and nucleus to convert nucleases acid to nucleotides.

It is a well established fact that the digestibility of protein is affected by several factors. Among them, one noteworthy factor is the availability of amino acids, the digestibility being affected in processed milk products. Heat processing in the presence of reducing sugar, glucose, and galactose, hinders the availability of lysine. Lactose reacts with lysine bringing about browning or the Millard reaction. This processing has an adverse effect on the digestibility of amino acids, particularly lysine. Protein Digestibility Corrected Amino Score (PDCAAS) is the official assay for evaluating protein quality in the human body.

32.1.3 Absorption

Digestion reduces food to a solution of fatty acids, glycerol, glucose, fructose, nucleotides, and amino acids. If these small, soluble molecules are to be of any use to the cells of the body, they must be moved out of the intestine into the bloodstream. The process of moving nutrients and water from the intestine to the blood constitutes absorption.

Since the small intestine is the place where nutrients and most water absorption takes place, we should expect it to have a large exposed surface area. This is exactly the case. The small intestine is quite long and is packed into the abdominal cavity as a series of coils. Besides, the surface of the small intestine also contains folds and enormous numbers of finger-like processors called Villi. Additionally, each villus is covered with epithelial cells, and the plasma membrane of finger-like projections, called microvilli, it further enhances the absorptive surface area. The residues of food that cannot be digested or absorbed, leave the small intestine and pass through the ileo-colonic valve into the large intestine. There, water and vitamins are absorbed, and waste materials are compacted into faeces.

The absorbed nutrients do not directly go into systematic circulation. Instead, everything is channeled into the portal vein, which goes to the liver, where it breaks up into tiny capillaries. The liver cells then process the absorbed food for proper use when they pass into the bloodstream through another vein, the venacava. The liver also stores absorbed and processed food for release into the bloodstream when required.

The study of nutrition based on the biochemical make-up of the diet, the action of digestive juices on it, the role of the pancreas, liver, etc., has given us valuable information on various aspects of nutrition. The information available is voluminous. Foods, in addition to nutritionally important components, contain a lot of other substances in small quantities, which have significant pharmacological activity, Also, cooking and food additives affect the nutritional value of food. The composition of food also varies depending on conditions of production and processing. Their effect varies from person to person. Although the information available on nutrition is voluminous, it is responsible for some contradictions one observes in the literature.

It has been accepted that an increase in energy expenditure, associated with the consumption of food, is approximately 10%. This is termed the Thermic Effect of Food (TEF), also referred to as Diet-induced Thermogenesis, DIT, or Specific Effect of Food (SEF). Further, TEF can be subdivided into efficacy and efficiency of metabolism, as Obligatory and adaptative or Facultative Thermogenesis. Obligatory Thermogenesis includes the energy required to digest, absorb, and metabolize, nutrients, synthesize and store protein, fat and carbohydrates. Adaptative or Facultative Thermogenesis is the excess energy expended in addition to the Obligatory Thermogenesis. In this case, the metabolism is inefficient, hence it affects sympathetic nervous activity.

According to the diet composition, TEF varies. Fat is metabolized efficiently with only 4% wastage, compared with 25% wastage in carbohydrates. This wastage is ascribed to the synthesis of carbohydrates to fat, which results in obesity.

Besides this, McCrory's study reveals that spicy meals enhance the metabolic rate by 33%, as compared to non-spicy meals, and the effects last for 3 hours. Similarly, it was observed that when coffee and nicotine are present, the effect is 8% to 11% increase in the metabolic rate. [Dulloo *et al* (1989) and Hofstetter (1886)].

The Thermic Effect on metabolism and digestibility brings about in turn physiological changes, which affect the psychological state. It is interesting to note that the utilization of food is best in fresh (*Sattvic*) foods, than in processed (*Rajasic*) foods, which is discussed in section 32.5.2 later in this chapter.

The wisdom the ancients had in the classification of foods into *Sattvic*, *Rajasic* and *Tamasic,* can now be understood, based on the effect of Thermogenesis in food. Based on their own human experiences, they inferred the psychological component of food and its impact on our nervous system, which is discussed in detail in Section 32.5.3 of this chapter.

These effects of Thermogenesis seem to last for three to four hours after food is ingested. The inefficient metabolic and digestive effects physiologically, in turn, affect the psychology. Mind, that is thus affected, to rise above its own level needs stability and purity. The chemical energy of metabolism can cause delay or damage the mind's state. There are other energy levels, including electromagnetic energy, which is refined subtle energy, that the mind needs to experience in pure silence. Therefore, the importance and the need for shift in the paradigm for spiritual health is because man has reached the zenith of the mind's development; the danger of falling below the sub-human level to animal behaviour has been noticed globally. The extinction of the human species is feared. Hence, his present nature has to evolve to his higher super divine nature; that is only the answer.

32.2 Health

Knowledge of nutrition helps man to know the types and quantities of different foods to be taken in our diet to maintain good health. According to ancient Indian concepts, health based on just the diet is *Arogya*—a state of no disease with which the, physician is primarily concerned. According to the World Health Organization (WHO), the term "health" means more than the presence or absence of symptoms and has a more comprehensive concept of a multi-dimensional, global well-being.

32.2.1 Dimensions of Health

Growth of psychological and social sciences has shown that illness is conditioned by psychological, social and cultural factors. Epidemiological diseases are due to social and cultural factors, while psychosomatic diseases are due to conditions of the mind. While the psycho-social concepts of health are important, they are not enough for the total well-being of man. For, as Dr. Bisht points out, "If the components of health are restricted only to physical, mental and social parameters, then a pack of wolves who are physically strong, mentally alert, and socially well-knit, would be ideally healthy!" If this is so, a group of human beings would be no better than a pack of wolves.

Man is a multi-dimensional being, and he has a spiritual perspective too that transcends other modalities of life. In this case, the definition of health should be enlarged to cover spiritual well-being in addition to physical, psychological and social well-being. The Sanskrit word for health is "*Swasth*," which means "rooted in the self"; true health exists only when man's consciousness is fixed in his spiritual self, the "*swa.*"

The term "Health" has been understood by physiologists, psychologists, and nutritionists, as per the available knowledge in each of these areas. Health is a subjective dynamic state of well-being, or *Swastya,* physically, vitally, mentally and spiritually. But physiologists describe this state as Homeostasis. Nineteenth Century physiologist Bernard (1879) stated that it is a "stable internal environment in face of changing external conditions." According to Cannon (1932), "it is a complex physiological mechanism where the internal milieu is maintained." To maintain this inner stabilized state, the nervous system of the parasympathetic, sympathetic in conjunction with the somatic motor system, regulates the behaviour of an organism, both in the normal and emergency states. The hypothalamus and amygdala in the brain bring about this regulation. Physiologists have conducted experiments on animals, controlling the appetite and hunger centres, to explain the state of Homeostasis. But this presents a mechanical physiological balance based on physiology.

In determining the impact of internal and external stimuli in retaining the state of Homeostasis, psychologists belonging to the Behaviourist school of thought adopted an objective approach based on observation and experimentation for the study of human behaviour. Once again the method they used to infer was based on experimentation with stimuli and the response in behaviour of rats and other animals and applying something similar to the human state. Pavlov, Skinner and J.B.Watson's observations were characterized by reductionism, which attempted to explain behaviour of the more evolved human organism in terms of physiological and biological principles applicable to less evolved animal organisms. Human beings are more than the Science of Physiology and Biology can tell. Their psychological components, therefore, cannot be simply related to animal experiments.

Human beings are more than their body. They have psychological components. Animal experiment results cannot be applied. According to Sri Aurobindo, ordinary psychology takes mind and the phenomena associated with it at the surface, assigning a surface value to it, but man's mind "reveals itself as a greater energy escaping from restrictions of the vital and physical formula of being. But even this is not all that man is or can be: he has in him the power to evolve and release still greater ideal energy, which in its turn escapes out of the restrictions of the mental formula of his nature and discloses the supramental form, the ideal power of a spiritual being." The human is a mentally growing being, and is in a subjective state of growth. Hence the term "*Teleosis*" is more applicable than the term "Homeostasis." *Teleosis* is more a subjective state where the human being synthesizes his inherent tendencies towards mental and supramental growth and maturity.

Vithoulkar (1996) observes such a state of *Teleosis* is "an inner urge for perfecting, resulting in a sense of completeness, the wholeness, maturity and happiness." Spiritual dimension is an evolving phase of higher state of consciousness and perfection, which includes understanding and realization of knowing that the Spirit is evolving, maturing, developing and perfecting in attaining ever higher levels of consciousness. This is an inner state. To arrive at this state, fusion of body and mind, the wholeness of well-being or S*wastya* is experienced.

To balance and to perfect the inner and outer states and experience well-being or *Swastya* is to feel the vibratory state of growth in consciousness of the Spirit.

When Homeostasis gives way to *Teleosis*, Bijlani, a leading physiologist, based on subjective experimentation, has given ample evidence that physiological clinical changes with Yogic practice leads to heightening one's growth of the evolving soul, which results in optimum spiritual benefits. Food, therefore, not only gives biological awareness (through nutrients for physical nourishment) but also triggers a source of consciousness or the Spirit.

The importance of knowledge of the *Gunas* of food lies in the fact that an agitated mind's view of life will be distorted, with problems and disharmony in the body as well as mind, but a food that gives peace alters the state of mind to receive higher spiritual light, where other dimensions of bliss and delight and "*Ananda*'" of existence give fullness of life. Thus a Yogic diet paves the way to the Yogic view of life. A comparison of the effects of the Yogic classification of food and the modern scientific classification is dealt with in the *Rajasic* foods section of this chapter.

Most persons believe that philosophy, religion, ethics, and morality, constitute spiritual health. These are only approaches to spiritual truth and not the Spirit itself. When we go beyond these misconceptions and understand the spiritual reality by identification, we discover that there is a unity of experience that cuts across the barriers of time and space. Therefore, spiritual health conveys a special concept of a holistic and integral viewpoint of health. The WHO, in its programme of health for all, has recognized the spiritual dimensions of health.

32.2.2 Spiritual Health

Spiritual health evokes different images to different persons. To the materialistic Western mind, it is paranormal healing, to the Eastern mind it is a boon or miracle of grace that heals our suffering and pain. To the materialist, spiritual health is either a hoax or faith healing, while to a true rationalist it is moral and ethical values in life, which help man become a better race. To some others, the word "spiritual" is a supreme something or someone whom none has known or can know. According to the *Vedas* and *Upanishads* (Indian scriptures), the spiritual state is a reality, which cannot be described but experienced. Seekers of consciousness have come in contact with spiritual reality and their life has been moulded by its influence. They have discovered in it something quite other than our customary notions of moral, ethical, and religious, values. Spiritual knowledge is a state of knowledge of that, the ultimate reality; it is revealed in a few, veiled in others, and present in all.

The seers, who have experienced and lived a spiritual life, affirm that "the spirit is other than the mind." It is unity and oneness while the mind is duality and division. It is peace and bliss, harmony and truth, while the mind dwells in pain, pleasure, and indifference. The mind also fumbles through error and ignorance. The spiritual state of health cannot be defined. It is best communicated and understood in the silence and stillness of our being. It is the highest perfection man is capable of through self-evolution.

This higher and greater consciousness is not tangible to the mass of humanity as yet. The next cycle of humanity will see the evolutionary emergence of this spiritual dimension. The resurgence of interest in Yoga, the debate over the possibility of consciousness, independent of material reality, the turn towards global life, the liberalization of spiritual pursuits, the growing need of man for freedom, love, and oneness, the inclusion of the spiritual dimensions in the field of psychology, education, health, and the findings in modern physics, are some areas indicative of such phenomena.

Those who have realized spiritual heights affirm that it is possible for man to enter and live in it, and with greater consciousness and power. If we attain that state, the disorders and conflicts that afflict humanity can be solved, and it will release us from the yoke of suffering and death, and impart harmony and peace that we so much lack now as a species. It is this that justifies and even makes it necessary to include the spiritual dimension as a factor with regard to health. This factor, being a source and origin of all, will also include lesser terms of our existence - mental, social, and even physical. The spiritual dimension is all-comprehensive, the simplest, and the most fundamental. It should be sought after by man, who is missing peace.

32.2.3 Science and Spirituality

Science is concerned with the matter. In its quest to understand the matter, science has acquired incredible powers and harnessed them to improve man's outer life. In the process, life has been reduced to a mechanical formula and man has been reduced to a machine among other machines.

Spirituality is the study of self and consciousness based on tapping the hidden powers of life and mind. Spirit or consciousness runs as a common thread through all phenomena. It is not an exclusive dimension that exists in isolation without any hold on the creature that inhabits it. The spiritual dimension includes the material and can intervene subtly to alter the laws and processes of the material universe and change the course of purely material and biological processes. Thus, spirituality not only helps in attaining a spiritual dimension but also subtly intervenes to alter the laws and processes of the material universe.

Science seeks the truth of matter and reality. Scientific methods and equipment can measure gross events. Scientific experiments can be seen, verified, and reproduced. Scientific observations and inferences can be codified, resulting in physical laws.

Spirituality seeks after the truth of the Spirit, which is quite another reality. Spiritual dimensions are a subtler truth, which cannot be measured by conventional equipment. Subtler levels can only be experienced. One must reach a level of experience, then go to the next level, to another, and on, and on, till reaching an awakened state. Here, life and mind are open systems and keep growing and evolving, which upset old experiences.

Thus, science and spirituality are proceeding on their lines of inquiry in search of a common goal. In the sincerity of their search, they will meet, and when they meet, they will realize that spiritual and material reality are two phases of one reality. The scientist would learn that "One Force" gives birth to the many. The spiritual scientist would discover that matter is created by a condensation of the Spirit of One Reality, which gives birth to various forms, phenomena and processes. This will result in the integration of human consciousness from a fragmented one when one experiences Bliss.

32.2.4 Evolution of Consciousness

Man's life is riddled with disease, death, and infirmity. His attempts to conquer them will remain precarious at his level of evolution. At best, he may arrive at a healthy equilibrium with his environment. All the stress and strain that besieges him, is a call to evolve to a state of consciousness more perfect than his.

Man's problems of want, greed and lust and desire, are due to his sense of self or individuality. His false sense of ego-self (I-ness) has to be shed off and replaced by true "I," the individual soul in him. This evolution of consciousness results in his feeling, peace, fullness and joy, with their immediate results of progress, health, and fitness, in the physical quietness and goodwill in the vital, with clear understanding and a general feeling of security and satisfaction. It will open the heart to a deep, pure and calm capacity to love without possessiveness and turbulent attachment. These will help one to be calm and balanced, free from fear, things which help in healthy living and even cure one of diseases.

It is possible for consciousness to evolve further when man will be immune from all types of diseases and even death. But, this type of consciousness is possible only for a few. Contact with such evolved persons will help others to awaken the sleeping soul in them, better than any other means.

32.3 The Concept of Spirit

To experience spiritual happiness, a concept of the Spirit is necessary. One's concept depends upon one's culture and religion. The Indian concept is based on the *Upanishads*, composed by persons who had some personal experience of the truths by their spiritual practices (Yoga), and who were familiar with the ideas of the *Vedic* and *Vedantic* Seers (5000 BC). The *Upanishads* are vehicles of illumination and not of instructions. One has to proceed from light to light, confirming one's intuitions, and verifying them by one's experience, not submitting to the ideas of the judgment of the logical reason. An attempt is made here to introduce this concept.

The one fundamental concept of the *Upanishads* is, that there is unity, oneness, and stability, behind all the flux and variety of phenomenal life. The unity behind all the bewildering whirl of motion, eternal variations, and perishing, is due to a guiding power, which is eternal, unalterable, and undecaying. The fundamental one and the absolute is a reality. It is as yet undefined and perhaps undefinable.

In the early period of Indian thought, there were endless speculations about the indestructible elements and origin of matter. Concepts like Time, Chance, Fate, Elements, Womb, Ego, were conceived. None of them could take a firm footing. Then, pure intellectual reasoning led to a dual concept of God and Nature, *Purusha* and *Prakruthi*, Spirit and Matter, and Ego and Non-ego. As both these aspects are perceivable, the old Indian Nihilists arrived at the false notion that Nothingness is the very stuff and reality of all existence. All this confusion led *Vedanta* to the conclusion that both *Purusha* and *Prakrithi* may be quite real, but they are different aspects of a Oneness higher than either. That unknown force was called *Brahman*. Spirit is pure consciousness, atma is formless and bodiless, whereas embodied consciousness is jivatman.

The seers of ancient India realized that all things and phenomena are merely the appearances of *Brahman*. Their Yogic experience led to three grand truths; they are: there is One Eternal in many transients, One Consciousness in many consciousnesses, and the Transcendental Self in individual man is complete as the Transcendental Self in the Universe. This led to the stupendous truth of *Vedanta*: He am I (*Aham Brahma Asmi*), I am *Brahman*, the Eternal.

32.3.1 Nature of the Absolute *Brahman*

Brahman is not definable, not describable and intellectually knowable. The *Brahman* in its ultimate reality is transcendent, absolute and infinite. The senses and the intellect are incapable of knowing *Brahman* and realizing its manifestations. Even the scientist believes there is some great ultimate reality, from which this Universe proceeds and on which all phenomena depend. But he is concerned only with the ultimate Nature and not its expression or manifestations, while the *Upanishads* consider both Nature and its manifestations.

The first step in the realization of *Brahman* is to know Him as manifested in the phenomenal universe. Western science seeks to know the Universe only through gross matter. Indian metaphysics has discovered a Universe of subtle matter penetrating and surrounding the gross. The Spirit of man, which withdraws partially into the subtle Universe for a brief time in sleep, is the source from which all psychic processes draw their origin. The link between this Universe and the gross material world is found in the phenomena of life and mind.

There is yet another Universe, the Universe of causal matter penetrating and surrounding both the subtle and the gross. This Universe to which the Spirit withdraws in the deepest states of sleep and trance is the source from which all perceptions take their rise. *Brahman* manifests Himself in each of these Universes, in the Universe of causal matter as Cause, Self and Inspirer (*Prajna*, the wise one), in the Universe of subtle matter as the Creator, Self and Container (life and form), and in the Universe of gross matter as the Ruler, Guide, Self and Helper (shining and mighty one). In each of these manifestations, He can be known and realized by the Spirit of man.

32.3.2 *ParaBrahman*

The great transcendental reality has been recognised by the human Spirit as it travels upwards culminating in the Supreme. Viewing downwards, the Spirit recognizes the manifestation of the Absolute in the Universe created by Him. The first step in this direction is the projection of *Brahman* as a luminous shadow of Himself, the *ParaBrahman*, which is called by different names such as God, the Eternal, the Supreme Spirit, Source, the Creator, and other terms. *Vedanta* refers to Him as *Sachidananda*, Existence, Consciousness, Bliss, or, in its subjective form, as Truth, Knowledge, and Infinity.

The Supreme is Pure Being, He alone is and nothing else exists in reality. Therefore, He exists by Himself, in Himself, and to Himself. He is beyond conceptions of Space, Time and Causality. Thus *ParaBrahman* is Absolute Existence, *Sat*.

The Supreme is also Pure Awareness, Absolute Consciousness, *Cit*. He is also *Sat*. Therefore, *Sat* and *Cit* are the same. Existence is consciousness. It follows then that *Brahman* is Consciousness, and in His transcendental reality, Absolute Consciousness.

The Supreme is, finally, Pure Ecstasy, Absolute Bliss, *Ananda*. If *Sat* and *Cit* are the same, then they are not different from *Anandam*. Conscious existence cannot endure without delight. This is the trinity of the Upanishads. Absolute Existence, which is, therefore, Absolute Consciousness, which is Absolute Bliss.

32.3.3 *Brahman*: God and the World

The Lord and the world seem to be different, but according to the *Upanishads*, they are not different from each other; they are one *Brahman*. God is one stable reality. He is beyond time and space and is immutable.

The world is a cyclic movement of Divine Consciousness in space and time. It exists by movement of Active Consciousness, creating oppositions of variety and multiplicity, divisions of time, and space and causality. All these things are real at the level of mental consciousness. But mental consciousness is not the power that creates the Universe. It is created by self-awareness of the Absolute unbound by any law of reality.

Unity is the eternal truth of things, diversity is a play of this unity. The sense of unity has therefore been termed knowledge (*Vidya*), the sense of diversity ignorance (*Avidya*). But diversity is not false, except when it is divorced from the sense of its true and eternal variety.

Brahman is one, not numerically, but in essence - numerical oneness does not exclude multiplicity. The many in the Universe are sometimes called parts of *Brahman*, as the waves are parts of the sea. Each soul is all *Brahman*.

Creation is not making something out of nothing or one thing out of another, but a self-projection of *Brahman* in conditions of space and time. Creation is not a making, but a becoming in terms and form of conscious existence. In this becoming, each individual is *Brahman*, variously represented and entering into various relations with Himself in the play of Divine Consciousness.

Brahman, therefore, by His immutable existence (*Sat*) is *Purusha*, God, Spirit, representing Himself as the Motional, by His power of Active Consciousness (*Cit*) is Nature, Force or World-principle (*Prakruthi, Shakti, Maya*). The play of these two principles is the life of the Universe.

Our consciousness has, therefore, to move forward to realize the Divine Consciousness, the *Brahman* within us. The self-unfolding is governed by the complexity of Consciousness in its cosmic action. Consciousness is not simple or homogeneous. It consists of seven forms or grades of conscious activity and descending from pure being to physical being; this interplay creates the worlds, determines all activities and constitutes all beings; *Brahman* self-extended in space and time is the Universe.

The seven states of consciousness in the human being co-exist in the Universe eternally and inseparably and are capable of being involved and ramified in each other. They can be withdrawn into pure infinite beings and can again be manifested out of it.

The infolding and unfolding of the one into the many, and the many in the one, is therefore the law of the eternally recurrent cosmic cycles.

Thus, the *Upanishads* teach us to perceive *Brahman* in the Universe and in our self-existence. He is both stable and moving. We have to see it in the eternal and immovable Spirit and in all the changing manifestations of the Universe and relatively. This transcendental, universal and individual *Brahman*, Lord, Continent, and *Atman,* is the object of all knowledge. Its realization is the way to immortality.

32.3.4 *Purusha* in *Prakruthi* or (Shiva or Shakti)

Some texts refer Purusha as Shiva and Prakruthi as Shakti or Shiva-Shakti.

Atman, the Self, represents itself differently in the seven-fold movement of Nature according to the dominant principle of the Consciousness in the individual being.

In the physical consciousness, *Atman* becomes the material being, *Annamaya purusha*.

In the vital or nervous consciousness, *Atman* becomes the vital or dynamic being, *Pranamaya purusha.*

In the mental consciousness, *Atman* becomes the mental being, *Manomaya purusha.*

In the supra-intellect consciousness, dominated by Truth (*Satyam*), *Atman* becomes the ideal being or great soul, *Vignanamaya purusha.*

In the consciousness proper to the universal Beatitude, *Atman* becomes the all–blissfull being or all enjoying and all-productive soul, *Anandamaya purusha.*

In the consciousness proper to the infinite Divine self-awareness, which is also the infinite all effective Will, *Atman* is the all-conscious soul that is the source and Lord of the Universe, *Caitanya purusha.*

In the consciousness proper to the state of pure Divine conscious existence, *Atman* is *Sat purusha*, the pure Divine Self.

Man, being his true self, one with the Lord, can live in any of these states of the self in the world. He can be anything he wants from the material to the all-blissful being.

It is possible for the soul to withdraw for an indefinite period into the pure state of *Sachidananda*, which is the aim of human existence. This is Spiritual Health.

32.3.5 Psychic Being or *Caitya-Purusha*

The soul or *Atman* is all conscious source and lord of the universe. According to Sri Aurobindo 'Soul is a spark of the divine, which is above the manifestation to support the evolution.'

The Psychic beings is formed by the soul in the evolving journey and it is *Caitya-Purusha*. On the mental plane it is the true mental being. *Manonmaya–Purusha*, on the vital plane it's the true vital being *Pranamaya-Purusha*, on Physical plane it is the true physical being, *Annamaya-Purusha*. The hidden purusha is in the mystic heart, according to Upanishad it is Hradayaguhagumyam. To transform human life to divine life, psychic beings is essential from *Annamaya-Purusha*, the inmost being has to develop as *Caitya-Purusha*. For psychic being to develop required yogic practices of aspiration, rejection and surrender in concentration, meditation and to be united with the inmost being. To make psychic being come forward to rule and develop itself needs spiritual experiences. Psychic gets organized along all the planes and influences and consolidates through spiritual experiences from life to life. All that is pure, good, true and beautiful is the realm of psychic proper. As it organized itself through spiritual experiences, it finds its guide, which is behind, above, supports the mind, body and life,

Psychisization, hence, opens the path of greater to spiritualization. To transform earth's existence and to evolve as a spiritual being is of at most value, therefore spiritual health is of great importance in one's evolutionary journey.

32.4 *Chakras*

Vedas and Tantra Shastras texts are interconnected Tan means to spread, Tantri comes from root word Tantri means origination or knowledge. Tantra is spread of knowledge, Tantra Shastra offers ascending centres of energy known as *Chakras*. They are popularly called *kundalini* or *Serpent* Power.

The *Chakra* system is a part of the subtle energy system that has been described for thousands of years in our spiritual traditions. Different cultures and many of the major religions validate the existence of subtle *Chakras*. The physical existence location of *Chakras* has been documented by scientific research. Dr. Motoyama 1985, has confirmed the relationship of *Chakras* to organs, glands and nerve flex by an instrument, which is called as AMI, or an apparatus for measuring functional conditions of meridians and their corresponding internal organs. His study shows that activated *Chakras* shows meridian energy supplied to specific organs around the specific *Chakra.* There seems to be general agreement that each *Chakra* has the specific, energetic nature that relates to colour, sound, number of Lotus Petals, geometrical shape, element, sense and sense experiences. Each *Chakra* is associated with certain mental states and with specific spiritual awareness. Each *Chakra* also seems to be associated with the physiology of specific glandular system, organ system and nerve plexus. These are in the subtle bodies and have subtle sounds or *shabda* and *Shakti* (power).

32.4.1 Location of *Chakras*

There are seven *Chakras* in the subtle physical body, as per Gopikrishna, Lead Beater, Woodroffe, Sri Aurobindo and Harish Johari. It is said eighth *Chakra,* the transpersonal *Chakra* is above the head. Their position in the subtle physical body corresponds to the points along the spinal cord. The anatomical, physical side is to explain that they include the central and sympathetic nervous sytem. The centres are thus connected to the brain or encephalon in the skull. Their placement in the spinal cord is within the vertebral column. It is necessary at this point to discriminate the difference between causal, subtle, and gross body. The gross body is the physical body, body-less energies are subtle bodies, which include seven subtle anomalies which are etheric, emotional, mental, astral, spiritual, causal, and soul bodies. For perfect physical health, the subtle bodies should be in tune with relevant colours, the *Chakras* should be open to release such energy, if they are blocked the energy around will have gaps through which the cosmic energies are not received but resisted. Any imbalance in health first takes place in the subtle bodies.

Table 32.1 Location of Chakras

Chakra	Colours	No. of Lotus Petals	Sound	Elements	Sense Organ	Sense Experience
Muladhara (at base of the spine)	Crimson Red	four	Lam	Earth	Nose	Smell
Svadhisthana (above genitals)	Orange	Six	Vam	Water	Tongue	Taste
Manipura (at the navel)	Yellow	Ten	Ram	Fire	Eyes	Vision
Anahata (behind the heart)	Green	Twelve	Yam	Air	Skin	Touch
Vishuddha (base of the throat)	Blue	Sixteen	Ham	Space/Either	Ear	Hearing
Ajna (between eyebrows)	Indigo	Two	Aum	Beyond Elements Third Eye (conscience)	Mind	Claireyoince (Trikala Drishti)
Sahasrara (at the skull cap)	Violet (Rainbow Colours)	Thousand (Petals arranged in variegated colours of the rainbow)	Sohum	Psyche (Chaitya Purusha)	Void or Shunya	Sat Chit Ananda

Note: The above Chakras has been worked out inclusive of traditional Tantras knowledge and colours as per Harish Johari and Cousen's.

A healthy gross body has a health aura. In Greek *Auric* means breeze, energies around the body. The water content in the body creates an electromagnetic field, that is luminous around living things. An auric field can be captured by Krilian photography or gas discharge visualization. Now, these are widely used for diagnostic purposes. An experimental study on gas discharge visualization has confirmed the aura of the experimental group had no gaps whereas, the control group showed gaps, confirming that knowledge or *Chakras,* concentration and meditation on *Chakras* create healthy aura, (Srilakshmi R., N. Shakuntala Manay 2008).

Another study of positive thought forms on aura and the growth of sprouts further adds value for positive response in receiving this energy directly from cosmos retaining the same in one's own auric field also release the same in one's atmosphere creates healthy vibration. (N. Shakuntala Manay or Sri Lakshmi, Qualitative vibration and thought energy on the environment 2003). According to the Mother of Sri Aurobindo Ashram "it is vibration that contains everything–a vibration which contains infinite power, infinite delight and infinite peace of vastness, it knows the difference between constructive and destructive vibrations.

32.5 Food Culture

Food is common, human, and divine. Food is more than nutrients (see Sec. 1.2). Food is the source of life. Human life grows and develops its potential, namely divine through food.

Vedic man elevated food not only as a continuation of life to live but also to worship food, discovers that food is sacrifice and therefore food is *Brahman. Rig-Veda* highlights act of eating is not only sacred but also social, an expression of communion with others, but also between man and God. Food imparts both physical and spiritual vigor, hence offered to Gods in rituals as a sacrifice. Hence food is not only nourishment for the body but it nurtures the soul. Eating is a sacred act because the food itself is holy.

Food is being consumed and assimilated but it does not dwindle, because it is imperishable, meaning it is given to Gods. The dynamic process of creation continues, food and life go together and they are inter-dependent.

The process of assimilation is a cosmic metabolism, which begins at the lowest strata of consciousness as hunger, continues to the highest state of the metaphysical state "I am Food, I am food, Who I am Food, Food eats the eater of the food". Eating and preparing food is human and divine action and both are required, which is Karma Yoga, the way of action, is integrated into the mystery of food. In Food, matter and spirit are united. Food of eternal life *Annam* Brahma, the following verse found in the Plates.

Chakra Samhita volume 2 further explains, "food's impact on mind, state of living things is food and the entire world seeks food, complexes, clarity, good voice, long life, understanding and happiness, satisfaction and growth intelligence etc., are all established in food". (see Sec. 32.2.2. spiritual health and 32.3 concept of spirit).

Culture is the living spirit, dynamic, evolving, expressed in art and architecture, dance, drama, literature, folklore, spiritual texts and scriptures. Every country has its own culture. Ours is *Vedic* and *Upanishadic* culture that is 5000 years old. The verses written are spiritual experiences experienced by *Rishis* or *Seers* of spiritual truth. They are written out as *Vedic* experiences, human birth is a culmination of cosmic birth among all living things. This is already mentioned in Sec. 32.2.2.

Vedic Anthology traces how human beings ultimately transform by becoming conscious of the divinity within them. God Phase of life gradually develops as the psychic being (see Sec. 32.3.5 psychic being and *Chaitya Purusha*), a spark that gradually germinates and grows. *Vedic* Revelations states a power that guides, gives direction, inspires the way of human to divine life.

For this development to take place, food through *Gunas* gives experiental growth of peace, purity, clearness of mind, is of great importance. The energy released by *Sattvic* food is better utilized than *Rajasic* and *Tamasic*. The thermogenic effect of food produced alpha waves in the brain. Hence, *Sattvic* food consumption regularly develops a mind that is at peace. (see Sec. 32.5 Food consciousness 32.5.1 Gunas).

Food *Sadhana, Sadhana* means practice, regular practice builds a union, through food with the divine. A Yogic diet thus nourishes both mind and body. *Vedic* culture has extensively elaborated on food, consumption of *Sattvic* food and food *sadhana*; all of these are related to the body.

Vedic knowledge aims at experiences, where the knowledge of knowing and known are one transparent state. *Tantric Chakras* in food and its vibration is an additional knowledge open to create one's own diet discussed in below Sec. 32.5.1 Rainbow Diet.

32.5.1 Rainbow Diet

Traditional *Tantra* has colours assigned to each *Chakra*. The colours of *Chakras* follow in rainbow and its vibration of colours are with a surface colour of the food. This is different from *Tantra Shastra's Chakra* Colours. The vibrational around the tongue and release of the saliva is a product of psychological and physiological response to Food. Food acts as an interface between nature on physical plane and colours of food is a biomolecular content of specific food as energy. Biomolecular nutrients will be of vibrational nature to the cells and tissues of the body. Rainbow colours thus are an intense relation between food and its impact on us. Vascular Atomic Signal (VAS), a technic used to measure the effect of subtle energy fields and biological etheric systems of the body. VAS is a clear smooth response of our blood vessels conducting the messages to the hypothalamic region of the brain. It is subjective response.

Testing of the body's altered state, is muscle testing technic known as Kinesiology as muscle testing technic. Therefore energy field from the food and the body is at a comfortable equilibrium. It is a perfect synchronism of interior and exterior vibration rhythms. This opens a channel of least resistance and one floats freely in the ocean of the phenomenal world of peace and plentitude without drowning. The human body is a perfect instrument for the expression of consciousness. The spectrum from minerals to man there are various levels in which consciousness exists. This system is a great generative rhythm of chemical, mechanical and electrical energy and has a fantastic network of nerves that serve as conductors between different systematic centres that *Tantric* tradition has recognized. This principle of *Tantra* has been retained as a union between individual consciousness and cosmic consciousness.

VAS is a term used by Doctor Nogier (father of arucular Acupuncture) which means an artificial pulse produces positive energy which enters the body's field of energy. According to Cousen's as SOEF (Subtle Organisation of Energy Force), the rainbow diet has direct correspondence between colours of food and *Chakras*. Here the spectrum of colours of rainbow is *intrinsically* connected with *Chakras*. Based on this colour of food and pigments (see Part I Section 8 pigments and colours), food and *Chakras* has been the knowledge behind Rainbow diet. The colours of the rainbow is found in the last *Chakras Thousand Petals* has been mentioned by Harish Johari. The *Chakras* aligned to the natural principle colour healing is a field by itself. Here the natural colours of the food and its meso nutrients performances with the body have been indicative of its observed results in experimentation. This is a different perception from macronutrients, carbohydrates, proteins and fats and micronutrients of vitamins and minerals. (see Part I Section 8, pigments and colours)

Consciousness of food is a realization of God through Food. Yogic diet culminates in experiencing non-material inner energies conserved by consciously consumption food and retaining essence of consciousness. Nature of this non-material energy is directly received from cosmos. *Annamaya Pursha* (physical consciousness) can be transformed to *Caitya Pursha*, the spark of the divine. This kindles psychic faculties or soul essence. This process is known as *psychicization*. This energy has the power to go beyond mind, vitality or *pranas* and the body. Universal spirit becomes one's existence filled with yogic Shakti, divine power. Dwelling in this is *Swasth* (see Sec. 32.2.1) This well being is spiritual also known as *yogakshema* wellbeing of all. Living in this is another dimension.

The Spectrum of Consciousness by Ken Wilber (1993) explains exhaustively non-material energy and which is spiritual. The potency of colours and its vibration is discussed below:-

Red Colour: It is the colour of basic *chakra* at the base of the spinal column, *muladhara*. The red colour of fruits and vegetables are lycopene belonging to carotenoids present in tomato, beets, apple, strawberry and pomegranates. This pigment reduces the risk of cancer of prostate, pancreas and stomach. Lycopene protects against oxidation damage due to ultra-violet rays.

Orange this colour is vermillion associated with *swadhistana* the second *chakra*. The orange pigment is lutein, zeaxanthin, and carotenoids. They are antioxidants, rich in vitamin A.

Yellow, third *Chakra*, *Manipura*, pigment is yellow, Lutein, zeaxanthin and carotenoids acts as antioxidants. prevent age-related muscular degeneration, (AMD), blurring of vision due to age and cataracts. Pineapples, and pumpkin, yellow pepper are good sources of Lutein and zeaxanthin.

Green, fourth *Chakra*, *Annahat*. Most of the leafy green vegetables broccoli and wheatgrass is examples of this colour. The pigment chlorophyll absorbs light in red and blue of the spectrum, reflects green, and is known to promote health. Chlorophyll rebuilds blood stream, it is non-toxic and has no side effects. It has high magnesium, promotes fertility by increasing active enzymes, and regulates sex hormones. It has antibacterial properties within and outside body. Deactivates toxin in the body, cleanses the liver, regulates problems related to blood sugar, reduces oral bacterial infection, and promotes healing rectal sores, reduces typhoid fever.

Blue, *Vishuddi chakra*, fifth chakra in the throat. Pigment blue smokey purple is found in eggplant, blueberries, plum are due to anthocyanin belonging to flavonoid group, they protect against ultra-violet rays, and they are phytonutrients that promote general health. Anthocyanin's intense blue or red colouration, has some limitations when there is temperature variability. They are highly soluble example; red cabbage may inhibit colour change to reddish-blue, or purple depending on pH. This pigment is non-toxic and potent antioxidant reduces Coronary heart disease, improves visual and viral activity. It reduces complications of diabetes and maintains insulin production in type I diabetes.

Indigo, white is a colour of sixth *chakra*, *Ajana*, between the two eyebrows, having same pigment as anthocyanin and has similar functions.

Violet is associated with *Sahasradala Chakra*. At this seventh *Chakras* all other colours configurate as in rainbow, as lustrous and whiter than full moon white colour. White and brown colours found in potatoes, cauliflower, turnip, corn, mushroom, parsnip. They make up the deficiency of all other nutrients; hence, its value cannot be underestimated.

A *yogic* diet is to gather all the subtle forces, colours and energy and be one with the Cosmos. So that our wholesome ancient food culture whose fundamental aim is to gain and establish spiritual health or establish oneself in *swa* and experience *swasthya*.

ANNAM BRAHMA

Rainbrow Diet : From the seven kinds of food

CEREALS, PULSES, FRUITS, VEGETABLES

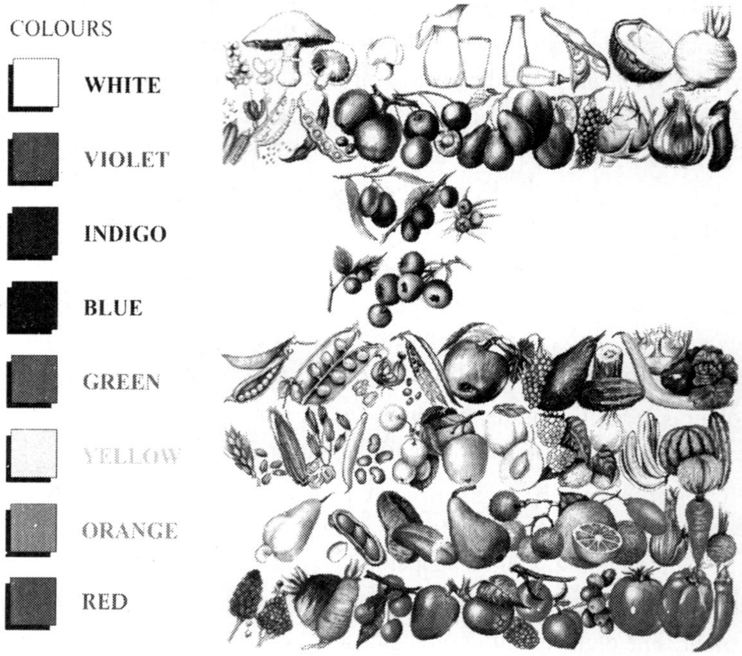

Courtesy : Ms. Kamlakshi, Chitrakala Parshit

ANNAM BRAHMA

From the seven kinds of food
Which the Father produced by intellect and ardor;
One of his foods was common to all beings,
Two he assigned to the Gods,
Three he made for his own use,
One he bestowed upon the animals.
On this, everything is based:
Both that which breathes and that which does not.
How is it then that these foods do not dwindle
When they are constantly eaten up
He who knows this permanence
Eats food with his mouth;
He goes to the Gods,
He lives on power.

(Bul, 5, 1-3)

32.5.2 *Sattvic* Foods

All fresh foods, which help one to be clear, peaceful, and harmonious, are *Sattvic* foods. They not only provide nourishment for the body, but also help to keep the body-mind-spirit complex in balance. They nourish the consciousness and help to experience inner strength, peace and balance. *Sattvic* foods are fresh fruits, vegetables, edible greens, all grains, grasses and legumes. Milk, particularly freshly drawn from the cow, is considered to be ideally *Sattvic*. These foods do not pull energy from the body and do not make one feel heavy. They give one alertness, energy, and create a keener consciousness.

In a study, fresh milk (*Sattvic*) and processed milk in the form of *khoa* (*Rajasic*) was given to two groups to assess the Thermogenic Effect of Food (TEF), discussed earlier in this chapter, it was found that, fresh milk was better utilized than the processed food, confirming, that *Rajasic* or processed food has higher TEF (Thermogenic Effect Food) than *Sattvic* food. In other words, *Sattvic* foods are better utilized than *Rajasic* foods (Sreelakshmi, R. and N. Shakuntala Manay, 2004).

32.5.3 *Rajasic* Foods

These foods stimulate the nervous system and speed up metabolism. One often feels some increased energy from eating them. The increased energy is not a balanced one, but tends to stimulate worldly activities, sensual pleasure, and "creature comforts." They are habit forming like coffee, tea, tobacco and spices. *Raja* means and pertains to kings or royalty, who deal in the area of domination, forcefulness and aggressiveness. *Rajasic* foods are, therefore, considered to be appropriate for rulers, military forces, politicians, and corporate executives, *Rajasic* foods include flesh foods, spicy foods, food cooked in oil, butter and cheese. These foods stimulate the taste buds, overheating the consumer leading to ill-health and chronic, degenerative imbalance.

The Thermogenic Effect of Food (Obligatory and Adaptive or Facultative Thermogenesis) and its effect on psychological moods and physiological changes in the body were studied. In this study, *Sattvic* foods (Obligatory Thermogenesis) produced Alfa readings, which signifies a vibratory state of mental peace and calm whereas *Rajasic* foods (Adaptive or Facultative Thermogenesis) induced negative impact on brain waves resulting in more Beta waves, causing restlessness and anxiety in mind. Readings of EEG (Electroencephalography) confirmed this fact. Further, the consumption of *Sattvic* food reduced body weight but weight gain was recorded in the case of *Rajasic* food (Sreelakshmi, R. and N. Shakuntala Manay 2006).

A significant correlation was found between *Yogic* classification (*Sattvic* – pure, *Rajasic* – over–stimulating, *Tamasic* – dull) and the modern science classification which considers diets rich in micronutrients and low in fats or cholesterol as having greater health attributes. *Sattvic* food was high in micronutrient density and low in fat content, while *Tamasic* food was low in micronutrient density and high in fat (Vaishali V. Agte and Shashi A. Chiplonkar, 2007).

To nourish oneself with food that is *Sattvic* is to get peace, calm and a stable mind. This inner state is highly required to evolve to a higher Divine Nature. The concept of *Teleosis* has to be promoted to attain overall well-being or *Swastya*.

32.5.4 *Tamasic* Foods

Foods, which are stale, decayed, decomposed, boiled, over-cooked, re-cooked, and processed foods, are *Tamasic*. All fast foods, alcohol and drugs belong to this category. They have no life-force, left in them and nourish only the grossest aspects of the body. They diminish our life-force. A diet, consistently comprising *Tamasic* foods, results in increase in body weight and causes diseases of degeneration. They cause a feeling of heaviness, lethargy and irritability. *Tamasic* diet may contribute to the degeneration of the moral fabric of a society.

Selected References

Chapter 1: Introduction

Aurand, L.W. and A.E. Woods, *Food Chemistry,* The AVI Publishing Co., Connecticut, 1973.

Briggs, G.M. and D.H. Calloway, *Nutrition and Physical Fitness,* W.B. Saunders Co., Philadelphia, 1984.

Finnema, O.R. (ed), *Food Chemistry,* Marcel Dekker, Inc., New York, 1996.

Jacob, M.B. (ed), *Chemistry and Technology of Foods,* Vol. I, Interscience Publishers Inc., New York, 1951.

Krause, M.V. and L.K. Mahann, *Food Nutrition and Diet Therapy,* W.B. Saunders Co., Philadelphia, 2000.

Meyer, L.H. *Food Chemistry,* Reinhold Publishing Corporation, New York, 1976.

Nutrition Foundation, Inc., Washington, D.C., *Present Knowledge in Nutrition,* 1976.

Peterson, M.S. and A.H. Johnson (eds), *Encyclopedia of Food Science,* The AVI Publishing Co. Inc., Connecticut, 1978.

PART I: FOOD CHEMISTRY

Chapter 2: Carbohydrates

Davidson, E.A., *Carbohydrate Chemistry,* Holt, New York, 1967.

Guthrie, R.D. and J. Honeyman, *An Introduction to the Chemistry of Carbohydrates.*

Clarendon Press, Oxford, 1968. Lennarz, WJ. (ed), *The Biochemistry of Glycoproteins and Proteoglycans,* Plenum, New York, 1980.

MacGregor, E. A. and C.T. Greenwood, *Polymers in Nature,* John Wiley & Sons, New York, 1980.

Pigman, W.W. and D. Horton (eds), *The Carbohydrates: Chemistry and Biochemistry,* Academic Press, New York, 1980.

Whistler, R.L. and J.N. BeMiller (eds), *Industrial Gums,* Academic Press, New York, 1972.

Chapter 3: Lipids

Ansell, G.B., J.N. Hawthrone and R.M.C. Dawson, *Functions of Phospholipids,* Elsevier, New York, 1973.

Gunstone, F.D., *An Introduction to the Chemistry and Biochemistry of Fatty Acids and their Glycerides.* Chapman and Hall, London, 1967.

Gurr, M.I. and A.T. James, *Lipid Biochemistry, An Introduction,* Cornell, Ithaca, New York, 1980.

Hilditch, T.P. and P.N. Williams, *The Chemical Constitution of Natural Fats,* Chapman and Hall, London, 1964.

Chapter 4: Proteins

Cherry, J.P., *Protein Functionality in Foods,* American Chemical Society, Washington D.C., 1981.

Dickerson, R.F. and I. Geiss, *Proteins: Structure, Function and Evolution.* Benjamin/Cummings, Menlo Park, California, 1983.

Greenstein, J.P. and M. Winitz, *Chemistry of Amino Acids,* John Wiley & Sons, New York, 1961.

Hascheraeyer, R. and A.H. Haschemeyer, *Proteins: A Guide to Study of Physical and Chemical Methods,* John Wiley & Sons, New York, 1973.

Hudson, B.J.F. (ed), *Development in Food Proteins,* Vol. I, Applied Science Publisher, London, 1991.

Schultz, G.E. and R.H. Schirmer, *Principles of Protein Structure,* Springer-Verlage, New York, 1985.

Chapter 5: Vitamins

Dyke, S.F., *The Chemistry of Vitamins,* Interscience Publishers Inc., New York, 1965.

Gyorgy, P. and W.N. Pearson (eds), *The Vitamin,* Vols. VI and VII, Academic Press Inc., New York, 1967.

Marks, J., *A Guide to the Vitamins: Their Role in Health and Disease,* University Park Press, Baltimore, 1975.

Sebrell, W.H. (Jr.), and R.S. Harris (eds), *The Vitamins,* Vols. I and II, Academic Press Inc., New York, 1967.

Williams, J., R.E. Eakin, E. Beersteeker, (Jr.) and W. Shine, *The Biochemistry of Vitamins,* Reinhold, New York, 1950.

Chapter 6: Minerals

National Science Academy, Washington D.C. *Recommended Daily Allowances,* 1980.

Prasad, A.S. and D. Oberleas (eds), *Trace Elements in Health and Disease,* Vols. I and II, Academic Press, New York, 1976.

Underwood, E.J. and W. Mertz, *Trace Elements in Human and Animal Nutrition,* Academic Press New York, 1987.

Chapter 7: Water

Bland, J.W. (ed), *Clinical Metabolism of Body Water and Electrolytes*, U.B. Saunders Company, Philadelphia, 1962.

Dick, D.A.T., *Cell Water*, Butterworth, Washington, 1966.

Eisenberg, D. and H. Kauzmann, *The Structure and Properties of Water*, Clarendon, Oxford, 1969.

Chapter 8: Pigments and Colours

Chichester, C.O. (ed), *The Chemistry of Plant Pigments,* Academic Press, New York, 1972.

Goodwin, T.W. *The Biochemistry of Carotenoids,* Vols. I & II, Academic Press, New York, 1980, 84.

Mackinney, G. and A.C. Little, *Colour of Foods,* The AVI Publishing Company, Connecticut, 1972.

Michael Eskin, N.A. *Plant Pigments, Flavours and Textures, Academic* Press, New York, 1979.

Chapter 9: Flavours

Birch, G.G., J.G. Brennan and K.J. Parker, *The Sensory Properties of Foods,* Applied Science Publication Ltd., London, 1977.

Gould, R.F. (ed), *Flavour Chemistry,* American Chemical Society, Washington, D.C., 1966.

Marton, I.D. and A.J. Macbod, *Food Flavours,* Elsevier Scientific Publishing Co., New York, 1982.

Chapter 10: Enzymes

Fersht, A., *Enzyme Structure and Mechanism,* W.H. Freeman & Co., 1985.

Palmer, T., *Understanding Enzymes,* John Wiley & Sons, New York, 1995.

Roberts, D.V. *Enzyme Kinetics,* Cambridge University Press, 1977.

Whitaker, J.R., *Principles of Enzymology for Food Science,* Marcel Dekker Inc., New York, 1994.

Chapter 11: Properties of Foods

Barrow, G.M., *Physical Chemistry for Life Science,* McGraw-Hill Book Company, New York, 1996.

Chang, R., *Physical Chemistry with Application to Biological System,* Collier Macmillan, International Edition, 1981.

Farrington, D. and A.A. Roberts, *Physical Chemistry,* John Wiley & Sons Inc., New York, 1962.

PART II: FOOD AND FOOD PRODUCTS

General

Bennion, M., *Introductory Foods,* Englewood Cliffs, Merrill / Prentice Hall, New Jersey, 1995.

Birch, G.C , A.G. Cameron, and M. Spencer, *Food Science,* Pergamon Press, New York, 1986.

Charley, H., *Food Science,* John Wiley and Sons, Inc., New York. 1982.

Council of Scientific and Industrial Research, New Delhi, *Wealth of India,* Vols. I and **XX.**

Jacob, M.B. (ed), *Chemistry and Technology of Foods,* Vol. II, Interscience Publishers Inc. New York, 1951.

Mcwilliams, M., *Food Fundamentals,* John Wiley & Sons, Inc., New York, 1979.

Paul, P.C. and H.H. Palmer, *Food Theory and Application,* John Wiley & Sons Inc., New York, 1972.

Peckham, G.G. and J.H. Freeland-Graves, *Foundations of Food Preparation,* Macmillan Publishing Co. Inc., New York, 1995.

Chapter 12: Beverages

Andrews, S., *Food and Beverage Science,* Tata McGraw Hill, Publishing Co. Ltd., New Delhi, 1980.

Charalambons, G., and G. Inglett, *The Quality of Foods and Beverages: Chemistry and Technology,* Vols I and II, Academic Press, New York, 1981.

Jasscler, D.K. and M.A. Joslyn (eds), *Fruit and Vegetables Juice,* The AVI Publishing Co. Inc., Connecticut, 1971.

Pamela, V.P., 4 *Directory of Wines and Spirits,* North Wood Publication, London, 1974.

Runeckles, V.C. and F.A. Loewus, *Recent Advances in Phytochemistry*, Vol. 11, Plenum Press, New York, 1977.

Schapira, J., *The Book of Coffee and Tea,* St. Martin's Press, New York, 1975.

Wellman, F.L., *Coffee,* Interscience Publishers, New York, 1980.

Chapter 13: Fruits

Duckworth, R.B., *Fruits and Vegetables,* Pergamon Press, New York, 1966.

Harrison, S.G., G.B. Masefield and M. Wallis, *The Oxford Book of Food Plants,* Oxford University Press, London, 1975.

Hunt, P. *(ed), Fruit and Vegetables,* Ward Lock Ltd., London, 1972.

Lal, G., G.S. Siddappa and G.L. Tandon, *Preservation of Fruits and Vegetables,* Indian Council of Agricultural Research, New Delhi, 1986.

Nagy, S., P.E. Shaw, and M.K. Veldhnis, *Citrus Science and Technology,* The AVI Publishing Co. Inc., Connecticut, 1977.

K.T. Achaya, *Indian Food–A Historical Companion*, Delhi, Oxford University Press, 1994

Chapter 14: Vegetables

Choudhury, B., *Vegetables,* National Book Trust, India, 1987.

Her Majesty's Stationery Office, London, *Domestic Preservation of Fruits and Vegetables,* 1982.

Katyal, S.L. *Vegetable Growing in India,* Oxford and IBH Publishing Co., New Delhi, 1985.

Nath, P. *Vegetables for the Tropical Region,* Indian Council of Agricultural Research, New Delhi, 1987.

Achaya, K.T. *Indian Food–A Historical Companion*, Delhi Oxford University Press, 1994.

Aman, *Medicinal Secrets of Your Food*, Printed in India by K.A. Korula at the Wesley Press, Mysore, 1969.

Chapter 15: Cereals

Singh, B., *Races of Maize,* ICAR, New Delhi, 1975.

Indian Council of Agricultural Research, *Wheat Research in India,* New Delhi, 1996.

Indian Council of Agricultural Research, *Jowar,* New Delhi, 1980.

Kent, N.L., and A.D Evers, *Technology of Cereals,* Pergamon Press, New York, 1994.

Matz, S.A., *Cereal as Foods and Feeds,* The AVI Publishing Co., Inc., Connecticut, 1991.

Matz, S.A., *Cereal Sciences,*The A VI Publishing Co. Inc., Connecticut, 1969.

Murthy, R.B., *Breeding Procedures in Pearl Millet,* ICAR, New Delhi, 1977.

Pal, B.P., *Wheat,* ICAR, New Delhi, 1966.

Antonella Pasqualone, *Traditional flatbreads spread from the Fertile Crescent: Production process and history of aking systems,* Journal of Ethnic Foods, February 2018.

Shabir Mir, Haroon Rashid Naik, Mahammad Maqbool Mir, *Indian Flatbreads: A Review Article* in Food and Nutrition Sciences, March 2014.

Sudha M. Lakshminarayan, *Wheat-Based Traditional Flatbreads of India,* Article in Critical Reviews in Food Science and Nutrition, June 2013.

Saee Koranne-Khandekar, *Crumbs!: Bread Stories and Recipes for the Indian,* Published by Hachette India; Latest edition 17 May 2016.

Indrani, D. and Venkateswara Rao, G. *Influence of surfactants on rheological characteristics of dough and quality of parotta.* International Journal of Food Science Technology, 38:47–54, (2003).

Indrani, D. and Venkateswara Rao, G. (2006), *Effect of additive on rheological characteristics and quality of wheat parotta.* International Journal of Texture Studies. 37:315–338.

Ilaria Parzanese, Dorina Qehajaj, Federica Patrinicola, Merica Aralica, Maurizio Chiriva-Internati, Sanja Stifter, Luca Elli, and Fabio Grizzi, *Celiac disease: From pathophysiology to treatment,* World Journal of Gastrointestinal Pathophysiology, 2017 May 15.

Pahwa Akanksha, Amarjeet Kaur, Ritika Puri, *Influence of Hydrocolloids on the Quality of Major Flatbreads: A Review,* Journal of Food Processing Volume January 2016.

Achayuthakan P. and M. Suphantharika, "*Pasting and rheological properties of waxy corn starch as affected by guar gum and xanthan gum,*" Carbohydrate Polymers, vol. 71, no. 1, pp. 9–17, 2008.

Elena-Madalina Stefan, Gheorghe Voicu, Gabriel Alexandru Constantin, Mariana Fwedes, *The effect of water hardness on rheological behavior of dough,* Article in Journal of Engineering Studies and Research, January, 2015.

Diamond J. Evolution, *Consequences and future of plant and animal domestication,* Nature 2002; 418:700e7.

Chapter 16: Cereal Products

Matz, S.A., *Bakery Technology and Engineering,* The AVI Publishing Co. Inc., Connecticut, 1992.

Matz, S.A., and T.D. Matz, *Cookie and Craker Technology,* The AVI Publishing Co. Inc., Connecticut, 1978.

Austin, A. and A. Ram, *Studies on Chapati-Making Quality of Wheat,* Indian Council of Agricultural Research, New Delhi, 1971.

Sultan, W. J., *Modern Pastry Cheff,* The AVI Publishing Co. Inc., Connecticut, 1977.

Whiteley, *P.P., Biscuit Manufacture,* Elsevier Publishing Co. Ltd., London, 1971.

Williams, A, (*ed*), *Bread Making,* Hutchinson, Benhan, London, 1975.

Chapter 17: Pulses

Aykrod, W.R. and J. Doughty, *Legumes in Human Nutrition,* FAO, Rome, 1982.

Kacharoo, P., *Pulse Crops of India,* ICAR, New Delhi, 1970.

Smartt, J., *Tropical Pulses,* Ixmgman Group Ltd., London, 1976.

Chapter 18: Nuts

Eley, G., *Wild Fruits and Nuts,* E.P. Publishing Ltd., Yorkshire, 1976.

Howes, F.N., *Nuts,* Fabers and Fabers Ltd., London, 1948.

Kadans, J.M., *Encyclopedia of Fruits, Vegetables, Nuts and Seeds,* Parker Publishing Co. Inc., New York, 1973.

Lloydryall, A. and W.T. Pendzer, *Handling Transportation and Storage of Fruits and Vegetables: Vol. II, Fruits and Peanuts,* The AVI Publishing Co. Inc., Connecticut, 1974.

Chapter 19: Oils and Fats in Foods

Holman, R.T. (ed), *The Progress in the Chemistry of Fats and Other Lipids*, Pergamon Press, New York, 1975.

Proceedings of the Symposium on Fats and Oils in Relation to Food Products and Their Preparation, Central Food Technological Research Institute, Mysore, 1976.

Swern, D, (ed), Bailey's *Industrial Oil and Fat Products*, Interscience Publishers Division, John Wiley & Sons, New York, 1982.

Weiss, T. J., *Food Oils and their Uses*, The AVI Publishing Co Inc., Connecticut, 1983.

Chapter 20: Spices

Ainaduraj, S.G., *A Review of Research on Spices and Cashew Nuts in India*, ICAR, New Delhi, 1966.

Chopra, R.N., I.C. Chopra, and B.S. Verma, *Supplement to Glossary of Indian Medicinal Plants*, C.S.I.R, New Delhi, 1969.

Commonwealth Secretariat, *Plantation Crops—Review*, Her Majesty's Stationery Office, London, 1969.

Frederic, R. (Jr.), *The Book of Spices*, Livingston Publishing Co., Wyne Wood, Pennsylvania, 1969.

Parry, J.W., *Spices*, Vols I & II, Chemical Publishing Co. Inc., New York, 1969.

Puruthi, J.S., *Spices and Condiments,* National Book Trust of India, New Delhi, 1976.

Chapter 21: Milk and Milk Products

Eckles, C.H., W.B. Combs and H. Macy, *Milk and Milk Products,* Tata McGraw-Hill, Bombay, 1980.

Ganguli, N.C., *Milk Proteins,* Indian Council of Agriculture Research, New Delhi, 1974.

Ranganna, K.S. and K.T. Achaya, *Indian Dairy Products,* Asia Publishing House, Bangalore, 1974.

Warner, J.N., *Principles of Dairy Processing,* Wiley Eastern Ltd., New Delhi, 1976.

Chapter 22: Eggs

Cambell, A.M., M.P. Penfield, and R.M. Griswold, *Experimental Study of Foods,* Houghton Miffin Co., Boston, 1980.

Stadlmare, W.J. and O.Y. Cotterill, *Egg Science and Technology,* The AVI Publishing Co. Inc., Connecticut, 1973.

Tandon, H.P., *Egg and its Care,* Ministry of Agriculture, Govt. of India, New Delhi, 1973.

Chapter 23: Meat

American Meat Foundation, *The Science of Meat and Meat Products,* W.H. Freeman and Co., San Francisco, 1971.

Forrest, J.C., E.D. Aberle, H.B. Hedrick, M.D. Judge, and R.A Merkel, *Principles of Meat Science,* Kendall Hunt Publishing Company., Dubuque IA, 1994.

Levie, A., *The Meat Hand Book,* The AVI Publishing Co. Inc., Connecticut,1967.

Paul, P.C. and H.H. Palmer, (eds) *Food Theory and Application,* John Wiley & Sons, Inc., New York, 1972.

Chapter 24: Poultry

Banerjee, G.C., *Poultry,* Oxford and IBH Publishing Co., New Delhi, 1979.

Jull, M.A., *Poultry Husbandry,* Tata McGraw-Hill Publishing Co. Ltd., New Delhi, 1977.

Rogers, C.A.C., *Profitable Poultry Keeping in India and the East,* Treasure House of Books, Bombay, 1966.

Chapter 25: Seafoods

Borgstrom, G., *Fish as Food,* Vols I & II, Academic Press, New York, 1962.

Chandy, M., *Fishes,* National Book Trust, India, 1970.

Simms, A.E. (ed), *Fish and Shellfish,* Virtue and Company Ltd, London, 1987.

Chapter 26: Sugar and Confectionery

Bachman, W., *Continental Confectionery,* Maclaren and Sons Ltd. London, 1955.

Juuka,W.R. and H.M. Pancoast, *Hand Book of Sugars,* The AVI Publishing Co., Inc., Connecticut, 1980.

Less, R. and E.B. Jackson, *Sugar Confectionery and Chocolate Manufacture,* Blackie Academic and Professional, London,1995.

Malik, R.K. and K.C. Dhingra, *Up-to-date Confectionery Industries,* Small Industry Research Institute, New Delhi, 1976.

Proceedings of Symposium on the Status and Prospects of Confectionery Industry in India, CFTRI, Mysore, 1979.

Chapter 27: Honey

Achaya, K.T. *Indian Food–A Historical Companion*, Delhi, Oxford University Press, 1994.

Aman, *Medicinal Secrets of your Food*, Printed in India by K.A. Korula at the Wesley Press, Mysore, 1969.

Geilling Natasha (22 August). "*The Science Behind Honey's Eternal Shelf life*" (http://smithsonianmag.com/science-nature/the-science-behind-honeys-eternal-shelf-life-1218690/?no-ist). Smithsonian. Retrieved 2017–01–28.

"Honey" (http://www.mayoclinic.org/drugs-supplements/honey/evidence/hrb-20059618). Mayo Clinic. 1 November 2013. Retrived 24 September 2015

"Full Report (All Nutrients): 19296, Honey" (http://ndb.nal.usda.gov/nbd/foods/show/6287?fg=&man=&Ifacet=&count=&max=35&sort=qlookup=honey& offset=format=Full&new=&new=&measureby=.USDA National Nutrient Database, Agricultural Research Service, Release 28. 2015. Retrieved 30 October 2015.

"Honey and Bees." (https://web.archive.org/web/20100305094736/hpp:honey.com/honey-at-home/learn-about-honey/how-honey-is-made). Archived from the original on 5 March 2010. Retrieved 17 November 2015 National Honey Board.

Binkley D (31 August 2014). "How bees make honey is complex process" (http://www.dispatch.com//content/stories/science/2014/08/31/how-bees-make-honey-is-complex-process.html). The Columbus Dispatch. Columbus. Ohio USA. Retrieved 17 November 2015

National Honey Board. "*Carbohydrates and the Sweetness of Honey*" (http://www.honey.corn/images/downlloads/carb.pdf). Last accessed 1 June 2012.

Crane, Ethel Eva (1999). *The World History of Beekeeping and Honey Hunting*. Routledge. ISBN 9781136746703.

PART III: FOOD PREPARATION, PRESERVATION AND PROCESSING

General

Borgstrom, G., *Principles of Food Science,* Vols I & II, The Macmillan Co., London, 1971.

Desrosier, N.C., *Food Preservation,* The AVI Publishing Co., Inc., Connecticut, 1977

Jacob, M.B. (ed), *The Chemistry and Technology of Food and Food Products,* Vol. Ill, Interscience, Inc., New York, 1951.

Matz, S.A., *Cereal Technology,* The AVI Publishing Co. Inc., Connecticut, 1970.

Peterson, M.S. and D.K. Tressler, *Food Technology the World Over,* The AVI Publishing Co. Inc., Connecticut, 1963.

Chapter 28: Cooking of Foods

American Home Economics Association, Washington, D.C., *Hand Book of Food Preparation,* 1992.

Arora, K., *Theory of Cooking,* K.N. Gupta & Co., Delhi, 1982.

Cesarean, V.S. Foskett, D., and R. Kintons, *Cookery,* Hodder & Stoughton, London, 1999.

Copson, D.A., *Microwave Heating,* The AVI Publishing Co. Inc., Connecticut, 1975.

Thangam, P.E., *Modern Cookery for Teaching and Trade,* Vol. I, Orient Longmans Ltd., Bombay, 1983.

The Home Science Association of India, *Food Preparation Hand Book,* 1973.

Chapter 29: Food Quality

Board, R.G., *A Modern Introduction to Food Microbiology,* Blackwell Scientific Publications. Oxford, 1983.

Gould, W.A. *Food Quality Assurance,* The AVI Publishing Co., Inc., Connecticut, 1977.

Ranganna, S. *Manual of Analysis of Fruit and Vegetable Products,* Tata McGraw-Hill Publishing Co. Ltd., New Delhi, 1984.

Thankamma, J., *Food Adulteration*, S.G. Wasani, New Delhi, 1976.

The Prevention of Food Adulteration Act, Naraina Industrial Area, New Delhi, 1981.

Chapter 30: Food Additives

Clydesdale, F. (*ed*), *Critical Review in Food Science and Nutrition,* Prentice-Hall, Inc., New Jersey, 1993.

Fennema; O.R., *Food Chemistry,* (Chap. 10) Marcell Dekker, Inc., New York, 1996.

Furia, T.E., *Hand Book of Food Additives,* Vol. I, C.R.C. Press, T.C. Ohio, 1980.

Chapter 31: Food Preservation and Processing

Hall, C.W., *Dictionary of Drying,* Marcel Dekker, Inc., New York, 1979.

Hobbs, B.C. (ed), *Food Microbiology,* Arnold-Heine Mann, New Delhi, 1983.

Mellor, J.D., *Fundamentals of Freeze-Drying,* Academic Press, London, 1978.

Potter, N.M. *Food Science,* The AVI Publishing Co., Inc., Connecticut, 1995.

Stumbo, C.R., *Thermobacteriology in Food Processing,* Academic Press, Inc., New York, 1973.

Throne, S., *Developments in Food Preservation,* Vol. I, Applied Science Publishers, London, 1989.

Sir John Woodroffe, The Serpent Power, Ganesh and company, Madras, All India press, Pondicherry 605001, India, 1992

Sir John Woodroffe, *Sakti and Sakta*, Ganesh and company, Madras, All India press, Pondicherry 605001, India, 187 C.W. Leadbeater, *The Chakras*, Theosophical Publishing House, India: USA; London, 1969.

Johri Harish, Chakras: "*Energy Centers of Transformations*", India Book distributors 195, Bombay-400021, 1934.

Shakuntala Manay N and Sreelakshmi R., *Psychological concept of health and Nutrition, Gunas* Qualitative Vibrations of food, NCTW, Psychological studies, published in Journal of the National Academy of psychology of India, Vol 51, o 2 & 3, 2005.

Sreelakshmi R. and Shakuntala Manay N. 2008, *Influence of Aroma on Human Aura*, qualitative Vibrations of Gunas psychological Studies, published in Journal of the National Academy of psychology of India, Vol 53, No. 21, 2008.

Shakuntala Manay N and Sreelakshmi R., *Quality Vibration of thought energy on environment*, Research Department, published in the journal Vol II, Issue-1, April 24, 2003.

Chapter 32: Nutrition, Health and Food Consciousness

Alok Pandey, *Health -Mental Vs. Spiritual Perspective*, NAMAH, JI of Sri Aurobindo International Institute for Integral Health and Research, Vol. 8, Issue 3,15 October 2000.

Gabriel Cousens, *Spiritual Nutrition*, Cassandra Press, P.O. Box. 868, San Rafa., CA- 94915, USA, 1986.

Gabriel Cousens, *Conscious Eating*, Essene Vision Books, P.O. Box.1080, Patagonia, AZ- 85624,1995.

Rudolph Ballentine, *Diet and Nutrition*, The Himalayan International Institution, Honesdale, Pennsylvania, USA, 1979.

Sri Aurobindo, *The Upanishads*, SABCL,Vol. 2 Sri Aurobindo Ashram, Pondicherry, 1977.

Sreelakshmi, R. and N. Shakuntala Manay, *Psycho-Physiological Concept of Health and Nutrition, Qualitative Vibration of Food.* Psychological Studies, Journal of the National Academy of Psychology, India Vol. 51: P 187-194, April –July 2006.

Sreelakshmi, R. N. Shakuntala Manay, and H.R. Nagendra, *Foods, Gunas and Their Utilization*, First National Convention on "Science & Tradition of Foods-India's Heritage of 5,000 Years", CFTRI, Mysore, July 2004.

Vaishali, V. Agte and Shashi A Chiplonkar, *Linkage of Concepts of Good Nutrition in Yoga and Modern Science,* Current Science, Vol. 92, Number 7, April 2007.

Bijlani, R. L., *Understanding Medical Physiology*, 3rd Edition, Jaypee Brothers Publishers, New Delhi, 2004.

Web Resources

www.fas.usda.gov
www.poultryeg.org
www.baddogcomputer.com
www.whfoods.com
www.americanheart.org
edis.ifas.ufl.edu/
www.foodadditivesworld.com
www.wikipedia.com
www.Indiacoffee.org
www.ico.org
www.teaboard.gov.in
www.nhb.gov.in
www.wikipedia.org
www.fao.org
www.statista.com
www.indexmundi.com
www.apeda.gov.in
www.brbee.com
www.wikipedia.org
www.pixabay.com
www.millets.res.in
www.dahd.nic.in
www.agricoop.nic.in

1 Appendix

Home Science Education, as an academic study came into existence in 1952. Foods and nutrition was one of the fields of study. Only in 1987, Food Science as a subject in home science education was introduced.

It was observed that this subject should be part of curriculum of home science. This was my research work for my master's degree. UGC grant to write textbook enabled me to bring out this as a book.

The science behind much of Indian cuisine had not been recognized, though every house hold prepares these dishes by skilled home makers. During my research I recognized, this is suitably categorised befittingly in relevant chapters.

Also books on Food Science were written by western authors, catering to their food preparation, example preparations like cheese, beef, bread and baked foods etc. These books do not cover our foods like pulses, spices, Indian confectionery and fermented products.

The production, processing and utilization of each food from Indian context are very different. Indigenous food products like idli dosa, chapatti, milk products like dhai, khoa, channa and sweet meats are unique. These now have received scientific principles behind their preparation and are appropriately studied in respective chapters.

Hence this book gives a comprehensive account of all foods and they are divided into four parts.

Part–1 *Food chemistry*: Consist of Chapter 1 to 11. These chapters deal with constituents of food. This section covers all nutrients, their classification and that of chemical and physical properties.

Part–2 *Food and Food products* Chapter 12 to 27. This covers all foods, their composition, nutritive values and their uses. This edition includes pictures of each food, black and white, as well as colour plates. In some foods additional varieties have been covered. Example: berries, leafy vegetables and millets, have undergone intensive revision. Covers all millets that have been recently recognised for their special nutritional values. Tables wherever required have been given. Honey has been part of this section, relevant tables covering varieties in different parts of world, also tables on physico chemical parameter and bio chemical analysis of honey have been given.

Part–3 *Food preparation, preservation and processing* Chapter 28 to 31. This section consists, food preparation, food quality processing and preservation. The effect of cooking, method of cooking, solar and microwave is covered. Evaluation of food quality both subjective and objective methods is discussed. Food adulterants and food additives form part of this section. Food preservation, processing, spoilage and the merits and demerits of these methods is covered.

Part–4 *Nutrition, Health and Food consciousness* Chapter 32. Food is of primordial importance and is central to life. It covers all aspects of life from beginning to the end of life. Nutrition aspect of yogic diet and its relevance to spiritual health is elaborately discussed. Science and spirituality merges. Our culture coming from the days of Vedas and Upanishads, where Rishis with their Tapas and yogic practices recorded their experiences in verses. It is saturated with spirituality. The concept of spirit as evolving consciousness as a soul is pointed out. The concept of Bhrahman or God, nature as purusha and prakrithi is explained.

Man is not mere body, mind and vitality. He has mood profiles. Selection and utilization of food determines his health . The health parameters as per WHO aims at attaining spiritual health. Recent knowledge on food has confirmed there is a difference in digesting and assimilating food. This is now being recognized as thermic effect of food (TEF) and thermogenesis has been given importance. This was already known and recognised as Sattvic, Rajasic and Tamasic foods. Based on these principles experimentation on human subject has been done. The results of these studies validate the principle behind this classification. Hence food influences quality of consciousness which in turn changes the mood profile of the subject.

To attain spiritual health which is purely an inner state where a being's body and mind are fused in becoming a wholesome being. Swastya is a term to be used, Swa means self or soul, self is vast. Well-being therefore is not only one's own self but self of all other beings. Soul or *Atman* is a spark of the divine, known as psychic being or *Caithya-Purusha*. It is a state of being in utter joy or Ananda.

According to Tanthra shastra, there are seven centres of energy situated on spinal cord. These are recognized world over as *Chakras*. Through yogic practices, this can be activated. All this energy centres interestingly have colours of rainbow. Upanishadic knowledge is practical scientific spiritual aspects of life. Hence the quality of life means "Consciousness " which is vast and all inclusive. This conclusive chapter assumes that those who use this book and have systematically acquired the knowledge from the initial chapters will be able to refine further their own understanding. The facts given in the book which become Principles, that in turn bring about inner Processing. The outcome will be wholesome spiritual living with peace and tranquillity or *Swasthya.*

This final chapter culminates with a quotation Brihad-Aranyaka Upanishad 1, 5, 1-3 thus updating our sacred place given to Food consciousness or Annam brahma.

Index

B

C

N

O